Studies in Surface Science and Catalysis 4

GROWTH AND PROPERTIES OF METAL CLUSTERS

Applications to Catalysis and the Photographic Process

Studies in Surface Science and Catalysis

Studies in Surface Science and Catalysis 4

GROWTH AND PROPERTIES OF METAL CLUSTERS

APPLICATIONS TO CATALYSIS AND THE PHOTOGRAPHIC PROCESS

Proceedings of the 32nd International Meeting of the Société de Chimie physique

Villeurbanne
24—28 September 1979

Editor

JEAN BOURDON

ORGANIZING COMMITTEE

J. Bourdon, Chairman
Mme R. Benard, M. Che, Mme A. Hugot-Le Goff, C.K. Jørgensen, A. Masson,
C. Naccache, J. Oudar, R. Parsons, J. Pouradier, and C. Troyanowsky
(General Secretary)

ELSEVIER SCIENTIFIC PUBLISHING COMPANY
Amsterdam — Oxford — New York   1980

ELSEVIER SCIENTIFIC PUBLISHING COMPANY
335 Jan van Galenstraat
P.O. Box 211, 1000 AE Amsterdam, The Netherlands

Distributors for the United States and Canada:

ELSEVIER/NORTH-HOLLAND INC.
52, Vanderbilt Avenue
New York, N.Y. 10017

Library of Congress Cataloging in Publication Data

Main entry under title:

Growth and properties of metal clusters.

English or French.
Bibliography: p.
1. Metal crystals--Growth--Congresses.
2. Catalysts--Congresses. 3. Photochemistry--
Congresses. I. Bourdon, Jean, 1927-   II. Société
de chimie physique.
QD921.G84   548   80-11089
ISBN 0-444-41877-6

ISBN 0-444-41877-6 (Vol. 4)
ISBN 0-444-41801-6 (Series)

Printed in The Netherlands

CONTENTS

VI

FOREWORD

The thirty-second international meeting of the Société de Chimie physique dealt with metal clusters, a theme which has induced a very high research activity, throughout the world, these past few years. A number of meetings have been held not so long ago on related subjects.

It is, however, far from being a novelty. If photography was born in 1839, with Daguerre and Talbot, it is because light, when impinging on a silver halide, gives birth to the latent image, the latter being nothing else than a very small cluster, as established later.

In a similar vein, specialists of heterogeneous catalysis noticed an increase in catalytic activity when the particle size of the catalyst was decreasing. This effect is the more striking when going from the "very large" particles (1,000 Å) to those of 100 or 10 Å or even less.

It was therefore more than chance if research people concerned with subjects seemingly so different as photographic science and catalysis were to meet some day in Villeurbanne to discuss and evaluate the formation and properties of metal clusters, in the company of inorganic chemists, specialists of surfaces, solid state physics, electrochemistry and quantum mechanics.

Nearly hundred and thirty persons attended the meeting, having come from the oil ,automobile or photographic industry as well as from the academic world.

The usefulness of a survey on metal clusters comes from the development and generalized use of a number of physical and physico-chemical techniques of remarkable efficiency for the formation of clusters (photochemistry, electrocrystallization or ion implantation) or their study: field emission microscope, high resolution and electron microscopes, ferromagnetic resonance, Mössbauer effect, N.M.R., E.X.A.F.S., SCF-X α-SW, plus an impressive theoretical contribution from quantum mechanics.

The aim of the Organizing Committee was thus to bring together people from various fields of research and help them, through the discussion of their common interests, to discover zones of overlapping importance, a common language, and perhaps unravel the mysteries of clusters electronic structure, the proper use of catalysis or the highly scientific beauty of photography.

I have pleasure in recording here the gratitude of the Société de Chimie physique to all those who helped in building this conference, and in the first place to authors : we owe them many new results and lively discussions.

The main themes were surveyed in a number of plenary lectures: nucleation, growth and electrocrystallisation of clusters, their structures and physico-chemical properties, their applications to photographic processes and to catalysis. The shorter contributions were presented either orally or in poster form. The poster technique was to us a "first" in an international meeting of the Société de Chimie physique, and it was a definite success : questions and comments in front of each poster were quite thorough, and so was it during the panel discussion that followed.

Nevertheless most of the poster discussions left no trace, as we seldom succeeded in having these extemporaneous remarks written down. Gathering written remarks appears to be easier after a conventional presentation. The reader must therefore not be surprised to find about twenty papers without discussion : the discussions took place, but to the sole benefit of those on the spot.

Somewhat surprisingly the panel discussion began with several minutes of a careful analysis of what constitutes a cluster : good proof that the simplest sounding questions can hide traps. How many atoms are needed to form a cluster? The mobility of atoms on a tungsten tip, strikingly visualized in a movie, seemed to establish that two atoms might be enough.

Some time was also devoted to the definition of terms usual in the cluster field: raft, bidimensional island, tridimensional cluster, bulk metal, and chiefly to the limits of each domain. These limits are visible in the crystalline structures: it can in particular be shown that the metal-metal bond is shorter in a cluster. They also manifest themselves in electronic structures, and evidently in the reactivity. And they are strongly dependent on the mode of formation or stabilisation -surface adsorption or stabilisation in an inert matrix-.

For the conditions in which this meeting took place we are deeply indebted to the Institut de Recherches sur la Catalyse and its director B. Imelik : from scientific participation to a most pleasant evening when we tasted lyonnese gastronomic specialities, "La Catalyse" brought us plenty. And our thanks go particularly to C. Naccache, who took an active part in the scientific work of the Committee before shouldering the whole burden of the local organization. In this he had the help of a team of young research people from the I.R.C., who took care of everything: secretarial tasks, collecting discussion papers and then deciphering -I should perhaps say decoding- the written notes which were our usual heirloom from discussion participants.

To conclude I wish to express my thanks to C. Troyanowsky, the général secretary of our Society. Once again he showed his efficiency in organizing a conference, able, unobtrusive and ever present. He put his stamp on this meeting as on former ones, creating a friendly climate that participants will remember, and ensuring the speedy publication of these Proceedings.

J. Bourdon
Chairman of the Organizing Committee

AVANT-PROPOS

Les petits agrégats métalliques étaient le thème de cette trente-deuxième réunion internationale de la Société de Chimie physique. C'est un sujet qui suscite depuis quelques années beaucoup d'activités dans de nombreux laboratoires de recherches à travers le monde.

Plusieurs congrès et réunions récents ont eu lieu sur ce sujet. Ce n'est pourtant pas un domaine nouveau. Si la photographie a vu le jour en 1839 avec Daguerre et Talbot, c'est parce que la lumière, agissant sur les halogénures d'argent, provoque la formation de l'image latente. Cette dernière n'est pas autre chose qu'un petit agrégat de quelques atomes de métal, ainsi que les chercheurs l'ont découvert par la suite. De même les spécialistes de la catalyse hétérogène ont constaté que l'activité des catalyseurs métalliques supportés croissait lorsque les dimensions des particules de métal allaient en diminuant, cet effet étant particulièrement marqué lorsqu'on passe des très larges particules de 1000 Å à celles de 100 Å, 10 Å et moins.

Ce n'est donc pas tout à fait le hasard si des chercheurs, travaillant dans des domaines aussi éloignés que la science photographique et la catalyse, se sont retrouvés un jour à Villeurbanne pour discuter de la formation et des propriétés des petits agrégats métalliques, en compagnie de spécialistes de la chimie minérale, des études de surface, de la physique du solide, de la mécanique quantique et de l'électrochimie.

Près de cent trente participants ont assisté à cete réunion. Les chercheurs des industries pétrolière, automobile, chimique ou photographique cotoyaient les chercheurs du domaine fondamental.

L'opportunité d'une mise au point sur les petits agrégats métalliques découle des développements récents de plusieurs techniques physiques ou physicochimiques qui permettent, soit de créer ces particules (voie photochimique, électrocristallisation ou implantation d'ions), soit de les étudier: microscopie à émission de champ, microscopie à très haute résolution, microscopie électronique, résonance ferromagnétique, effet Mössbauer, R.M.N., E.X.A.F.S., S.C.F.-X.α-S.W., sans oublier l'apport considérable de la mécanique quantique.

En organisant cette réunion, les membres du Comité d'organisation cherchaient à provoquer la rencontre de spécialistes provenant de domaines très variés, dans un contexte où ils pourraient trouver un langage commun et découvrir, peut-être, les mystères de la structure électronique des petits agrégats, l'utilité de la catalyse ou la beauté, très scientifique, de la photographie.

J'ai plaisir à exprimer la gratitude de la Société de Chimie physique aux uns et aux autres, et plus spécialement aux auteurs: tous ont efficacement contribué à construire une réunion profitable.

Les conférences plénières ont passé en revue les principaux thèmes: nucléation, croissance, électrocristallisation des petits agrégats métalliques, leurs structures et propriétés physicochimiques, leurs applications à la photographie et à la catalyse. Les communications furent présentées oralement ou par affiches. Ce dernier mode de présentation, plus connu sous le nom de "poster", constituait une expérience nouvelle dans une réunion

XII

internationale de la Société de Chimie physique. Une table ronde suivait la session de "posters". L'animation des discussions devant chaque panneau, aussi bien qu'au cours de la table ronde, montrèrent qu'un langage commun avait effectivement été trouvé, et que la présentation par affiches a bien acquis droit de cité.

Certaines discussions devant les posters n'ont pas laissé de traces, et l'essai de les faire rédiger n'a pas eu grand succès. Que le lecteur ne s'étonne donc pas de trouver une vingtaine de communications sans discussions à la suite: les discussions ont eu lieu, - nous pouvons en témoigner -, mais la rédaction des remarques semble mieux au point après les présentations de type traditionnel.

De façon un peu surprenante, une partie de la discussion générale porta sur .. la définition des petits agrégats métalliques, preuve que les questions apparemment simples peuvent parfois masquer des pièges.

Combien d'atomes faut-il pour constituer un agrégat? Un film, visualisant de façon frappante la mobilité d'atomes à l'extrémité d'une pointe de tungstène, semble indiquer que deux atomes constituent déjà un agrégat.

Les mots les plus familiers du langage des clusters ont été rediscutés: "raft", radeau, ilôt, bidimensionnels, et cluster, agrégat, particule, tridimensionnels, métal massif, et surtout les limites de validité de ces termes.

Quelle est la frontière entre le métal massif et le petit agrégat? Cette frontière apparait dans la structure cristalline: il peut être montré, en particulier, que la liaison métal-métal est plus courte dans le petit agrégat. Elle apparait aussi dans les propriétés électroniques, et évidemment dans la réactivité. Elle dépend du mode de formation, du mode de stabilisation: adsorption sur une surface, stabilisation dans une matrice inerte.

Comme toujours, la qualité de la réunion a du beaucoup à l'organisation locale. Nous sommes en particulier profondément obligés à l'Institut de recherches sur la Catalyse et à son directeur B.Imelik: des concours scientifiques à une bien plaisante dégustation de spécialités lyonnaises, "la Catalyse" nous a beaucoup apporté.

Nos remerciements vont tout particulièrement à C.Naccache, qui a pris une part active au travail scientifique du Comité d'organisation, et a ensuite endossé la charge de toute l'organisation matérielle sur le plan lyonnais. Il a été aidé en cela par un groupe de jeunes chercheurs de l'Institut de recherches sur la Catalyse, qui ont assuré aussi bien les tâches de secrétariat que la collecte des discussions, et le déchiffrage des notes que les participants aux discussions nous ont léguées.

Je terminerai en adressant mes remerciements très vifs au secrétaire général de la Société, Clément Troyanowsky. Il a fait la preuve, une fois de plus, de sa compétence pour organiser une réunion internationale. Son efficacité, sa présence, son dévouement inlassable et discret ont apporté à cette réunion, comme à celles qui ont précédé, un cachet, une ambiance cordiale que chacun se rappellera.

Jean BOURDON
Président du Comité
d'organisation

ACKNOWLEDGEMENTS

The 32nd International Meeting of the Société de Chimie physique was organized with the financial help of the following organizations:

- Commissariat à l'Energie Atomique
- Direction des Recherches Etudes et Techniques
- Ministère des Universités
- European Research Office (U.S. Army)

and the following firms and industrial groups:
-Agfa-Gevaert
-Institut Français du Pétrole
-Kodak-Pathé
-Thomson - C.S.F.

This help is gratefully acknowledged

LIST OF PARTICIPANTS

C. APESTEGUIA, Catalyse organique, 86022 Poitiers

P. AUJOUANNET, Lumière S.A., B.P. 336, 69800 Saint Priest

J. BANDIERA, Institut de recherches sur la catalyse 69626 Villeurbanne

J. BARBIER, Catalyse organique 86022 Poitiers

J. BARRAULT, Catalyse organique 86022 Poitiers

J. BELLONI Mme, Physicochimie des rayonnements bâtiment 350 91405 Orsay

A. BENIS, 224 av. Jean Lolive 93500 Pantin

Y. BEN TAARIT, Institut de recherches sur la catalyse 69626 Villeurbanne

A. BERTHET Mme, Lumière S.A., B.P. 336 69500 Saint Priest

H.P. BONZEL, Inst. für Grenzflächenforschung Kernforschungsanlage Jülich R.F.A.

E. BORELLO, Istituto di Chimica Fisica, C.M. D'Azeglio 48 10125 Torino, Italie

Y. BOUDEVILLE, Institut de recherches sur la catalyse 69626 Villeurbanne

J. BOURDON, Kodak Pathé, rue des vignerons 94300 Vincennes

M. BOURG, Univ. de Provence, Place V. Hugo, 13331 Marseille cedex 3

P. BRACCONI, réactivité des solides , Faculté des sciences Mirande B.P. 138 21004 Dijon

M. BRIEU, Laboratoire de physique structurale, 118, route de Narbonne 31077 Toulouse

E. BUDEVSKI, Central Lab. of Electrochemical Power Sources, Acad. of Sciences Sofia, Bulg.

C. CACHET, Institut de recherche sur la catalyse 69626 Villeurbanne

R. CALSOU Mlle, Laboratoire physique structurale, 118, route de Narbonne 31077 Toulouse

H. CHARCOSSET, Institut de recherches sur la catalyse 69626 Villeurbanne

M. CHE, Chimie des solides, Univ. Paris VI, 4, place Jussieu Paris

S. de CHEVEIGNE Mlle, GPSENS, tour 23 2, place Jussieu 75221 Paris cedex 05

P. CORNAZ, Physique expérimentale, E.P.F., Lausanne, Suisse

C. COSSE Mme, Spectroscopie infra-rouge, Univ. de Bordeaux I, 33405 Talence cedex

G. COUDURIER Mme, Institut de recherches sur la catalyse 69626 Villeurbanne

M. COULON, E.N.S.E.E.G. 38401 St Martin d'Hères

A. CRUCQ, Laboratoire de catalyse FNRS, Ecole Royale Militaire B-1040 Bruxelles Belgique

F. CYROT-LACKMANN Mme, C.N.R.S. groupe des transitions de phases, 166 X 38042 Grenoble

J.P. DAUDEY, Physique quantique, Univ. P. Sabatier 31077 Toulouse

D. DADYBURJOR, Rensselaer Polytechnic Inst. Troy NY 12181 U.S.A.

J. DAVENAS, Physique des matériaux, Univ. Cl. Bernard 69621 Villeurbanne

D. DELAFOSSE Mme, Chimie des solides, Tour 54-55 Paris VI, 4 place Jussieu 75230 Paris

M.O. DELCOURT Mme, Physicochimie des rayonnements Bâtiment 350 91405 Orsay

J. DEMUYNCK, ERA 139 (CNRS) Univ. Louis Pasteur Strasbourg

G.J. DEN OTTER, Koninklijke/Shell-Laboratorium, Badhuisweg 3, Amsterdam, Pays Bas

M. DUFAUX, Institut de recherches sur la catalyse 69626 Villeurbanne

L.C. DUFOUR, Réactivité des solides, Faculté Mirande B.P. 138, 21004 Dijon

D. DUPREZ, Chimie IV (Catalyse organique) Faculté des sciences 86022 Poitiers

C. DUPUY Mme, Physique des matériaux C.N.R.S., Villeurbanne

P. EHRBURGER, Physico-Chimie des Surfaces Solides, 68200 Mulhouse

G. EHRLICH , University of Illinois, Urbana Champaign, Illinois 61801 U.S.A.

F. FIGUERAS, C.N.R.S., E.N.S.C.M. 8, rue de l'Ecole Normale 34075 Montpellier

J.P. FRAISSARD, Chimie des surfaces, Univ. Paris VI, 4, Place Jussieu 75230 Paris

M. FREUND I.F.P. rue de Bois Préau 92 Rueil Malmaison

M. FROMENT, Physique des liquides et électrochimie, Univ. Paris VI, 4, Place Jussieu Paris

P. GALLEZOT, Institut de recherche sur la Catalyse   69626 Villeurbanne

E.D. GARBOWSKI, Institut de recherche sur la Catalyse 69626 Villeurbanne

F. GARIN, Laboratoire de Catalyse, Université Louis Pasteur Strasbourg

P. GELIN, Institut de recherche sur la Catalyse 69626 Villeurbanne

P.G. de GENNES, Collège de France 75231 Paris Cedex 05

M. GILLET, Microscopie et diffraction électroniques St Jérome   13397 Marseille Cedex 4

H.L. GRUBER, University of Innsbruck, Physical Chemistry Autriche

J.F. HAMILTON, Eastman Kodak Co, Research Laboratories, Rochester, NY 14650 U.S.A.

M. HARDING Ilford Ltd, the Drive, Warley Brentwood, Essex, England

J.M. HERRMANN, Institut de recherche sur la Catalyse 69626 Villeurbanne

L. HILAIRE Laboratoire de Catalyse Université Louis Pasteur Strasbourg

A. HOFFMAN the Weizmann Institute of Sciences Rehovot Israel

R. HOOGEWIJS, Laboratorium voor kristallografie Krijgslaan 271 B-9000 Gent Belgique

B IMELIK Institut de recherche sur la Catalyse 69626 Villeurbanne

P.A. JACOBS, Centrum Oppervlaktescheikunde K.U. L B-3030 Heverlee Belgique

R. JENKINS Miss Kodak Limited Research Division Harrow HAI 4 TY Angleterre

A. JULG, Chimie théorique Université de Provence, place V. Hugo 13331 Marseille Cedex 3

J. KIWI Institut de chimie physique CH 1015 Lausanne Suisse

U. KREIBIG, Universität des Saarlandes Saarbrucken R.F.A.

L.W. KETELLAPPER Agfa Gevaert N.V. Mortsel 2510 Belgique

M. LANDRIVON, Lumière S.A. B.P. 336 69800 Saint Priest

L. LAFOURCADE, Physique structurale, Univ. Paul Sabatier, 118, route de Narbonne Toulouse

G. LECLERCQ Mme, Catalyse organique , Université de Poitiers 86022 Poitiers

L. LECLERCQ, Catalyse organique, Université de Poitiers 86022 Poitiers

B. LEVY, Polaroid Corp. 750 Main Street Cambridge, MA 02139, U.S.A.

J. LIETO, I.P.S.O.I. Centre de St Jérôme, rue H. Poincaré 13397 Marseille Cedex 4

I. MARKOV, Inst. of Physical Chemistry, Bulgarian Academy of Sciences Sofia Bulgarie

J. MALINOWSKI, Bulgarian Academy of Sciences, Central Laboratory of Photoprocesses Sofia

C. MARQUARDT, Naval Research Laboratory Washington, D.C. U.S.A.

G.A. MARTIN, Institut de recherche sur la catalyse 69626 Villeurbanne

T.P. MARTIN, Max Planck Inst. für Festkörperforschung Stuttgart R.F.A.

G. MARTINO, Cinétique et catalyse I.F.P. 92500 Rueil Malmaison

A. MASSON, Physico-chimie des surfaces, E.N.S.C.P. rue Pierre et Marie Curie Paris

R. MAUREL, Directeur scientifique au C.N.R.S.   15, quai anatole France Paris

P. MAURET, Chimie organique structurale, 118, route de Narbonne 31077 Toulouse

G. MAURIN, Physique des liquides et électrochimie Paris VI

T. MEJEAN Mlle, Spectroscopie infrarouge, Université Bordeaux I, 33405 TALENCE

J.C. MENEZO, Catalyse organique Univ. de Poitiers 86022 Poitiers

L.C. de MENORVAL, Chimie des surfaces Paris VI, 4, place Jussieu 75005 Paris

D. MERCIER, 27, rue des Boulangers 75005 Paris

J.J. METOIS, C.R.M.C$_2$ Traverse de la Barasse 13.397 Marseille cedex 4

J.M. MIQUEL, Microscopie et diffraction électroniques Faculté de St Jérome 13397 Marseille

C. MINOT, Chimie théorique 91405 Orsay Bâtiment 490

E. MOISAR, Agfa-Gevaert AG D 5090 Leverkusen R.F.A.

A. MOLENAAR, N.V. Philips, Nat. Lab WA, Eindhoven Pays Bas

C. NACCACHE, Institut de recherche sur la catalyse 69626 Villeurbanne

M. NASTASI, Lumière S.A. B.P. 336 69800 Saint Priest

J. OUDAR, Physicochimie des surfaces , E.N.S.C.P., 11, rue Pierre et Marie Curie Paris

D. OLIVIER Mme , Chimie des solides, Université Paris VI, 4, Place Jussieu 75230 Paris

M. PASTERNAK, Department of Physics Ramat Aviv, Tel Aviv, Israel

J.P. PIRARD,   Université de Liège, 2, rue A. Stevart Liège Belgique

H. PRALIAUD Mme, Inst. de recherches sur la catalyse 69626 Villeurbanne

P. RABETTE, Chimie des solides Univ. Pierre et Marie Curie 4, Place Jussieu 75230 Paris

A.J. RENOUPREZ, Institut de recherche sur la catalyse 69626 Villeurbanne

M. RIVECCIE, Kodak-Pathé, C.I.D.S.T., 30, rue des Vignerons 94300 Vincennes

E. RUCKENSTEIN, S.U.N.Y. Faculty of Engineering, Buffalo N.Y. 14214

M.R.V. SAHYUN 3M Co, 3 M Center 201- 3 E St Paul Mim 55101 U.S.A.

L. SALEM, Chimie théorique, Université de Paris Sud 91405 Orsay

A. SIMOENS, Faculté universitaire, N.D. de la Paix Namur Belgique

G. SIMON, Rhone Poulenc Centre de recherches des Carrières 69190 St Fons

S. STOYANOV, Institute of Physical Chemistry, Bulgarian Academy of Sciences 1040 Sofia

XVIII

B. THOMAS, Kodak Ltd, Research Division, Headstone drive, Harrow (HAI 4 TY) U.K.

M. TRANQUILLE, Spectroscopie I.R. Université Bordeaux I , 33405   Talence

C. TROYANOWSKY, E.P.C.I., 10, rue Vauquelin 75005 PARIS

R. VANHOREBEEK, Agfa Gevaert 2510 Mortsel Belgique

F. VAN STEEN, Physics Department , Univ. of Antwerp B. 2610, Wilrijk Belgium

  VEDRINE, Institut de recherche sur la catalyse   69626 Villeurbanne

 VERGNON , Univ. Cl Bernard, Chimie LA 231   69621 Villeurbanne

F. VERGAND Mme, Chimie physique   -   Univ. Pierre et Marie Curie, 75231 Paris Cedex 05

T. WELKER, Max Planck Institut für Festkörperforschung Stuttgart R.F.A.

R. WIART, C.N.R.S., Physique des liquides et électrochimie 4, Place Jussieu Paris

D.T. WILLIAMS, I.C.I. 24, Penrith close, Fordsham Cheshire   Angleterre

P. WYNBLATT, Ford Motor Company, Research Laboratory, P.O. Box 2053, Dearborn MI 48121 U.S.A.

M.J. YACAMAN, Instituto di Fisica, U.N.A.M. Apartado postal 20-364 Mexico 20,

D.J.C. YATES, Corporate Laboratory, Exxon Research and Engineering P.O. Box 45 Linden
        New Jersey U.S.A. 07036

J. YUDELSON, Eastman Kodak, Research Laboratory, Rochester N.Y. U.S.A. 14610

A. ZECCHINA, Istituto di chimica fisica Corso M'D'Azeglio 48 10125 Torino   Italie

M. ZOBRIST, Ciba-Geigy Photochemie AG CH-1701 Fribourg Suisse

J. BOURDON (Editor)
Growth and Properties of Metal Clusters, pp. 1—14
© 1980 Elsevier Scientific Publishing Company — Printed in The Netherlands

SURFACE DIFFUSION OF METAL CLUSTERS ON METALS[†]

Gert Ehrlich and Kaj Stolt

Coordinated Science Laboratory*, Department of Metallurgy and Mining Engineering, and
Materials Research Laboratory, University of Illinois, Urbana, IL 61801, USA

The behavior of metal clusters is of considerable interest in the nucleation and growth of crystals and films, as well as in homogeneous and heterogeneous catalytic reactions. In fact, molecular clusters constitute an exciting branch of inorganic chemistry, and a fair amount of information is already available about their structure and energetics. In contrast, little is known about clusters on metals; what there is has been revealed by examination with the field ion microscope (FIM), which provides a view of surfaces on the atomic level [1]. Our aim will be to summarize briefly some of the quantitative information obtained in this very direct way about clusters on metals. Experimental effort up to date has been limited; only the behavior of rhenium atoms on the (211) plane of tungsten has been at all extensively examined. It is upon this particular system that we will therefore focus here to convey an idea of the detail that can be obtained by direct examination of clusters on surfaces.

I. OBSERVATIONS OF INDIVIDUAL RHENIUM ADATOMS

To understand the behavior of surface clusters, it is useful to first examine the properties of single metal atoms bound to a surface. The (211) plane of tungsten is particularly advantageous for this. It is made up of rows of close-packed lattice atoms; as shown in Fig. 1, these form channels, which can be expected to restrict the motion of atoms to one dimension. This is indeed the behavior actually observed [2]. In Fig. 2, a single rhenium atom has been deposited upon a (211) plane of tungsten formed in a highly perfect state by field evaporation at low temperatures. Observations in the field ion microscope reveal that this atom moves only along surface channels in the $[\bar{1}11]$ direction, never across them [3,4]. It should be noted that the act of observation has no perceptible effect upon the system, despite the fact that observations are made at very high electric fields, usually $\approx 4V/\text{Å}$, and that during observation there is electron bombardment of the surface [5-7]. Field ion microscopy is done only with the surface at $\approx 20°$K. Repeated observations do not cause any change in the location of the atom. Atom locations are never examined at room temperature, where mobility is pronounced and where the field is likely to have a significant effect. The motion evident in Fig. 2 is thus typical of diffusion in an ordinary thermal environment.

It is customary to view the surface migration of an adatom as a random walk [8], for which the mean-square displacement in one dimension, $\langle \Delta x^2 \rangle$, is related to the diffusion coefficient D and the diffusion interval t by

[†]Supported by the National Science Foundation under Grant DMR 77-23723.
*Operated with support from the Joint Services Electronics Program under Contract N00014-79-C-0424.

$$\langle \Delta x^2 \rangle = 2Dt \; . \tag{1}$$

The diffusion coefficient is in turn given by [9]

$$D = (\nu \lambda^2/2) \, \exp(\Delta S_m/k) \exp(-\Delta E_m/kT) = D_0 \, \exp(-\Delta E_m/kT) \tag{2}$$

$$D_0 \equiv \nu_0 \lambda^2/2, \; \nu_0 \equiv \nu \, \exp(\Delta S_m/k). \tag{3}$$

Here ν is an effective vibrational frequency for an adatom, and λ is the root-mean-square jump distance, assumed to correspond to one lattice spacing; ΔS_m is the change in entropy as an atom moves from its normal site to the saddle position, and ΔE_m represents the activation energy for the diffusion process. The diffusion barrier can be obtained from

$\leftarrow [\bar{1}11]$

Fig. 1. Hard-sphere model of the (211) plane of tungsten. Outermost layer of lattice atoms in dark grey, second layer in white, adatom in black.

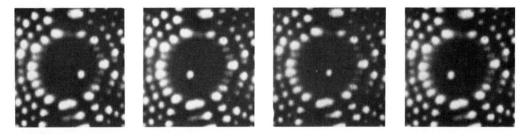

Fig. 2. Motion of single Re adatom on W(211), as observed by FIM. Diffusion occurs along a [$\bar{1}$11] channel, during an interval of 30 sec at 351°K.

the temperature dependence of the mean-square displacement, as indicated in Fig. 3. For a single rhenium atom moving along the [$\bar{1}$11] channels of W(211), the diffusion parameters [4] found by the usual Arrhenius analysis are $\Delta E_m = 19.8 \pm 0.7$ kcal/mole, $D_0 = 2.2(\times 2.8^{\pm 1}) \times 10^{-3}$ cm^2/sec. If we assume that $\Delta S_m = 0$, this value for the prefactor leads to a vibrational frequency of 5.9×10^{12}/sec, an entirely reasonable value quite close to kT/h, as expected.

It would now be of great interest to know the desorption energy of a rhenium atom from the (211) plane of tungsten, so as to establish a standard by which to judge the magnitude of the migration barrier. After all, the latter gives us an idea of the potential confining an atom to its normal binding site on a surface, whereas the desorption energy measures the barrier confining an atom to the surface itself. Regrettably, this information is not available. Attempts have been made to derive the desorption energy of metal atoms from a

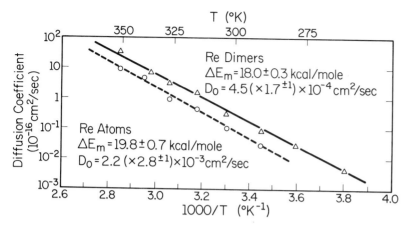

Fig. 3. Temperature dependence of diffusion coefficient for single Re adatom, and for a
cross-channel Re dimer, on W(211) [4].

tungsten surface by field desorption measurements [10,11]. While these studies are simple
to execute, their interpretation depends crucially on assumptions about the mechanism of
field desorption that still remain to be validated by experiment. In addition, the results
must be corrected for the polarizability of the adatom, for which data are scarce [12]. In
view of the lack of quantitative data, only a qualitative statement is warranted: the
barrier to atomic motion is probably small compared to that for desorption.

That the motion of individual atoms on the surface does in fact conform to a one-
dimensional random walk as assumed can be established directly. This is done by measuring
the probability $p_x(t)$ that during a time interval t an atom will have moved to a position x
sites away from the origin [4]. If the atom jumps only to nearest neighbor sites and the
jump rate is α, then the probability $p_x(t)$ is given by [13-15]

$$P_x(t) = \exp(-\alpha t)I_x(\alpha t), \tag{4}$$

where I_x is the modified Bessel function of order x. An actual distribution [16] is compared with these expectations in Fig. 4. It is evident that Eq. (4) provides a reasonable
approximation but that there are some deviations from what is expected for a simple random
walk. Equation (4) describes the actual motion only if an atom always jumps to a neighboring site. The possibility of longer jumps cannot be discounted, however. Little is known
about the trajectories, or about the rate at which thermalization occurs after a migrating
atom collides with the lattice. If we postulate a model which also allows jumps to second-
nearest neighbor sites at a rate β, then the probability $p_x(t)$ becomes [17]

$$P_x(t) = \exp[-(\alpha + \beta)t] \sum_{k=-\infty}^{\infty} I_k(\beta t)I_{x-2k}(\alpha t). \tag{5}$$

A least-squares fit of Eq. (5) to the data in Fig. 4 yields a ratio $\beta/\alpha = 0.1$. Thus
roughly one jump out of 10 appears to span a distance of 2 lattice spacings. The small
value of β indicates, however, that the migration of a single adatom conforms quite well
to the simplest notions about diffusion. We can thus confidently turn to the examination
of more complicated systems.

4

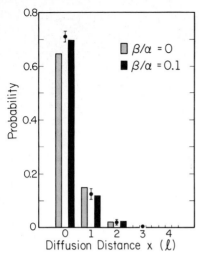

Fig. 4. Distance distribution function for tungsten atom diffusing on W(211) [16].
Shaded bar indicates fit of experimental data to Eq. (4), black bar to Eq. (5).

II.   PROPERTIES OF CROSS-CHANNEL DIMERS

The adatoms studied in the field ion microscope arrive at the surface in question at
random, during evaporation from a nearby incandescent wire. Occasionally, therefore, more
than just a single atom is deposited on a plane. Subsequent collisions between migrating
atoms can be expected to lead to the formation of clusters. This possibility was pointed
out long ago by Moore [18]. Although clusters can easily be identified in early field ion
images, they were ignored until their existence was recognized by Bassett [19].

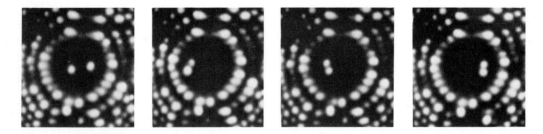

Fig. 5.   Coalescence of two Re atoms in adjacent channels into a dimer, and its subsequent
migration. Diffusion occurs during 3 sec intervals at $375^{o}K$.

A very simple cluster, formed when two rhenium atoms are placed on a (211) plane of
tungsten and are then allowed to diffuse, is shown in Fig. 5. The two individual atoms are
initially in adjoining channels. Once they approach each other they coalesce into a pair;
the resulting dimer moves as a stable unit. The migration of this pair has been studied
quantitatively at different temperatures [4], and the Arrhenius plot for the diffusion
coefficient of the center of mass is shown in Fig. 3. Surprisingly enough, this rhenium
dimer moves more rapidly than single rhenium atoms on the same plane. The activation
energy for dimer motion amounts to only 18.0 ± 0.3 kcal/mole. The prefactor
$D_0 = 4.5(\times\ 1.7^{\pm\ 1}) \times 10^{-4}\ cm^2/sec$ is just a bit smaller than that characteristic of single
adatoms. The question is--how can this come about?

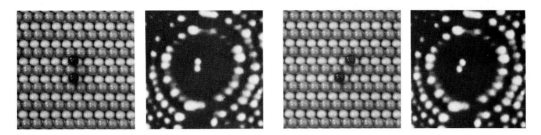

Fig. 6. Configurations of cross-channel dimers of rhenium on W(211). Left: Straight or
0-configuration. Right: Slanted or 1-configuration.

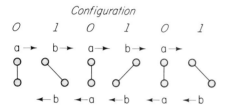

Fig. 7. Schematic of atomic jumps in the diffusion of a cross-channel dimer [24].

Observations of diffusion at low temperatures and short times can isolate the elementary
step in the diffusion of the dimer. Such measurements [4] have established that the dimer
moves as the individual atoms in it jump one lattice spacing at a time, rather than by the
coordinated motion of the dimer as a whole [20]. It has been found in a number of
laboratories that a dimer can exist in two stable forms [4,21-23]. In the straight or
0-configuration, the two atoms are lined up with each other in adjoining rows; in the
slanted or 1-configuration, they are separated by one lattice spacing, as illustrated in
Fig. 6. Diffusion involves two different rate processes, indicated schematically in Fig. 7:
the jump of an atom transforming a straight into a slanted configuration at a rate $\underline{a}$, and
the reverse process, which occurs at a rate $\underline{b}$. The diffusion coefficient for the center of
mass of a dimer moving in this way is given by [24,25]

$$D = \langle \Delta x^2 \rangle / 2t = ab\ell^2/2(a + b), \tag{6}$$

where ℓ is the distance between nearest neighbor sites.

Obviously, an experimental determination of the mean-square displacement alone is
insufficient to define the individual jump rates. An independent determination of the ratio
a/b of the two can, however, be obtained from observations of the equilibrium population of
dimers in the two states. The population probabilities P_1 and P_0 are related to the jump
rates $\underline{a}$ and $\underline{b}$ through the expression [4,26]

$$\frac{P_1}{P_0} = \frac{L - 1}{L}\frac{a}{b} = \frac{2(L - 1)}{L}\,\exp(S_1 - S_0)/k\,\exp\text{-}(E_1 - E_0)/kT, \tag{7}$$

in which L stands for the number of atomic sites in the diffusion channels, and $S_1 - S_0$ is
the difference in entropy of the two configurations. Observations of the population
ratio P_1/P_0 at different temperatures [27] can thus yield E_1-E_0, the difference in energy
between the two dimer states, as well as the ratio of rate constants a/b.

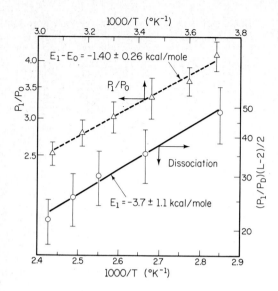

Fig. 8. Temperature dependence of the equilibrium distribution of rhenium dimers [27]. Upper curve: relative occurrence of 0- and 1-configuration. Lower curve: dimers in 1-configuration compared to number dissociated.

Such measurements have been carried out and the results are shown in Fig. 8. They reveal an energy difference of 1.5 kcal/mole between states 1 and 0. Combined with the migration measurements these data also yield the individual jump rates for atoms in the dimer, given in Fig. 9. It is of particular interest to note that the faster diffusion of dimers, as compared to that of single atoms, arises from the smaller barrier confronting atoms in the dimer when they attempt a jump. The dynamics of the jump process, as reflected in the prefactor, are not significantly different for an isolated adatom and a rhenium atom joined to another in a dimer.

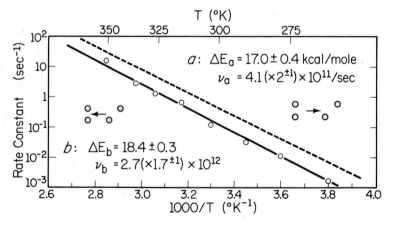

Fig. 9. Jump rates for Re atoms in cross-channel dimer on W(211).

To better understand how this lowering of the diffusion barrier arises in dimers it is useful to concentrate upon the energetics of the situation. It has already been shown that the slanted configuration has a lower energy than the straight. The question now is--how strongly are the two rhenium atoms bound to each other? This has been answered by measurements of the equilibrium between bound and dissociated dimers [27]; among the latter are included all pairs with atoms separated by more than one lattice spacing. The ratio of dimers in state 1 to the number dissociated is given by

$$P_1/P_D = [2/(L - 2)] \exp(S_1/k) \exp(-E_1/kT), \tag{8}$$

with the thermodynamic quantities referenced to the properties of dissociated pairs. The temperature dependence of this ratio is given in Fig. 8. There is too much statistical scatter for extracting meaningful values of the entropy difference between dissociated and bound dimers. However, the dissociation energy of dimers is found to be 3.7 ± 1.1 kcal/mole, and we can now draw at least an approximate potential energy diagram for this system, as in Fig. 10. It appears from the measurements that the effective interactions between rhenium atoms are strongest at a separation corresponding roughly to the saddle point position for an atomic jump between the straight and the slanted configuration. This lowers the barrier to such a jump compared to the barrier confronting an isolated adatom on the same surface, and brings about the more rapid diffusion of dimers.

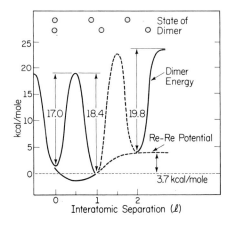

Fig. 10. Potential diagram for Re cross-channel dimer on W(211) [27].

The magnitude of the dissociation energy itself is of interest. It is quite small, comparable to the heat of vaporization of xenon, which amounts to 3.83 kcal/mole. In contrast, the dissociation energy of Re_2 in the gas phase has been estimated at > 95 kcal/mole [28]; the Re-Re bond energy in the $Re_2(CO)_{10}$ cluster is $\approx$ 44.7 kcal/mole [29]. In comparing these values it must be kept in mind that on W(211) the spacing between rhenium atoms is quite large. The lattice positions corresponding to the 0-configuration are separated by 4.48 Å and those in the 1-configuration by 5.25 Å [30]. Distances between rhenium atoms in molecular clusters vary. In the triangular rhenium halide cluster $Re_3X_{12}^{3-}$, the Re-Re spacings are less than 2.5 Å [31]; in $Re_2(CO)_{10}$ the bond is longer but still only 3.04 Å [32]. The spacing between rhenium atoms on W(211) is 50% larger than in molecular clusters.

However, on W(211) the interactions are obviously mediated by the lattice, with which the atoms individually are in strong interaction [33]. A simple comparison with the energetics of molecular clusters is thus not warranted.

Another surprising aspect of rhenium dimers on W(211) is their stability despite a very small dissociation energy. Even at temperatures above 400°K less than 1/3 are dissociated. This comes about because of the small difference in configurational entropy for bound and dissociated dimers. In the equilibrium constant of Eq. (8) the configurational term amounts to $2/(L - 2)$ with L less than 30 for the small planes on which observations have been made. The number of states accessible to dissociated dimers is thus quite limited, and dissociation is not strongly favored by this effect.

Only for rhenium dimers on W(211) are detailed quantitative data available. However, there is enough known about other systems to indicate that we can expect a significant effect of the structure and chemical identity of the substrate, as well as of the chemical constitution of the interacting adatoms upon cluster properties. On W(110) for example there are rough indications that the dissociation energy of Re_2 is vanishingly small [34]. For iridium on W(211) the diffusion of atoms and dimers is just the converse of that found for rhenium: single iridium atoms move rapidly over a significantly smaller barrier than do iridium dimers [35]. These are effects about which it will be desirable to know much more.

III. OTHER RHENIUM CLUSTERS

When a third rhenium atom is placed on W(211) in a channel adjacent to a dimer, as in Fig. 11, a trimer is formed. The number of energetically distinct configurations is now increased to four and diffusion involves nine different jump rates [36], indicated in Fig. 12. A complete analysis of the mobility of such a trimer is not yet available; however, quantitative measurements of the migration of the center of mass have been made [37]. The temperature dependence of the diffusion coefficient is surprising. Despite the availability of diffusion paths quite different from those of dimers, the diffusion parameters of trimers are the same as those of dimers within the limits of the measurements: $D_0 = 5.2(\times 2.3^{\pm 1}) \times 10^{-4}$ cm^2/sec and $\Delta E_m = 18.2 \pm 0.5$ kcal/mole. Although it is not clear how this comes about, the results indicate that on W(211) at least, mass transport by higher clusters is likely to be important compared to that of single adatoms. Larger clusters are also stable; tetramers (Fig. 13) and higher clusters of rhenium have been observed.

In any attempt to interpret the behavior of these larger entities the range of the atomic interactions plays an important role. To shed some light on this, measurements of the distance distribution function for two tungsten adatoms on W(211), separated by an intervening empty channel, have been carried out [26]. After equilibration at $\approx 300^{\circ}$K no significant deviation from a random distribution was detected. At the distances involved, which amount to at least 8.95 Å, interactions between the adatoms are evidently smaller than kT. In rhenium trimers on W(211) direct interactions between the two end atoms should therefore be small also. However, it must be noted that measurements have been reported [34,38] of the distribution of rhenium atoms on W(110) showing long range interactions at separations > 10 Å. A thorough statistical analysis of these data has not yet been done, and the first of these studies [38] appears marred by inadequate equilibration. A careful

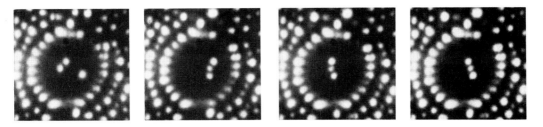

Fig. 11. Combination of three Re atoms, in separate but adjacent channels on W(211), into a trimer, and its subsequent migration as a unit. Diffusion occurs during 60 sec intervals at 315°K.

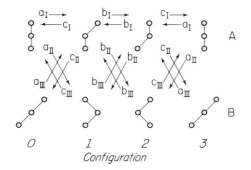

Fig. 12. Schematic of atomic jumps and configurations in the diffusion of a cross-channel trimer on W(211) [36].

investigation [39] of the interactions between a tungsten and a palladium adatom on W(110), carried out recently, does suggest a potential with two separate attractive regions: a shallow well in the vicinity of 10 Å, and another one, ≈ 700 cal/mole deeper, at 3 Å. It will be inportant to search for such effects on other planes as well.

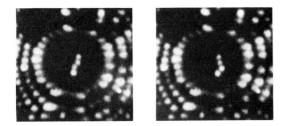

Fig. 13. FIM images of cross-channel tetramer of rhenium atoms on W(211).

The emphasis so far has been upon clusters formed from rhenium atoms in adjacent rows of W(211); their behavior appears straightforward. However, a new set of phenomena is observed when in-channel clusters are formed by depositing more than one atom in the same diffusion channel. In Fig. 14 is shown the formation of such a dimer by combination of two rhenium atoms [40]. Diffusion of an in-channel dimer is much slower than that of cross-channel dimers composed of rhenium atoms in adjacent rows. Quantitative measurements

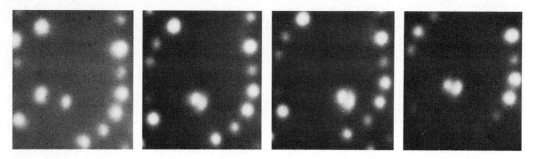

Fig. 14.   Formation and subsequent motion of in-channel Re dimer on W(211) [40].
Diffusion interval: 15 sec at 369°K.

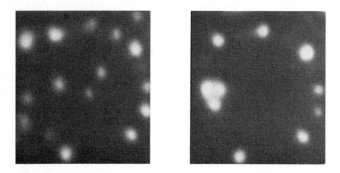

Fig. 15.   Formation of triangular Re trimer on W(211) [40].

are still in progress, but it appears that the activation energy of an in-channel dimer
is ≈ 3 kcal/mole higher than that of a single rhenium adatom.   The addition of another
rhenium atom to form an in-channel trimer further inhibits mobility; however, if a third
rhenium atom is added in an adjacent channel, as in Fig. 15, the mobility of the
triangular trimer so formed is comparable to that of an in-channel dimer [40].   Interactions across the rows of lattice atoms are thus clearly less significant than along the
channels.   Most important for the moment, however, is the realization that cluster
properties are strongly affected by their atomic conformation.

IV.   SUMMARY

A consistent picture of the behavior of metal clusters, and of the interactions between
the atoms in them, still has not emerged even for the one system most intensively studied
so far--rhenium on W(211).   However, it is clear from the available data that clusters do
contribute significantly to surface transport.   All indications are that the behavior of
surface clusters is markedly affected by the atomic arrangement of the substrate.   There
are also very significant specificities depending upon the chemical constitution of the
interacting atoms.   Although little is available in the way of systematic information
about these effects, it has been amply demonstrated that field ion microscopy can provide
such information in a routine fashion.   It now remains to explore these trends.

ACKNOWLEDGEMENTS

We are indebted to D. Coulman and D. A. Reed for many discussions, as well as for permission to use their unpublished material in this review.

REFERENCES

1   E. W. Müller and T. T. Tsong, Field Ion Microscopy, American Elsevier, New York, 1969.
2   G. Ehrlich and F. G. Hudda, J. Chem. Phys., 44(1966)1039-1049.
3   D. W. Bassett and M. J. Parsley, J. Phys. D:, 3(1970)707-716.
4   K. Stolt, W. R. Graham, and G. Ehrlich, J. Chem. Phys., 65(1976)3206-3222.
5   G. Ehrlich and F. G. Hudda, Philos. Mag., 8(1963)1587-1591.
6   D. W. Bassett, Brit. J. Appl. Phys., 18(1967)1753-1761.
7   A. E. Bell, L. W. Swanson, and D. Reed, Surf. Sci., 17(1969)418-429.
8   J. R. Manning, Diffusion Kinetics for Atoms in Crystals, Van Nostrand, Princeton, 1968.
9   C. P. Flynn, Point Defects and Diffusion, Clarendon Press, Oxford, 1972, Ch. 7.
10 G. Ehrlich and C. F. Kirk, J. Chem. Phys., 48(1968)1465-1480.
11 E. W. Plummer and T. N. Rhodin, J. Chem. Phys., 49(1968)3479-3496.
12 T. T. Tsong, J. Chem. Phys., 54(1971)4205-4216.
13 E. W. Montroll, in W. M. Mueller (Ed.), Energetics in Metallurgical Phenomena, Vol. III, Gordon and Breach, New York, 1967, pp. 123-187.
14 W. Feller, SIAM (Soc. Ind. Appl. Math.) J. Appl. Math., 14(1966)864-875.
15 G. Ehrlich, J. Chem. Phys., 44(1966)1050-1055.
16 D. Coulman, personal communications.
17 M. E. Twigg, M.S. Thesis, Department of Metallurgy, University of Illinois at Urbana-Champaign, 1978.
18 A. J. W. Moore, J. Aust. Inst. Met., 11(1966)220-226.
19 D. W. Bassett, Surf. Sci., 23(1970)240-258.
20 D. W. Bassett, J. Phys. C:, 9(1976)2491-2503, has concluded that the motion of clusters of up to four platinum atoms on W(110) can be rationalized on the same picture.
21 T. T. Tsong, Phys. Rev. B:, 6(1972)417-426.
22 W. R. Graham and G. Ehrlich, J. Phys. F:, 4(1974)L212-214.
23 T. Sakata and S. Nakamura, Surf. Sci., 51(1975)313-317.
24 D. A. Reed and G. Ehrlich, J. Chem. Phys., 64(1976)4616-4624.
25 U. Landman and M. F. Shlesinger, Phys. Rev. B:, 16(1977)3389-3405.
26 W. R. Graham and G. Ehrlich, Phys. Rev. Lett., 32(1974)1309-1311.
27 K. Stolt, J. D. Wrigley, and G. Ehrlich, J. Chem. Phys., 69(1978)1151-1161.
28 A. R. Miedema and K. A. Gingerich, J. Phys. B:, 12(1979)2081-2095.
29 J. A. Connor, Topics in Current Chemistry, 71(1977)71-110.
30 American Institute of Physics Handbook, 3rd edn., D. E. Gray (Ed.), McGraw-Hill, New York, 1972, p.9-7.
31 M. J. Bennett, F. A. Cotton, and B. M. Foxman, Inorg. Chem. 7(1968)1563-1569.
32 N. I. Gapotchenko, N. V. Alekseev, N. E. Kolobova, K. N. Anisimov, I. A. Ronova, and A. A. Johannson, J. Organomet. Chem., 35(1972)319-320.
33 An extensive review of the subject has been given by T. L. Einstein, CRC Crit. Rev. Solid State Mater. Sci., 8(1978)181-208.
34 D. W. Bassett and D. R. Tice, Surf. Sci., 40(1973)499-511; also in E. Drauglis and R. I. Jaffee (Ed.), The Physical Basis of Heterogeneous Catalysis, Plenum, New York, pp. 231-245.
35 D. A. Reed and G. Ehrlich, Philos. Mag., 32(1975)1095-1099.
36 J. D. Wrigley, D. A. Reed, and G. Ehrlich, J. Chem. Phys., 67(1977)781-792.
37 K. Stolt and G. Ehrlich, Abstracts, 1979 TMS-AIME Fall Meeting, Milwaukee, Wisconsin, Sept. 16-20, 1979.
38 T. T. Tsong, Phys. Rev. Lett., 31(1973)1207-1210.
39 H. W. Fink, K. Faulian, and E. Bauer, Abstracts, 26th Internat'l Field Emission Symposium, West Berlin, Sept. 3-8, 1979.
40 D. A. Reed, personal communication.

DISCUSSION

G. EHRLICH, K. STOLT

Ruckenstein - I expect the entropic contribution to play a larger part in determining the diffusion coefficient because, by clustering, some translational degrees of freedom are lost. Obviously the diffusion coefficient has to pass through a maximum with an increase in the number of atoms ; the entropic effect is probably in part responsible for this.

Ehrlich - The diffusion coefficient of clusters migrating via individual atomic displacements depends, of course, upon the rate constants for these displacements. For a dimer made up of atoms in adjacent channels of W(211), for example, two rate constants suffice. The magnitude of any one jump rate Γ is, as usual, affected by the entropy of activation in the form

$$\Gamma = \nu \, \exp \, (\Delta S_m/k) \, \exp \, - \, (\Delta E_m/kT)$$

here ΔS_m is just the difference in the entropy of the transmition state and the normal state of the jumping atom. As the size of the cluster increases, the number of rate constants rapidly increases. For trimers, nine different constants enter ; detailed expressions have been worked out by J.D. Wrigley, D.A. Reed, and G. Ehrlich, J. Chem. Phys. 67, 781 (1977). However, these expression are too complicated to provide any immediate intuitive feeling about the contribution of various physical factors. The importance of entropic effects is more immediately apparent in the equilibrium between bound and dissociated dimers. Ther term 2/(L-2) that appears in the equilibrium constant is just a reflection of the difference in the number of configurations accessible to the two entities.

At the moment, comparative values for diffusion coefficients are available only for dimers and trimers in adjacent rows of W(211). Within the limit error, these are the same and provide no indication of any pronounced trends with size. As the number of atoms in a cluster increases, the measurements rapidly become more time consuming, and studies on significantly larger clusters are therefore not attractive.

Martin - Are rhenium atoms more mobile on tungsten surfaces than when dissolved into bulk tungsten ? Did you compare surface and bulk diffusion coefficients ?

Ehrlich - The mobility of metal atoms on the low index planes we have studied is much higher than their mobility in the bulk. For example, the diffusion of Re atoms on W(211) occurs with an activation energy of ∼ 20 kcal/mole. By comparison, bulk diffusion of Re atoms in tungsten requires an activation energy of ∼ 141 kcal/mole (L.N. Larikov, V.M. Tyshkevich, and L.F. Chorna, Ukr. Fiz. Zh. 12, 983 (1977)). More extensive data are available for tungsten. The barrier to motion of a tungsten atom on W(211) is ∼ 18 kcal/mole. The barrier to monovacancy motion in bulk tungsten is 41 kcal/mole ; the energy of vacancy formation, a prerequisite to diffusion in the bulk, amounts to 83 kcal/mole (K.D. Rasch and H. Schultz, Philos. Mag. 37, 567 (1978)). The much higher energy for atom motion in the solid as compared to motion over the surface is not surprising. For an atom to jump into an adjacent vacancy, it must push aside the lattice atoms surrounding it. At the surface, the number of lattice atoms around an adatom is much reduced, and the activation energy for motion should therefore also be much less, as is in fact observed.

Levy - Is there a possibility of partial electron transfer from the clusters to the substrate ? Would this be responsible for some or all of the motions of the clusters ?

Ehrlich - As suggested by the Hellmann-Feynman theorem, there is always likely to be some rearrangement of charge around an atom upon binding to a surface. This has actually been observed. For exemple, K. Besocke and H. Wagner, Phys. Rev. B8, 4597 (1973) reported a dipole moment of ∼ 1D for tungsten atoms absorbed on W(110) ; however, this amounts to the transfer of only a small fraction of an electron to the surface. The adatoms are therefore most appropriately viewed as slightly polarized entities. These dipoles will contribute to repulsive interactions between two adatoms, but up to now the magnitude of such repulsive interactions has not been directly measured.

Abon - 1°/ Do you think that metal adatoms could move more easily on flat planes, such as W(1̄10), than on rough planes ?

  2°/ Is it possible to study the diffusion of adatoms by FIM on very rough planes with steps ?

Ehrlich - The behavior of the (110) plane of tungsten is surprising : metal atoms do not move more easily over this plane, the most densely packed of the bcc lattice, than over the (211) or (321) plane. However, the situation is quite different for fcc metals. On rhodium, for example, Guy Ayrault found some time ago that diffusion over the close packed (111) occurs at 50°K, with a very small activation energy. On rougher planes, such as (311) and (110), surface mobility becomes important only when the temperature is raised more than 100°K higher. To this extent at least, the fcc metals seem to conform more closely to the classical notions about surface mobility. However, it must be noted that the fcc metals are surprising in other respects. On platinum, for example, D.W. Bassett and P.R. Webber have observed frequent jumps of metal atoms across the close packed rows of lattice atoms that make up the (110) plane. On Ir(110), John Wrigley has found that such cross-channel jumps predominate, and that they involve an exchange, between the adatom deposited on the (110) plane and an atom from the substrate. So it seems we still have a lot to learn about the dependence of atomic diffusion on the structure of the substrate surface.

  In principle, there is little to prevent studies of atomic diffusion on highly stepped surfaces using the field ion microscope. In practice, however, diffusion on very rough surfaces occurs at much higher temperatures than on relatively smooth ones. This introduces additional problems : diffusion of contaminants up the shank of the emitter, and the dissolution of the highly perfect surface, formed by field evaporation at low temperatures. Diffusion on rough planes should still be accessible to observation in the field ion microscope, but will clearly require a considerable experimental effort.

Oudar - What is the influence of W monoatomic steps on the motion of adsorbed atom ?

Ehrlich - The effect of steps on atomic motion is quite surprising. In the earliest observations of surface diffusion using the field ion microscope, it was already observed that tungsten adatoms are usually reflected at the descending step bounding the (110) plane of tungsten. This is contrary to the theory of crystal growth phenomena, in which it is generally assumed that an atom reaching a step will be incorporated into it regardless of whether the atom approaches the step from above or below. However, reflection at descending steps was postulated by Drechsler as early as the 50's, and is in any event quite responsible. In order for an atom to move from a plane and be incorporated into a descending step, it must pass over the top edge of the step. In this position, the overlap with the lattice atoms is reduced to a minimum. The atom should therefore pass over a potential higher than that confronting an atom on a flat plane. Reflection by this high potential at the plane edge rationalizes the observations.

  The phenomena observed on other planes, especially W(211), are rather more complicated. These adatoms are often observed to be localized at the plane edge, close to a descending step, without rolling over the edge. They can be freed again by small increases in the temperature. The probability of such capture is sensitively dependent upon the chemical identity of the adatom. For example, rhenium adatoms are captured more frequently than tungsten adatoms, and for iridium the capture probability is higher still. The detailed geometry of the step also plays an important role ; for example, the edge of the (211) closer to the (111) appears stickier than that facing the (100) plane. It appears that there are many interesting phenomena involving the interplay between adatoms and steps that merit further study.

Budevski - Your experiment seems to show a rather high atomic interaction. Can you give us some figures at dissociation energies for the different positions and have you ever observed nucleation effects for the formation of monoatomic layers or three-dimensional phases ?

Ehrlich - From the work presented here we cannot obtain absolute values of the binding energy of a metal atom at different sites on a surface. Attempts to derive such information from field desorption experiments have been made in the past, by G. Ehrlich and C.F. Kirk, J. Chem. Phys. 48, 1465 (1968), and E.W. Plummer and T.N. Rhodin, J. Chem. Phys. 49, 3479 (1968). These attempts were based on a particular model of the desorption process in a high field (a model which may not be applicable) and in addition neglect some important physical effects. Reliable values of the binding energy of an atom to its own lattice are thus still lacking. As regards nucleation effects, I must stress that our studies have been concentrated upon the behavior of single adatoms and clusters. However, the clusters can be viewed as nuclei for a new layer of atoms, and the measurements of the dissociation energy of dimers, for example, constitute a first step in quantifying our notions about the energetics of such nuclei.

Cyrot-Lackmann - 1°/ Can you interpret your results in term of long range interaction forces, alternative or repulsive, due to electrons ? In particular, for the differences between Re and Ir.

2°/ There seems to exist no diffusion between different rows. Have you an interpretation for this ?

Ehrlich - From our studies of rhenium and iridium dimers on W(211) we can deduce potential curves describing the effective interactions between the two atoms. The differences in the motion of these two dimers lead us to believe that the distance dependence of the interactions is quite different for rhenium and for iridium. For the former, the attractions peak as one of the atoms moves through the saddle point separating the straight from the staggered configuration ; for iridium, the attractions are strongest in the straight configuration. It would now be very desirable to have an understanding of how to rationalize this in terms of the electronic structure of the interacting atoms.

On W(211), diffusion is observed to occur along the direction of the close packed lattice atoms, and not across them. That is what we intuitively expect, as motion over the protruding lattice rows that make up the diffusion channels should be very expensive in energy. However, on Ir(110), and to a lesser extent on Pt(110), motion occurs across the channels. John Wrigley in our laboratory has established that these jumps occur by exchange of an adatom with a lattice atom. It should also be noted that these cross channel jumps occur on a plane restructured from the ideal envisioned in the bulk. Precisely why this occurs on some metals, but not on others, is not at all clear right now.

J. BOURDON (Editor)
Growth and Properties of Metal Clusters, pp. 15—33
© 1980 Elsevier Scientific Publishing Company — Printed in The Netherlands

PARTICLE NUCLEATION AND GROWTH IN SUPPORTED METAL CATALYSTS

P. Wynblatt
Research Staff, Ford Motor Company, Dearborn, Michigan 48121

ABSTRACT

This paper will focus on the loss of activity which results from the exposure of supported metal catalysts to high temperatures, and in particular, on the mechanisms of nucleation and growth of the catalytically active metal particles. Attention will be confined primarily to the case of platinum particles supported on alumina substrates, as this has been the most widely studied system. However, the concepts discussed will be sufficiently general to provide insights into the behavior of related metal cluster systems. The following topics will be covered in some detail. a) The nucleation processes which lead to the formation of either metallic or oxidic particles. b) The phenomenon of "redispersion." c) Mechanisms of growth and associated particle growth kinetics for particles supported on flat substrates. d) Influence of substrate curvature on mechanisms of growth.

I. INTRODUCTION

Supported metal catalysts consist of a finely divided, catalytically active metal phase dispersed on the surface of a microporous ceramic oxide support. The active metal can be present either in the metallic state or in the form of an oxide and can range in dispersion from individual isolated molecular or atomic units all the way to particles several tens of nanometers in size. The activity of these catalysts tends to decrease during service as a result of various chemical and physical phenomena. In this review, we shall focus on one of these phenomena, namely, the loss of active surface area which results from the agglomeration and growth of the supported metal entities. Also, attention will be confined primarily to the case of platinum supported on alumina, as this has been the most widely studied system. However, the concepts presented here should be generally applicable to other related systems.

This paper will be divided into four principal sections. In the first section, the nucleation processes which lead to the formation of either metallic or oxidic particles of the catalytically active phase will be described. The second section will briefly summarize some recent progress which has been made in the understanding of so-called "redispersion" phenomena. In the third section, the major concepts which have been developed to model the growth of particles in supported catalysts will be reviewed in the context of particles supported on flat substrates. The fourth and final section will address the effects of substrate curvature on the growth of metal particles in supported catalyst systems.

II. NUCLEATION

II.1. Initial catalyst configuration

It is worthwhile to begin with a brief description of the methods used to prepare supported metal catalysts, since the initial state of the catalyst must clearly play an important role in the early stages of particle nucleation and growth. Since the detailed procedures which have been used in catalyst preparation are quite varied, the following descriptions can only give a broad outline of the most common methods.

Supported metal catalysts are prepared by impregnating a high surface area support with the catalytically active component. In Pt/Al_2O_3 catalysts, the support is typically a lightly sintered, microporous, γ-alumina having a surface area in the range 50 to 250 m^2/g. Platinum is introduced in the form of aqueous solutions of such compounds as chloroplatinic acid (H_2PtCl_6) or platinum amines (e.g., $Pt(NH_3)_4Cl_2$)).

In some cases, the support is immersed in the solution, and the molecules of the platinum compound are adsorbed out of the solution onto the support surface. The support is then dried and the platinum compound decomposed to yield either Pt metal or oxide. This procedure tends to produce the highest degrees of metal dispersion. In other cases, the solution may be sucked into the pores of the support by capillary action. Here also, the support would be dried and the compound decomposed to metal or oxide. However, in these cases, the drying process can produce small crystals of the platinum compound which would presumably decompose to yield aggregates of metal atoms or oxide molecules, leading to a lower degree of dispersion of the active component.

The methods used for decomposition of the platinum compound are also quite varied. The compound may be decomposed thermally either in air (calcination) to yield platinum oxide, or in inert gas, vacuum or reducing gases to yield metallic platinum. Other procedures, such as precipitation of platinum as the sulphide, by treatment with H_2S before the catalyst is dried, may also be used.

The concentration of metal in the catalyst is commonly reported in terms of the weight percent of the metal and generally falls in the range 0.1 to 5%. These figures taken together with the typical range of support surface area translates into average metal coverages, θ, in the range 10^{-3} to 0.3 monolayers of metal or 1.5×10^{-3} to 0.45 monolayers of oxide on the support surface.

As soon as the platinum compound is decomposed, the processes of particle nucleation and growth can begin. These processes are expected to be quite different depending on whether the impregnated platinum compound is decomposed to metal or to oxide, and so will be considered separately in the following discussion.

II.2. Nucleation in systems containing metallic platinum

The general scheme outlined here for modelling the formation of metal particles follows the lines proposed originally in a previous review of the subject (ref. 1), namely, a description of the process in terms of a sequence of transitions, as illustrated schematically in Fig. 1. Thus, the formation of particles is viewed as a stepwise process beginning with a transition from individual metal atoms (monomers, Fig. 1a) to two-dimensional islands (Fig. 1b), followed by a transition from two-dimensional (2-D) islands to 3-D clusters (Fig. 1c) and culminating in the formation of quasi-macroscopic particles (Fig. 1d). While the concept of nucleation was implicit in the previous review, explicit estimates based on nucleation theory were not presented. In this paper, we provide such estimates in the remainder of this section.

Chemisorption measurements of the metal dispersion (i.e., the fraction of metal atoms present in the surface of platinum aggregates) in Pt/Al_2O_3 catalysts have shown that some of the preparation techniques described above can be used to produce catalysts in which every metal atom is accessible to the gas phase. Under those circumstances, the metal phase must exist either as monomers on the substrate or in the form of 2-D islands (or rafts), as shown in Figs. 1a and 1b. Clearly, the latter of these two forms is the more stable, as it allows Pt-Pt bonds to be formed, each of which lowers the

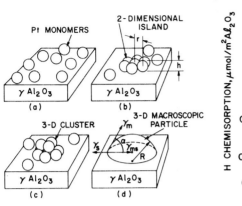

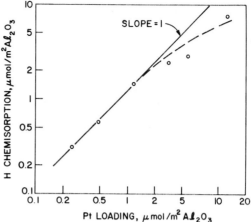

Fig. 1. Schematic indicating the different possible configurations of platinum on alumina substrates: a) monomers, b) 2-D islands, c) 3-D clusters, and d) quasi-macroscopic particles.

Fig. 2. Dependence of metal surface area (as measured by hydrogen chemisorption) on catalyst platinum loading, for a series of Pt/Al_2O_3 catalysts heated in hydrogen at 573K for 2 hours (after Yao et al ref. 9).

energy of the system by ⨯ 90kJ/mol. Whether one or the other of these two forms is present will therefore depend on kinetic factors, such as the rate at which stable 2-D nuclei can be formed.

II.2.1. Transition from monomers to 2-D islands. In order to address this issue, we assume (for the sake of simplicity) that the impregnated platinum compound in the catalyst is reduced instantaneously to produce a random distribtuion of Pt monomers on the support surface, at the temperature of interest, and proceed to investigate nucleation phenomena from that point.

Nucleation theory (ref. 2) defines the radius of a disc shaped critical sized nucleus, as:

$$r_c = -\varepsilon / \{ (\gamma_m + \gamma_{sm} - \gamma_s) + h \Delta G_v \} , \tag{1}$$

where ε (energy/unit length) is the edge energy of the nucleus; γ_m, γ_{sm} and γ_s (energy/unit area) are the interfacial energies associated with the metal-vapor, substrate-metal and substrate-vapor interfaces, respectively; h is the height of the disc; and ΔG_v is the free energy per unit volume of disc. The latter quantity is defined by:

$$\Delta G_v = -\frac{kT}{\Omega} \ln (n_s/n_s^o) = -\frac{kT}{\Omega} \ln (\theta/\theta^o) \tag{2}$$

where k is the Boltzmann constant; T is the absolute temperature; Ω is the atomic volume of the disc material; n_s and n_s^o (monomers/unit area of substrate) are the actual and equilibrium surface concentrations of monomers, respectively; and θ and θ^o (area of monomers/unit area of substrate) are the respective coverages.

Under the present assumptions, θ is the surface coverage of monomers which would be inherited on decomposition of the precursor platinum compound used in the preparation of the catalyst. The equilibrium monomer coverage θ^o, may be defined by equating adsorbing and desorbing fluxes at the substrate surface:

$$\theta^o = \sigma n_s^o = \beta \, p_{PtO_2} \, \exp \{H_{des}/kT\} \, /(1 + \beta \, p_{PtO_2} \, \exp \{H_{des}/kT\}) \,, \qquad (3)$$

where: $\beta = \sigma/\{v_s(2\pi mkT)^{\frac{1}{2}}\}$, σ is the area occupied by a monomer on the substrate, v_s is the vibration frequency of a monomer on the substrate, H_{des} is the heat of desorption of a monomer, p^o is the equilibrium vapor pressure of the monomer material and m is the mass of the monomer. It should be pointed out that Eq. (3) is just the Langmuir adsorption isotherm, and that for the case of dilute coverage, $\theta^o \ll 1$, the deninator of Eq. (3) approaches unity, yielding a simpler form. Finally, p^o can be obtained from the free energy of sublimation of the particle material, ΔG_{subl}:

$$p^o \, (atm) = \exp (\, -\Delta G_{subl}/kT) \,. \qquad (4)$$

Evaluation of r_c by means of Eq. (1) requires a knowledge of all the quantities in Eqs. (1) to (4). These are known except for v_s and H_{des}. The quantity v_s is approximated here as $3 \times 10^{12} sec^{-1}$, a reasonable value for an adsorbed atom (ref. 3). The quantity H_{des} is estimated crudely from the work of adhesion of Pt on Al_2O_3, W_a (energy/unit area), defined as:

$$W_a = \gamma_m + \gamma_s - \gamma_{ms} \,. \qquad (5)$$

The work of adhesion is a measure of the energy which must be expended to break the bonds across a Pt - Al_2O_3 interface. These same types of bonds must be broken during the desorption of a Pt monomer from an alumina surface. Thus, for the purpose of the present estimates it will be assumed that:

$$H_{des} \simeq W_a \sigma N_A \,, \qquad (6)$$

where N_A is Avogadro's number. However, the sensitivity of this assumption will be tested by allowing H_{des} to adopt values ranging from twice to one half the value given by Eq. (6). Other values used in these estimates are: γ_m, γ_s, γ_{ms} = 2100, 770, 1050 mJ/m^2, respectively (ref. 4); $\Delta G_{subl}/kT = 63490/$ T - 15.57 (ref. 5); h is taken as the atomic diameter of Pt: 0.277mm; σ is taken as 6.6×10^{-20} m^2; n_s is set at 10^{-17} atoms/m^2 (this corresponds to a surface coverage of $\theta = n_s \sigma = 6.6 \times 10^{-3}$, i.e., a fairly low metal loading); $\Omega = 1.51 \times 10^{-2}$mm^3; and ϵ is set equal to 0.2 hγ_m, a value consistent with previous studies (ref. 6).

Values of r_c computed from Eq. (1) are given in Table 1 for several temperatures, and show that the size of the critical nucleus is smaller than atomic dimensions for all conditions. The subatomic size of the critical nucleus indicates that there exists no nucleation barrier to growth in the case of Pt monomers on Al_2O_3 substrates. Thus, as Pt monomers encounter each other, they will tend to form stable 2-D aggregates that are unlikely to dissociate.

Since there exists no nucleation barrier to growth, the rate of formation of 2-D aggregates will depend merely on the concentration of monomers and their mobility. If we consider the reaction between two monomers, to form a dimer, then the initial (fractional) rate of decrease in monomer coverage may be approximated by:

$$\frac{1}{\theta}\frac{d\theta}{dt} = - \theta v_s \, \exp \, (-H_m^s/kT) \,, \qquad (7)$$

where H_m^s is the activation energy for migration of a monomer over the substrate surface. Taking θ = 10^{-3} (the lowest value in supported catalysts) and $H_m^s \simeq H_{des}/2$ (an upper bound), we find: $(1/\theta) \, (d\theta/dt) \simeq$ -2000 sec^{-1} at 300K. Thus, the initial rate at which monomers decrease is extremely large, and the transition from a monomer dispersion to 2-D islands will be very rapid even at temperatures as low as room temperature. It seems intuitively clear that the size of the 2-D islands produced by this transition will depend on the initial metal loading of the catalysts. However, at the present time, no model is available for relating the initial monomer concentration to the resulting mean island size.

TABLE 1

Radius of critical sized disc nucleus (in nm) of Pt on Al_2O_3

Assumed Value of H_{des} (kJ/mol)	Temperature		
	300K	500K	800K
36	9.8×10^{-3}	1.0×10^{-2}	1.1×10^{-2}
72	1.1×10^{-2}	1.1×10^{-2}	1.2×10^{-2}
144	1.4×10^{-2}	1.4×10^{-2}	1.6×10^{-2}

Once a distribution of 2-D islands of various sizes is formed, it is possible to address the problem of the growth of these islands by transport of Pt monomers between islands. This problem has been treated previously (ref. 1), for the case of growth by transport of Pt monomers between islands; however, because of the extremely low value of n_s^o, essentially negligible growth is predicted by this process at temperatures below the 2-D to 3-D transition. While growth of these 2-D islands could occur by island migration, collision and coalescence, a process which may be faster than growth by monomer transport, no theory is available for growth by that mechanism.

II.2.2. Transition from 2-D islands to 3-D clusters. The transition from 2-D islands to 3-D clusters (Figs. 1b and 1c) is also driven by the resulting increase in the number of Pt - Pt bonds. Methods analogous to those outlined above for the nucleation of disc shaped particles may be used to compute the radius of a critical sized 3-D cluster. The results obtained are similar to those displayed in Table 1, indicating that as in the case of 2-D islands, there exists no nucleation barrier confronting the formation of 3-D clusters. However, the kinetics of the transition from 2-D islands to 3-D clusters depend on the rate at which platinum atoms diffuse over other platinum atoms, i.e., platinum surface self diffusion. This process is associated with an activation energy of $\sim$125 kJ/mol (ref. 7), and is thus much slower than the diffusion of Pt monomers over an Al_2O_3 substrate.

The kinetics of the transformation from 2-D islands to 3-D clusters may be estimated crudely from the known kinetics of thin film break-up (ref. 8). As a 2-D island transforms to a 3-D cluster, the initial rate of shrinkage of its projected radius, r_p, is given approximately by:

$$\frac{1}{r_p}\frac{dr_p}{dt} \simeq -\frac{D_s \Omega^2 \gamma_m \sqrt{\pi}}{\sigma \, kT h^{3/2} r_p^{5/2}}, \tag{8}$$

where D_s is the surface self diffusivity ($D_s = 0.014 \exp\{-15000/T\}$ cm^2/sec for platinum (ref. 7)). For an island having a projected radius r_p = 2.5 nm, Eq. (8) gives $(1/r_p)$ $(dr_p/dt) \simeq 10^{-10}$ sec^{-1} at 300K and 10 sec^{-1} at 600K. Thus it is expected that the transition will become rapid at or about 600K.

The values of the interfacial energies: γ_m, γ_{ms}, and γ_s, given above, indicate that a macroscopic platinum particle in local equilibrium with an alumina substrate will adopt an essentially hemispherical shape (contact angle = α = $\cos^{-1}$ { $[\gamma_s - \gamma_{ms}]/\gamma_m$ } = 98°). If it is assumed that an equilibrated 3-D cluster will also have that general shape, then the ratio of the accessible surface area of a hemispherical cluster to the surface area of a disc shaped 2-D island of radius r will be: $2\{3h/(2r)\}^{2/3}$. For r = 2.5 nm, the area ratio is ~ 0.6.

Some experimental results obtained on highly dispersed supported Pt/Al_2O_3 catalysts are shown in Fig. 2 (refs. 9, 10). The data give results obtained after heating the fresh catalysts in hydrogen at 573K for two hours. Lightly loaded catalysts (0.2 to 1 µmol. Pt/m^2, corresponding to metal coverages $\theta \simeq 1$ x 10^{-2} to 4 x 10^{-2}) show that essentially every Pt atom is accessible to the gas phase, indicating the presence of very small clusters, whereas more heavily loaded catalysts (3 to 12 µmol Pt/m^2, corresponding to $\theta \simeq 0.12$ to 0.5), show that progressively fewer atoms are accessible to the gas phase. These results are generally consistent with the picture presented above.

II.3. Nucleation in systems containing oxidized platinum.

In order to develop a coherent picture of the behavior of platinum oxide supported on alumina substrates, it is useful to begin with a brief review of the equilibrium between platinum and oxygen and of the state of platinum oxide on alumina substrates.

II.3.1. The equilibrium between platinum and oxygen. Berry (ref. 11) has recently studied the equilibrium between solid platinum metal, oxygen and solid platinum dioxide:

$$Pt_{(s)} + O_{2(g)} \rightleftharpoons PtO_{2(s)} \quad , \quad \Delta G^{\circ}_{(9)}/kT = -21090/T + 24.8, \quad \quad (9)$$

where $\Delta G^{\circ}_{(9)}$ is the standard free energy change for the reaction. (The subscript (9) is used to associate the value of the standard free energy change to the reaction of Eq. (9). This subscript system will be used for subsequent chemical reactions.) Thus, under one atmosphere of oxygen, solid PtO_2 is the stable phase below 850K, whereas at higher temperatures, the metal is the stable phase. (In air, the dissociation temperature of the oxide is $\sim 800K$.)

The characteristics of the equilibrium between solid platinum, oxygen and gaseous PtO_2 have been known for some time from high temperature measurements (ref. 12) and may be expressed as:

$$Pt_{(s)} + O_{2(g)} \rightleftharpoons PtO_{2(g)}, \quad \Delta G^{\circ}_{(10)}/kT = 20785/T - 1.5 . \quad \quad (10)$$

Combination of Eqs. (9) and (10) yields:

$$PtO_{2(s)} \rightleftharpoons PtO_{2(g)}, \quad \Delta G^{\circ}_{(11)}/kT = 41875/T - 26.3 , \quad \quad (11)$$

where $\Delta G^{\circ}_{(11)}$ is the sublimation free energy of PtO_2. Thus, at any oxygen partial pressure, the partial pressure of PtO_2 in the vapor phase will follow different trends depending on whether bulk PtO_2 is stable, or not. In particular, under one atmosphere of oxygen, the partial pressure of PtO_2 may be expressed as:

$$p^o_{PtO_2} \text{ (atm)} = \exp(-G^o_{(11)}/kT) \ , \ T \le 850K \tag{12a}$$

$$p^o_{PtO_2} \text{ (atm)} = \exp(-\Delta G^o_{(10)}/kT) \ , \ T \ge 850K \ . \tag{12b}$$

III.3.2. State of PtO_2 on $\gamma - Al_2O_3$. Yao et al (refs. 9, 10) have studied the behavior of Pt/Al_2O_3 catalysts of various metal loadings after heat treatment in oxygen at 500^oC (where PtO_2 is the thermodynamically stable phase). Their results yield the following picture of the state of oxidized platinum supported on alumina substrates.

At low metal loadings (up to $\curvearrowright 2.2$ μmol $PtO_2/m^2 Al_2O_3$, corresponding to 1.32×10^{18} monomers/m^2) all the platinum in the catalysts is present in the form of individual PtO_2 monomers dispersed on the substrate. As the metal loading is increased beyond this value, the monomer phase becomes saturated and exists in equilibrium with a bulk 3-D PtO_2 phase. It should be emphasized that this behavior is generally no different from the case of metallic platinum, where there is always some finite metal monomer concentration in equilibrium with either 2-D islands or 3-D particles. The major difference resides in the magnitudes of the monomer concentrations of the metal and the oxide.

The concentration of PtO_2 monomers in equilibrium with bulk PtO_2, at 500^oC, corresponds to the quantity n^o_s of Eqs. (2) and (3) (or to $\theta^o = \sigma \, n^o_s = 0.14$, where σ for PtO_2 is taken as $1.05 \times 10^{-19} m^2$ (ref. 13)). Thus, at that temperature, there will be a driving force for nucleation of aggregated PtO_2 only in cases where $\theta > 0.14$. The availability of a value of n^o_s in this case makes it possible to extract an experimental value of the heat of desorption of a PtO_2 monomer from an alumina surface, by means of Eq. (3). Using $\theta^o = 0.14$, $\nu_s = 3.3 \times 10^{12} \text{sec}^{-1}$, and p^o for PtO_2 from eq. (12a), at 500^oC, one obtains: $H_{des} = 237$ kJ/mol. Putting this value of H_{des} back into eq. (3) allows computation of θ^o, the saturated PtO_2 monomer coverage at any temperature. Equation (3) even allows computation of the PtO_2 monomer concentration which would be in equilibrium with 3-D platinum metal particles at temperatures above the decomposition temperature of bulk PtO_2. At those temperatures PtO_2 still exists in the gas phase at a partial pressure defined by Eq. (12b). Thus, for temperatures above 850K and under one atmosphere of oxygen, θ^o may be obtained from Eq. (3), using Eq. (12b) for $p^o_{PtO_2}$. The resulting temperature dependence of θ^o is shown in Fig. 3. It is interesting to note that the saturation PtO_2 monomer coverage increases with temperature to a peak value at 850K, and then decreases with temperature when bulk PtO_2 is no longer stable.

II.3.3. Nucleation of 3-D PtO_2. The formation of 3-D PtO_2 particles should follow the general scheme of transitions outlined in Fig. 1. However, so little is known of the properties of PtO_2 that an evaluation of the type made above for the case of metallic platinum is not possible. Thus, we confine our attention here just to the nucleation of 3-D particles from monomers.

The radius of curvature of a critical nucleus in the shape of a spherical segment (see Fig. 1d) is given by (ref. 2):

$$R_c = -2\gamma_p/\Delta G_v \tag{13}$$

where γ_p is the interfacial energy of the particle-vapor interface, and ΔG_v is defined as in eq. (2) (Ω for PtO_2 is 0.035 nm^3 (ref. 13)). The quantity θ^o for this case is as computed in Fig. 3. In order to proceed with estimates of R_c we assume γ_p is equal to the Al_2O_3-vapor interface energy, i.e. $\gamma_p = 770$mJ/m^2.

Unlike the case of metallic platinum, R_c for PtO_2 is found to adopt a wide range of values which depend strongly on θ (the initial PtO_2 monomer coverage assumed to be inherited from the

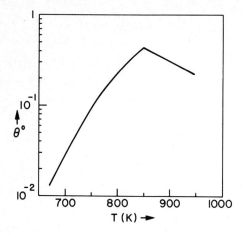 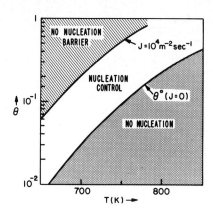

Fig. 3. Saturation coverage of PtO_2 monomers on Al_2O_3 substrates, in the presence of 1 atm of O_2, as a function of temperature (after Yao et al ref. 10).

Fig. 4. Nucleation map for bulk PtO_2 on Al_2O_3 substrates, see text.

decomposition of the precursor platinum compound) and on temperature. In order to define a range in which nucleation phenomena may control the rate of particle formation, it is necessary to compute the nucleation rate, J (nuclei per unit area per unit time) given by (ref. 2):

$$J = \frac{Z\theta 2\pi R_c b \sin(\alpha) \nu_s}{\sigma 2} \qquad \exp(-H^s_m/kT) \exp(-\Delta G_c/kT) , \qquad (14)$$

where: $\Delta G_c = \frac{16\pi \gamma_p^3 \alpha_1}{3\Delta G_v^2}$, $\alpha_1 = \{2 - 3\cos(\alpha) + \cos^3(\alpha)\}/4$,

α is the contact angle for a PtO_2 particle on the substrate, b is the distance between substrate sites (0.273nm), ΔG_c is the free energy of formation of a critical nucleus and Z is the Zeldovich factor (0.01). Evaluation of J requires knowledge of additional unavailable quantities, however, we proceed with a rather uncertain evaluation merely to gain qualitative insights into the expected behavior. It is assumed that $H^s_m = H_{des}/2$ (as in the case of metallic platinum), and since wetting of alumina by PtO_2 is likely to be much better than that by the metal, we assume $\alpha = 30°$. Finally, we use the usual criterion of $J = 10^4$ nuclei $m^{-2}sec^{-1}$ (ref. 2) as constituting the dividing line between fast and slow nucleation.

A nucleation map is given in Fig. 4. Two lines are drawn on the figure. One line is labelled J = 0, and corresponds to $\theta = \theta°$, or $\Delta G_v = 0$. This line is identical to the curve of Fig. 3 and represents the equilibrium between PtO_2 monomers and bulk PtO_2. The other line is labelled $J = 10^4 m^{-2}sec^{-1}$ corresponds to the onset of fast nucleation. These curves delineate regimes where: a) no nucleation can take place, b) formation of particles is controlled by nucleation, and c) growth is spontaneous and there exists no nucleation barrier to growth.

It should be stated that the location of the $J = 10^4 m^{-2}sec^{-1}$ boundary is quite sensitive to the assumed values of γ_p and α. Thus, in view of the limited knowledge of bulk PtO_2 properties, it is felt that this is as far as it is reasonable to pursue an analysis of nucleation phenomena in this regime.

III. REDISPERSION IN Pt/Al_2O_3 CATALYSTS

It is worthwhile to digress here briefly in order to present the results of a recent analysis of the phenomenon of redispersion (ref. 10), based on the differences in behavior between alumina-supported metallic and oxidized platinum which have been outlined in Section II.

Over the past 20 years or so, several investigators have noted that the accessible platinum surface area in Pt/Al_2O_3 catalysts can be increased by heat treatment in oxygen (or air) atmospheres at temperatures below about $550^{\circ}C$. This phenomenon has been referred to as "redispersion". The results of Fiedorow and Wanke (ref. 14), shown in Fig. 5, provide an example of this type of behavior. The figure is a plot of metal dispersion obtained after heat treatment in oxygen for one hour at various temperatures. The dispersion in the "fresh" catalyst (reduced in H_2 at $500^{\circ}C$ after preparation) is indicated by the cross. It is clear that the dispersion increases with heat treatment temperature up to $\sim 550^{\circ}C$, and then drops off rapidly at higher temperatures.

This type of experimental result has previously been considered to be at odds with the expectation that surface area should decrease at high temperatures, as a result of the surface energy driving force for particle growth. However, if the initial configuration of the catalyst is one where 3-D metallic platinum entities are present (e.g., as a result of heating under reducing conditions) then subsequent heating in the presence of oxygen will lead to the formation of large PtO_2 monomer concentrations, as shown in Fig. 3, with a resulting increase in the amount of platinum accessible to the gas phase. Indeed, the general shape of Fig. 3, showing a maximum in PtO_2 monomer concentration (and hence in dispersion) at 850K, is quite similar to that of Fig. 5. On the basis of the results of Fig. 3, it is even possible to explain instances of increased dispersion in catalysts heated initially in oxygen at, say 950K, followed by heat treatment in the same atmosphere at 850K.

This approach to the interpretation of redispersion phenomena has been given recently by Yao et al (ref. 10), and generally similar, though less specific hypotheses have been proposed by Fiedorow and Wanke (ref. 14).

IV PARTICLE GROWTH ON FLAT SUBSTRATES

In this section we shall address primarily those cases where the bulk metal is present in metallic form, as the properties of the oxide are not known well enough for the purposes of this discussion.

The 3-D clusters or particles formed by the processes described in Section II, can continue to grow. The driving force for growth is still the maximization of the number of Pt - Pt bonds, or in other words, the minimization of surface energy. Two types of mechanism have been proposed for the growth of supported particles: growth by a process of particle migration leading to interparticle collisions and coalescence, and growth by some form of interparticle mass transport. These processes have been treated in some detail in previous reviews (refs. 1, 15) and so will be dealt with here rather briefly.

IV.1. Growth by particle migration, collision and coalescence

Ruckenstein and Pulvermacher (ref. 16, 17) have developed a binary collision model for particles migrating over planar substrates in which the rate controlling step for particle growth can be either particle migration or particle coalescence. For slow migration and fast coalescence, the migration process would be rate controlling, and vice versa. In both of these cases, their solutions yield expressions relating accessible metal surface area to time. For the purposes of comparison with other models, it is convenient to give an approximate form of their expression in terms of particle radii (refs 1, 15):

$$(\bar{R}/\bar{R}_o)^n \simeq 1 + Qt, \qquad (15)$$

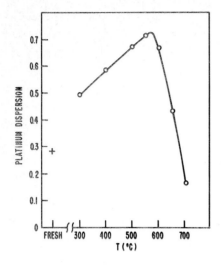

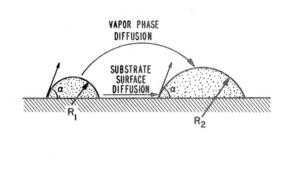

Fig. 5. Dispersion of a Pt/Al$_2$O$_3$ catalyst heat treated in O$_2$ for 1 hour at several temperatures (after Fiedorow and Wanke ref. 14).

Fig. 6. Schematic of the modes of inter-particle transport.

where $\bar{R}_o$ and $\bar{R}$ are the average particle radii of curvature at times t = o and t = t, respectively; n is an integer and Q is a rate constant. The values of n and Q depend on the detailed mechanisms of growth. Ruckenstein and Pulvermacher did not attempt to formulate physical models for either the particle migration or particle coalescence processes. In order to obtain physically meaningful estimates of particle growth by these processes, it is necessary to postulate specific models of particle migration and coalescence and graft these onto Eq. (15). It is convenient to assume that both of these processes take place by surface diffusion, as existing models may then be adapted readily to the present purposes.

There exists no net driving force for the migration of a particle over a planar substrate. However, particles can migrate over this type of substrate in a random thermal motion, akin to Brownian motion, by the movement of atoms over the particle surface (refs. 1, 15). As an approximation to the particle diffusivity, D_p, we make use of a result derived by Gruber (ref. 18) for the migration of pores in solids by surface diffusion:

$$D_p = 0.3\, D_s \left(\frac{a_o}{R} \right)^4 \qquad , \qquad (16)$$

where a_o is the interatomic (or intermolecular) spacing in the particle, and R is the particle radius. It is possible to obtain a lower bound estimate of the time for particle migration between collision events from Eq. (16), by taking the time required for a particle to migrate a distance equal to 10 times its radius. This distance is small compared with interparticle spacings even in high metal loading catalysts, once 3-D particles are present. Thus, the migration time is experessed as:

$$\tau_{mig} = \frac{(10\,R)^2}{4 D_p} = \frac{83.3\, R^6}{D_s a_o^4} \qquad . \qquad (17)$$

The process of coalescence of two identical spherical particles of radius R, by surface diffusion, has been treated by Nichols and Mullins (refs. 19, 20). They have shown that the relaxation time for complete coalescence may be written:

$$\tau_{coal} = \frac{0.89\ R^4 kT\sigma}{D_s \gamma_m \Omega^2} \cdot \qquad (18)$$

Recognizing that the quantity $(\sigma\ a_o^4 /\Omega^2) \simeq 10$ for metals, we may write the ratio of the coalescence time to the migration time as:

$$\frac{\tau_{coal}}{\tau_{mig}} \simeq \frac{0.1\ kT}{\gamma_m R^2} \qquad (19)$$

The r. h. s. of Eq. (19) is much smaller than unity for any reasonable values of the parameters, indicating that the coalescence process is always much faster than the migration process. Thus, particle growth by particle migration collision and coalescence will always be controlled by the migration process.

Combining the Ruckenstein and Pulvermacher formalism, Eq. (15), with Eq. (16) one obtains (ref. 24):

$$\left[\frac{\bar{R}}{\bar{R}_o}\right]^7 \simeq 1 + \left\{ 16\pi D_p(\bar{R}_o)\ N_o / \ln\left[\frac{2D_p(\bar{R}_o)\ \Gamma}{\bar{R}_o^2}\right]\right\} t \quad , \qquad (20$$

where N_o is the initial number of particles per unit area of substrate, Γ is a characteristic time and D_p must be evaluated at $R = \bar{R}_o$. This expression will be used for later comparison with models of growth by interparticle transport.

IV.2. Growth by interparticle transport

Expressions for the rates of particle growth by interparticle transport have been developed for the cases of diffusion between particles either through the vapor phase, or over the substrate surface (refs. 1, 6); as illustrated schematically in Fig. 6. The approach used has been based on the classical treatments of Ostwald ripening (refs. 21-23).

The chemical potential, μ, of a particle in the shape of a spherical segment depends on its radius of curvature R, according to the relationship:

$$\mu = \mu_o + 2\gamma_m \Omega / R = kT\ \ln\left\{ p(R)/p^o \right\} \quad , \qquad (21)$$

where μ_o is the value of μ for an infinite sized particle and $p(R)$ is the vapor pressure in equilibrium with a particle of radius R. Thus, since supported particles will generally display a distribution of radii of curvature, the larger particles with lower chemical potential will grow at the expense of smaller particles with higher chemical potential. Under those conditions, some particles will grow, and others will dissolve away, leading to an overall increase in average particle size.

For the case of substrate diffusion, it can be shown that particles grow according to the relation (ref. 1, 6):

$$\left[\frac{\bar{R}}{\bar{R}_o}\right]^4 = 1 + K_D t \ , \quad K_D \simeq \frac{0.37\ D_1\ n_s^o\ \gamma_m \Omega^2}{\bar{R}_o^4\ \alpha_1\ kT} \cdot \qquad (22)$$

Similarly, for vapor phase transport, the particle growth law may be stated as:

$$\left[\frac{\bar{R}}{\bar{R}_o}\right]^2 = 1 + K_V t , \quad K_V \simeq \frac{0.79 \alpha_2 \gamma_m \Omega^2 p^o}{\bar{R}_o^2 \alpha_1 kT(2\pi mkT)^{1/2}} \quad , \tag{23}$$

where $\alpha_2 = \{1 - \cos(\alpha)\}/2$.

IV.2.1. Effects of ambient atmosphere. We consider first the case of growth under conditions where particles are heated under a reducing atmosphere, (e.g. H_2). Under those circumstances, the constants K_D and K_V of eqs. (22) and (23) refer to metallic platinum particles and/or monomers. Evaluation of the rate constants (ref. 24) shows that the expected rate of growth by interparticle transport is negligible, because of the very low values of n_s^o and/or p^o. Thus, even the relatively low rates of particle growth which have been observed experimentally in H_2 atmospheres (refs. 1, 25) must therefore be presumed to occur by the process of particle migration, collision and coalescence.

Next, we consider the growth of particles under an oxygen containing environment. As mentioned above, it is not useful to consider in detail the regime where bulk PtO_2 is stable, in view of the limited knowledge available on that material. However, it is clear from Fig. 4 that for metal loadings and temperatures corresponding to the "no nucleation" regime, PtO_2 monomers are the only stable species on the substrate, and no growth of particles could be expected since particles are not stable. Above the line labelled $J = 0$, particle growth can take place, but at rates which cannot readily be predicted until more is known about the properties of bulk PtO_2. However, it is possible to consider particle growth in systems heated to temperatures above the decomposition temperature of bulk PtO_2. Under those conditions, metallic platinum is the stable bulk phase and it exists in equilibrium with O_2 and PtO_2 vapor (see eq. (10)). Because of the large heat of desorption of PtO_2 monomers, discussed in Section II.3.2., bulk metallic platinum supported on Al_2O_3 will also exist in equilibrium with PtO_2 monomers (adsorbed) on the substrate. For any partial pressure of O_2 other than 1 atm, eq. (12b) may be rewritten as:

$$p^o_{PtO_2} (atm) = P_{O_2} (atm) \exp\{- \Delta G^o_{(12)}/kT\} = P_{O_2} (atm) K^{eq} , \tag{24}$$

where K^{eq} is the equilibrium constant for the reaction of Eq. (10). Thus, for growth in oxygen atmospheres, we can rewrite the rate constants K_V and K_D of Eqs. (22) and (23) as (ref. 6):

$$K_V \simeq \frac{0.79 \alpha_2 \gamma_m \Omega^2 P_{O_2} K^{eq}}{\bar{R}_o^2 \alpha_1 kT (2\pi mkT)^{1/2}} \quad , K_D \simeq \frac{0.37 a^2 \gamma_m \Omega^2 P_{O_2} K^{eq}}{\alpha_1 kT (2\pi mkT)^{1/2}} \exp (H_{des} - H_m^s)/kT . \tag{25}$$

For oxygen partial pressure values of interest (such as those encountered for example over oxidation catalysts), evaluation of K_V and K_D from these expressions yield reasonable rates of particle growth. Furthermore, the predicted trends of increasing growth rate with increasing oxygen partial pressure are qualitatively consistent with experimental findings for both particles supported on flat substrates (ref. 26) as well as in conventional supported catalysts (ref. 24).

IV.3. Comparison of growth rates predicted by the different models

In order to provide some indication of the regimes where different models are likely to operate, we provide some estimates of the relative rates of growth by the processes described above.

It has already been stated that the modest rate of particle growth observed under reducing

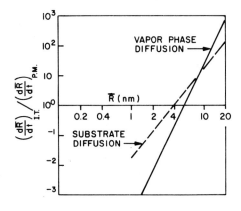

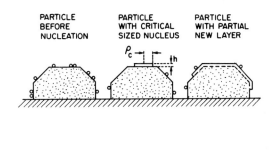

Fig. 7. Ratio of the rate of growth by interparticle transport to the rate of growth by particle migration, as a function of average radius, for Pt particles on a flat Al_2O_3 substrate (T = 700°C, p_{O_2} = 0.02 atm).

Fig. 8. Stages in the growth of perfect faceted particles.

conditions is most likely controlled by particle migration processes in all regimes of temperature and particle size. In the presence of oxygen, however, quite different results are projected. In order to make a simple comparison, we compute the derivatives $d\bar{R}/dt$ (evaluated at time t = 0) from Eq. (20), for growth by particle migration, and from Eqs. (22) and (23) using the values of K_D and K_V obtained from Eq. (25), for growth by interparticle transport. The evlaluation is made at 700°C for an oxygen partial pressure of 0.02 atm. The results are shown in Fig. 7 as a plot of the ratio of the derivatives versus average particle radius, where $(d\bar{R}/dt)_{I.T.}$ refers to interparticle transport either by vapor phase transport or by substrate diffusion, and $(d\bar{R}/dt)_{P.M.}$ refers to growth by particle migration. It should be recognized that since all these processes occur in parallel, the fastest process will be rate controlling. The figure shows that for particle sizes below ~ 4nm, particle migration processes contribute most to growth. In the range from 4nm to ~ 8nm substrate diffusion is the dominant process, and vapor diffusion is the rate controlling mechanism at higher particle sizes.

Generally speaking, one may conclude that the particle migration process will be rate controlling for small particles and that interparticle transport will dominate for large particle sizes.

IV.4. Nucleation inhibited interparticle transport

While the theoretical framework presented thus far in Section IV is generally useful in that it identifies the physical processes which play a role in the particle growth processes of interest in catalysts, it is not capable of accounting quantitatively for experimental observations even in model experimental systems where metal particles are supported on flat substrates. When the observed experimental kinetics have been forced to conform to the general form of Eq. (15), it has been found that the exponent n can adopt wide-ranging values as large as 12 (refs. 24, 26-28), which fall outside the physical range $2 \leq n \leq 7$. Furthermore, these "effective" exponents frequently show a time dependence, increasing with increasing time. These results, coupled with the electron microscope observation that growing particles tend to facet, have led to the development of the so-called "nucleation inhibited" growth models (refs. 6, 24, 29, 30).

It is well known from crystal growth theory (ref. 31) that growth of (perfect) faceted crystals requires repeated nucleation events, leading to rates of growth that are lower than those of unfaceted particles. This nucleation process is illustrated schematically in Fig. 8. As a faceted particle grows, incoming monomers will tend to settle at energetically favorable sites such as kink and ledge sites. Eventually, all such sites will be consumed leading to a perfect crystallite. At this point, further growth will have to await the nucleation of an atomic step before large numbers of monomers can once again be accommodated on the particle. After nucleation, a whole new monolayer of growth can occur, as shown in the figure, before another nucleation event is required.

The rate of particle growth under those constraints can be formulated by combining classical nucleation theory with the Ostwald ripening formalism used in the derivation of eqs. (22) and (23), (ref. 6). The resulting equations are complex and can only be solved numerically for comparison with experiment. However, closed form asymptotic solutions can be obtained in certain limiting cases (refs. 29, 30), and are useful in that they indicate the general form of the results; e.g., for the case of substrate diffusion:

$$t = \frac{kTC_1}{2\gamma_m \Omega} \int_{\bar{R}(t=0)}^{\bar{R}(t)} \bar{R}(t)^{-3/2} \exp\left[\frac{C_2 \pi \epsilon^2 \bar{R}(t)}{2h\gamma_m kT} - \frac{2\gamma_m \Omega}{kT\bar{R}(t)}\right] d\bar{R}(t) , \qquad (26)$$

where C_1 and C_2 are constants. By expansion of the exponential terms, eq. (26) may be reduced to a power series in $\bar{R}$. As time proceeds, the dominant term in the series shifts, so that the effective growth exponent increases with time and can achieve large values. Thus, this type of model can account for the awkward features of experimental results, and has been useful in the interpretation of the kinetics of growth of alumina - supported platinum particles (refs. 26, 27) and platinum - palladium particles (ref. 28).

It should be mentioned that the concepts of nucleation inhibition can in principle be applied to models of growth by particle migration (ref. 1). In that case also, one would expect to obtain particle growth laws with time dependent exponents.

V. PARTICLE GROWTH ON CURVED SUBSTRATES

The previous Section has dealt with the major modes of particle growth, as they apply to particles supported on <u>flat</u> substrates. In conventional supported metal catalysts, however, the particles reside on the surface of a highly curved substrate, and as has been discussed qualitatively in the past (refs. 1, 15, 24), substrate curvature can profoundly influence both particle migration and interparticle transport phenomena. More recently, Ahn <u>et al</u> (ref. 32) have developed a formalism for describing the interaction between particle growth processes and substrate curvature effects, and have confirmed the predicted trends by studying the growth of particles supported on sinusoidally curved surfaces. The results of this latter study are summarized below.

V.1   Effects of substrate curvature on growth by particle migration

Particle migration over flat substrates occurs under zero driving force by random thermal process analogous to Brownian motion. In contrast, particles on a curved substrate experience a driving force for migration as illustrated in Fig. 9. Consider the particles at positions 1 and 2. In order for these particles to be in local equilibrium with the substrate, they must make equal contact angles, α, with the substrate. Thus, particles having equal volumes will display a smaller radius of curvature at position 1, R_1, than at position 2, R_2. Compared with the radius of curvature, R_f, of an equal volume particle supported on a flat substrate, $R_1 < R_f < R_2$. Hence, the chemical potential of the particle at position 1 will be higher than the particle at position 2 (see Eq. 21) and there will be a driving force for migration from 1 to 2. This type of particle migration process has been referred to as "biased" or "driven" migration. It can also be seen from the figure, that unless the curvature of the substrate is comparable to that of the particles, the driving force for migration will tend to vanish.

Assuming a surface diffusion mechanism for the migration process, the time required for a particle to migrate from position 1 to position 2 (ref. 32) is given by:

$$t_{mig} \simeq - \frac{\pi^3 kt\sigma}{8D_s \gamma_m \Omega^2} \frac{\ln(R_1/R_2)}{\frac{1}{R_s^2}\left[\frac{1}{R_2} - \frac{1}{R_1}\right]^2} \quad , \tag{27}$$

where R_s is the radius of curvature of the substrate, and the contact angle, α, has been taken as 90°. Table 2 gives sample calculations of the migration time at several temperatures, using values of the parameters within the range of interest for conventional catalysts. It can be seen that the migration time is less than 1 hour at all temperatures, i.e., very much shorter than catalyst lifetimes.

TABLE 2

Time required for "driven" particle migration from convex to concave sites on curved supports, $R_s = 10$ nm, $R_2 = 2.2$ nm, $R_2/R_1 = 1.2$, after Ahn et al (ref. 32)

Temperature	$300^\circ C$	$500^\circ C$	$700^\circ C$	$900^\circ C$
t_{mig} (hours)	6×10^{-1}	9.2×10^{-4}	2.2×10^{-5}	1.9×10^{-6}

Thus, it is possible to summarize the role of particle migration phenomena in the metal surface area loss of conventional microporous supported catalysts, as follows. If a catalyst containing an initially random distribution of particles is heated, and the radius of curvature of the substrate is comparable to that of the particles, then particles will migrate rapidly from regions of substrate convexity to regions of substrate concavity. Particles which arrive at the same concave site will collide and coalesce, leading to particle growth. However, once this process is complete, no further growth by this process is likely, since particles will tend to be trapped at concave sites by the chemical potential barrier confronting the migration of particles away from those sites.

The actual extent of particle growth resulting from this process, in a conventional microporous catalyst, may vary from large to insignificant, depending on the number of particles which are present within a given pore (or topological catchment area), i.e., depending on the number of particles per unit area as well as on the pore size. In any event, the effects of particle migration are likely to occur in the early stages of growth, and then cease to be a major factor. Beyond that point, continued particle growth must depend on interparticle transport processes.

V.2.   Effects of substrate curvature on growth by interparticle transport

As shown in the previous section, when particles reside on substrates having curvatures comparable with particle curvature, particles will migrate rapidly to concave regions of the substrate. Thus, in the limit of strong substrate curvature effects, we only need be concerned with the growth of particles residing in concave sites. This problem has also been treated by Ahn et al (ref. 32).

In that treatment, the surface area of particles growing on a substrate having the general shape shown in Fig. 9 has been calculated . A sample of the results obtained is given in Fig. 10 as a plot of

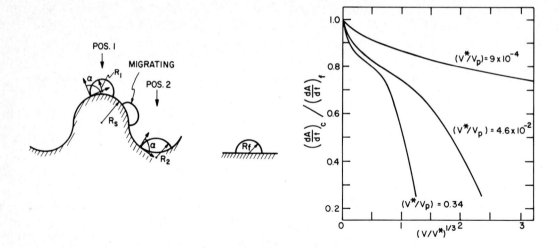

Fig. 9. Schematic of particles supported on an idealized curved substrate constructed from semi-circular segments.

Fig. 10. Ratio of the rate of metal surface area loss on curved substrates to that on flat substrates, plotted against normalized particle size, see text (after Ahn et al ref. 32).

$(dA/dt)_c/(dA/dT)_f$ versus $(V/V*)^{1/3}$, for the case of interparticle transport by substrate diffusion. The quantities $(dA/dt)_c$ and $(dA/dt)_f$ represent the rates of change of the exposed surface area of the particles in concave substrate sites and on flat substrates, respectively. The ratio has been calculated as a function of dimensionless particle size, $(V/V*)^{1/3}$ for several values of $(V*/V_p)$, which represents the ratio of average particle volume to pore volume. The figure shows that as the dimensionless particle size approaches zero or as the pore size approaches infinity, $(dA/dt)_c/(dA/dt)_f$ approaches unity; these conditions represent the limit of vanishing substrate curvature. For other conditions, the effect of the concave substrate is to suppress the rate of particle growth. Furthermore, this suppression arises primarily from geometric factors; thus, in a general sense, the results of Fig. 10 will hold even in the case of nucleation inhibited growth.

V.3.   Closing comments

The detailed results presented thus far in this section apply to particle growth on a substrate having the idealized form shown in Fig. 9. The growth of particles in pores having more realistic shapes has been discussed qualitatively in previous reviews (refs. 15, 24). The conclusions which can be drawn from general considerations are that growing particles will be confined to pores, and that pore size will largely dictate the ultimate particle size. However, as growth proceeds, and particles fill up the pores in which they reside, a progressively smaller fraction of the particle surface will be available to the gas phase, thus partially offsetting the apparent benefits of limited particle size.

It is clear, therefore, that in conventional catalysts, the rates of both of the major processes of particle growth - particle migration and interparticle transport - depend sensitively on the details of substrate topography and particle distribution. Consequently, the quantitative prediction of metal surface area loss is rendered difficult by the complexity of conventional supported catalyst systems. However, the fact that it is possible to discuss the issues cogently, and identify the areas of ignorance, is in itself an indication that the tools required for the understanding of those systems are now well in hand.

REFERENCES

1. P. Wynblatt and N. A. Gjostein, in J. O. McCaldin and G. Somorjai (Eds.), Prog. Solid State Chem., Pergamon, New York, 9 (1975) 21.
2. J. P. Hirth and G. M. Pound, in B. Chalmers (Ed.), Prog. Mater. Sci., Macmillan, New York, 11 (1963) 1.
3. P. Wynblatt, Phys. Stat. Sol., 36 (1969) 797.
4. M. McLean and E. D. Hondros, J. Mater. Sci., 6 (1971) 19.
5. A. S. Darling, Int. Metall. Rev., 18 (1973) 91.
6. P. Wynblatt and N. A. Gjostein, Acta Metall., 24 (1976) 1165.
7. N. A. Gjostein, in J. J. Burke, N. L. Reed and V. Weiss (Eds.), Surfaces and Interfaces, Syracuse Univ. Press, Syracuse, (1967) 271.
8. R. Brandon and F. J. Bradshaw, Royal Aircraft Establishment Tech. Report No. 66095, (1966).
9. H. C. Yao, M. Sieg and H. K. Plummer, Jr., J. Catal., in press.
10. H. C. Yao, P. Wynblatt, M. Sieg and H. K. Plummer, Jr., Proc. 5th Int. Conf. Sintering and Related Phenomena, Notre Dame, June 18-20, 1979, in press.
11. R. J. Berry, Surface Sci., 76 (1978) 415.
12. H. Schaffer and A. Tebben, Anorg. Chem., 304 (1960) 317.
13. O. Muller and R. Roy, J. Less Common Metals, 16 (1968) 129.
14. R. M. J. Fiedorow and S. E. Wanke, J. Catal., 43 (1976) 34.
15. P. Wynblatt and T-M. Ahn, in G. C. Kuczynski (Ed.), Mater. Sci. Research, Vol. 10, Sintering and Catalysis, Plenum Press, New York, (1975) 83.
16. E. Ruckenstein and B. Pulvermacher, AIChE J., 19 (1973) 356.
17. E. Ruckenstein and B. Pulvermacher, J. Catal., 29 (1973) 224.
18. E. E. Gruber, J. Appl. Phys., 38 (1967) 243.
19. F. A. Nichols and W. W. Mullins, Trans. AIME, 233 (1965) 1840.
20. F. A. Nichols, J. Appl. Phys., 37 (1966) 2805.
21. C. Wagner, Z. Electro Chem., 65 (1961) 581.
22. I. M. Lifshitz and V. V. Slyozov, J. Phys. Chem. Solids, 19 (1961) 35.
23. B. K. Chakraverty, J. Phys. Chem. Solids, 28 (1967) 2401.
24. P. Wynblatt, R. A. Dalla Betta and N. A. Gjostein, in E. Drauglis and R. I. Jaffee (Eds.). The Physical Basis for Heterogeneous Catalysts, Plenum Press, New York, (1975) 510.
25. R. M. J. Fiedorow, B. S. Chahar and S. E. Wanke, J. Catal. 15 (1978) 193.
26. P. Wynblatt, Acta Metall., 24 (1976) 1175.
27. T-M. Ahn, P. Wynblatt and J. K. Tien, in preparation.
28. R. W. Clark, P. Wynblatt and J. K. Tien, in preparation.
29. T-M. Ahn and J. K. Tien, J. Phys. Chem. Solids, 37 (1976) 771.
30. T-M. Ahn, S. Purushothaman and J. K. Tien, J. Phys. Chem. Solids, 37 (1976) 777.
31. W. K. Burton, N. Cabrera and F. C. Frank, Phil. Trans. Roy. Soc. (London), A243 (1950) 299.
32. T-M. Ahn, J. K. Tien and P. Wynblatt, submitted for publication.

DISCUSSION

P. WYNBLATT

Charcosset - Have you been considering the possibility of surface reduction of alumina during sintering of Pt/Al_2O_3 under reducing atmospheres ?

Wynblatt - In the present paper, I have ignored the possibility of surface reduction of alumina in the presence of reducing atmospheres. However, it has been implicitly assumed that the conditions which prevail during an experiment will remain constant throughout the experiment. As long as that is true, I do not think reduction effects would present any problems.

I have also performed some experiments which suggest a reaction between Pt and Al_2O_3 under hydrogen at temperatures of $\sim 1000°$ C. However, these experiments are incomplete and somewhat ambiguous, so that I would rather not take any definite position at the present time.

Yates - With regard to the PtO_2 monomers that you propose to exist, do you think that it would change the argument if rafts were present instead ?

For the system Pt on Al_2O_3, we have many times heated such catalysts in air under a variety of conditions. We find particles in X-ray diffraction, after this, of between 100 and 1000 A. However, these are always of Pt not PtO_2 ! Obviously, if the particles are covered with a larger of oxygen, we would not see this in the X-ray spectrum. Do you have any comments on this ?

Wynblatt - As I explained in my talk, there exists a range of metal loading (expressed as a coverage, θ) and of temperature, where PtO_2 will be present as monomers. Outside this range, and below the decomposition temperature of bulk PtO_2, PtO_2 monomers could exist in equilibrium with either 2-D islands (rafts) or 3-D clusters of PtO_2. Thus, rafts could co-exist with monomers under certain conditions.

Yao et al (my ref-9) observed the presence of bulk PtO_2 by chemical methods (temperature programmed reduction). As far as the apparent absence of X-ray evidence for PtO_2 in the Pt/Al_2O_3 catalysts which you have examined, I would comment that the conditions under which bulk PtO_2 is formed are rather restricted. Now that we know where to look for it, PtO_2 may be easier to find by X-ray techniques.

Imelik - Do you have some experimental proof for different particle shapes you have presented in your talk. In particular, concerning the hemispherical shape, which could indicate a rather strong interaction between the metal and the support.

Wynblatt - The shape of a particle existing in local equilibrium with a substrate will be determined by the values of the three interfacial energy terms which act upon it, namely : the particle surface energy, the substrate particle interface energy, and the substrate surface energy. In the case of "macroscopic" metallic platinum entities in equilibrium with alumina, McLean and Houdros (my ref. 4) have shown that the contact (or wetting) angle is $\sim 98°$. This corresponds to a nearly hemispherical shape, and to a relatively weak interaction between Pt and Al_2O_3 of ~ 72 kJ/mole. Il have myself confirmed by means of tilting experiments in the transmission electron microscope, that Pt particles in the size range 100-200 Å are also nearly hemispherical.

Yacaman - 1°/ It is generally established that for the case of critical nuclei size of one atom the classical nucleation theory is no longer valid and one has to go to an atomistic-rate type of theory. Would you comment on the implications of this to your results.

2°/ In what range size will you locate your "macroscopic" 3-D clusters.

Wynblatt - I only used the nucleation theory formalism as a rough method of ascertaining that no nucleation barrier was present to impede the agglomeration of metallic Pt monomers. I dont think that an atomistic formalism would have been any more significant, in view of the sub-atomic size of the critical nucleus.

It is difficult to estimate the size at which a cluster will begin to display macroscopic properties. My guess would be that this happens when the number of atoms in a particle lies somewhere between several hundred and several thousand.

Martin - If one compares iron and plazinum catalysts, for instance, one observes that iron particles are larger, and that degrees of reduction of iron-based catalysts are smaller. Thus, we are led to the idea that sintering and oxidability are relazed, and my question is the following : in the case of interparticle transport via the substrate, in what chemical state is the atom ? Is it in the metallic state, or rather, in the ionic state ?

Wynblatt - In the presence of oxygen, we presume that the transport species is a PtO_2 molecule, whereas under reducing conditions, it is assumed that the transport species is a metallic atom. However, in the latter case there could be some charge transfer between the atom and the substrate, and I have no idea how important that might be or how it could affect the transport process.

Ruckenstein - Concerning the comment of Dr Yates I would like to observe that it is very difficult to detect the presence of a single monolayer of PtO_2 on a substrate by X-ray diffraction. Even when a lattice of PtO_2 is formed, the amount of crystalline PtO_2 required for the X-ray method is quite large. The electron diffraction method is able, however, to detect the formation of such smaller amounts of crystalline material. We have determined the presence of PtO_2 by electron diffraction after heating Pt islands deposited on a thin layer of graphite at very low pressure of O_2 (Chu and Ruckenstein, Surface Science, 1977). Concerning the comment of Dr Charcosset, I mention that we have detected by electron diffraction the formation of a Pt-Al alloy but at very high temperatures (Chu and Ruckenstein J. Catal., 1978).

Concerning the paper of Dr Wynblatt I would like to comment about the Lifshitz-Slyozov theory of the Ostwald ripening mechanism of sintering. This theory is based upon a continuity equation similar to that used in hydrodynamics. A stochastic formulation of the problem developed by Ruckenstein and Dadybujor (J. Catal. 1977) revals, however that the "hydrodynamic approach" is approximate.

Wynblatt - Thank you for your comment.

Dadyburjor - Calculations to clarify the role of strain-induced cracking in the redispersion of Pt/Al_2O_3 indicate that "small" particles (~ 40 Å) will exist as Pt oxide, while larger particles contain a surface layer of oxide over a core of Pt metal, when an oxidizing atmosphere is present.

These results may explain the apparent discrepancy between the absence of oxide as noted by Dr Yates above, and the results of Dr Yao.

Wynblatt - Clearly, under conditions where the kinetics of oxidation of metallic platinum are slow, both metallic platinum as well as PtO_2 could be present for extended periods of time.

Pasternak (remark to Martin) - In the case of Sn metal clusters in an oxide matrix, Mössbauer effect observations suggest that the Sn outer layer does not react with the oxide host. No charge transfer is observed.

Wynblatt - Thank you for your comment.

J. BOURDON (Editor)
Growth and Properties of Metal Clusters, pp. 35—38
© 1980 Elsevier Scientific Publishing Company — Printed in The Netherlands

MECANISME DE COALESCENCE DYNAMIQUE D'AGREGATS

J.J. METOIS

Centre de Recherche sur les Mécanismes de la Croissance Cristalline - C.N.R.S.,
Centre Scientifique de Saint-Jérôme, 13397 Marseille Cedex 4 (France)

Le dépôt d'un film mince sur un substrat débute par la nucléation d'une phase
condensée à partir d'une couche d'atomes adsorbés. Dans le cas où les énergies
d'interaction dépôt-substrat sont faibles par rapport aux liaisons entre atomes du
dépôt, il y a formation d'une distribution discontinue de germes tridimensionnels.
Le remplissage progressif de la surface de support résulte de l'action simultanée
de deux phénomènes : la croissance des germes qui est contrôlée par un mécanisme de
diffusion de surface des adatomes et la coalescence entre les germes.
Lors des premières études concernant les dépôts sous vide, théoriciens et expérimen-
tateurs considéraient que les germes formés sur le substrat étaient immobiles et que
la coalescence survenait lorsque, durant leur croissance, des germes voisins deve-
naient jointifs. Cette conception a été rapidement mis en doute par des auteurs tels
que : Bassett, Phillips, Masson et Kern. Un modèle dynamique est proposé dans lequel
on suppose que les germes sont mobiles sur le substrat et que la coalescence résulte
du choc entre deux germes.

Dans tout ce qui suit nous nous intéresserons au cas de la condensation sous UV
des couches minces d'or sur une surface (001) KCl fraîchement clivée. Les difficultés
rencontrées dans l'étude de la formation des films minces résident dans le fait que
les expériences antérieures étaient menées de telle manière que nucléation, orientation
et coalescence avaient lieu simultanément. Pour s'affranchir de ces inconvénients, nous
avons condensé de faibles quantités d'or (10^{13} cm^{-2} sec^{-1}, 30 sec) sur KCl à température ambiante. Les populations de grains ainsi obtenues, reproductibles et ayant une
granulométrie parfaitement connue, constituent notre état de référence. Après le
dépôt, les échantillons sont recuits à des températures constantes T et pendant des
temps déterminés. Les populations de grains ainsi obtenues sont analysées pour être
comparées à notre référence. Cette manière d'opérer permet de s'assurer que le phénomène nucléatoire ne joue aucun rôle dans la modification de la granulométrie avant et
après recuit.

Dans une première phase nous nous sommes attachés à montrer expérimentalement que
la migration des cristallites sur le substrat était une réalité. Pour ce faire, il
est nécessaire de dissocier les phénomènes : mobilité de grains et coalescence. Ayant
observé que des recuits à température T ≤ 100° C ne modifiaient en rien l'histogramme
de taille de l'état de référence (nombre de grains, taille et dispersion de taille
constants) nous avons étudié la mobilité des grains dans ce domaine de température.

En utilisant une technique d'ombrage de hauts gradins par un flux d'or oblique, afin d'introduire une discontinuité dans la distribution des cristallites d'or sur (100) KCl, nous avons montré que la limite entre la zone contenant des cristallites et la zone qui en est dépourvue s'étale lorsque les échantillons sont recuits à des températures $T > 80°$ C. Compte-tenu du fait que la granulométrie du système reste conservative au cours du recuit si $T \leq 100°$ C, nous en avons conclu que l'étalement de la limite était la conséquence de la migration des grains d'or en tant qu'entité (ref. 1). La mobilité des grains a été confirmée en établissant les distributions radiales des cristallites. Sur des surfaces exemptes de gradins nous avons relevé les coordonnées (x,y) d'environ 3000 cristallites et calculé les distances intercristallites : r. Les distributions de fréquence de r permettent de calculer très aisément la distribution radiale des grains g(r). Nous avons constaté que bien que l'histogramme de taille des cristallites soit inchangé au cours des recuits ($80°$ C $< T < 100°$ C), la forme de la distribution radiale se modifie. Cette modification ne peut être donc attribuée qu'à la mobilité des grains (ref. 2). L'analyse de la forme des distributions radiales g(r) après recuit a permis de détecter la présence d'interactions répulsives entre les cristallites. Ces forces d'interaction ont une origine élastique. En effet, lorsque les paramètres du dépôt sont différents de ceux du support, à l'interface cette différence tend à être minimisée d'où la présence d'un champ de tension. Ce champ de tension se propage dans le support au voisinage du cristallite et lorsque deux cristallites s'approchent l'un de l'autre, leurs champs de tension de même signe interagissent pour créer des forces qui tendent à les éloigner (ref. 3).

Dans un M.E. permettant de réaliser sous UV le clivage, le dépôt et le recuit, nous avons pu observer sur le système Au/MgO la mobilité des grains. Les trajectoires empruntées par les cristallites semblent éviter la collision, ce qui pourrait résulter de l'action des forces répulsives entre cristallites (ref. 4).

Dans une seconde phase, nous avons étudié des échantillons recuits à des températures plus élevées ($200°$ C $< T < 350°$). Pour ces conditions expérimentales, l'histogramme de taille des grains diffère de celui de l'état initial. La densité diminue, la taille moyenne et la dispersion de taille augmentent, tous ces facteurs résultent de la coalescence intercristallites. L'étude de l'évolution des histogrammes de taille des cristallites, en fonction du temps de recuit et pour différentes températures, a permis de tester une théorie originale de la coalescence par chocs intergranulaires (réf. 5). Cette théorie s'inspire de celle de la coagulation des colloïdes de Smoluchowski. Les hypothèses de base de cette formulation sont dictées par les résultats expérimentaux obtenus lors de l'étude de la migration des cristallites. On considère une population de cristallites animés d'un mouvement brownien. Leur coefficient de diffusion D est calculé à partir de la relation reliant D avec la température et la taille du cristallite. Cette relation a été établie expérimentalement pour des recuits $T \leq 100°$ C (ref. 6). Toutes les collisions inter-cristallites n'entrainant pas nécessairement la coalescence, il existe un coefficient d'efficacité ($\delta < 1$) de la coalescence. De plus, nous avons pu montrer que les cristallites résultant des actes de coalescence sont immobiles car ils présentent une orientation épitaxique particulière. Des équations différentielles décrivant le mécanisme de coalescence par chocs ont été établies et nous avons proposé une solution numérique. Connaissant la distribution de taille de cristallite dans l'état de référence (dépôt 20° C), cette formulation permet d'établir l'évolution des histogrammes de taille en fonction du temps et de la température de recuit. La confrontation expérimentale avec la théorie formulée a montré qu'il existait un coefficient d'efficacité δ de la coalescence. Ce facteur δ dépend d'une part de l'orientation azimutale mutuelle des cristallites durant l'acte de coalescence et d'autre part de l'énergie d'activation nécessaire pour surmonter les forces répulsives entre cristallites afin d'établir le contact.

Lors de la formation des couches minces, la coalescence dynamique joue un rôle important car elle peut agir dès les premiers stades de la condensation. Chapon et al (ref. 7) ont pu montrer, grâce à une technique de visualisation indirecte par du Cd, que des cristallites d'or d'un diamètre inférieur à 7 Å peuvent coalescer sur NaCl même à température ambiante. D'ailleurs dans les théories récentes de la nucléation, le mécanisme de coalescence dynamique est inclu.
Les travaux décrits précédemment peuvent trouver une application en catalyse hétérogène. En effet, on sait que le vieillissement des catalyseurs est lié à la diminution du rapport surface/volume, or cette diminution peut être attribuée à la coalescence dynamique entre les grains. La coalescence dynamique étant liée à la mobilité qui est elle-même liée à l'épitaxie, on peut concevoir des conditions expérimentales telles que la mobilité des grains soit minimisée et par voie de conséquence la durée de vie du catalyseur augmentée.

REFERENCES
1. A. Masson, J.J. Métois et R. Kern, Advances in Epitaxy-Endotaxy, H.G. Schneider and V. Ruth (Ed.), Vol. II, Deutscher Verlag für Grundstoffindustrie Leipzig, 1971, p. 103.
2. J.C. Zanghi, J.J. Métois et R. Kern, Phil. Mag. 29, 5 (1974) 1213.
3. J.C. Zanghi, J.J. Métois et R. Kern, Surf. Sci. 52 (1975) 556.
4. J.J. Métois, K. Heinemann et H. Poppa, App. Phys. Letters 29, 3 (1976) 134.
5. J.J. Métois, J.C. Zanghi, R. Erre et R. Kern, Thin Solid Films 22, 3 (1974) 331.
6. R. Kern, A. Masson et J.J. Métois, Surf. Sci. 27 (1971) 483.
7. C. Chapon, C. Henry et B. Mutaftschiev, J. Cryst. Growth 33 (1976) 291.

DISCUSSION

J.J. METOIS

Yacaman - In the diffraction patterns that you show, there was a (111) ring possibly due to multiple twinned particles that disappeared after annealing. That seems to imply that the icosahedral particles (or decahedral) will change to pyramidal shaped epitaxial particles and thus a better rearrangement is being produced on the cristallites. Is your activation energy enough to account for this ?

Metois - We observe an orientation change from (111) to (100) when a dynamical coalescence occurs between particles. This takes place during reheating at $T \geqslant 200°C$, this an experimental observation which is difficult to explain at present. The activation energy of this orientation change is perhaps low since the (111) particles have paracristalline structures which are destabilized when the particles grow. This is of course a tentative explanation.

Ruckenstein - Computations performed some years ago by Hoare and Pal have shown that the small clusters have isosahedral configuration. Only when the crystallites become sufficiently large do they acquire an fcc structure. This I believe can explain the results of Dr Metois.

Metois - I do not think that a size increance is sufficient to explain the change from (111) to (100). In effect we have been able to show that for increasing particle sizes, this change occurs only when there is coalescence of particles.

We think that the orientation change takes place when two particles come into contact and coalesce.

Lafourcade - Avez-vous tourné votre échantillon de façon à faire apparaitre les points de macle et les doubles diffractions associées.

Metois - Non, je n'ai pas effectué ce type de mesures car, lors de l'étude de la cinétique de la coalescence dynamique des clusters, je n'ai pas abordé les problèmes concernant la structure des particules multimaclées. Le seul point qui représentait de l'intérêt pour moi dans ce travail, était de connaître le plan de contact dépôt-support et ceci ne nécessite pas de tourner l'échantillon.

Froment - Pouvez vous faire intervenir la formation de défauts dans la cinétique de coalescence ? En effet, lors de la coalescence de germes faiblement désorientés, peuvent se former des dislocations. Est-ce possible de voir ces défauts lors des observations en microscopie électronique ?

Metois - Pour le système Au/KCl, nous avons constaté que la cinétique de coalescence est régie par la diffusion des germes sur le support ; l'acte de coalescence proprement dit est un processus très rapide. Nos mesures, basées sur la comparaison des histogrammes avant et après recuits ne nous permettent donc pas d'obtenir des informations sur l'influence de défauts dans la cinétique de l'acte de coalescence.

Concernant la deuxième partie de votre question, les observations au microscope électronique font apparaitre de nombreux défauts dans les grains dont on ne connait pas l'origine. Pour connaître l'origine d'un défaut, il faudrait pouvoir suivre, au cours du temps, la coalescence de deux grains. L'appareillage expérimental utilisé au laboratoire, n'est pas adapté pour des observations in-situ.

J. BOURDON (Editor)
Growth and Properties of Metal Clusters, pp. 39—46
© 1980 Elsevier Scientific Publishing Company — Printed in The Netherlands

MOLECULAR DYNAMICS SIMULATION OF A CLUSTER MOTION ON FOREIGN SUBSTRATE

S. STOYANOV

Institute of Physical Chemistry, Bulgarian Academy of Sciences
1040 Sofia, Bulgaria

ABSTRACT

One-dimensional Frenkel-Kontorova model was used to simulate the motion
of a cluster in the periodic field, created by the substrate. An "equilibrated" cluster showed a Brownian-like motion above a certain total energy.
Completely different type of motion was shown to exist at considerably lower
energy under specialy chosen initial conditions.

INTRODUCTION

The mobility of small clusters on a foreign substrate is an well established fact [1]. A direct theoretical approach to this problem is provided
by the method called molecular dynamics. A computer can solve the Newton
equations of motion of all atoms of the substrate and the clusters on it.
Thus one can follow the motion of the clusters as entities. Such an approach
automatically accounts for the elastic forces between the cluster pairs, due
to the overlap of the strain fields induced by the clusters in the substrate.

Computer time and memory limitations, however, restrict the number of
atoms in the system (substrate and clusters on it). That is why it seems
reasonable to choose a relatively simple model and to concentrate on revea-
ling the mechanism of a clusters motion.

MODEL

The model analised in this paper is shown in fig. 1. The cluster is
simulated by a linear chain of atoms connected one to the next by identical
springs of natural length b and force constant α. The substrate is also a
chain of atoms which are assumed to be fixed in place, whereas the upper
chain can move.

The lower chain creates a sinusoidal potential having an amplitude A. The
substrate lattice parameter is a and the natural misfit between the unstrained chain and the substrate is $B = (b - a) / a$.

This model (at $B = 0$) has been used by Frenkel and Kontorova [2], and
by Seeger et al. [3] to study the propagation of a crystal dislocation. The
statics of the model has been analysed by Frank and van der Merwe [4],

Snyman and van der Merwe [5], Markov et al. [6] in studing the equilibrium structure of the substrate - overgrowth interface.

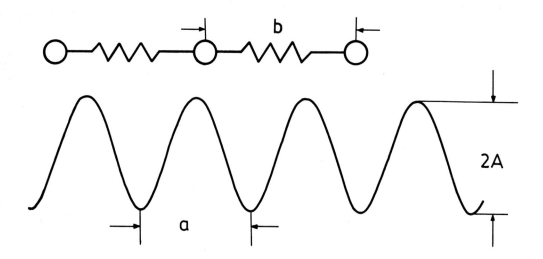

Fig. 1. One - dimensional model of a cluster on a foreign substrate. The lattice constants of the substrate and the cluster are a and b. The amplitude of the potential field created by the substrate is A; the force constant of the springs is α.

COMPUTATIONAL PROCEDURE

The Runga-Kutta-Gill algorithm [7] was applied to solve the equations of motion of the atoms, belonging to the chain. This algorithm computes the values of the atom coordinates and velocities at a moment t + Δt, provided that the values of these quantities at a moment t are known. The initial values of the coordinates and the velocities of the atoms, necessary to start the computation, were chosen in two completely different ways.

The first type initial conditions were intended to represent an "equili-brated" cluster. The values of the coordinates and velocities were obtained as a result of slowly "heating" the chain, starting from a low energy state, satisfying the equipartition law. The "heating" of the chain was realized by solving the equations of motion with the atom velocitites being multiplied by 1.02 after each 500 time steps (after a time interval 500 Δt). The total energy of the chain was thus slowly increased to values at which a mobility of the chain as an entity occured. The temperature of the chain, calculated from the time average kinetic energy, also increased during this procedure, justifying the term "heating".

The atom coordinates and velocities needed to start the "heating" were obtained in the following way. Since the "heating" starts from a low energy state, the atoms belonging to the chain vibrate about their equilibrium positions. These equilibrium positions can be easily obtained by numerically solving the algebraic equations, describing the lowest energy state of the chain.

As far as the motion of the atoms is concerned, it is a superposition of the normal vibrations of the system. From a dynamical point of view the amplitudes of the normal vibrations are arbitrary constants of integration. From a point of view of the statistical mechanics, however, the amplitudes must satisfy the law of equipartition of the energy among the degrees of freedom

$$m_i \omega_i^2 C_i^2 = kT$$

Here m_i, ω_i and C_i are the equivalent mass, the frequency and the amplitude of the i-th normal oscilator. The first two quantities are known in the case of zero misfit (B = 0). Using them as an approximation and choosing sufficiently low temperature one can calculate the amplitudes C_i.

The exact solution of the linearized equations of motion ($\sin x \approx x$) at B = 0 includes also phase constants, which do not appear in the expression for the energy of chain. Thas is why their values (between 0° and 360°) were chosen by random number generator. This exact solution (at B = 0) was used to give both the velocities of the atoms and their deviations from the equilibrium positions at B = 0. This is, in fact, an approximation used to calculate the initial conditions, necessary to start the "heating" of the chain.

The motion of the chain was followed in long runs, consisting of 10^5 time steps. To avoid the effect of error accumulation an energy correction was incorporated in the program. The correction was realized after each 500 time steps by changing the velocity of the left atom to adjust the total energy of the chain to its initial value. Since one is not interested in paricular trajectories of the chain but in its mobility at a fixed energy, the correction does not interfier with the aim of this investigation.

Two runs at each energy value were carried out covering a total time interval $\tau = 6000$. Here $\tau = t \, (2\pi A/ma^2)^{1/2}$ is a dimensionless time, m is the mass of one atom and t - a real time. Assuming typical values $m = 3 \times 10^{-22}$g, $a = 3 \times 10^{-8}$cm, A = 0.3 ev one obtains $t = 2.992 \times 10^{-13}\tau$ sec. The motion of the chain is therefore simulated for a real time interval $t = 1.795 \times 10^{-9}$ sec.

The simulation based on the first type initial conditions is in some way a passive approach to the problem. The computer is expected to do the whole work and to give us the mean square displacement as a function of the temperature (the time average kinetic energy per atom). This approach however, cannot be successful, due to the too short interval, covered by the simulation. Even if the chain makes 10^5 jumps per second, which is considerably higher than the experimentally observed value (the diffusion coefficient $D = 10^{-13}$cm^{2}sec^{-1} [1] corresponds to 10^2 jumps/sec) one has to cover a time

42

interval 10^{-5} sec in order to simulate a single jump. (The chain is assumed
to have made a single jump, when both atoms at its ends have entered the
neidhbouring substrate potential wells, provided that the number of misfit
dislocations has not changed.)

The basic idea in choosing the second type initial conditions is to
simulate particular trajectories, which rarely occur but lead to a migration
of a chain, having a relatively low energy. Since the model under consideration can be approximetaly described by the well known sine-Gordon equation
[8], the traveling wave solutions of this equation were used as a guide in
searching the desired initial conditions. No precise procedure of calculating the atom coordinates and velocities was developed and only 20% of the
runs turned out to be succesful. In the successful runs the chain moved in
one direction at a distance from 5a to 17a in a time interval τ = 100,
depending on the total chain energy. No energy correction was applied during
these relatively short runs (5000 steps, $\Delta\tau$ = 0.02). The energy change, due
to computational errors, was less than 0.1%.

RESULTS AND DICUSSION

The results obtained in molecular dynamics simulation of a chain of 24
atoms with parameters B = 0.23, $\alpha a^2/2\pi A$ = 34.4. are shown in fig. 2. As seen,
the second type initial conditions (black circles) make the chain moving at
energies much lower than the energy at which mobility occurs under the firts
type initial conditions (empty circles). In addition the black circles show
distances covered in a time interval τ = 100, whereas the empty circles
reffer to τ = 6000. A qualitative difference also exists between the chain
motions started with different types initial conditions. The first type
conditions initiate Brownian - like motion whereas the second type conditions lead to one - directional motion with a constant mean velocity.

Besides the simulations covering time interval τ = 100, about 20 runs
were carried out with τ = 200. Only two of them turned out to be successful
with distances covered by the chain 18a and 33a, depending on the total
energy. In the remaining 18 runs the one - directional motion was destroyed
(in some cases after a time τ = 150, in others after the first one or two
jumps).

The temperature of the chain, calculated from the time average kinetic
energy is shown in. fig. 3 as a function of the energy per atom. The data
in the low energy region (empty circles) were calculated in the "heating"
procedure, whereas results, obtained in the long runs are presented in the
high energy interval.

Two branches, corresponding to the two types of motion can easily be
distinguisged. The empty circles reffer to the motion, initiated by the
firts type initial conditions and the black ones - to the one-directional

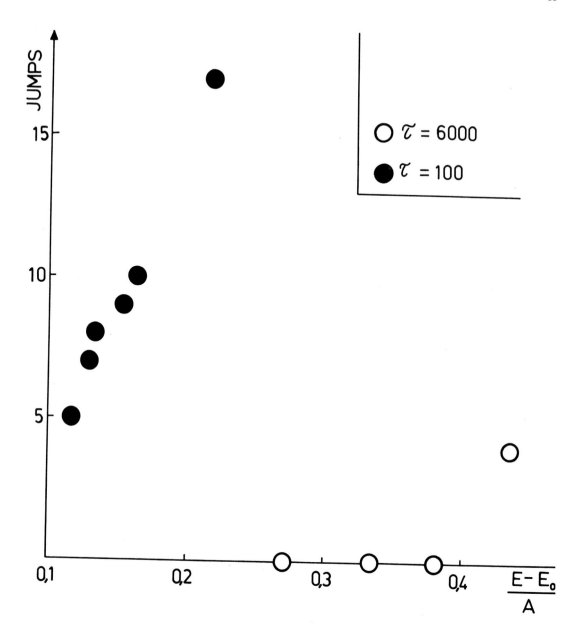

Fig. 2 . The number of jumps as a function of the energy per atom. E is the total energy per atom and E_o is the potential energy per atom in the lowest energy state of the chain. Empty circles reffer to the first type initial conditions, black circles - to the second type initial conditions.

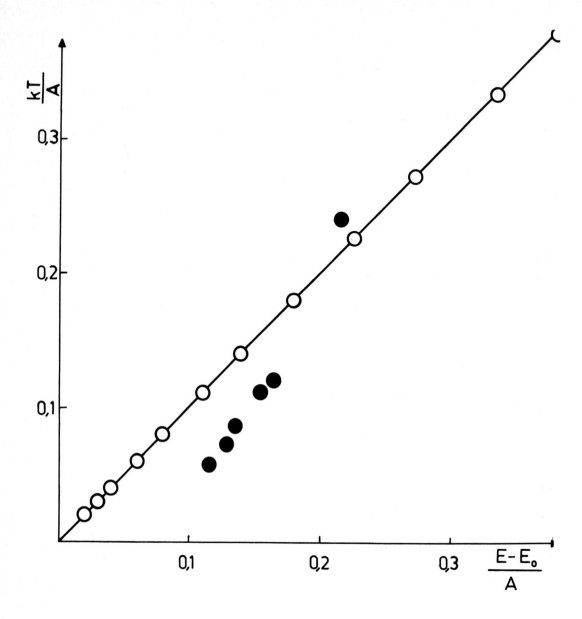

Fig. 3. The temperature of the chain, calculated from the time average
kinetic energy per atom. The empty circles represent results obtained in
the simulations, started with the first type initial conditions (equilibrated clusters). The black circles reffer to the second type initial conditions i.e. to one-directional motion of the chain.

motion strated by the second type initial conditions.

As a matter of fact, all empty circles reffer to an immobile chain and show a heat capacity per atom equal to k , in accordance with the classical statistical mechanics. A chain moving along the substrate show a higher heat capacity (the black circles in fig. 3). This fact suggests that although equivalent from dynamical point of view, the two types of motion of the chain are significantly different from a point of view of the statistical mechanics.

In its equilibrium state, the chain is immobile and its atoms vibrate about their equilibrium positions. As a result of these vibrations, the atom coordinates and velocities sometimes (very rarely) accept values similar to these, used in the simulation as second type initial conditions. Then the chain began to move along the substrate.

The lowest velocity obtained in the simulations was $v = 5000$ cm/sec. The chain moving with this show a temperature $T = 150^{o}K$ under the assumption $A = 0.3$ ev. As pointed out, however, such motions of the chain occur very rarely and therefore the real temperature of the chain is determined by the first type motion at the same energy (the line connecting the empty circles). Thus the lowest temperature at which chain mobility was observed in the simulations is $T = 300^{o}K$.

The model under cosideration does not account for the termal motion of the substrate atoms. This motion is likely to interfier with the correlated motion of the chain atoms, thus decreasing the distance covered by the chain. On the other hand, elastic waves in the substrate can be expected to stimulate mobility of the clusters on it.

REFERENCES

1. R. Kern, G. Le Lay and J.J. Metois, in E. Kaldis (Ed), Current Topics in Materials Science, Vol.III, North - Holland, Amsterdam, 1979, Ch.3, p.130

2. J. Frenkel and T. Kontorova, Journ. Phys. USSR 1 (1939) 137

3. A. Seeger, H. Donth, A. Kochendörfer, Z. Phys., 134 (1953) 173

4. F.C. Frank and J.H. van Merwe, Proc. Roy. Soc. (London) A 198 (1949) 205

5. J.A. Snyman and J.H. van der Merwe, Surface sci., 42 (1974) 190.

6. I. Markov and V. Karaivanov, Thin Solid Films (in press).

7. A. Ralston and H. Wilf, Matematical Methods for Digital Computers, Wiley, New York, 1966.

8. A. Barone, F. Esposito, C.J. Magee and A.C. Scott, Rivista del Nuovo Cimento, 1 (1971) 227.

DISCUSSION

S. STOYANOV

Moisar - Is there a physical background to choose a particular time step Δt (e.g. connected to vibrational frequency) for the calculation program ?

Stoyanov - Yes. The time step Δt must be sufficiently smaller than the vibrational period in order to achieve a good accuracy in numerical integration of the equations of motion. The most suitable value of Δt was "experimentally" determined, using the total energy conservation law as a criterion for the accuracy of the computations.

Wyntblatt - I believe that the one-dimensional model which you have used is very restrictive. There are many features of the movement of a particle on a substrate which are necessarily two-dimensional. In particular, surface diffusion models of particle migration are excluded from your 1-D model. Would you care to comment ?

Stoyanov - One-dimensional chains and their mobility have been observed by Bassett (Thin Solid Films, 48, (1978), 237). The model used in the modecular dynamics simulation is quite close to these observations. On the other hand, it can be used for an approximate description of the translation of 2-D and 3-D particles. This model, however, cannot be used in investigating the rotation of the particles and the achievement of epitaxial orientation. That is why a consideration of a 2-D model is highly desirable.

J. BOURDON (Editor)
Growth and Properties of Metal Clusters, pp. 47—55
© 1980 Elsevier Scientific Publishing Company — Printed in The Netherlands

ON THE MOBILITY OF SMALL EPITAXIAL ISLANDS - ONE-DIMENSIONAL MODEL

I. MARKOV and V. D. KARAIVANOV
Institute of Physical Chemistry, Bulgarian Academy of Sciences,
1040 Sofia, Bulgaria

ABSTRACT
    A misfit dislocation slip mechanism is proposed for the mobility of
small crystallites on the surface of a foreign substrate. The crystallites
are represented by finite chains of atoms connected with springs. The
activation energies required for the reversible motion of the chains
as entities are calculated as a function of the interaction forces,
the misfit and the chain length. It is found that an observable mobility
of small epitaxial islands could be expected if the natural misfit is
greater than the critical one, when misfit dislocations can be introduced
spontaneously at the free ends of the chains. In the opposite case mobility has to be assumed for very small clusters only whose sizes are comparable with the size at which a chain containing one misfit dislocation
becomes energetically favoured.

INTRODUCTION
    The first theoretical treatment of both the rotation and translation
of small clusters as entities on foreign substrates[1] appeared in 1968
after the first experimental observation of this phenomenon made by
Bassett[2] in 1960. Reiss[1] considered a finite two-dimensional island
with a simple cubic lattice placed in the two-dimensional sinusoidal potential field of a substrate with a quadratic symmetry. Both the overgrowth island and the substrate were assumed rigid. The calculation of
the change of the potential energy associated with the island's rotation
and translation has shown that the motion of initially misoriented clusters does not require large activation energies.
    In the last decade a series of experimental investigations of this
phenomenon was performed[3-12]. Besides, the mobility of clusters as entities had to be accepted to occur in some experiments on the initial
stages of the growth of thin films in order to give a satisfactory theoretical interpretation of the data[13]. The great scatter of the data
for the cluster mobility obtained in the above cited papers was the reason Kinosita and Takeuchi[14] to emphasize the role of the experimental
conditions. On the other hand, different values of the cluster mobility
have to be expected in different systems accounting for the interaction

forces and the lattice misfit. This is the aim of the present paper to derive a theoretical criterion for prediction of the cluster mobility which is high enough to affect considerably the epitaxial growth of the thin films. The overgrowth crystallites are simulated by chains of atoms with a finite length as a first approximation. The mechanism of the motion of the chains as entities is analogous to that suggested by Frenkel and Kontorova[15] in the late fourties to explain the plastic deformations in crystals. It consists of thermally activated movement of misfit dislocations[16] in one direction which leads to a shift of all atoms of the chain in the opposite direction. It is clear that the translation of the chain at one lattice parameter of the substrate requires an escape of a misfit dislocation at the one free end of the chain and an introduction of a new dislocation at the other end.

In their paper Frenkel and Kontorova have considered the motion of edge dislocations as a propagation of waves in an infinite chain of atoms representing the one half of the crystal in the sinusoidal potential field of the other half of the same crystal. Obviously, the translation of crystallites on foreign substrates can be formally considered as a "plastic flow" of the crystallites with respect to the substrate. The term "worm-like motion" used by Frenkel and Kontorova themselves appears to be very suitable to describe also the phenomenon of the cluster mobility. It is to be noted that the model is similar to that proposed by Masson et al[17] for translation of three-dimensional crystallites in epitaxial orientation. However, in the latter paper no calculations have been made. In the present paper the activation energy for surface diffusion of the chains as entities is calculated as a function of the energetic parameters included in the model, the misfit and the chain length.

MODEL

A chain consisting of a finite number of atoms $N+2$ is placed on a substrate which is a source of an invariable periodic potential $V(X)$ with a period a. The atoms are connected with springs(force constant μ, unstrained length b) which replace the quasi-elastic interatomic forces between the nearest neighbours. The left-hand end atom is chosen as an origin $n = 0$. The potential energy of the above system can be written in the form[15,16]

$$U = \frac{1}{2}\mu a^2 \sum_{n=0}^{N}(X_{n+1} - X_n - P)^2 + \sum_{n=0}^{N+1} V(X_n) \tag{1}$$

where aX_n is the displacement of the nth atom from the bottom of the nth potential trough of the substrate and $P = (b-a)/a$ is the natural misfit.

Usually a sinusoidal representation of the periodic potential is accepted[15,16]

$$V(X) = \frac{1}{2}W(1 - \cos 2\pi X) \tag{2}$$

where W is the depth of the potential troughs.

In some cases in order to obtain explicit solutions the periodic potential of the substrate is represented by simple parabolic archs[18-20]

$$V(X) = \tfrac{1}{2}\lambda x^2, \quad |x| \leqslant \tfrac{1}{2} a \tag{3}$$

the depth of the potential troughs being $W = \lambda a^2/8$.

The condition for equilibrium of the chain atoms

$$dU/dX_n = 0 \tag{4}$$

leads to the following system of algebraic equations:

$$\mu a^2(X_1 - X_0) = dV/dX_0 + P$$

$$\mu a^2(X_{n+1} - 2X_n + X_{n-1}) = dV/dX_n \quad (n = 1, 2, 3 \ldots \ldots N) \tag{5}$$

$$\mu a^2(X_{N+1} - X_N) = -dV/dX_{N+1} + P$$

where the first and the last equations appear as boundary conditions.

It is worth noting that Frenkel and Kontorova have used the condition

$$-dU/dX_n = m(d^2X_n/dt^2)$$

instead of (4), m and t being the atom mass and the time, respectively. Then, a system of differential equations for the particle motion is obtained.

In the case of the parabolic potential representation the equations in system (5) are linear and an exact explicit solution for the atom displacements is easyly obtained[20-22]. Moreover, on substituting the solution in equation (1) the following exact expression for the potential energy is obtained[22]:

$$U_M/\tfrac{1}{2}\mu a^2 = U_0/\tfrac{1}{2}\mu a^2 - 2MP + \beta M\frac{chq(N+2)}{shq(N+2)} + 2P\sum_{j=1}^{M} chq((N-2N_j)/2)/chq((N+2)/2) -$$

$$- \beta(\sum_{j=1}^{M} chq(N-2N_j) + 2(\sum_{\substack{i,j=1 (j>i)}}^{M}(chq(N-N_j-N_i) - chq(N-N_j+N_i+2)))/shq(N+2) \tag{6}$$

Here M is the number of the misfit dislocations, N_1+1, $N_2+1\ldots\ldots N_M+1$ are the numbers of atoms from the left-hand end to the first, second.... Mth dislocations, respectively. U_0 is the potential energy of a chain with the same length but not containing misfit dislocations[20,21]:

$$U_0/\tfrac{1}{2}\mu a^2 = P^2(N + 1 - \frac{2}{e^q-1}\frac{1 - (e^q-1)e^{-q(N+2)} - e^q e^{-2q(N+2)}}{(1 + e^{-q(N+2)})^2}) \tag{7}$$

The parameters μ and λ are included through the quantities β and q

$$\beta = (e^q-1)/(e^q+1) \tag{8}$$

$$a = \ln(\frac{k+2}{2} + (\frac{(k+2)^2}{4} - 1)^{1/2}) \qquad (9)$$

where $k = \lambda / \mu$.

Note that in the case of the parabolic potential the misfit dislocation is equivalent to empty trough when the misfit is positive($b > a$) and to pair of atoms in one trough in the opposite case($b < a$)[20-22]. When the substrate potential is represented by the fluent sinusoid the misfit dislocation is represented either by empty trough(or a pair of atoms in one trough) or by an atom on the hill between two adjacent troughs[23](Fig.1).

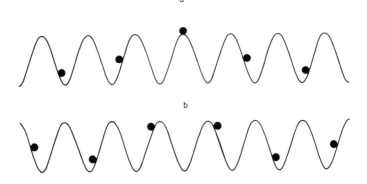

Fig. 1. Atom-on-hill (a) and empty-trough (b) configurations of the misfit dislocations.

As shown in refs.24 and 25 the atom-on-hill configuration appears only in the case of odd number of atoms and odd number of dislocations in the chain. In some cases(longer chains, lower values of the misfit) except of the positive dislocations(empty troughs) negative dislocations(pair-of-atoms in one trough) can appear. However, chain configurations with negative dislocations have much greater values of the potential energy [24,25] so they appear of no importance for our analysis.

Thus it is possible to investigate the energetic behaviour when the dislocations are moving in the chains, being introduced or escaped at the free ends. As will be shown the latter is of major importance for the process of cluster mobility assuming the dislocation slip mechanism.

Bearing also in mind the rather unrealistic shape of the parabolic potential, the same problem can be numerically solved using the sinusoidal potential representation as this is done in refs. 24 and 25.

MECHANISM OF MOTION

As was stated above the dislocation slip mechanism of motion of the chains(or crystallites) requires an introduction of a dislocation at the one free end and an escape of an initially existing one at the other end. Both the introduction and the escape of dislocations were studied by Frank and van der Merwe[16], the activation energies associated with these processes having been calculated. Because of the significance of this question it will be treated more thoroughly here using the parabolic potential representation for simplicity[22].

As shown by Stoop and van der Merwe[20] the absolute values of the displacements of the end atoms increase with the chain length. If the natural misfit P is smaller than the critical one P_{ns} for metastability od chains not containing dislocations[16,20,21] the displacements tend to a constant value smaller than 0.5. In the opposite case the displacements of the end atoms reach 0.5(the atoms reach the hills) at some critical length[20-22]. Longer chains can exist only if they contain misfit dislocations.

Let us now consider a chain with a length greater than the critical one and containing one dislocation in the lowest energy state as is shown in fig.2a(conf.1). If the dislocation moves, say, to the right-hand end all atoms are shifted to the left. Then, a critical configuration is reached(associated with a particular site of the dislocation) such that if the dislocation moves at one more lattice parameter to the right the first atom will overpass the left-hand hill of the trough. A new dislocation will be spontaneously introduced. The escape of the first dislocation leads then to reestablishment of the initial state but the chain is moved as entity at one lattice parameter. In fig.2b the change of the potential energy associated with this process is shown. The sharp peaks reflect the crests of the periodic potential and the minima represent the energies of the equilibrium configurations shown in fig.2a.

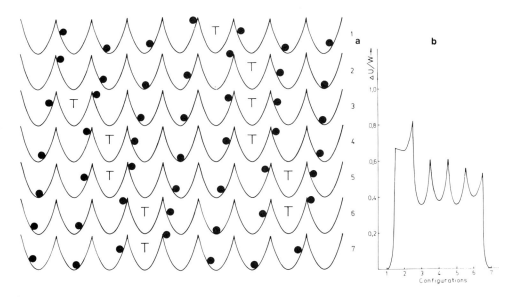

Fig. 2. The consecutive configurations (a) and the potential energy change (b) of a chain consisting of 7 atoms and initially containing one dislocation in the process of reversible translation(parabolic potential representation.

In the opposite case when the chain is shorter than the critical size
or the natural misfit P is smaller than the metastability limit P_{ms} the
existing dislocations can move and escape without the introduction of new
ones[22]. The displacements of the end atoms reach the values they would
have in a chain not containing a dislocation. The introduction of a new
dislocation at the ends requires then an additional energy compared with
the previous case.

Similar results are obtained when the sinusoidal potential profile is
used[25]. In fig.3a the consecutive equilibrium configurations ocupied
by a chain consisting of 11 atoms and containing one dislocation initially
are shown in a reduced form. The dislocation having initially atom-on-hill
configuration(odd number of atoms and one dislocation) escapes at the
one end and a configuration without a dislocation is reached. Then a new
dislocation is introduced at the other end and the initial lowest energy
state is reestablished. A case when the natural misfit is greater than
the metastability one is demonstrated in fig.3b. The chain consists again
of 11 atoms but contains now two dislocations with empty-trough configurations. As seen the introduction of a new dislocation occurs before
the escape of the initial one.

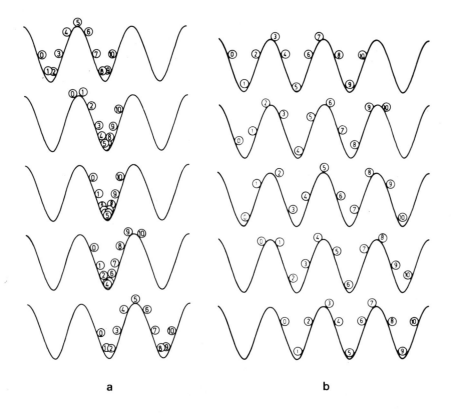

a   b

Fig. 3. The consecutive equilibrium configurations in the process of reversible translation of a chain consisting of 11 atoms:(a)-P = 15%, (b)-
P = 26.8%,(P_{ms} = 17.1%).

ACTIVATION ENERGIES FOR SURFACE DIFFUSION

The change of the potential energy connected with the reversible
chain motion shown in fig.3 is given in fig.4b. The maxima are associated with the asymmetrical configurations when a dislocation is introduced or escaped at the free ends. As seen such configurations are energetically unstable[24]. The relative minimum represents the energy of
the symmetrical configuration of the chain containing one dislocation
more or less compared with the lowest energy configuration. The change
of the potential energy of a chain containing more than one dislocations
in the case when $P < P_{ms}$ is shown in fig.4c. The consecutive maxima of
the left-hand and the right-hand sides are associated with the escape
and the introduction of the first, second, etc. dislocations, respectively. The consecutive relative minima represent the energies of the
symmetrical configurations containing one, two, etc. dislocations less
than in the lowest energy one. The highest relative minimum represents
always the energy of the chain without a dislocation. In this case the
chain has to cover as many lattice spacingsas the number of the dislocations in the lowest energy state in order to reestablish it. In the
case of very short chains(5-6 atoms) asymmetrical configurations do not
usually exist and the change of the potential energy has the form shown
in fig.4a.

Obviously, the difference between the energies of the lowest energy
state and the highest maximum connected with introduction or escape of
dislocations represents the activation energy for surface diffusion of
the chain as an entity. They are shown in fig.5 in units of the depth
of the potential troughs W as a function of the chain length at different values of the misfit. Aconstant value of the parameter $l_o^2 = \mu a^2/2W$
[16] is taken corresponding to the system Au/(001)NaCl[26]. The critical
misfit $P_{ms} = 1/l_o$ is equal to 17.1%. Two types of behaviour are observed.
When the natural misfit P is greater than P_{ms} the activation energies
oscilate around a nearly constant value lower than unity. This is obviously due to the fact that the slip of the dislocations to the one end
leads to a spontaneous introduction of a new dislocation at the other
end. In the opposite case($P < P_{ms}$) when this condition is not fulfilled
the activation energy increases monotoneously with the chain length after a minimum associated with the critical length at which a chain containing one dislocation becomes energetically favoured[20-22].

CONCLUSION

Bearing in mind all approximations connected with the one-dimensional
models and with the neglect of the entropy change in our considerations
the following criterion can be drawn:

1. If $P > P_{ms}$ an observable mobility of larger crystallites is expected.
2. If $P < P_{ms}$ an observable mobility of larger crystallites should not

be experimentally established. Mobility could be assumed for small clusters only with a size comparable with the critical one at which a chain containing one dislocation becomes energetically favoured.

Moreover, the azimuthal misorientation of the crystallites could be effectively expressed as an increase of the natural misfit. Then if $P < P_{ms}$ a cluster mobility could be observed while the crystallites are epitaxially misoriented.

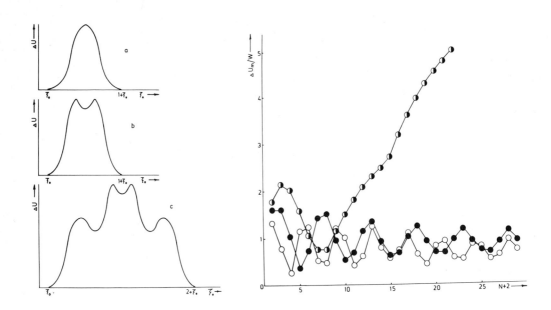

Fig. 4. Change of the potential energy acompanying the reversible translation:(a)-Bell-shaped curve when only two symmetric configurations exist, (b)-Bimodal curve when $P > P_{ms}$ or $P < P_{ms}$ but M=1, (c)-Polymodal curve when the chains contain more than one dislocations(M>1) and $P < P_{ms}$.
Fig. 5. Dependence of the activation energy for surface diffusion on thenumber of atoms N+2 in the chains(l_o=5.855 - Au/(001)NaCl); ◐ - P = 15%, ● - P = 20% and ○ - P = 26.8%.

Let us now consider some particular cases. The natural misfit for the system Au/(001)NaCl -26.8% is greater in absolute value than the critical one P_{ms} = 17.1%. Hence, an observable mobility of small epitaxial islands has to be expected. The case Au/(001)KCl is more complicated. According to Chan et al.[26] the potential troughs on the (001) plane of KCl are not equidistant. A network of potential troughs possessing nearly a distorted hexagonal structure is formed, the distances between the troughs being 2.84Å and 3.33Å. So that two misfits +1.4% and -13.6% exist both smaller in absolute value than the metastability limit P_{ms} = 27%. According to the above criterion Au crystallites in epitaxial orientation could not migrate. However, a migration has to proceed when the crystallites are epitaxially misoriented as this has been experimentally established by Masson et al.[3].

REFERENCES

1 H. Reiss, J. Appl. Phys., 39(1968)5045.
2 G.A. Bassett, Proc. Europ. Conf. Electron Microscopy, 1(1960)270.
3 A. Masson, J.J. Metois and R.Kern, Surf. Sci., 27(1971)465.
4 J.J. Metois, M. Gauch, A. Masson and R. Kern, Surf. Sci., 30(1972)43.
5 G. Honjo, K. Takayanagi, K. Kobayashi and K. Yagi, Jap. J. Appl.
  Phys., Suppl. 2, Part 1, 13(1974)357.
6 K. Heinemann and H. Poppa, Thin Solid Films, 33(1976)237.
7 J.J. Metois, K. Heinemann and H. Poppa, Appl. Phys. Lett., 29(1976)134.
8 J.J. Metois, K. Heinemann and H. Poppa, Phil. Mag., 35(1977)1413.
9 R.T.K. Baker and P. Skiba, Carbon, 15(1977)233
10 J.C. Zanghi, J.J. Metois and R. Kern, Phil. Mag., 31(1975)743.
11 H. Schmeisser, Thin Solid Films, 22(1974)83,99.
12 C.R. Henry, C. Chapon and B. Mutaftschiev, Thin Solid Films, 46(1977)
   157.
13 V.N.E. Robinson and J.L. Robins, Thin Solid Films, 20(1974)155.
14 K. Kinosita and K. Takeuchi, Paper presented at International Conference on Solid Films and Surfaces, 1978, Tokyo, Japan.
15 J. Frenkel and T. Kontorova, J. Phys.,Acad. Sci. USSR, 1(1939)137.
16 F.C. Frank and J.H. van der Merwe, Proc. Roy. Soc.,(London), A 198
   (1949)205.
17 A. Masson, J.J. Metois and R. Kern, in H.G. Schneider and V. Ruth
   (Ed.), Advances in Epitaxy and Endotaxy, VEB Deutscher Verlag für
   Grundstoffindustrie, Leipzig, 1971, Ch. 2, p. 103.
18 J.H. van der Merwe, J. Appl. Phys., 34(1963)117.
19 J.H. van der Merwe, Surf. Sci., 31(1972)198.
20 L.C.A. Stoop and J.H. van der Merwe, Thin Solid Films, 17(1973)291.
21 I. Markov and V. Karaivanov, Bulg. J. Phys., 5(1978)379.
22 I. Markov and V. Karaivanov, Thin Solid Films, 61(1979)115.
23 J. Kratochvil and V.L. Indenbom, Czech. J. Phys., B13(1963)814.
24 J.A. Snyman and J.H. van der Merwe, Surf. Sci., 42(1974)190.
25 I. Markov and V. Karaivanov, Thin Solid Films, in press.
26 E.M. Chan, M.J. Buckingham and J.L. Robins, Surf. Sci., 67(1977)285.

J. BOURDON (Editor)
Growth and Properties of Metal Clusters, pp. 57—63
© 1980 Elsevier Scientific Publishing Company — Printed in The Netherlands

SINTERING AND REDISPERSION OF SUPPORTED METAL CATALYSTS

E. Ruckenstein
State University of New York at Buffalo
Faculty of Engineering and Applied Sciences
Buffalo, New York, 14214, U.S.A.

ABSTRACT

The free energy of formation $\sigma(h)$ of a film of metal of thickness h on a substrate is used to identify conditions under which sintering or redispersion of the metal crystallites over the substrate can take place. If $\sigma(h)$ is positive for all values of h the metal cannot spread over the substrate. In this case migration and coalescence is the mechanism of sintering. However, when $\sigma(\infty) > 0$ but $\sigma(h) < 0$ for $h < h_o \ll \infty$ a thin film (probably a submonolayer) can coexist with the crystallites. As long as the surface concentration in this film is lower than the saturation concentration corresponding to the largest crystallite present, all the crystallites will lose molecules to the substrate. On the other hand, if the surface concentration becomes larger, then the crystallites with sizes smaller than a critical value will decrease in size, while those with larger sizes will grow (Ostwald ripening).

This thermodynamic point of view is used to explain experimental data concerning sintering and redispersion of Pt crystallites deposited on a thin film of alumina heated alternatively in oxygen and hydrogen.

I. INTRODUCTION

Supported metal catalysts contain a large number of metal crystallites 1 to a few tens of nm in size dispersed over the large internal surface of a highly porous material. The heating of the catalyst in vacuum and, in particular, in various chemical atmospheres, leads generally to the decay of the exposed surface area of the metal (ref. 1-4). The decay is a result of sintering which occurs either via crystallite migration over the surface of the substrate (ref. 5-9) and/or via Ostwald ripening (ref. 10-12). In the latter mechanism, the small crystallites lose atoms to a surface phase of single metal atoms on the surface of the substrate whereas the large crystallites gain such atoms from that phase. Ostwald ripening occurs when the surface concentration in metal atoms of the surface phase is larger than the surface concentration of single atoms in equilibrium with the large crystallites but smaller than the surface concentration of single atoms in equilibrium with the small crystallites. In addition and in contrast to Ostwald ripening, direct ripening involving only two or a few neighboring particles which are not in contact can also occur (ref. 13). In direct ripening single atoms are transferred directly from a smaller to a larger particle without the intermediate accumulation in a supersaturated surface phase of single atoms which covers the entire substrate. Consequently, direct ripening is a kind of fluctuation which can occur locally even for unsaturated global concentrations of the surface phase of single atoms.

There are, however, circumstances under which redispersion of the crystallites also takes place (ref. 14-18). In a recent experiment (ref. 18) we observed using electron microscopy that when Pt crystallites with an average size of about 4 nm, deposited upon a thin film of alumina, were heated alternatively in oxygen and hydrogen, several cycles of heating were needed before redispersion of crystallites occurred during heating in oxygen. Thereafter, redispersion and sintering could be produced periodically by changing the chemical atmosphere from oxygen to hydrogen.

Thermodynamic and kinetic arguments are used in the present paper to explain the above phenomena. The free energy of formation of a thin film on a substrate, σ, is the main quantity used in the thermodynamic analysis. The range of the interaction forces between one atom of the film at its free surface and the substrate is, in the cases of interest here, larger than the thickness of the film. For this reason, the film is not treated as a bulk phase and σ becomes a function of the thickness h of the film. The thermodynamic analysis allows us to associate Ostwald ripening and redispersion with a particular kind of phase separation, namely, the coexistence of a two-dimensional film with crystallites. When such a phase separation cannot occur, or when the surface concentration of atoms in the two-dimensional film is too low, migration and coalescence becomes the dominant mechanism of sintering. Although there are conditions under which vaporization, followed by vapor transport, gives rise to sintering, this case is not considered here.

II. ROLE OF WETTING IN SINTERING AND REDISPERSION

1. Thick Films

Consider a thick film of metal transferred from a large reservoir to a substrate. The free energy of formation of such a film is equal to the difference between the free energy of the final and initial states. Since the formation of the thick film involves the formation of a metal-gas interface and a metal-substrate interface and the disappearance of the substrate-gas interface, the free energy of formation of a film on a uniform substrate per unit area, σ_∞, is given by the expression

$$\sigma_\infty = \sigma_{mg} + \sigma_{ms} - \sigma_{sg}. \tag{1}$$

Here the subscript ∞ indicates that the film is thick and σ_{mg}, σ_{ms}, and σ_{sg} are the interfacial tensions between film and gas, film and substrate, and substrate and gas, respectively.

When $\sigma_\infty < 0$, the material composing the film wets the substrate (it spreads over its surface). In the opposite case the material does not wet the substrate and therefore islands of metal form which, in order to decrease the free energy of the system, tend to coalesce into a single island. In vacuum, the metals have large surface tensions, while the oxides have surface tensions several times smaller. Therefore, the metals do not wet the oxides. Islands of metal form which, in order to achieve a minimum free energy configuration, tend to coalesce into a single island. On the other hand, in an oxygen atmosphere the metal is oxidized, its surface tension decreases and, in some circumstances, σ_∞ may become negative. Then the metal oxide will spread over the substrate oxide with a rate which can be, however, extremely low.

2. Thin Films

In the cases of interest here, the loading of the substrate is low and the corresponding film is extremely thin. The range of the interaction forces between one atom at the free surface of the film and the substrate is larger than the thickness of the film and the film can no longer be treated as a bulk phase. Under these circumstances the free energy of formation of the film per unit area, σ, becomes a function of the thickness h of the film.

Neglecting the interactions with the gas phase, the free energy of formation σ is equal to the free energy σ_1 due to the interactions between the atoms of the film and those of the substrate minus the free energy σ_2 due to the interactions between the atoms of the film and the semi-infinite layer of the same metal atoms of the large reservoir.*

To compute the dependence of σ on h pairwise additivity is assumed and the Lenard-Jones potential

$$u(R) = -\varepsilon [2(\tfrac{\Omega}{R})^6 - (\tfrac{\Omega}{R})^{12}] \tag{2}$$

is used as the interaction potential between two atoms. Although for metals and oxides the interactions are poorly represented by the 6-12 potential, its simplicity makes this potential extremely attractive. Here R is the distance between two atoms, $\varepsilon = |u(\Omega)|$ and Ω is the position coordinate of the minimum in the curve u = u(R). To further simplify the problem, the free energy is approximated by the internal energy.

The interaction potential between one molecule of the film located at a distance z from a semi-infinite substrate is computed from the integral (ref. 19,20),

$$U_{ms}(z) = \int n_s u_{ms}(R) 2\pi R^2 dR \sin \theta \, d\theta, \tag{3}$$

where n_s is the number of molecules of substrate per unit volume and θ is the angle between the radius vector and the normal to the surface of the substrate. As before, the subscript ms refers to the interactions between metal and substrate. The energy of interaction per unit area between the film and substrate, σ_1, is given by

---

*It is instructive to demonstrate that for $h \to \infty$, $\sigma_1 - \sigma_2 \equiv \sigma_\infty$. Indeed, σ_1 is the free energy change when a semi-infinite substrate is brought, from infinite distance, in contact with the metal; in other words,

$$\sigma_1 = \sigma_{sm} - \sigma_{sg} - \sigma_{mg}.$$

Similarly, σ_2 is the free energy change when two parts of the same metal are brought, from infinite distance, in contact; hence,

$$\sigma_2 = -2\sigma_{mg}.$$

Consequently,

$$\sigma_1 - \sigma_2 = \sigma_{sm} + \sigma_{mg} - \sigma_{sg} \equiv \sigma_\infty.$$

$$\sigma_1 = \int_{\delta_{ms}}^{h} n_m U_{ms}(z)dz \equiv -\frac{\pi}{6}\varepsilon_{ms}\Omega_{ms}{}^6 n_s n_m (\frac{1}{\delta_{ms}{}^2} - \frac{1}{h^2}) + \frac{\pi}{360}\varepsilon_{ms}\Omega_{ms}{}^{12} n_s n_m (\frac{1}{\delta_{ms}{}^8} - \frac{1}{h^8}), \tag{4}$$

where n_m is the number of atoms of metal per unit volume and δ_{ms} is the minimum distance between one atom of metal and a molecule of substrate. Similarly one obtains that

$$\sigma_2 = -\frac{\pi}{6}\varepsilon_{mm}\Omega_{mm}{}^6 n_m{}^2 (\frac{1}{\delta_{mm}{}^2} - \frac{1}{h^2}) + \frac{\pi}{360}\varepsilon_{mm}\Omega_{mm}{}^{12} n_m{}^2 (\frac{1}{\delta_{mm}{}^8} - \frac{1}{h^8}), \tag{5}$$

where the subscript mm refers to the metal-metal interactions and δ_{mm} is the minimum distance between two metal atoms. Consequently,

$$\sigma = \frac{\pi}{6}(\frac{\varepsilon_{mm}\Omega_{mm}{}^6 n_m{}^2}{\delta_{mm}{}^2} - \frac{\varepsilon_{ms}\Omega_{ms}{}^6 n_m n_s}{\delta_{ms}{}^2}) - \frac{\pi}{360}(\frac{\varepsilon_{mm}\Omega_{mm}{}^{12} n_m{}^2}{\delta_{mm}{}^8} - \frac{\varepsilon_{ms}\Omega_{ms}{}^{12} n_m n_s}{\delta_{ms}{}^8})$$

$$ -\frac{\pi}{6}\frac{\varepsilon_{mm}\Omega_{mm}{}^6 n_m{}^2 - \varepsilon_{ms}\Omega_{ms}{}^6 n_m n_s}{h^2} + \frac{\pi}{360}\frac{\varepsilon_{mm}\Omega_{mm}{}^{12} n_m{}^2 - \varepsilon_{ms}\Omega_{ms}{}^{12} n_m n_s}{h^8}. \tag{6}$$

At large values of h, Eq. (6) reduces to

$$\sigma_\infty = \frac{\pi}{6}(\frac{\varepsilon_{mm}\Omega_{mm}{}^6 n_m{}^6}{\delta_{mm}{}^2} - \frac{\varepsilon_{ms}\Omega_{ms}{}^6 n_m n_s}{\delta_{ms}{}^2}) - \frac{\pi}{360}(\frac{\varepsilon_{mm}\Omega_{mm}{}^{12} n_m{}^2}{\delta_{mm}{}^8} - \frac{\varepsilon_{ms}\Omega_{ms}{}^{12} n_m n_s}{\delta_{ms}{}^8}). \tag{7}$$

Consequently the dependence of σ on h can be rewritten as

$$\sigma = \sigma_\infty + \frac{\alpha}{h^2} - \frac{\beta}{h^8}, \tag{8}$$

where

$$\alpha \equiv -\frac{\pi}{6}(\varepsilon_{mm}\Omega_{mm}{}^6 n_m{}^6 - \varepsilon_{ms}\Omega_{ms}{}^6 n_m n_s) \quad \text{and} \quad \beta \equiv -\frac{\pi}{360}(\varepsilon_{mm}\Omega_{mm}{}^{12} n_m{}^2 - \varepsilon_{ms}\Omega_{ms}{}^{12} n_m n_s). \tag{9}$$

Because of the continuum approach used in its derivation, Eq. (8) holds only for film thicknesses sufficiently large compared to molecular spacing. It is worth mentioning, however, that in a more rigorous theory of the dispersion interactions (ref. 21) based upon the macroscopic field equations and not involving the pairwise additivity of the potential, the same dependence on the thickness h was obtained. In this more detailed treatment, the coefficient α is expressed in terms of dielectric permeabilities.

3. Thermodynamic Stability of a Thin Film

$\sigma < 0$ is a necessary condition for the film to be stable from a thermodynamic point of view. Mechanical stability requires the additional condition $d\sigma/dh < 0$. Of particular significance in the present context is the case in which only very thin films of thickness h_o can wet the substrate. In other words $\sigma_\infty > 0$, but $\sigma(h_o) < 0$ and $(d\sigma/dh)_{h_o} < 0$. Such a situation may occur when α and β are negative and σ_∞ is positive but not too large. In Fig. 1 we plot σ against h for the latter case. If the loading of the substrate corresponds to a thickness h such that $h_c < h < h_m$, where h_c and h_m are defined in Fig. 1, then both σ and $d\sigma/dh$ are negative and the film is stable. If, however, $h > h_m$, the mechanical stability condition is violated and the film of thickness h is no longer thermodynamically

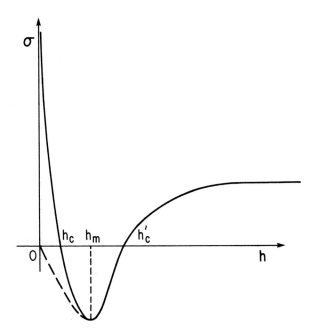

Fig. 1.

stable. In this case, in order to decrease the free energy, the system undergoes a process similar to a phase separation; one phase is a film of thickness h_m, whereas the second phase consists of a single crystallite containing the rest of the atoms.

Even though $\sigma_\infty > 0$, $\sigma(h)$ can become under certain circumstances negative for $h < h_c'$. To evaluate the thickness h_c' at which σ becomes zero, let us assume that h_c' is sufficiently large so that the terms in Eq. (6) due to the Born repulsion could be neglected. One then obtains

$$(h_c')^2 = \frac{\varepsilon_{mm}\Omega_{mm}^6 n_m - \varepsilon_{ms}\Omega_{ms}^6 n_s}{(\frac{\delta_{ms}}{\delta_{mm}})^2 \varepsilon_{mm}\Omega_{mm}^6 n_m - \varepsilon_{ms}\Omega_{ms}^6 n_s} \, \delta_{ms}^2 . \tag{10}$$

Since in the situation under consideration $\sigma_\infty > 0$, one can write (ignoring for the sake of simplicity the Born repulsion) that

$$\varepsilon_{mm}\Omega_{mm}^6 n_m > (\frac{\delta_{mm}}{\delta_{ms}})^2 \, \varepsilon_{ms}\Omega_{ms}^6 n_s . \tag{11}$$

When, in addition to inequality (11),

$$\varepsilon_{mm}\Omega_{mm}^6 n_m - \varepsilon_{ms}\Omega_{ms}^6 n_s < 0 \tag{12a}$$

is also satisfied, $\sigma(h)$ does not change the sign for any value of h. The more interesting case is that in which in addition to (11),

$$\varepsilon_{mm}\Omega_{mm}^6 n_m - \varepsilon_{ms}\Omega_{ms}^6 n_s > 0 \tag{12b}$$

holds. Then, the critical thickness h_c' becomes several interatomic distances thick when $(\frac{\delta_{ms}}{\delta_{mm}})^2 < 1$, but is smaller than the interatomic distance δ_{ms} when the opposite inequality is valid. Since the thickness of the repulsion range is of the order of δ_{ms} and since Eq. (10) was established ignoring the repulsive forces, values of h_c' somewhat smaller than δ_{ms} resulting from Eq. (10) are likely to imply that the free energy of formation σ cannot become negative. For metals on oxides it is reasonable to assume that $\delta_{mm} < \delta_{ms}$ and σ does not become zero for any value of h as argued above. For some oxides on oxides the inequalities $\delta_{ms} < \delta_{mm}$, (11) and (12b) may be simultaneously satisfied and therefore σ can become zero for a film thickness of several interatomic distances. Since the Born repulsion is short range one can expect under such conditions a negative minimum of σ at about a mono-layer (or possibly a submonolayer). To account for the zero value of σ when the amount of metal is zero, the full curve (in Fig. 1) has to be replaced for $h < h_m$ by the dotted curve. Of course, a more detailed approach has to better account for the partially filled mono-layer. Eq. (8) is not strictly valid from a quantitative point of view for the small thicknesses involved. However, the qualitative conclusions probably are in the right direction.

Consequently, if $\sigma < 0$ and $d\sigma/dh < 0$ in a given range of thicknesses $h_c < h < h_m$, total spreading will occur in that range. If $h > h_m$, then, at least, the mechanical stability condition is violated. Under such circumstances the phase separation already described takes place via the formation of a film of thickness h_m in contact with a single crystal-lite containing the remaining atoms.

III. DISCUSSION

Let us start the discussion by considering a large number of crystallites on a substrate. When σ_∞ is positive and $\delta_{mm} < \delta_{ms}$, $\sigma(h)$ does not become zero for any value of h and no spreading can occur. In order to achieve a minimum free energy the crystallites will migrate over the substrate and coalesce to achieve the smallest possible areas of the metal-gas and metal-substrate interfaces. Since the migration of the larger crystallites is extremely slow, only sufficiently small crystallites migrate at an appreciable rate and therefore large crystallites can survive for the entire life of the supported metal. Metals supported on oxides probably satisfy under vacuum and in hydrogen some of the above condi-tions.

When, however, σ_∞ is positive and not too large and, in addition, $\varepsilon_{mm} \Omega_{mm}^6 n_m > \varepsilon_{ms} \Omega_{ms}^6 n_s$ and $\delta_{mm} > \delta_{ms}$, $\sigma(h)$ becomes negative for values of h_c' equal to several inter-atomic distances. Under these circumstances, appreciable redispersion is expected under the form of a mono-molecular (or perhaps submonomolecular) film. This may happen in an oxygen atmosphere because the interfacial tension σ_{mg} becomes much smaller than in vacuum and if δ_{mm} becomes larger than δ_{ms}. Starting with metal crystallites, the heating in oxygen leads to metal oxide which in this case spreads through the leading edge of the crystallites over the substrate. As long as the surface concentration of the surface phase of single metal atoms is lower than the equilibrium surface concentration correspon-ding to the largest crystallite present, all the crystallites will lose atoms to the surface of the substrate. When, however, the surface concentration becomes larger, the crystallites with sizes smaller than a critical value will lose molecules to the surface of the substrate, whereas those with larger sizes will gain such molecules from the surface of the substrate. This is the Ostwald ripening mechanism. A crystallite is said to have the critical size when its equilibrium surface concentration in monomolecules is equal to the surface concentration of the surface phase. In the case just discussed, the overall behavior is redispersion as long as the exposed surface area of the oxidized metal increases, or is sintering in the opposite case. The ultimate thermodynamic equilibrium state will consist of a single crystallite in contact with a thin film.

Concerning the phenomena observed during alternating heating in oxygen and hydrogen (ref. 18) it appears likely that the first five or six cycles enhance the oxidation of crystallites and also cause some reconstruction of the substrate. After this initiation process, platinum oxide spreads, during heating in oxygen, over the surface of the substrate. By reducing platinum oxide to platinum during heating in H_2, the two-dimensional film recondenses into metal crystallites, being either recaptured by the existing crystallites or generating new ones. This happens because the metal does not wet the substrate.

The thermodynamic analysis developed in the present paper is able to explain some of the features of sintering and redispersion. It associates redispersion and sintering via Ostwald ripening with the occurrence of a two-dimensional phase in contact with the crystallites. When such a two-dimensional phase does not occur or when the amount of molecules forming the two-dimensional phase is low, migration and coalescence constitute the dominant mechanism of sintering.

REFERENCES

1 G.A. Mills, S. Weller, and E.B. Cornelius, Proc. 2nd Congr. Catal., (1960)2221.
2 R.A. Herrmann, S.F. Adler, M.S. Goldstein and R.M. deBaun, J. Phys. Chem., 65(1961)2189.
3 H.L. Gruber, J. Phys. Chem., 66(1962)48.
4 H.J. Maat and L. Moscou, Proc. 3rd Int. Congr. Catal. II(1965)1277.
5 A. Masson, J.J. Métois and R. Kern, Surface Sci., 27(1971)483.
6 Y.F. Chu and E. Ruckenstein, Surface Sci., 67(1977)517.
7 J.J. Métois, K. Heineman and H. Poppa, Phil. Mag., 35(1977)1413.
8 Y.F. Chu and E. Ruckenstein, J. Catal., 55(1978)281.
9 E. Ruckenstein and B. Pulvermacher, J. Catal., 29(1973)224.
10 B.K. Chakraverty, J. Phys. Chem. Solids, 28(1967)2401.
11 P. Wynblatt and N.A. Gjostein, Progr. Solid State Chem., 9(1975)21.
12 E. Ruckenstein and D.B. Dadyburjor, J. Catal., 48(1977)73.
13 E. Ruckenstein and D.B. Dadyburjor, Thin Solid Films, 55(1978)89.
14 S.F. Adler and J.J. Keavney, J. Phys. Chem., 64(1960)208.
15 F.L. Johnson and C.D. Keith, J. Phys. Chem., 67(1963)200.
16 S.W. Weller and A.A. Montagna, J. Catal., 20(1971)394.
17 E. Ruckenstein and M.L. Malhotra, J. Catal., 41(1976)303.
18 E. Ruckenstein and Y.F. Chu, J. Catal., 59(1979)109.
19 J. Frenkel, Kinetic Theory of Liquids, Clarendon Press, Oxford, 1946.
20 E. Ruckenstein, J. Crystal Growth (in press).
21 E.I. Dzyaloshinskii, E.M. Lifshitz and L.P. Pitaevskii, Adv. Phys., 10(1961)165.

J. BOURDON (Editor)
Growth and Properties of Metal Clusters, pp. 65—70
© 1980 Elsevier Scientific Publishing Company — Printed in The Netherlands

CREATION PAR IMPLANTATION IONIQUE DE PETITS AGREGATS PIEGES DANS DES
MATRICES ISOLANTES :
Influence des défauts cristallins et des liaisons chimiques induites par implantation sur les processus de nucléation.

J. DAVENAS, J.P. DUPIN, C. DUPUY, M. GUERMAZI, A. PEREZ et P. THEVENARD
Groupe de Radiolyse et Radiométrie des Matériaux

C. DIAINE, J. DUPUY et J.L. GISCLON
Groupe de Physicochimie des Matériaux
43 Bd du 11 Novembre
69622 VILLEURBANNE CEDEX

Résumé

        L'implantation ionique couramment utilisée pour le dopage, peut dans certaines conditions de concentration et de préparation avoir pour conséquence la précipitation des ions étrangers (amas extrinsèques) ou des ions de la matrice (amas intrinsèques) ainsi que la production de nouvelles phases dont les dimensions varient avec les traitements. Il apparaît donc une voie "nouvelle" de production de petits agrégats. Ce papier définit les conditions de formation ainsi que les principales propriétés des agrégats formés. L'étude a été faite par absorption optique dans un certain nombre de matrices naturellement transparentes et dans lesquelles la formation d'agrégats donne naissance à des bandes d'absorption. Dans des cristaux en partie covalents comme TiO_2, il a été observé, en fonction des électronégativités respectives du cation implanté et du titane, la possibilité de stabiliser l'implant dans le réseau par formation d'une liaison chimique avec les ions de la matrice, ou de précipiter les ions implantés sous forme d'amas à caractère métallique. Dans les cristaux ioniques , tels que MgO ou LiF, les ions implantés précipitent sous forme d'agrégats élémentaires faisant intervenir quelques ions ou sous forme d'amas à caractère métallique de dimensions plus importantes. Les défauts cristallins jouent alors le rôle prépondérant dans le processus de nucléation de ces amas. AgCl constitue un cas intermédiaire entre les cristaux ioniques et TiO_2.

Abstract

        Ion implantation which is frequently use as a doping technique, may in particular conditions of concentration and preparation be responsible of the precipitation of the foreign atoms (extrinsic clusters) or of the matrix ions (intrinsic clusters) and also of the production of new phases, the size of which depends on the annealings. It appears then a "new way" of production of small aggregates. This paper gives the conditions of formation and the main properties of the formed aggregates. Optical absorption has been used for the study of normally transparent crystals, in which the formation of clusters give rise to absorption bands. In covalent crystals like TiO_2, it has been observed, in function of the respective electronegativity of the implanted cation and of titanium, the possibility to have a stabilization of the implanted atom in the lattice through the formation of a chemical bond with the normal ions of the matrix, or to get the precipitation of implanted ions that give metallic clusters. In ionic crystals, like MgO or LiF, implanted ions have a tendency to cluster to give small aggregates involving a few number of ions or metallic clusters of larger size (typically of the order of 100 Å). In that case the lattice defects play the major role in the nucleation process of the clusters. AgCl presents an intermediate character between ionic crystals and partially covalent crystals, like TiO_2.

1. INTRODUCTION

Les cristaux considérés dans cet article sont étudiés par différents "groupes" du Département de Physique des Matériaux et ont la propriété commune de présenter une zone de transparence très large dans laquelle les défauts ponctuels peuvent donner des bandes d'absorption optique. Ces bandes d'absorption optique sont souvent responsables de la coloration de cristaux naturellement transparents et permettent de caractériser en partie les défauts. Elles ne correspondent cependant pas à un mécanisme unique d'absorption d'énergie. Elles peuvent être dues :
- à des transitions électroniques entre différents niveaux d'énergie d'un défaut ponctuel
- à des transitions internes à un défaut à caractère moléculaire.
Dans ce deuxième cas la bande d'absorption sera pratiquement celle de la molécule à l'état libre, avec éventuellement une perturbation due à la distorsion de la molécule par le réseau cristallin.
- à des oscillations électroniques collectives.
Ces oscillations de plasma peuvent être excitées optiquement dès qu'apparaît le caractère métallique d'un amas relativement important. Il pourra y avoir plusieurs bandes d'absorption associées à un même amas dès que sa forme s'écarte de la symétrie sphérique.

Nous rappellerons pour commencer quelques caractéristiques du processus d'implantation qui permettront de situer, dans la chaîne des évènements qui découlent de l'implantation d'un ion, le stade dans lequel se produit le réarrangement des liaisons chimiques dans le cristal.

2. L'IMPLANTATION D'IONS

Avant de s'arrêter dans le réseau, un ion incident perd son énergie cinétique suivant différentes formes d'interaction ion-matière. L'implantation d'ions constitue un mode de coloration très inhomogène car les défauts qui résultent d'une forme d'interaction sont localisés dans des formes cylindriques autour de la trajectoire individuelle de chaque ion et dont le rayon dépend fortement de l'énergie (1). Les défauts sont cependant le résultat d'une succession de processus dynamiques très rapides qui ont pour origine les différentes formes d'excitations du cristal par l'ion incident, au voisinage immédiat de sa trajectoire. On peut définir une chronologie des évènements qui découle des différents temps de propagation de chaque excitation. Ces temps sont étroitement liés à la portée des excitations. On distingue d'une part des évènements chauds qui se développent très près de la trajectoire de l'ion, comme les cascades de collisions, et d'autre part des évènements thermalisés, qui correspondent à une énergie qui s'est dissipée dans le volume du cristal. Ces deux types d'évènements sont décrits correctement, soit par la physique des excitations élémentaires, soit par la physique statistique. Cependant il existe une zone de temps intermédiaire qui est celle des recombinaisons spontanées et de la formation de liaisons chimiques nouvelles. Ces réactions secondaires sont beaucoup plus mal connues et la complexité des processus mis en jeu rend très difficile la solution du problème par des méthodes physiques. L'emploi d'arguments de type physico-chimique permet cependant d'interpréter un certain nombre de résultats.

Chocs

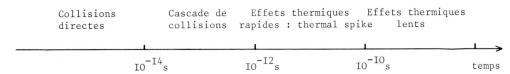

Ionisation : exemple des halogénures alcalins

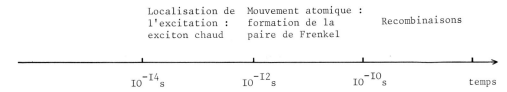

3. EFFETS CHIMIQUES LIES A L'IMPLANTATION DANS TiO_2

Une première étude comparative (2) de l'implantation de particules α ou de deutons dans des monocristaux de rutile a mis en évidence l'apparition d'une bande à 1,35 μm dans le spectre d'absorption optique des cristaux implantés avec des deutons. L'absence de bande d'absorption dans le spectre (0,4-2 ξm) des cristaux de TiO_2 implantés avec des particules α indique que les défauts intrinsèques créés ne donnent pas de bande d'absorption dans cette partie du spectre.

Des techniques complémentaires ont été utilisées pour caractériser (3) le défaut responsable de l'absorption à 1,35 μm :
- le profil de coloration à 1,35 μm déterminé par microspectrophotométrie correspond à la distribution d'ions implantés
- le spectre d'absorption infra-rouge montre l'apparition d'une bande à 2480 cm^{-1} caractéristique de la liaison O-D
- le profil de conductivité fait point par point en fonction de la profondeur fait apparaître une augmentation importante de la conductivité dans la zone d'implantation. Ces différentes observations permettent de conclure à la formation d'une liaison chimique

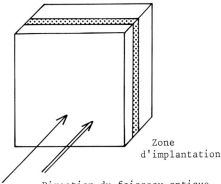

Zone d'implantation

Direction du faisceau optique
Direction du faisceau d'ions

entre le deuton implanté et un ion oxygène du réseau selon la réaction : $TiO_2 + D \longrightarrow TiO(OD)$ qui entraîne un changement de valence du titane qui passe de Ti^{4+} à Ti^{3+}. La force d'oscillateur faible (10^{-3}) permet d'attribuer la bande d'absorption à 1,35 μm à la transition "interdite" d-d de l'ion Ti^{3+} avec une perturbation due au réseau.

L'étude systématique de l'implantation avec différents ions, que l'on résume dans le tableau 1, montre l'apparition de la bande d'absorption due à l'ion Ti^{3+} pour les échantillons de TiO_2 implantés avec des ions alcalins, alors que l'on observe la formation de précipités métalliques dans des cristaux implantés avec des ions argent ou or.

Tableau 1 (Electronégativité du titane 1,5)

	DEUTONS	Li^+	K^+	Rb^+	Ag^+	Au^+
$\lambda(OD_{max})$ observé	1350 nm	1000 nm	900 nm	850 nm	450 nm	620 nm
λ calculé bande colloïdale		555 nm	1040 nm	1130 nm	450 nm	610 nm
Electronéga-tivité		1	0,8	0,8	1,9	2,4

Ce tableau fait apparaître le rôle essentiel des électronégativités respectives dans le type de défaut formé par implantation dans TiO_2.

4. INFLUENCE DES EFFETS CHIMIQUES SUR LA FORMATION DES COLLOIDES D'ARGENT INDUITS PAR IMPLANTATION IONIQUE DANS AgCl

Des travaux antérieurs ont montré (4,5) que les défauts qui résultent des pertes d'énergie électroniques ou des pertes d'énergie par chocs étaient de deux types très différents et qu'il était possible de les distinguer par la température d'implantation.
- A la température de l'azote liquide le processus photographique est bloqué et on observe la croissance d'une bande d'absorption à 500 nm pendant implantation. C. Diaine (6) a montré que cette bande pouvait être attribuée à la formation de colloïdes d'argent.
- A température ambiante on observe le spectre caractéristique du processus photographique, qui est une bande d'absorption composite centrée à 580 nm, et la bande d'absorption à 500 nm qui était aussi formée par implantation à basse température. La discussion porte sur les colloïdes d'argent produits à la température de l'azote liquide.

En considérant des implantations réalisées avec des ions alcalins de diverses énergies nous avons reporté en figure 2 (pour une même dose totale d'ions implantés) le nombre de colloïdes d'argent N_c en fonction de l'énergie dissipée par chocs dans le cristal ΔE_n. La variation observée est linéaire et montre que la formation de colloïdes d'argent est étroitement liée aux collisions atomiques.

Cependant les chocs ne constituent que le mécanisme primaire de la formation de défauts et les processus secondaires de recombinaison jouent un rôle important dans la production de défauts stables. La figure 2 fait apparaître que les ions alcalins implantés dans AgCl permettent de stabiliser les paires de Frenkel initialement créées par formation de liaisons chimiques avec les ions chlore. En effet, pour une même énergie d'implantation, l'efficacité de collisions est à peu près la même pour des ions argon ou potassium et l'électronégativité des ions alcalins qui est inférieure à celle des ions argent permet la formation préférentielle de liaisons chimiques entre ions alcalins implantés et ions chlore du cristal d'AgCl. Inversement l'implantation d'ions chlore s'accompagne du piégeage de nombreux ions argent déplacés par choc et explique la faible taux de formation de colloïdes d'argent alors observé.

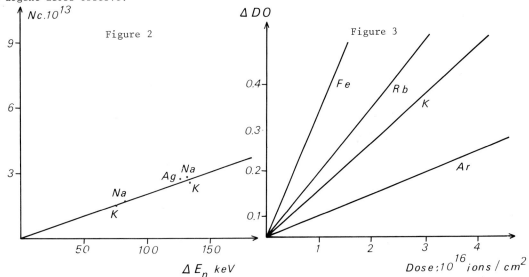

La formation de colloïdes peut être expliquée par l'intervention d'un effet thermique et d'un effet faible d'ionisation.

5. OBSERVATION DE DIFFERENTS PROCESSUS DE COALESCENCE DES IONS IMPLANTES DANS LE FLUORURE DE LITHIUM

Les halogénures alcalins sont caractérisés par une liaison à caractère ionique très marqué et parmi ceux-ci le fluorure de lithium possède la liaison cristalline la plus forte. Les liaisons chimiques rompues par les déplacements atomiques sont en fait plus facilement satisfaites que les liaisons covalentes, par piégeage d'électrons qui rétablissent la neutralité électrique locale. C'est ainsi que les défauts produits préférentiellement par irradiation sont le centre F et l'interstitiel halogène, qui est stabilisé dans le réseau par formation d'amas halogènes à température ambiante. Les ions implantés ont alors tendance à former des agrégats plus ou moins importants suivant la température d'implantation.
- A température ambiante les ions implantés précipitent (7,8) sous forme de colloïdes métalliques pendant implantation. Le processus de précipitation continue au cours de recuits. Ces amas sont responsables de bandes d'absorption colloïdales caractéristiques de l'ion implanté.
- A basse température le processus de formation de colloïdes est bloqué et on observe à partir d'une dose critique d'ions implantés un phénomène de coalescence des ions implantés qui s'apparente à une transition de percolation (9). Un film à caractère métallique est alors formé comme l'ont montré des mesures de conductivité. Par exemple, la conductivité passe de $10^{-16} \ \Omega^{-1}$ à $10^{-5} \ \Omega^{-1}$ pour une dose d'ions potassium implantés de 3.10^{16} ions/cm^2. Cette couche implantée continue se transforme au voisinage de la température ambiante pour donner une couche granulaire analogue à celle obtenue par implantation à température ambiante.

La valeur faible (5 %) de la concentration critique pour laquelle on observe cette transition non métal-métal laisse penser qu'elle pourrait être due à la coalescence d'agré-gats allongés en forme de batonnets et orientés au hasard. En effet de tels agrégats (10) peuvent être responsables de concentrations critiques bien inférieures à la concentration critique de l'ordre de 30 % que l'on obtient en général en considérant la coalescence de domaines à symétrie sphérique

6. CONCLUSION

Les réactions secondaires jouent un rôle essentiel dans la stabilisation des défauts formés par implantation ionique. Alors que dans les halogénures alcalins les défauts de neutralité électrique, dus aux déplacements d'atomes du réseau, peuvent facilement être compensés par piégeage d'électrons, les liaisons chimiques, rompues par l'irradiation dans des cristaux partiellement covalents, ont tendance à se rétablir, avec les ions implantés si cette nouvelle liaison est plus stable que la liaison cristalline initiale.

REFERENCES

1 P. Thévenard, G. Guiraud, C. Dupuy et B. Delaunay, Rad. Effects, 32 (1977) 83-93
2 M. Guermazi, P. Thevenard, P. Faisant, M.G. Blanchin et C. Dupuy, Rad. Effects, 37 (1978) 99-104
3 M. Guermazi, Thèse de 3e cycle, Lyon, 807 (1978)
5 C. Diaine, J.L. Gisclon, J. Dupuy, Phys. Stat. Solidi (b), 87,(1978) 293-300
5 J.L. Gisclon, J.F. Jal, J. Dupuy, Rad. Effects, 34 (1977) 35-42
6 C. Diaine, Thèse d'Etat Sciences Pharmaceutiques, Lyon, 154 (1978)
7 J. Davenas, A. Perez, P. Thevenard, C. Dupuy, Phys. Stat. Solidi (a), 19 (1973)679-686
8 J. Davenas, A. Perez, C. Dupuy, J. de Phys., coll C7 37 (1973) 531-535
9 J. Davenas, J.P. Dupin, Vu Thien Binh, C. Dupuy, J. de Phys. (à paraître)
10 G.E. Pike, C.H. Seager, Phys. Rev. B, 10,4 (1974) 1421-1434

J. BOURDON (Editor)
Growth and Properties of Metal Clusters, pp. 71—76
© 1980 Elsevier Scientific Publishing Company — Printed in The Netherlands

METALLIC AGGREGATE FORMATION OF INDIUM IMPLANTED IN LiF STUDIED
BY OPTICAL AND NUCLEAR HYPERFINE METHODS

A. PEREZ and J. P. DUPIN
Département de Physique des Matériaux

G. MAREST and R. HAROUTUNIAN
Institut de Physique Nucléaire (et IN2P3)

Université Claude Bernard Lyon-I
43, Bd du 11 Novembre 1918 - 69622 Villeurbanne Cedex, France

ABSTRACT

Optical absorption and nuclear hyperfine method such as time dependent perturbed angular correlation have been associated to study the formation of metallic clusters in LiF crystals implanted at room temperature with 2.10^{16} stable indium ions/cm^2 and 4.10^{10} radioactive ^{111}In ions/cm^2. The maximum fraction of implanted ions aggregated into metallic clusters reaches 37% at 350°C and a dissolution phenomena is observed above. Influence of the host matrix on the structure of metallic aggregates and the existence of indium-defect interactions are discussed.

I. INTRODUCTION

Ion implantation is a powerful technique to introduce into materials controlled concentration of impurities in well defined zones. In ionic crystals implanted with high dose of metallic ions ($> 10^{16}$ ions/cm^2), the formation of small metallic clusters have been observed in addition to point defects (refs 1, 2). The coloration of the irradiated crystal can be analysed by optical absorption technique. In the particular case of small metallic aggragates the associated absorption band is due to the plasma resonance of the free electrons. Due to the extreme complexity of high dose implanted systems, optical studies cannot give complete "microscopic" information on the sites of the implanted ions and associated defects. Nuclear techniques such as time differential perturbed angular correlation (TDPAC) seem to be well suited to this problem (ref. 3). It consists to determine the time dependence of the angular correlation between two nuclear radiations, e. g. two γ-rays, in coincidence through an isomeric intermediate nuclear state. The distribution pattern can be strongly influenced by hyperfine interactions (hfi) such as the coupling eQV_{zz} of the electric quadrupole moment eQ of the intermediate state with the electric field gradient (efg) V_{zz} at the nucleus, arising from the electronic charge-distribution. This interaction and consequently the TDPAC spectra will reflect the microscopic environment of the nuclear probe.

For TDPAC experiments ^{111}Cd fed by ^{111}In radioactivity is a very sensitive and convenient probe. Every nuclear parameter of the ^{111}Cd decay and the quadrupole moment of the isomeric 247 keV level are well known (ref. 4).

II. EXPERIMENTAL PROCEDURE AND RESULTS

1. Sample preparation

High purity LiF single crystals were implanted with 100 keV stable indium ions at room temperature (R. T) using the isotope separator of the Institut de Physique Nucléaire de Lyon. The total dose was 2.10^{16} ions/cm^2. Under identical conditions 4.10^{10} ions/ cm^2 radioactive ^{111}In were implanted in the same zone. Subsequent thermal treatments for 30 minutes at 150, 250, 350, 400, 450, 500 and 650°C were performed.

In order to control the evolution of the implanted ion distribution after each annealing step, Rutherford backscattering (R. B. S.) measurements (ref. 5) have been performed using 1 MeV α-particles produced in the 2.5 MeV Van de Graaff accelerator of the Département de Physique des Matériaux. The mean penetration depth of implanted In is about 200 Å with a half-maximum distribution full width of $\sim$ 550 Å. Taking into account the total implanted dose the maximum In concentration is 6% at. No significant change of the In depth profile has been observed during the annealing procedure.

2. Optical absorption measurements

Optical spectra were recorded at RT using a Cary 17 double beam spectrophotometer. After implantation the spectrum exhibits a band located at 215 nm (Fig. 1). Between R.T and 350°C this band splits into two bands (200 nm and 235 nm) which are well resolved at 350°C. Above 350°C the peak at 200 nm disappears and a continuous decrease of the 235 nm band is observed. In the absorption spectra just after implantation we also observe a weak absorption band near 440 nm due to F_2^--centers. From this band we can roughly estimate that the implanted zone is saturated with F-type defects ($\sim 10^{20}$ cm^{-3}).

Due to the large indium concentration in the implanted zone we can assume the possible formation of small indium aggregates. From the Doyle's theory (ref. 6) we find that small metallic aggregates of indium in LiF would give an optical absorption band at about 240 nm. This is in accordance with the 235 nm band observed at 350°C. Thus from the optical absorption spectra evolution we can deduce that small metallic aggregates are formed up to 350°C. Above this temperature the dissolution of precipitates into the matrix seems to occur.

3. Hyperfine measurements

The TDPAC measurements of the 173-247 keV γ-γ cascade of ^{111}Cd were performed using two NaI(Tl) detectors and standard fast-slow coincidence electronics (ref. 7). Due to the fact that the implanted zone is completely saturated with defects we assume that In ions experience randomly oriented h f i. In this case the correlation function is theoretically (ref. 8) given by :

$$W(\theta, t) = A_2 Q_2 G_2 (t) P_2(\cos \theta)$$

Where A_2 is the angular correlation coefficient, Q_2 a correction factor taking into account the finite solid angles of detection, $P_2(\cos \theta)$ the Legendre polynomial. The perturbation factor $G_2(t)$ contains the whole information on external interactions. $G_2(t)$ is experimentally determined by measuring the coincidence counting rates when the second detector is positioned at angles $\theta = \pi$ and $\pi/2$ with respect to the first one. Three typical experimental $G_2(t)$ curves (R. T , 350°C and 500°C) are presented in figure 2.

In the case of randomly oriented axially symmetric quadrupolar interactions in the intermediate spin $I = 5/2^+$ level of ^{111}Cd, $G_2(t)$ is theoretically given by :

$$G_2(t) = \sum_{n=0}^{3} s_{2n} \exp \left[- 1/2 (2\pi \delta \nu_o t)^2 \right] . \cos (2\pi n \nu_o t)$$

where s_{2n} are tabulated factors (ref. 7) and $\nu_o = \dfrac{3}{2I(2I-1)} \nu_Q .$ $\nu_Q = \dfrac{eQV_{zz}}{h}$ is the quadrupole interaction frequency. For an implanted sample we can assume that implanted ions are not exposed to an unique e f g but rather to a gaussian frequency distribution around a mean value ν_o, with $\sigma = \delta \nu_o$ the distribution width.

Moreover many contributions to the perturbation factor may be present. For the analysis of the experimental $G_2(t)$ curves we have considered the following possibilities :

-   a fraction a_o of indium ions sees an unperturbed surrounding (cubic sites)
-   a'_o of ^{111}In nuclei experience a spread of weak e f g's due to defects at rather large distance (distribution δ_o around ν_o)
-   different fractions a_i of ^{111}In nuclei may interact with different e f g's having gaussian distributions (different ν_{Qi} with different δ_i)

To determine the principal interaction frequencies present in the experimental $G_2(t)$ factors we have performed their Fourier transform analysis (ref. 9). This analysis gives four preponderant interaction frequencies located around ν_{Q_1} = 15 MHz, ν_{Q_2} = 90 MHz, ν_{Q_3} = 150 MHz and ν_{Q_4} = 200 MHz.

In the least-square-fit of the experimental $G_2(t)$ factors, assuming the different contributions previously considered, we have injected four frequency regions centered around the ν_{Q_i} values found above. The best fits are reported in figure 2 (solid lines).

No indium atoms in unperturbed cubic sites have been found, even after the different annealing steps. A fraction a'_o = 35% of indium atoms experiencing a spread of weak e f g's due to defects at large distances exists after implantation. This fraction decreases continuously up to 350°C (a'_o = 18%) to reach rapidly a zero value at 400°C (Fig. 3). Previous works in LiF crystals bombarded with different energetic ions in the same dose range shown that point defects such as F-centers are stable up to 350°C and are rapidly annealed above (refs 10, 11). The fraction a'_o given by the fits can then be attributed to the great density of point defects created during implantation.

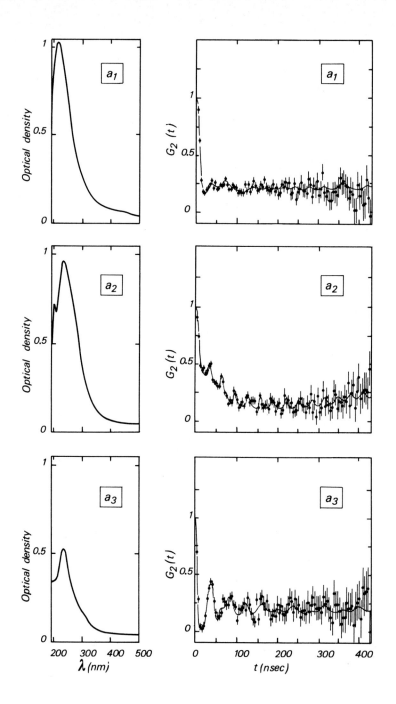

Fig. 1. Optical absorption spectra of In implanted LiF obtained after implantation (a_1), after thermal annealing at 350°C (a_2) and 500°C (a_3).

Fig. 2. Perturbation factors $G_2(t)$ obtained with In implanted LiF after implantation (a_1) after thermal annealing at 350°C (a_2) and 500°C (a_3). The solid lines represent the best fits obtained

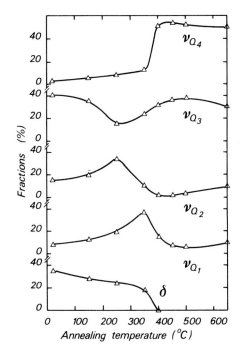

Fig. 3. Annealing temperature dependence of the different indium fractions deduced from weighted least-square fits of TDPAC spectra. Solid lines are only to guide the eye.

Among the rather well defined interaction frequencies we want specially to discuss the lower one $\nu_{Q_1} \simeq 15$ MHz. This frequency is very close to the 17.6 MHz interaction frequency of ^{111}Cd into tetragonal metallic indium (ref. 12) and may be attributed to the location of ^{111}In into metallic indium clusters. On figure 3 we see that the fraction of clustered indium atoms is 8% after implantation, reaches a maximum of 37% at 350°C and decreases strongly after this step. This is in good agreement with the evolution of the observed 235 nm optical absorption band attributed to metallic indium clusters. The exact value of ν_{Q_1} obtained from the least square fit is 13.5 MHz after implantation but increases to attain 15 MHz around 350°C. This can be interpreted by assuming that the metallic aggregates are influenced by the surrounding cubic matrix and evolve towards the normal structure of metallic indium. Another information is given by the frequency distribution factor δ_1 which continuously increases from 0.01 at R.T to 0.33 at 350°C. This seems to indicate that after implantation the strong influence of the cubic matrix on the small aggregates confers them a rather well defined structure. During their growth a more important structure dispersion between them occurs.

The evolution of the three other interaction frequencies are reported in figure 3. The fraction associated to ν_{Q_4} fastly increases above 350°C when the one attributed to metallic clusters decreases. In the same way a_2 associated to ν_{Q_2} is maximum at 250°C when a_3 is minimum. Several possibilities can be considered for indium ions which do not belong to the metallic precipitates or for ions which evaporate from them : well defined sites, association with defects, bonding with the halogen of the matrix. More experimental works are needed to ascribe these interaction frequencies to defined structures.

III.   CONCLUSION

The association of classical solid state physics techniques with an hyperfine interaction method (TDPAC) is very helpful to study the formation and the thermal evolution of metallic clusters in high dose implanted ionic crystals.

It is remarkable that small clusters exist even after the implantation at R. T. and that the maximum fraction of implanted atoms which participate to the aggregate formation does not exceed 37 % at 350°C. Above this temperature a dissolution mechanism is observed.

More microscopic information on non-aggregated indium atoms could be obtained in the future.

REFERENCES

1   J. Davenas, A. Pérez, P. Thevenard and C.H.S. Dupuy,   Phys. Stat. Sol. (a),
    19 (1973) 679
2   J. Davenas, A. Pérez and C.H.S. Dupuy, J. de Phys., Suppl. No 12, 37 (1976) 531
3   E. Recknagel,   in A. Pérez and R. Coussement (eds), Site Characterization and
    Aggregation of Implanted Atoms in Materials, Plenum Pub. Co, New York, 1979,
    ch. p. 223
4   R.S. Raghavan, P. Raghavan and J.M. Friedt, Phys. Rev. Lett, 30 (1973) 10
5   W.K. Chu, J.W. Mayer, M.A. Nicolet (Eds), Backscattering Spectrometry, Acade-
    mic Press, New York, 1978
6   W.T. Doyle, Phys. Rev., 111 (1958) 1067
7   G. Marest, Thesis, Univ. Claude Bernard Lyon-I, (1969)
8   W.D. Hamilton, in W.D. Hamilton (Ed.), The Electromagnetic Interaction in Nuclear
    Spectroscopy, North-Holland, Amsterdam, 1975, Ch. 14
9   A. Pérez, J. Davenas, J.P. Dupin, G. Marest and R. Haroutunian,   Proc. 8th Int.
    Conf. Atomic Collisions in Solids, Hamilton, Canada, August 13-17, 1979, Nucl.
    Instr. and Meth. (to be published)
10 J. Davenas, Thesis, Univ. Claude Bernard Lyon-I, (1972)
11 A. Pérez, Thesis, Univ. Claude Bernard Lyon-I, (1974)
12 R. Vianden, in R.S. Raghavan and D.E. Murnick (Eds), Hyperfine Interactions IV,
    North-Holland, Amsterdam, 1978, pp. 956-976

J. BOURDON (Editor)
Growth and Properties of Metal Clusters, pp. 77—83
© 1980 Elsevier Scientific Publishing Company — Printed in The Netherlands

AGGREGATE FORMATION IN HIGH DOSE IRON IMPLANTED MgO SINGLE CRYSTALS STUDIED BY OPTICAL ABSORPTION AND CONVERSION ELECTRON MÖSSBAUER SPECTROSCOPIES

A. PEREZ and J.P. DUPIN
Département de Physique des Matériaux,   Université Claude Bernard Lyon-1
69622 Villeurbanne Cedex, France

O. MASSENET
Laboratoire des Transitions de Phases, C.N.R.S., 166 X, 38042 Grenoble Cedex, France

G. MAREST
Institut de Physique Nucléaire (et IN2P3), Université Claude Bernard Lyon-1
69622 Villeurbanne Cedex, France

P. BUSSIERE
Institut de Recherche sur la Catalyse, C.N.R.S., 69626 Villeurbanne Cedex, France

ABSTRACT

The association of optical absorption, Rutherford backscattering and conversion electron Mössbauer spectroscopies have been applied to the study of high dose (6.10^{16} ions.cm^{-2}) iron implantation phenomena in MgO single crystals. After implantation defects in the oxygen sublattice (F-type centers) and in the magnesium sublattice (V-type centers) have been observed as well as superparamagnetic iron precipitates (size $\sim 20\,\overset{\circ}{A}$) and Fe^{2+} ions. After thermal annealing at 700°C in argon atmosphere all the iron species are converted mainly into Fe^{3+} ions. A part of them is magnetically ordered even at room temperature, the other part remaining paramagnetic down to 4.2 K. This could correspond to a bipartition in the Fe_2O_3 particle sizes : 50 to 80 $\overset{\circ}{A}$ and < 20 $\overset{\circ}{A}$ respectively.

INTRODUCTION

Intrinsic and extrinsic aggregates can be produced in implanted ionic crystals. The intrinsic aggregates are due to the precipitation of the atoms of the matrix displaced during bombardment when the extrinsic ones are due to the aggregation of implanted impurities themselves. The implantation doping technique is very convenient to create metallic extrinsic aggregates in such insulating materials (ref. 1) : it allows to introduce a precise impurity concentration in a well defined zone of the target and a great choice in the matrix-impurity combination is possible. However in high dose implanted systems ($> 10^{16}$ ions.cm^{-2}), large concentrations of defects are also created.

In the particular case of $^{57}Fe^+$ ions implanted in MgO single crystals, the association of optical absorption, Rutherford Backscattering (RBS) and Conversion Electron Mössbauer Spectroscopies (CEMS) is very powerful to study the phenomena in the implanted zone. In addition these techniques are very sensitive and non destructive. The optical absorption spectroscopy allows to reveal the ponctual defects created in the oxygen sublattice (F-type centers) and in the magnesium one (V-type centers) (ref. 2). Absorption bands due to iron ions can also be observed (refs 2, 3). The RBS technique is very convenient to analyse the implantation depth profile (ref. 4). The Mössbauer spectroscopy (ref. 5) is an useful method for studying the state of an impurity : its local microscopic environment, charge state and relative concentrations involved in the formation of precipitated phases. In an implanted system, the concentration in the stopping zone can be important but the total quantity of implanted matter remains very low. In addition traces of the considered impurities in the bulk of the sample may be present with a total amount as large as the dose of implanted atoms near the surface. In this case the CEMS technique (ref. 6) is better suited than the conventional method which measures the γ-ray resonant absorption through the sample.

In this paper are presented the complementary results obtained with the three techniques (optical absorption, RBS and CEMS) in MgO single crystals implanted with high dose $(6.10^{16}$ $cm^{-2})$ of $^{57}Fe^+$ ions. Thermal annealing effects after implantation are also reported.

EXPERIMENTAL PROCEDURES AND RESULTS

Sample preparation and implantation.

MgO crystals were cleaved into plates of 25 x 10 x 0,5 mm from a "spicer" single block. $^{57}Fe^+$ ions have been implanted at room temperature using the isotope separator of the Institut de Physique Nucléaire de Lyon. The beam energy was 100 keV and the current density around 1 μA cm^{-2}. During implantation the samples were scanned in order to obtain an homogeneous implanted surface of 1.5 x 10 mm.

Optical absorption study.

The optical absorption spectra were performed using a Cary 17 double beam spectrophotometer. The Fe^{3+} ions in MgO exhibit an absorption band located at 4.3 eV (ref. 3). From this band measured in our MgO samples before implantation, we deduced the Fe^{3+} impurities concentration in the bulk of about $9.10^{17} cm^{-3}$. This emphasizes the usefulness of the CEMS technique in the case of implanted systems. For the optical absorption measurements in the implanted samples, the unimplanted sides of the crystals were used as references in order to eliminate the absorption due to iron impurities in the bulk.

The optical absorption spectrum of a MgO sample implanted with 6.10^{16} $^{57}Fe^+$ ions cm^{-2} at room temperature is shown in figure 1(a). The broad absorption in the UV region of the spectrum is due to the sum of several bands which are not resolved. However, a tentative fit using a sum of Gaussian bands gave evidence for the presence of the follo-wing defects : F and F^+ centers (band at 5 eV) (ref. 2), unfilled oxygen vacancies (band at 5.75 eV) (ref. 7), F_2-centers (band at 3.42 eV) (ref. 2) and V^--centers (band at 2.3 eV) (ref. 2). The two bands (5.65 eV and 4.3 eV) (ref. 7) associated with Fe^{3+} ions are also present. The Fe^{2+} ions in MgO exhibit a band in the near IR (~ 1 to 1.7 eV) (ref. 3) but the oscillator strength of this band is very low. Taking into account the low quantity of implanted matter, we did not observe the Fe^{2+} band in our implanted crystals.

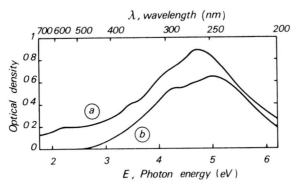

Fig. 1. Optical absorption spectra of a MgO single crystal implanted with 6.10^{16} $^{57}Fe^+$ ions.cm^{-2} at R.T. (a) As implanted, (b) annealed for one hour at 700°C in argon at-mosphere.

After thermal annealing for one hour at 700°C in an argon atmosphere, a significant change appeared in the optical absorption spectrum (figure 1(b)). The V^--band disappea-red indicating a rearrangement in the magnesium sublattice. The F_2-centers were also annealed but the F, F^+-band seemed always present. Normally in MgO bombarded with heavy ions, the F-type centers are annealed between 500 and 600°C (ref. 8). In our case, the presence of such defects above these temperatures could be due to the stabilization of Frenkel pairs resulting from the capture of interstitial oxygens at the Fe^{3+} ions (ref. 7). Moreover the Fe^{3+} band at 4.3 eV is clearly present in the annealed sample spectrum. Finally, the optical study allows to obtain a qualitative information on the defects in the oxygen and magnesium sublattices and also on the implanted impurities. Unfortunately, due to the extreme complexity of the optical spectra in such high dose implanted systems, it would be quite difficult to extract quantitative results.

Rutherford backscattering analysis.

The RBS measurements were performed using 1.8 MeV α-particle beam produced in the 2.5 MeV Van de Graaff accelerator of the Département de Physique des Matériaux The mean penetration depth of the 100 keV iron ions measured in the crystal implanted with 6.10^{16} ions cm^{-2} is about 400 Å. The full width at half maximum of the iron depth distribution is ~ 950 Å. This allows to determine the maximum iron concentration in the implanted zone of the order of 12 % at. No significant change of the iron depth profile is observed after thermal annealing for one hour at 700°C.

Conversion electron Mössbauer study.

For these measurements we used the apparatus of the Laboratoire des Transitions de Phases which was described in a previous paper (ref. 6). In figure 2 are shown the CEMS spectra obtained at 293, 77 and 4.2 K with the MgO sample implanted with 6.10^{16} $^{57}Fe^{+}.cm^{-2}$. The Mössbauer parameters of these spectra obtained by computer fitting are reported in table 1. All the isomer shifts (IS) are given with respect to metallic iron. In the room temperature (RT) spectrum the single line with IS =-0.1 mm s^{-1} can be attributed to small metallic particles of iron and the quadrupole doublet to Fe^{2+} ions. The IS value (1.15 mm s^{-1}) for this last one is close to the value reported for Fe^{2+} in MgO by Leider et al. (1.05 mm s^{-1}) (ref. 9) but the large quadrupole splitting (QS = 1.27 mm s^{-1}) is an evidence for Fe^{2+} ions in non pure cubic sites. In addition the width of the lines is large (0.9 mm s^{-1}) compared to the theoretically expected value (0.26 mm s^{-1}). This may result from the various positions of iron ions in the highly perturbed lattice as reported in the optical study. At 4.2 K the single line has vanished and we observe a broad spectrum without defined value of magnetic hyperfine field (HF). This indicates that at 4.2 K the iron aggregates are in a relaxation regime with a relaxation time comparable to the Larmor precession time of iron nucleus ($\sim 10^{-8}$ s.). At 77 K we still are in the regime of fast relaxation since no significant change of the single line with respect to the RT one is observed. This allows to estimate the size of the iron precipitates ~ 20 Å in diameter or less. The possible presence of Fe^{3+} ions in the implanted crystal before annealing was discussed in the optical study. From the Mössbauer spectra it seems that the Fe^{3+} fraction is quite small compared to the other iron components since it does not show up in these spectra.

After thermal annealing for one hour at 700°C in argon atmosphere, substantial change appears in the CEMS spectra (figure 3) with respect to those of the unannealed sample. The Mössbauer parameters of these spectra are given in table 2. The main component of the RT spectrum is a quadrupole doublet with IS = 0.34 mm s^{-1} and QS = 0.89 mm s^{-1} which is attributed to paramagnetic Fe^{3+} ions (ref. 9). A magnetic sextuplet coming from magnetically ordered Fe^{3+} ions is also present. At RT this sextuplet exhibits a large linewidth (1.46 mm.s^{-1}) and a rather weak HF value (402 k Oe). This reduced value of the field indicates some relaxation effects coming from the larger particles for which a size of about 80 Å is calculated. At 77 and 4.2 K more iron atoms contribute to the sextuplet (55% instead of 36%) while the HF value of 520 k Oe is in good agreement with the measured value for Fe^{3+} in Fe_2O_3 (ref. 10). The similitude between the 77 and 4.2 K spectra suggests to calculate the smaller particle size from the blocking of the spins at 77 K. In this case we obtain a value of about 50 Å. As to the iron fraction which remains paramagnetic down to 4.2 K, this could be due to Fe_2O_3 particles, the sizes of which are lower than about 20 Å.

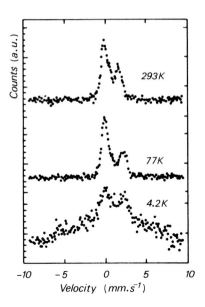

Fig. 2. CEMS spectra of a MgO single crystal implanted with 6.10^{16} $^{57}Fe^+$ ions.cm^{-2} at R.T.

Table 1. Mössbauer parameters from the fitting of the CEMS spectra shown in figure 2. The I.S are given with respect to metallic iron.

	Single Line			Quadrupole Doublet			
T K	I S mm. s^{-1}	W mm. s^{-1}	Relative Intensity %	I S mm. s^{-1}	W mm. s^{-1}	Q S mm. s^{-1}	Relative Intensity %
293	-0.11	0.62	37	1.15	0.90	1.27	63
77	-0.06	0.64	37	1.31	1.02	1.88	63

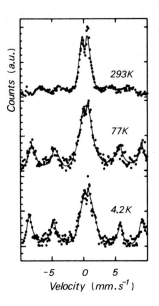

Fig. 3.   CEMS spectra of a MgO single crystal implanted with 6.10^{16} $^{57}Fe^+$ ions.cm^{-2} at R.T. and subsequently annealed for one hour at 700°C in an argon atmosphere.

Table 2.   Mössbauer parameters from the fitting of the CEMS spectra shown in fig. 3. All the I.S are given with respect to metallic iron.

T K	Quadrupole Doublet				Magnetic Sextuplet			
	I.S mm.s^{-1}	W mm.s^{-1}	QS mm.s^{-1}	Relative Intensity %	I.S mm.s^{-1}	W mm.s^{-1}	H.F kOe	Relative Intensity %
293	0.34	0.78	0.89	64	0.24	1.46	402	36
77	0.46	1.02	0.86	45	0.43	1.16	504	55
4.2	0.44	0.92	0.88	46	0.41	0.84	520	54

A careful examination of the annealed MgO spectra (figure 3) suggests the possible presence of some Fe^{2+} (IS = 1.15 mm s^{-1}) which at RT appear as a bump on the right hand side of the Fe^{3+} quadrupole doublet and which is more visible at 4.2 K. This would correspond to Fe^{2+} ions substitutionally located in cubic symmetry sites and thus giving a single line at RT. Similar behaviour was observed by Leider et al. (ref. 9) and Simkin et al. (ref. 11) in highly doped MgO crystals ($>$ 10%).

CONCLUSION

In MgO single crystals implanted with high dose of iron ions and subsequently annealed at 700°C in neutral atmosphere, the three following configurations are observed : metallic aggregates, Fe^{2+} and Fe^{3+} ions. After implantation at RT, the most abundant species are iron precipitates and Fe^{2+} ions. The metallic precipitates behave superparamagnetic thus indicating a typical size $\sim 20 \overset{\circ}{A}$. The thermal annealing effect is to convert the iron mainly into Fe^{3+} ions. A part of them is magnetically ordered even at RT, the other part remaining paramagnetic down to 4.2 K. This could be due to a bipartition in the Fe_2O_3 particles sizes : 50 to 80 $\overset{\circ}{A}$ and smaller than 20 $\overset{\circ}{A}$ respectively. Complementary informations about the point defects present in the oxygen sublattice and in the magnesium one are obtained from the optical absorption study.

REFERENCES

1.   J. Davenas, A. Perez, P. Thévenard and C.H.S. Dupuy, Phys. Stat. Sol. (a), 19 (1973) 679
2.   E. Sonder and W.A. Sibley, in J.H. Crawford and L.M. Slifkin (Eds), Point defects in solids, Plenum Press, New York, 1972, p. 201
3.   F.A. Modine, E. Sonder and R.A. Weeks, J. Appl. Phys., 48 (1977) 3514
4.   W.K. Chu, J.W. Mayer and M.A. Nicolet (Eds), Backscattering Spectrometry, Academic Press, New York, 1978
5.   H. De Waard, in A. Perez and R. Coussement (Eds), Site Characterization and Aggregation of Implanted Atoms in Materials, Plenum Press, New York, 1979
6.   O. Massenet, Nucl. Instr. Meth., 153 (1978) 419
7.   A.S. Kuznetsov and I.V. Yaek, Sov. Phys., Sol. State, 18 (1976) 2051
8.   B.D. Evans, J. Comas and P.R. Malmberg, Phys. Rev., B-6 (1972) 2453
9.   H.R. Leider and D.N. Pipkorn, Phys. Rev., 165 (1968) 494
10. L.H. Bowen, Mössbauer Effect References and Data Journal, 2 (1979) 76
11. D.J. Simkin, P.J. Ficalora and R.A. Bernheim, Phys. Lett., 19 (1965) 536

J. BOURDON (Editor)
Growth and Properties of Metal Clusters, pp. 85—100
© 1980 Elsevier Scientific Publishing Company — Printed in The Netherlands

NUCLEATION PHENOMENA IN ELECTROCRYSTALLIZATION

E.Budevski, G.Staikov and V.Bostanov

Central Laboratory of Electrochemical Power Sources
Bulgarian Academy of Sciences, Sofia 1040, Bulgaria

I. THE FREE ENERGY OF NUCLEUS FORMATION

It is well known that the formation of a new phase is impeded in its initial stages by the fact that small aggregates of the new phase are unstable and tend to dissolve back into the parent phase. The most straightforward way to calculate the Gibbs free energy of formation and the size of the critical cluster is to use the classical equation

$$\Delta G_N = - N\Delta\mu + \Phi(N) \tag{1}$$

where $\Phi(N)$ is the excess free energy of the cluster surface. $\Phi(N)$ includes not only the surface free energy σS of the cluster-solution interface (area S and specific surface energy σ) but the energy of the cluster-substrate interface $S^*(\sigma^* - \sigma_s) = S^*(\sigma - \beta)$ as well. The asteric refers to the cluster-substrate interface and the index s to the substrate-solution interface. $\beta = \sigma + \sigma_s - \sigma^*$ has been introduced by Kaischew [1] as the cluster-substrate interaction per unit contact area. If the cluster of the new phase has a regular crystalline structure the surface free energy is given by the sum $\sum\sigma_i S_i$, so that

$$\Delta G_N = - N\Delta\mu + S^*(\sigma - \beta) + \sum\sigma_i S_i \tag{2}$$

Using the Gibbs-Wulff-Kaischew theorem [1] for the equilibrium form a relation between N, S_i and S^* can be found allowing the differentiation of ΔG_N with respect to N and the evaluation of ΔG_c and N_c for the critically sized cluster for which $d\Delta G_N/dN = 0$:

$$\Delta G_c = \frac{4}{27} B \frac{v_m^2 \sigma^3}{\Delta\mu^2} \Phi^* \tag{3a}$$

and

$$N_c = \frac{8}{27} B \frac{v_m^2 \sigma^3}{\Delta\mu^3} \Phi^* \tag{3b}$$

B is a factor depending on the geometrical form of the cluster ($B = 36\pi$ for a sphere and $B = 6^3$ for a cube). v_m is the atomic volume and Φ^* is a function of σ and β accounting for the cluster-substrate interaction and according to Kaischew [1] is given by the ratio V^*/V of the volumes of the critical cluster in contact with the substrate and that in the homogeneous phase at the same supersaturation.

When the cluster-substrate interaction β becomes higher, i.e. closer to 2σ, the crystalline cluster becomes flatter, its thickness being defined by $h = h_o(2\sigma_o - \beta)/\sigma_o$. Here h_o is the distance from the Wulff point of the face o parallel to the surface of the substrate and σ_o its specific surface energy. (As the contact plane normally belongs to one of the equilibrium form faces there is always a face on top of the crystal lying parallel to the substrate surface). With $\beta \rightarrow 2\sigma$ the thickness of the crystal diminishes and the crystal becomes two-dimensional. In the two-dimensional case the term $S^*(\sigma_o - \beta)$ cancels with the corresponding $S_o\sigma_o$ term in the sum $\sum\sigma_i S_i$ (because with $\beta \rightarrow 2\sigma_o$ the contact plane area S^* tends to S_o) leaving a surface energy contribution from the side faces only. This is found in the case of formation of nuclei on an equilibrium form crystal face of the same material. As the σ_i values of the peripherial faces diminish with height h of these faces it is better to introduce here the peripherial energy $\sum\varepsilon_i L_i$ instead of $\sum\sigma_i S_i$. Where the ε_i represent the specific periphery energies, J cm^{-1}, of the sides of the two-dimensional cluster and L_i their lengths. Using the same technique as in the three-dimensional case one obtains for

$$\Delta G_c = b\frac{s\varepsilon^2}{\Delta\mu} \tag{4a}$$

and for

$$N_c = b\frac{s\varepsilon^2}{\Delta\mu^2} \tag{4b}$$

where b is a geometrical factor ($b = \pi$ for a circle and $b = 4$ for a square) and s the area occupied by one atom on the surface of the cluster.[+]

With increasing supersaturations N_c decreases sharply reaching in most of the cases of three-dimensional nucleation a value of less than ten atoms. The use of bulk quantities as volume, surface, surface energy etc loses its physical meaning in such cases and the use of atomic forces of interaction becomes more reasonable. The atomistic approach has been used first by Walton [2,3] and was developed later to a general nucleation theory by Stoyanov, Milchev and Kaischew [4,5].

It can easily be shown that $\Phi(N)$ in this case can be calculated from

---

[+]Strictly speaking if more than one type of faces or sides confine the equilibrium form of the three- or two-dimensional crystalline nucleus, σ and ε have the meaning of average values defined by $\sum\sigma_i S_i/\sum S_i$ or $\sum\varepsilon_i L_i/\sum L_i$.

the difference between the dissociation energy $\varphi_0 N$ of N atoms from the bulk crystal phase (where φ_0 is the bond energy of an atom on a kink site) and the dissociation energy $\sum \psi_i$ of the cluster of N atoms. The sum $\sum \varphi_i$ includes not only forces of interaction between the cluster atoms themselves but also forces acting between them and the substrate.

$$\Phi(N) = N\varphi_0 - \sum_1^N \varphi_i \qquad (5)$$

and

$$\Delta G_N = -N\Delta\mu + N\varphi_0 - \sum_1^N \varphi_i \qquad (6)$$

The dependence of $\Phi(N)$ and ΔG_N at different $\Delta\mu$ values on N calculated by Stoyanov [6] for a close packed, five-fold symmetry of a small cluster of up to 15 atoms is given in Fig. 1. Forces ψ acting between first neighbours only have been taken into account and the forces of interaction ψ_a with the substrate are assumed to be $\psi_a = \psi$. It is essential to note that in large intervals of $\Delta\mu$ values the number of atoms of the critical cluster (ΔG_N = max) remains constant in contrast to the large cluster model where dN is considered as an infinitesimal quantity.

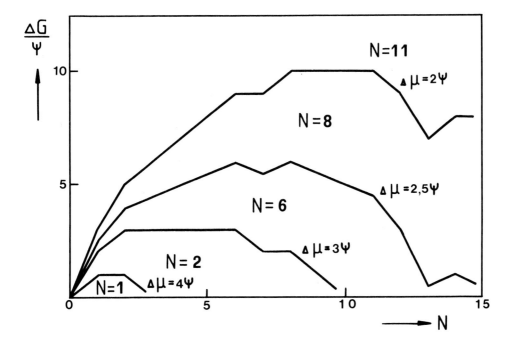

Fig. 1. Calculated free energies of cluster formation as function of number of atoms [6]. Five-fold symmetry close-packed structure of the cluster is assumed. ΔG_N is calculated from eq. (6) with $\varphi_0 = 6\psi$ and $\psi_a = \psi$.

II. THE NUCLEATION RATE

The first nucleation rate equation $J = k_1 \exp(-\Delta G_c/kT)$ was given by Volmer and Weber in 1927. Theories based on the Becker and Döring model or the Zeldovich equation have disclosed factors affecting the value of the frequency factor k_1. The most common way in expressing the nucleation rate is

$$J = \omega_{a,c} \Gamma N_o \exp(- \Delta G_c/kT) \qquad (7)$$

where N_o and Γ are the number of adsorption sites and the Zeldovich factor respectively. $\omega_{a,c}$ is the attachement frequency of single atoms to the critical cluster. The nucleation rate dependence on supersaturation, or the cathodic overpotential $\eta = \Delta\mu/ze_o$ in the electrocrystallization case, can easily be obtained from (7) using (3a) or (6) for ΔG_c:

$$J = \omega_{a,c} \Gamma N_o \exp\left[- \frac{4}{27} B \frac{v_m^2 \sigma^3 \phi^*}{(ze_o\eta)^2 kT} \right] \qquad (8)$$

Theoretically when analysing J as a function of η , the dependence of $\omega_{a,c} \sim \exp (1 - \alpha)ze_o\eta/kT$ and Γ have to be taken also into account, but they contribute insignificantly to the general $J - \eta$ relation and are very often neglected at lower η values.

For large η values, i.e. for the small cluster case, ΔG_c depends linearly on η and the contribution of the $\omega_{a,c}$ dependence on η can not be neglected. Then from (7) and (6) [4,5]:

$$J = k \exp\left[\frac{[N_c + (1 - \alpha)] ze_o\eta}{kT} \right] \exp(- N_c\varphi_o + \sum \varphi_i) \qquad (9)$$

In full analogy the rate of two-dimensional nucleation can be obtained from (7) and (4a):

$$J = N_o \Gamma \omega_{a,c} \exp(- \frac{bs\varepsilon^2}{ze_o kT\eta}) \qquad (10)$$

III. EXPERIMENTAL VERIFICATION OF THE NUCLEATION RATE EQUATIONS

The most straightforward test of the nucleation rate equation is to have a plot of the number of nuclei per unit area as function of time at different overpotentials. The double pulse technique developed by Scheludko and Todorova [7] has been successfully used in a wide range of systems [8-10]. For the purpose the electrode is conditioned at the equilibrium potential of the deposited metal and a short overpotential pulse is applied. The nuclei formed during this nucleation pulse are grown with a second, lower overpotential pulse. The amplitude of this growth pulse is set at an overpotential lower than the critical value so that no nucleation can proceed. The duration of the pulse is chosen so that the nuclei

formed during the first pulse can grow to a size visible under the microscope. The nuclei are then counted and related to time and overpotential.

Fig. 2 shows experimental plots of the number of nuclei vs. time at
different overpotentials in the electrodeposition of mercury on platinium.

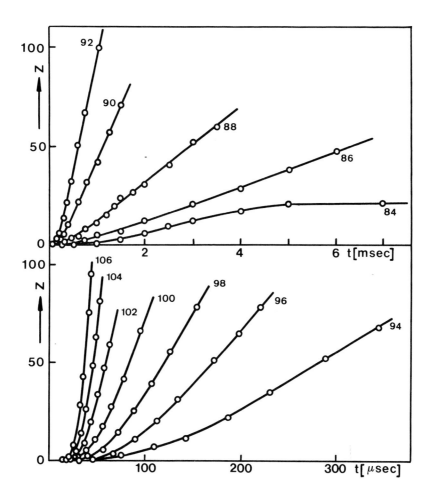

Fig. 2. Experimental plots of the number of nuclei vs. time in the elec -
tro deposition of mercury on platinium after Toshev and Markov [10]. The
figures denote the corresponding overvoltage in mV.

From the linear parts of the N/t curves the steady-state nucleation rate J
for different overpotentials can be evaluated. Fig. 3a represents a typical ln J vs. $1/\eta^2$ plot of the results presented in Fig. 2. The analysis
of this data according to eq. (8) shows that in the overpotential interval
of 84 to 106 mV studied the value of ΔG_c varies between 8,4 and 5.3×10^{-20} J,
while the number of atoms forming the critical nucleus varies between 13
and 6. The low number of atoms discredits the use of eq. (8). The same
results are represented in Fig. 3b in a ln J vs. η plot according eq. (9).

90

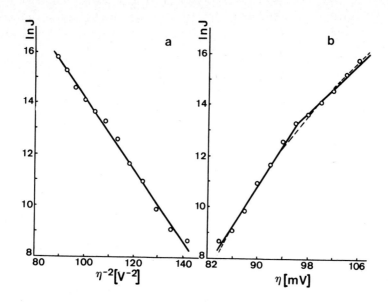

Fig. 3. Experimental data on steady-state nucleation rate J from Fig. 2. (a) in a ln J vs. $1/\eta^2$ plot; (b) in a ln J vs. η plot.

The curve shows a cusp as required by eq. (9) dividing two overpotential regions, where a 10 and a 6 atomic clusters are playing the role of the critical nucleus.

The impediments of the nucleation rate theory evolve from the fact that up to now only small clusters were found experimentally so that the use of eq. (8), with its possibilities to reveal ΔG_c and ϕ^*, i.e. to come closer to informations about surface energies and forces of interaction, was prohibited. On the other side in all cases known up to now only one cusp in the ln J – η curves has been found, so that the only information obtained was about the number of atoms of the critical cluster. Two cusps in this curve would give an additional information about forces of inter-action and are mostly desired. Some new promising results in this field have been recently reported by Milchev et al. [11].

The same double pulse technique has been applied to two-dimensional nu-cleation. The techniques of preparation of dislocation free single crystal faces by growing a crystal into a capillary has been reported elsewhere [12,13]. The most characteristic behaviour of dislocation-free faces is that there is an overpotential threshold of about 5-8 mV below which no nucleation, i.e. no growth, can proceed. On a pre-polarized cell, with an overpotential not exceeding that value, current can only flow if a nucleus is produced, e.g. by application of a nucleation pulse. This nucleation pulse can be adjusted in such a way that only in 50% of the pulse applica-tions a nucleus is produced. The criterion that only one nucleus is produced is given by the current-time curve following the nucleation pulse. The duration of the pulse can be considered as the time lapse $\tau_{0.5}$ needed for the formation of the nucleus with a probability of 0.5 and is inversely proportional to J : $\tau_{0.5}$ = 1/JSln2. Fig. 4 represents a lg J vs. $1/\eta$ plot.

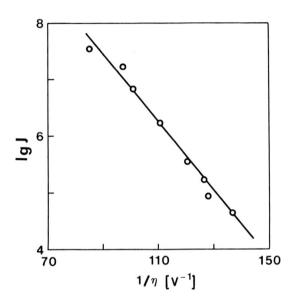

Fig. 4. Experimental data on two-dimensional nucleation rate J in a lg J vs. $1/\eta$ plot, in the electrodeposition of silver on a screw dislocation-free (100) face of a single silver crystal.

The relation of this two quantities is linear as required by eq. (10). From the slope the edge energy has been estimated $\varepsilon \cong 2 \times 10^{-13}$ J cm^{-1} and from (4a) and (4b) ΔG_c and N_c have been found to vary in the range of 10 to 6.9×10^{-20} J and 80 to 36 atoms respectively.

IV. THE TWO-DIMENSIONAL NUCLEATION MECHANISM OF GROWTH

1. The steady state

If a dislocation-free face of area S is polarized at an overpotential above the nucleation threshold nucleation and propagation of the new layers takes place simultaneously. At lower overpotentials when the nucleation rate is slow enough to give time to one nucleus to spread over the face before the second is formed, the rate of growth is determined by the nucleation rate only. The average current $\bar{I}$ is given then by

$$\bar{I} = q_{mon} Sk_1' \exp\left(- \frac{bs\varepsilon^2}{ze_o kT\eta} \right) \tag{11}$$

where q_{mon}, A s cm^{-2}, is the amount of electricity needed for the deposition of the monoatomic layer. The growth proceeds in this case by consecutive deposition of layers. The instantaneous current i(t) is unstable and is characterized by periodic pulsations connected with the nucleation and propagation of every new layer. With growing overpotentials, the nucleation rate grows much faster than the propagation rate. The time between two nucleations becomes much shorter than the time needed for the nucleus to spread over the face, so that more nuclei are formed on the same level. Nucleation proceeds, however, not only on the same level but also on top of the already growing nuclei. This mechanism is known as multinuclear multilayer growth. The problem has been extensively theoretically investigated consecutively by Hillig [14], Brovinskii and Zindergosen [15], Armstrong and Harrison [16] and Rangarajan [17] all based on the Kolmogorov-Avrami theory and by Bertocci [18] and Gilmer [19] using Monte-Carlo simulation. The steady state current density is given by

$$i_\infty = q_{mon} \beta (bJv^2)^{1/3} \tag{12}$$

where J and v are the nucleation and monolayer propagation rates. β is a constant varying in the range of unity from theory to theory. A log i_∞ vs. $1/\eta$ plot gives a possibility for the evaluation of the exponential term in J, see eq. (10) and the estimation of ε and ΔG_c, because the overpotential variation of v being linear can be neglected in the logarithmic presentation.

2. The transitional period

An additional information about the value of the Jv^2 product can be obtained from the current transient at constant overpotential. The initial part of the current transient is connected with the formation and propagation of nuclei of the new lattice net. With nucleation constantly proceeding with time the current for the formation of the first layer, taking into account the overlapping of the growing patches in a later period, is given by [20]

$$i_1 = q_{mon} bJv^2 t^2 \exp(-bJv^2 t^3/3) \tag{13}$$

In an early stage, before overlapping has occured, the current follows the quadratic equation given by the pre-exponential term in eq. (13). This gives a possibility for the determination of the product Jv^2 from an experimental i. vs. t^2 - plot [21].

In the case where nucleation proceeds in an initial very short period of time, e.g. instantaneously on a limited number of active centers, the current transient is given by [20].

$$i = q_{mon} 2bv^2 N_o t \exp(-bv^2 N_o t^2)$$

where N_O is the number of the instantaneously produced nuclei at the beginning of the overpotential pulse. If no new nuclei are formed in the following period of time this relation can be used for the estimation of the product $N_O v^2$ from an experimental log i/t vs. t^2 plot. The double pulse technique described earlier can be used in this case to produce instantaneously a certain number of nuclei during the first (nucleation) pulse, $N_O = J\tau_1$, which will produce a current according eq. (14) at the second lower overpotential pulse where no nuclei can be formed. If the propagation rate v of the monoatomic layers is known N_O can be determined and with known parameters: amplitude η_1 and duration τ_1 of the first nucleation pulse, the value of J as a function of η can be evaluated [22].

In the further course of the current transient at constant overpotential the progressively formed nuclei begin to form also on top of the already formed layers. The theoretical calculation shows that after the initial rise the current transient passes through several oscillations and calms down to the steady-state value.

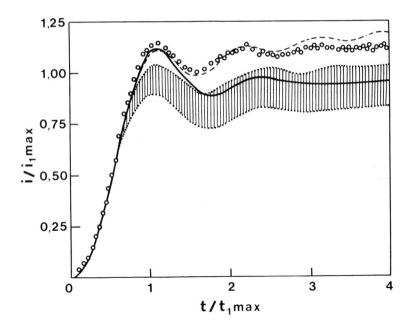

Fig. 5. Normalized theoretical and experimental current transients for multinuclear multilayer growth. − − − − and ——— analytical methods [15] and [16]; o Monte Carlo simulation [19]; the hatched area represents the range of variation of the experimental i − t curves obtained at different overpotentials.

On Fig. 5 theoretical current-time transients are represented as calculated by different authors. All transients are normalized to the parameters $i_{1,max}$ and $t_{1,max}$ of the maximum value of the formation of the first layer given by the product Jv^2 acc.eq. (13): $i_{1,max} = q_{mon}(4bJv^2)^{1/3} e^{-2/3}$

and $t_{1,max} = (2/bJv^2)^{1/3}$. We would not like to go into details of the obviously existing differencies in the various theoretical calculations. They are connected with the different way of calculating the probabilities for nucleation of the n + 1st layer on top of the nth layer. The most reliable results seem to be obtained by the nucleation and disc growth Monte Carlo simulation (circles in Fig. 5) calculated by Gilmer.

3. The rate of propagation of monoatomic steps

A very essential quantity in the determination of J from the product Jv^2 of the preceding paragraph is the knowledge of the propagation velocity of monoatomic steps and its dependence on overpotential. The current-time dependence after a nucleation act can be used for this determination. If only one nucleus has been formed during the nucleation pulse, in the double pulse technique, the i - t dependence in the following growth pulse can be used for the determination of the propagation rate, since $(di/dt)_{t=0} = q_{mon}2bv^2$, which follows directly from (14) for $N_o = 1$. Using this and similar techniques [22,23] values of v were found to vary with overpotential η according to the linear relation $v = \varkappa\eta$ with the constant $\varkappa$ varaying between 1 and 2 cm s^{-1} V^{-1}.

4. Experimental verification on screw dislocation-free (100) silver single crystal faces.

The most simple way to verify the multinuclear mechanism of growth is to record a potentiostatic transient on a dislocation-free face with its typical transitional oscillations [24]. Fig. 6 shows a potentiostatic i - t

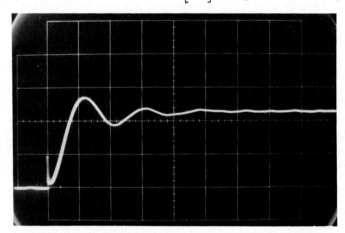

Fig. 6. Experimental current transient for multinuclear multilayer growth. η = 14 mV. Vertical sensitivity: 2 μA/division. Time base: 5 ms/division.

transient. The general time course of the current corresponds remarkably well to the theoretical curve. A set of i - t transients recorded at different overpotentials can be used for the evaluation of ΔG_c and ε as given

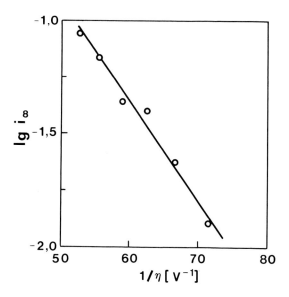

Fig. 7. Experimental data on steady state current density i_∞ in a lg i_∞ vs. $1/\eta$ plot.

in paragraph 1. A lg i_∞ vs. $1/\eta$ plot is shown in Fig. 7. From the slope of the curve the periphery energy ε was found $\varepsilon \cong 2.5 \times 10^{-13}$ J cm^{-1}. ΔG_c and N_c have been calculated from (4a) and (4b) and were found to vary in the range 9.3 to 6.5×10^{-20} J and 40 to 20 atoms. It is difficult to compare the i - t

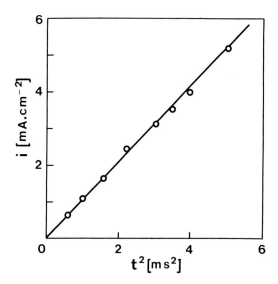

Fig. 8. The initial part of the transient given in Fig. 6. in a i vs. t^2 plot.

transients to those theoretically calculated because the value of Jv^2 is needed for the normalization of the current and time coordinates. If any of the β values from the different theories is used to calculate Jv^2 from i_∞ according eq. (13), a large deviation is observed from the theoretical curves in the initial parts (the $i - t^2$ region) of the $i - t$ transient. In Fig. 8 the initial part of the transient given in Fig. 6 is presented in a $i - t^2$ plot. The linear dependence between i and t^2 can be used as a criterion for the validity of the multinuclear model with constant nucleation rate. Another evidence that this mechanism holds quantitatively in the monolayer region can be found in an analysis of $\lg J$, calculated from Jv^2

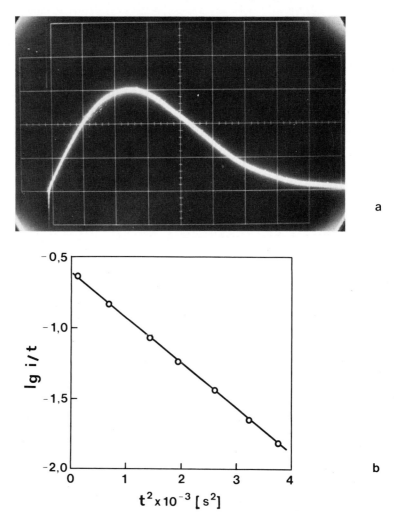

Fig. 9. (a) Experimental current transient for instantaneous nucleation. η_1 = 17 mV, τ_1 = 120 μs, η_2 = 4 mV. Vertical sensitivity: 0.4 μA/division Time base: 10 ms/division.
(b) $\lg i/t$ vs. t^2 plot of the transient given in (a)

and v, as function of $1/\eta$ giving value of ε = 2 to 2.8×10^{-13} J cm^{-1} [21].
The validity of the suggested mechanism can be checked also by the double-
pulse method described in paragraph 2. The nuclei formed during the initial, nucleation pulse (pulse parameters varying in the ranges η_1 = 14 to
20 mV and τ_1 = 0.1 to 3 ms) are grown at an overpotential below the critical nucleation overpotential. A typical i - t transient is represented
in Fig. 9a. It shows a bell-shaped course of the current-time curve as
required by eq. (14). From the lg i/t vs. t^2 plots. Fig. 9b the product
$N_0 v^2$ and $J = N_0/\tau_1$ have been calculated. The lg J vs. $1/\eta$ analysis gives
value of ε = 2 to 2.8×10^{-13} J cm^{-1} confirming in a quantitative way the
theoretical model [22].

Now the values of Jv^2 from the initial parts of the i - t transients
can be used for the normalization of the i,t coordinates. Transients recorded at different overpotentials and normalized in this way give a pack-
age of curves lying in the hatched region of Fig. 5. The steady-state
parts of the transients are lying in a range well below any of the theoretical curves. The most important fact, however, is that the first maximum
of the experimental transients lie in a range around or below the maximum
of the current-time curve of the first layer formation calculated from
(13), which is obviously impossible within the model of homogeneous nucleation. One possible explanation is to assume that nucleation proceeds on
active sites. An attempt to make a model for nucleation on active centers
has been made by Obretenov et al. [25] recently, suggesting a progressive
nucleation on a given number nucleation sites, constant for all layers.
There is evidence that active centers play a role in two-dimensional nucleation even in this believed-to-be very simple case of electrocrystallization of silver.

In conclusion a significant progress has been made in the three-dimensional nucleation theory with the introduction of the atomistic model.
From an experimental point of view, however, little progress has been made
because with a new theory, qualitatively fitting better to the experimental results, the possibility to evaluate nucleation parameters like energy
of formation, specific surface energy or energy of interaction with the
substrate was lost. The two-dimensional case seems to render more reliable
results and allows a more detailed analysis of the general behaviour of
the solid-solution interface. In contrast to the three-dimensional case,
however, where a number of systems have been investigated the two-dimensional case has been studied on one or two systems only up to now. Both
theory and experiment have to be further developed in the effort of a better understanding of the nucleation and growth processes on solid surfaces.

REFERENCES

1 R. Kaischew, Bull. Acad. Bulg. Sc. (Phys.), 1(1950)100; ibid, 2(1951)
   191; Arbeitstagung Festkörperphysik, Dresden, 1952, p.82.
2 D. Walton, J. Chem. Phys., 37(1962)2182; Phil. Mag., 7(1962)1671.
3 D. Walton, T. Rhodin and R. W. Rollins, J. Chem. Phys., 38(1963)2698.
4 S. Stoyanov, Thin Solid Films, 18(1973)91.
5 A. Milchev, S. Stoyanov and R. Kaischew, Thin Solid Films, 22(1974)255;
   ibid, 22(1974)267.
6 S. Stoyanov, in E. Kaldis (Ed.), Current Topics in Materials Science,
   Vo. 3, North-Holland Publ. Co., Amsterdam, 1978, Ch. 4, p.421.
7 A. Scheludko and M. Todorova, Bull. Acad. Bulg. Sc. (Phys.), 3(1952)61.
8 R. Kaischew and B. Mutaftschiev, Electrochim. Acta, 10(1965)643.
9 R. Kaischew, S. Toschev and I. Markov, Comm. Dept. Chem., Bulg. Acad.
   Sc., 2(1969)463.
10 S. Toschev and I. Markov, Ber. Bunsenges. Physik. Chem., 73(1969)184.
11 A. Milchev, E. Vassileva and V. Kertov, in preparation.
12 E. Budevski, V. Bostanov, T. Vitanov, Z. Stoinov, A. Kotzeva and
   R. Kaischev, Electrochim. Acta, 11(1966)1697.
13 R. Kaischev and E. Budevski, Contemp. Phys., 8(1967)489.
14 W.B. Hillig, Acta Metall., 14(1966)1868.
15 L.A. Borovinski and A.N. Zindergosen, Dokl. Akad. Nauk SSSR, 183(1968)
   1308.
16 R.D. Armstrong and J.A. Harrison, J. Electrochem. Soc., 116(1969)328.
17 S.K. Rangarajan, J.Electroanal. Chem., 46(1973)125.
18 U. Bertocci, J. Electrochem. Soc., 119(1972)822.
19 G. Gilmer, submitted to J. Cryst. Growth.
20 M. Fleischmann and H.R. Thirsk, in P. Delahay (Ed.), Advances in Electrochemistry and Electrochemical Engineering, Vol.3, Wiley (Interscience), New York, 1963, p.123.
21 G. Staikov, V. Bostanov and E. Budevski, Electrochim. Acta, 22(1977)
   1245.
22 W. Obretenov, G. Staikov, V. Bostanov and E. Budevski, in preparation.
23 V. Bostanov, G. Staikov and D.K. Roe, J. Electrochem. Soc., 122(1975)
   1301.
24 V. Bostanov, W. Obretenov, G. Staikov, D.K. Roe and E. Budevski, in
   preparation
25 W. Obretenov, I. Petrov, I. Nachev and G. Staikov, in preparation.

DISCUSSION

E. BUDEVSKI, G. STAIKOV, V. BOSTANOV

Wiart - For silver deposition the nucleation theory predicts that nucleation cannot proceed for an overpotential lower than 5-8 mV. In nitrate electrolytes, we have obtained steady state polarization curves exhibiting a much steeper increase of current with overpotential. Can you comment these results which appear in discrepancy with the theoretical predictions ?

Budevski - An overpotential threshold of 5-8 mV or even higher as predicted by the theory, can only be expected when dislocation-free faces are involved. Normally crystal faces are pierced by screw-dislocations, so that, according to Frank's spiral growth theory they can grow at substantially lower supersaturations. The existence of an overpotential barrier, as found in your case, may be explained by blocking of the screw-dislocations clusters by adsorption. The activation of a blocked screw-dislocation can proceed at low overpotentials as found in your case. In any case, the existence of an overpotential threshold in the process of growth is not necessarily connected with two-dimensional nucleation.

Ehrlich - A small point about the formalism may be in order. In nucleation theory, it is the reversible work of forming the critical nucleus that is of interest. The change in the Gibbs function, ΔG, only gives this work if the pressure is constant, a condition not met in nucleation experiments. Il would appear more appropriate to represent the reversible work by the change in the Helmholtz free energy, which seems to be the quantity in fact you have calculated.

Budeveski - In electrocrystallization this is not very true because in all electrodeposition conditions, the pressure is really constant, so that the use of the Gibbs free energy can be used without any concern. Generally speaking, however, the question is reasonable but the small contribution of the pressure change due to supersaturation can very often be neglected compared with the capillarity pressure term so that the use of the Gibbs free energy can also be applied in most nucleation cases.

Williams - I understood your figures to show that three-dimensional nucleation occurred on an overpotential pulse with no current being drawn. Is this correct ? and if so how do you explain it ?

Budevski - If you keep the nucleation pulse sufficiently short, the clusters normally having a size of a few atoms, have no time to grow further and the current is so low that it cannot be measured at least under the conditions used up to now in the double pulse nucleation technique.

Williams - You say you can alter the nucleation density by controlling the duration of this pulse and then grow the "nuclei" into larger clusters without further nucleation. What size distribution do you achieve and can you control it ?

Budevski - The second phase, where the "nuclei" are grown to a visible size so that the crystals or droplets produced could be counted, is so large compared to the nucleation pulse, that small differences in the cluster sizes arising during the nucleation pulse, are completely levelled out.

Froment - In the first part of your conference, you have presented experiments of three-dimensional nucleation to test the atomistic theory. What is the system used (substrate-deposit) in this case ?

Budevski - The result presented refer to the electrodeposition of mercury on spherical platinum single crystals of Toschev et al. Recent studies have been made by Milchev et al. on systems like Ag or Pt or Ag on glassy carbon, etc.

Ruckenstein - Concerning the comment of Dr Williams, I would like to observe that the size distribution can be probably controlled to some extent by using a succession of pulses of adequate duration.

Budevski - This is an absolutely reasonable idea. It has been actually tried in some work of Toschev, but to my knowledge, without major success.

Oudar - Did you study the underpolarization of any metal using a different metal substrate by your method.

Budevski - Yes Staykov, Lorenz, Jüttner and myself have studied the deposition of Tl on electrolytically grown silver single crystals. We have found a strong effect of the underpotential-deposited monoatomic layer of Tl on the nucleation of the same metal in the overpotential region.

Wynblatt - In the case you have discussed, of nucleation in electrolyte environments, how does one account for the effects of adsorption of ions, or of the solvent itself, on both the substrate and the nuclei ?

Budevski - In most of the cases referred to in my talk quite sophisticated measures have been taken to exclude as much as possible contamination and adsorption effects.

In electrochemistry adsorption is studied in different ways, one technique being the measurement at the double layer capacity. An other technique is the potential sweep method or the thin-layer method of Schmid as used for the underpotential deposition.

Adsorptive effects upon nucleation have been measured by Keischew, Mutaftschiev, and Toochev and recently by Staykov, Lorenz, Jüttner and myself. But I do not believe that we have a clear picture of the effect of adsorption.

What one normally is trying to do is to create as much as possible pure and reproducible surface conditions believing that adsorption effects are excluded or at least minimized.

J. BOURDON (Editor)
Growth and Properties of Metal Clusters, pp. 101—113
© 1980 Elsevier Scientific Publishing Company — Printed in The Netherlands

AGREGATS ET STRUCTURES MULTIMACLEES EN ELECTROCRISTALLISATION

G. MAURIN

Groupe de Recherche n°4 du CNRS "Physique des Liquides et Electrochimie"
associé à l'Université Pierre et Marie Curie, 4, Place Jussieu 75230 Paris, Cedex 05.

RESUME

Les dépôts électrolytiques de métaux C.F.C. sont fréquemment constitués de cristallites multimaclés à pseudo-symétrie pentagonale. On étudie les modalités de la nucléation et de la croissance de l'argent et du nickel, métaux ayant des comportements électrochimiques très différents. On montre que la transformation des agrégats icosaédriques ou décaèdriques en particules multimaclées est favorisée par une sursaturation élevée et par une inhibition par divers adsorbats.

I. INTRODUCTION

La nucléation et la croissance cristalline par voie électrolytique présentent le grand intérêt de se prêter à un contrôle direct par l'intermédiaire de deux paramètres particulièrement commodes : le potentiel électrique V appliqué à la cathode et l'intensité I du courant électrique traversant la cellule d'électrolyse. En effet, dans un système réversible, la surtension $\eta = V - V_o$ par rapport au potentiel V_o d'équilibre est donnée par la relation classique :

$$\eta = \frac{RT}{zF} \, \text{Log} \, \frac{a}{a_o} \tag{1}$$

avec R : constante des gaz parfaits, T la température, F le Faraday, z la valence de l'ion actif. Le rapport a/a_o des activités ioniques – a au potentiel considéré, a_o au potentiel d'équilibre – joue le rôle de la sursaturation. D'après la loi de Faraday, le courant I est proportionnel au nombre d'ions déchargés par unité de temps.

Les modalités de la nucléation dépendent de façon complexe des conditions expérimentales: nature et état de surface du substrat, propriétés physico-chimiques du métal déposé, composition de l'électrolyte etc ... . Par exemple, Budevski et Col. (réf. 1-2) en prenant pour substrat une face (100) parfaite d'un monocristal d'argent exempt de dislocation, ont mis en évidence que l'argent est déposé par nucléation bidimensionnelle et croissance d'une couche monoatomique. Mais il s'agit là d'un cas idéal ; habituellement l'interface métal-électrolyte comporte des imperfections géométriques et se trouve être l'objet d'une compétition de recouvrement entre divers adsorbats. En outre, le passage de l'ion métallique à l'atome déchargé fait intervenir une succession de réactions couplées pouvant faire intervenir des intermédiaires adsorbés. L'occupation de la surface contrarie la cristallisation et peut aller jusqu'à bloquer complètement la progression latérale des couches de croissance.

On assiste alors à une nouvelle phase de nucléation dont l'orientation est désormais indépendante de celle du substrat, et qui va déterminer en grande partie les caractéristiques
structurales du dépôt formé ultérieurement. Nous allons présenter quelques résultats
concernant la nucléation indépendante du substrat dans deux cas caractéristiques. Le premier
est celui de l'argent déposé à partir de solutions aqueuses de nitrate ou de perchlorate.
Dans ce système, le transfert électronique est particulièrement rapide. La nucléation sera
effectuée sur un substrat neutre pour obtenir d'emblée des germes isolés et pour pouvoir
en étudier la cinétique de croissance. Nous mentionnerons des résultats relatifs au plomb
qui se comporte de façon analogue à l'argent. Nous examinerons ensuite l'électrocristallisation du nickel. Celle-ci est caractérisée par un transfert électronique lent, en
plusieurs étapes et aussi par la formation concomitante d'hydrogène. Tous ces métaux à
maille cubique à faces centrées, en dépit de leurs comportements électrochimiques dissem-
blables présentent le phénomène commun d'être fréquemment constitués de cristallites multimaclés à pseudosymétrie d'ordre cinq. Nous montrerons que ces structures s'établissent dès
le stade de la formation des premiers agrégats et qu'elles sont favorisées par une sursaturation élevée ainsi que par une inhibition importante.

II. NUCLEATION DE L'ARGENT ET DU PLOMB SUR SUBSTRAT NEUTRE

1. Cinétique de nucléation de l'argent

Lorsqu'on utilise comme électrolyte des solutions aqueuses de sels d'argent non
complexés, nitrate ou perchlorate, la réaction de transfert électronique $Ag^+ + e^- \rightarrow Ag_{métal}$
est très rapide. Il s'ensuit que le courant est limité par le processus de nucléation ainsi
que par la vitesse du transport par diffusion des cations du sein de l'électrolyte en
direction de l'interface cathodique. Nous utilisons la technique de double impulsion potentiostatique (réf. 3) dont nous rappelons le principe. La cathode est constituée d'un
matériau neutre, c'est-à-dire que sa structure et son orientation ne sont pas susceptibles
d'influencer la nucléation par épitaxie. Ce matériau peut être du platine dont le caractère
neutre provient de la couche d'oxyde superficielle, ou, de préférence, du carbone vitreux.
Pour créer les germes, on utilise le dispositif expérimental schématisé sur la figure 1.
Une double impulsion rectangulaire est appliquée à la cathode par le potentiostat, le
potentiel étant repéré par rapport à une électrode auxiliaire en argent, faisant office de
référence. La première impulsion (quelques dizaines de millivolts) déclenche la nucléation
et assure un premier grossissement des germes, la seconde, de niveau très bas, sert uniquement à entretenir la croissance jusqu'à ce que les cristaux atteignent une taille
compatible avec le moyen d'observation utilisé et sans en altérer la structure. Le courant
transitoire I = f(t) traversant la cellule est mémorisé dans un enregistreur analogique-
digital puis restitué sur table traçante. La cathode est ensuite observée directement au
microscope électronique à balayage en vue du comptage des germes et de l'étude de leurs
morphologies. Des observations complémentaires ont été entreprises en microscopie électronique par transmission. Le transfert des germes sur une membrane de carbone reste délicat
et actuellement le diamètre minimum des particules pouvant être étudiées est de l'ordre
de 200 Å .

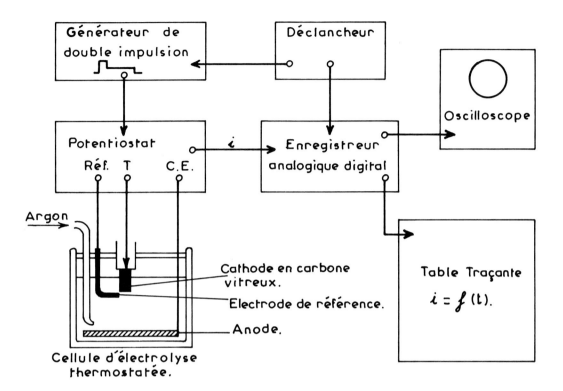

Fig. 1. Schéma du dispositif expérimental pour l'étude de la cinétique de nucléation de l'argent ou du plomb.

Les courbes transitoires I = f(t) ont typiquement l'aspect présenté sur la figure 2a. Dans ce cas, elles correspondent à des impulsions de 13 mS de divers niveaux de potentiel. Chaque courbe débute par un pic de courant très intense dû à l'établissement de la double couche à l'interface carbone-électrolyte ; après un passage par un minimum, le courant croît sous le double effet de l'augmentation du nombre des germes et de l'accroissement de la superficie de chacun d'eux. Ce comportement est tout à fait conforme au modèle développé par FLEISCHMANN et THIRSK (réf. 4) relatif à la croissance de germes hémisphériques contrôlée par la diffusion radiale des cations. On montre que dans ces conditions, le courant i relatif à un germe unique est proportionnel à $t^{1/2}$. Pour un ensemble de N germes apparaissant suivant une relation statistique N = f(t) le courant total sera donné par

$$I = \int_{o}^{t} i\,(u)\,\left(\frac{\partial N}{\partial t}\right)_{t=(t-u)} du \qquad\qquad (2)$$

Expérimentalement il a été constaté que le nombre de germes tend vers une limite N_o ce qui peut s'exprimer par

$$N = N_o (1 - e^{-At})\tag{3}$$

on constate alors que l'intégrale (2) n'admet pas de solution analytique générale. Toute-fois une expression simple peut être obtenue dans deux cas limites. Si A est grand, la nucléation est dite instantanée, le courant est de la forme :

$$I_{inst} \sim K_2 N_o t^{1/2}\tag{4}$$

Si A est petit, $N(t) \stackrel{\sim}{\sim} A N_o t$ la nucléation est dite progressive, alors :

$$I_{prog} \sim \frac{4}{3} K_2 A N_o t^{3/2}\tag{5}$$

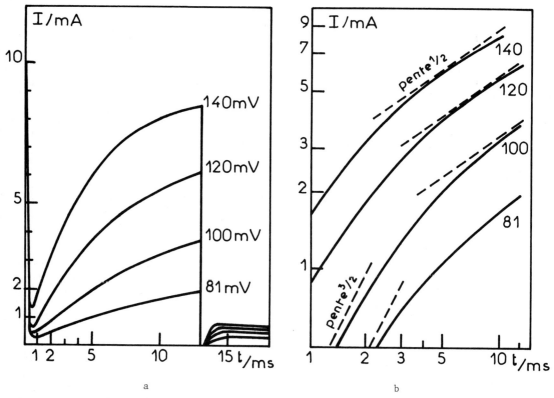

a   b

Fig. 2. Courbes i = f(t) correspondant aux premiers instants de la croissance de germes d'argent sur carbone vitreux
            a) en coordonnées linéaires   b) en coordonnées logarithmiques

Lorsqu'elles sont tracées en coordonnées logarithmiques (figure 2b), on vérifie que les courbes I = f(t) sont assimilables dans leurs parties hautes à des droites de pente 1/2, et dans leurs parties basses à des droites de pentes 3/2.

On retiendra de ces résultats et de leur interprétation à partir du modèle de FLEISCHMAN et THIRSK, que pour des impulsions d'un niveau supérieur à 50 mV la nucléation est essentiellement tridimensionnelle et qu'il s'établit immédiatement autour de chaque germe un régime de diffusion radiale. Les mêmes conclusions ont été obtenues par GUNAWARDENA et col. (réf. 5) sur l'électrocristallisation du mercure. Pour des surtensions plus faibles, selon PANGAROV et VELINOV (réf. 6) la nucléation de l'argent sur le platine serait plutôt du type bidimensionnel, et dans ces conditions, l'orientation des germes serait déterminée par la surtension.

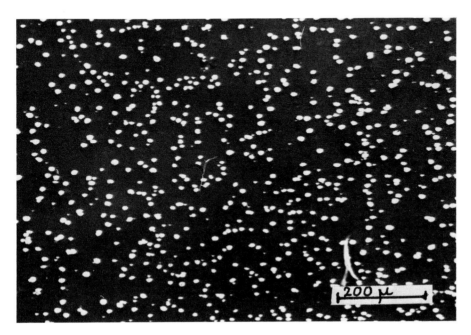

Fig. 3. Germes d'argent déposés sur une cathode de carbone vitreux à partir d'un électrolyte Ag NO_3 1M + HNO_3 1M - Préimpulsion de 200 mV, 13 mS.

2. Morphologie des germes d'argent ou de plomb

Nous étudions de façon systématique les caractéristiques structurales des germes obtenus par la technique décrite plus haut. La seconde impulsion de potentiel est maintenue pendant plusieurs secondes pour obtenir des germes de quelques microns - aisément observables en microscopie à balayage -. Cette durée est assez courte pour que la probabilité de coalescence demeure très faible (Figure 3). Nos résultats ont déjà été présentés (références 7 et 8) ; nous en retiendrons essentiellement que les germes peuvent être classés en trois catégories : à faible surtension, ils présentent la morphologie habituelle pour la structure cubique à faces centrées ; le faciès est du type cuboctaèdrique {111} + {100} . Dans certaines conditions se développent des faces vicinales {211} . Dès que l'amplitude de la première impulsion excède ∿ 50 mV, une proportion importante des germes présentent des symétries apparentes d'ordre 5. Nous distinguons la structure monopentagonale qui apparaît de façon prépondérante dans la gamme ∿ 50 mV, ∿ 80 mV, et la structure multipentagonale majoritaire au-delà de 80 mV. Les examens détaillés de leurs morphologies complétés par des observations en microscopie électronique par transmission permettent d'affirmer qu'il s'agit toujours d'édifices multimaclés parfaitement définis.

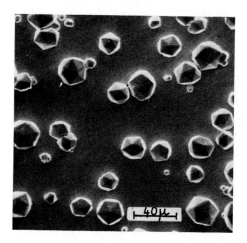

Fig. 4.   a   b
        cristallites multimaclés d'argent obtenus à partir d'une solution de nitrate
        d'argent
        a) décaèdres
        b) icosaèdres

Un édifice monopentagonal est constitué par l'accolement de 5 secteurs tétraèdriques ayant
un axe [110] commun, chaque secteur étant en position de macle (111) par rapport à ses
deux voisins . La structure d'un multipentagonal est plus complexe puisqu'il est formé
de 20 tétraèdres ayant un sommet commun au centre de l'édifice, chaque tétraèdre étant
en position de macle par rapport à ses 3 voisins. Lorsque la surface est constituée de
plans denses (111), les cristaux monopentagonaux prennent l'aspect de décaèdres (bipy-
ramides pentagonales) (Figure 4a) tandis que les multipentagonaux sont des icosaèdres
(20 faces triangulaires) (Figure 4b). En jouant sur les conditions de croissance, nous
pouvons obtenir des décaèdres ou des icosaèdres excédant 100 microns de diamètre. Le
faciès n'est pas nécessairement toujours aussi simple, les cristallites monopentagonaux
exhibent fréquemment 5 faces (100) et parfois des faces vicinales (211). Les cristallites
monopentagonaux deviennent rapidement difficiles à identifier quand apparaissent des
faces vicinales (réf. 9). Lorsque l'électrolyte est une solution de perchlorate d'argent,
le faciès est constitué de plans (110) et les multipentagonaux apparaissent sous la forme de
dodécaèdres pentagonaux. On détecte les traces de 5 plans de macle convergeant au centre
de chaque face à contour pentagonal. Il semble donc, que l'énergie de surface, théoriquement minimum pour les faces (111), ne joue pas un rôle primordial dans la stabilité de ces
gros édifices multimaclés. Par contre, nous avons mis en évidence que les plans de macle
sont susceptibles de privilégier la croissance dans la direction de leur axe commun [110]
au point de provoquer la formation de dendrites aciculaires pseudopentagonales, en particulier lorsqu'on utilise un électrolyte très dilué (réf. 10).

Les travaux récents de PALMISANO et Col. (réf. 11) sur la cinétique de nucléation du plomb à partir de solutions chlorhydriques aboutissent aux mêmes conclusions que les nôtres, à savoir que la nucléation est tridimensionnelle et que la croissance est contrôlée par un régime de diffusion radiale conformément au modèle de FLEISCHAMNN et THIRSK. De notre côté, nous avons étudié la structure et la morphologie de petits germes de plomb préparés par la technique de double impulsion potentiostatique, à partir de solutions de nitrate. Nous avons trouvé les mêmes catégories de structure précédemment décrites pour l'argent. En particulier, nous avons obtenu, ce pour la première fois à notre connaissance, des cristallites de plomb multimaclés décaédriques ou icosaédriques (réf. 12) (figure 5). Il existe une quatrième catégorie de structure ; les germes sont très plats et contiennent dans leur épaisseur un défaut bidimensionnel assimilable à un joint de torsion, pouvant être décrit comme résultant de l'accolement de deux plans (111) après une rotation de l'un d'eux d'un angle compris entre 20 et 35 degrés (réf. 13). Ce défaut remarquable qui doit apparaître dès les premiers stades de la nucléation, a la propriété encore plus marquée que les macles multiples de provoquer une croissance dendritique (réf. 12).

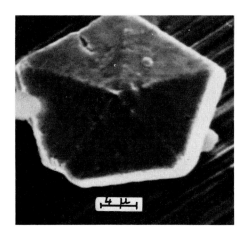 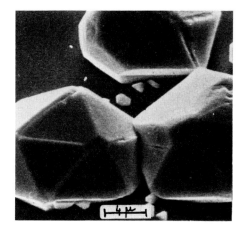

Fig. 5.   a   b

Cristallites multimaclés de plomb déposés à partir d'une solution de nitrate de plomb.

a) cristallite monopentagonal   b) cristallite multipentagonal

108

III. FORMATION DES TEXTURES DANS LES DEPOTS DE NICKEL

Le nickel déposé à partir de l'électrolyte le plus courant c'est-à-dire la solution de Watts (à base de sulfate, chlorure et acide borique) est connu pour un processus réactionnel lent. Le passage du cation solvaté Ni^{++} à l'atome métallique incorporé dans un réseau cristallin se fait par une série de réactions couplées faisant intervenir des intermédiaires adsorbés tels que $Ni\ OH_{ads}$ et Ni_{ads}. Par ailleurs, le nickel étant moins noble que l'hydrogène,il ne peut se déposer que grâce à la réduction simultanée d'ions H^{+}. Ces circonstances font que la cinétique de nucléation est difficile d'accès par les méthodes de cinétique électrochimique et c'est donc essentiellement par des techniques d'étude structurale que nous avons abordé le problème de l'étape de nucléation qui initie le dépôt polycristallin. Nous avons montré que lorsqu'on dépose ce métal sur une face d'un monocristal de nickel ou du cuivre, l'épitaxie se conserve jusqu'à une certaine épaisseur H à partir de laquelle la croissance couche par couche dégénère et se déclenche la formation d'une structure polycristalline indépendante des couches épitaxiales sous jacentes et présentant une texture de fibre souvent très marquée. L'épaisseur H varie de façon considérable suivant la face cristalline de départ et suivant les conditions expérimentales d'électrolyse (réf. 14). Pour étudier cette phase de transition, des observations en microscopie électronique à haute tension (1 MeV) ont été effectuées sur des lames minces découpées au voisinage de l'épaisseur H (réf. 15). Il a pu ainsi être mis en évidence que dans certaines conditions, apparaissent des microcristallites multimaclés mono ou multi-pentagonaux parfaitement identiques aux germes d'argent décrits plus haut. Par exemple, sur la figure 6, on reconnait la structure d'un germe monopentagonal décaédrique. Celui-ci s'est formé sur un dépôt monocristallin (100) épais qui apparaît en fond clair sur le cliché. L'étude des contrastes de tels germes met en évidence qu'ils peuvent présenter statistiquement toutes les orientations par rapport au dépôt monocristallin.

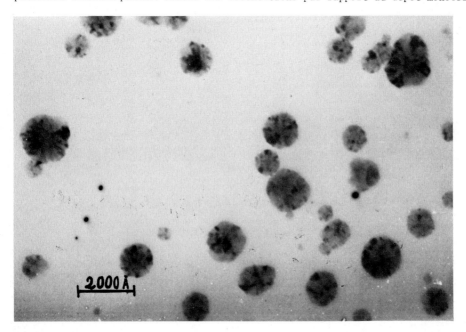

Fig. 6. Observation en microscopie électronique à 1 MEV de germes multimaclés de nickel formé spontanément sur un dépôt monocristallin (100).

Les petits germes pentagonaux, jouent un rôle considérable dans le développement
ultérieur du dépôt désormais polycristallin puisqu'ils sont susceptibles d'initier les
textures de fibre d'axes préférentiels [110] ou [211] très communément rencontrés. Les
grains issus de ces germes croissent préférentiellement dans la direction d'un axe
quinaire de germes décaèdriques ou icosaèdriques pour la texture [110][A], dans la direction
d'un axe binaire d'icosaèdre pour la texture [211].

Fig. 7. Aspect de la surface d'un dépôt électrolytique de nickel polycristallin texturé
d'axe [110][A]. L'extrêmité de chaque grain a l'aspect d'une pyramide à cinq faces.

D'après les travaux antérieurs (réf. 16-17), nous savons que les dépôts électrolytiques de nickel, peuvent, suivant les conditions expérimentales, présenter une grande
variété de textures de fibre, les principales orientations préférentielles étant [110][A]
et [211] déjà mentionnées, mais aussi : [100] , [210] , [110][B] et plus rarement [111]. Les
dépôts d'une autre texture que [110][A] ou [211] contiennent aussi des macles, mais ces
défauts sont totalement aléatoires et nullement corrélés au mécanisme de croissance. Pour
la solution de WATTS à 50°C par exemple, la figure 8 précise les conditions de pH et de
densité de courant (mesurée sur une électrode tournante) qui président à la stabilité des
quatre textures [110][A], [211] , [100] , [210]. Une étude comparative sur une grande
quantité de données a permis de mettre en évidence que chaque texture est associée à des
conditions particulières d'inhibition de l'interface métal-électrolyte. Ainsi, la texture
[100] est caractéristique d'une croissance "libre" et s'obtient généralement avec de bons
rendements faradiques. La texture [210] dans des conditions correspondant à un fort
dégagement d'hydrogène. Enfin et surtout, les deux textures correspondant au développement
uniaxial à partir de germes pentagonaux, s'obtiennent dans des conditions de forte inhibition. La texture [211] est associée à la formation de l'espèce stable NiOH dans le

catholyte tandis que la texture [110]^A est associée à la présence d'hydrogène H$_{ads}$ fortement adsorbé (réf. 18).

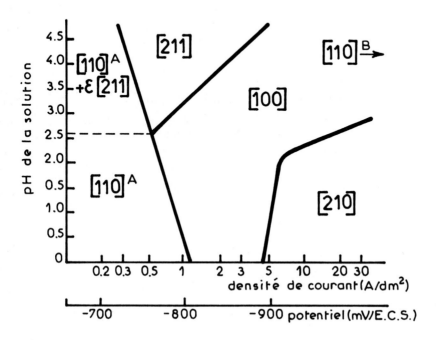

Fig. 8. Conditions de stabilité des principales textures de fibre des dépôts électrolytiques de nickel préparés à partir d'une solution de WATTS sur électrode tournante.

III. ORIGINE DES STRUCTURES MULTIMACLEES

Les structures multimaclées pseudopentagonales constituent un phénomène de caractère général pour les dépôts électrolytiques des métaux à maille cubique à faces centrées, que ces dépôts soient dendritiques polycristallins texturés ou formés de grains isolés. S'il est désormais clair qu'elles se développent à partir de petits édifices décaédriques ou icosaédriques, il reste à comprendre comment ces derniers peuvent se former et grossir jusqu'à des dimensions aussi importantes que celles que nous avons trouvées.

PANGAROV et Col. (réf. 19) admettent que le maclage se produit dans le cours de la croissance, par suite d'une nucléation bidimensionnelle en position erronée sur une face (111) d'un cristal. Ils montrent que la probabilité de ces erreurs dans l'ordre d'empilement des plans (111) croît avec la surtension appliquée. Ce serait donc par une succession de telles erreurs sur différentes faces qu'on aboutirait aux structures pentagonales. Cette explication ne rend pas compte de façon satisfaisante des résultats expérimentaux ; une séquence de maclages aléatoires peut donner un nombre quasi infini d'édifices multimaclés dont la complexité devrait croître avec la dimension alors qu'on ne trouve que deux types dont les caractéristiques parfaitement définies n'évoluent pas en cours de croissance. Ces caractéristiques sont déjà parfaitement établies dans les plus petits germes que nous avons pu observer (réf. 8) . Il y a donc tout lieu de penser que les symétries pentagonales s'établissent dès les premiers stades de la nucléation.

Des structures pentagonales ont très fréquemment été observées dans des germes métalliques (Au, Pt ...) obtenus le plus souvent par condensation sous vide (réf. 22-24). INO a calculé la stabilité des édifices décaédriques et icosaédriques constitués par des accolements de tétraèdres (réf. 24). Il tient compte de l'énergie de macle spécifique du métal considéré ainsi que de l'énergie de contrainte nécessaire à la déformation des tétraèdres pour les accoler parfaitement. L'énergie totale dépend de la taille de l'édifice. Dans le cas de l'argent, le diamètre maximum est de 76 Å pour l'icosaèdre, de 2900 Å pour le décaèdre, au-delà de ces valeurs c'est le cuboctaèdre qui présente l'énergie minimale. Le modèle d'Ino est cohérent avec toutes les observations expérimentales sur des germes obtenus par condensation puisque la taille des multimaclés n'excède pas quelques centaines d'angtroems, mais il est moins explicite quant à l'origine des symétries pentagonales. KOMODA a apporté des éléments très intéressants en montrant que les très petits germes pentagonaux d'or ($\phi \sim 20$ Å) ne contiennent ni dislocation, ni impureté centrale, ni défaut de fermeture (réf. 25). Il a pu également mettre en évidence une légère courbure des plans réticulaires. YANG, YACAMAN et Col. (réf. 26) considère que le métal cristallise dans le système orthorhombique centré pour les particules décaédriques ou dans le système rhomboèdrique pour les particules icosaèdriques. Cette hypothèse rendrait mieux compte des images de particules d'or obtenues en microscopie à haute résolution.

Divers travaux théoriques sur la structure d'agrégats d'atomes liés entre eux par divers types de potentiels, aboutissent à la conclusion commune que les arrangements icosaèdriques ou décaédriques parfaits peuvent être plus stables que l'arrangement cubique à faces centrées normal (réf. 27,28). Toutefois lorsque de tels agrégats croissent, ils devraient spontanément se transformer dans la forme cubique. On peut néanmoins concevoir une transition continue entre les petits agrégats pentagonaux et les édifices multimaclès décrits par INO par un processus de croissance couche par couche combiné à l'organisation de plans de macle (réf. 29).

Dans le cas de l'électrocristallisation, nous avons montré que la formation et le développement des structures pentagonales sont favorisées par deux facteurs : une forte surtension de cristallisation et/ou la présence de substances fortement adsorbées à l'interface métal-électrolyte. On peut supposer que la stabilité des pentagonaux est maintenue pour des dimensions supérieures à celles prévues par les calculs théoriques, grâce à une modification du rapport de l'énergie de surface à l'énergie de corps due à la tension superficielle de la couche d'adsorbats. Cet effet pourrait être important pour le nickel dont on connaît la faculté d'adsorber l'hydrogène. Le second effet de l'adsorption est une conséquence de l'inhibition du substrat. Les atomes ou molécules fixées en surface font écran à l'échange électronique nécessaire à la décharge des cations et sont également susceptibles de faire obstacle à la progression des couches de croissance. La nucléation ne peut plus s'effectuer que sur un nombre limité de sites ponctuels, où la barrière énergétique se trouve localement ou momentanément affaiblie, et elle ne pourra être que tridimensionnelle.

Les travaux de CACHET et Col. (réf. 30) illustrent bien ce phénomène : les dépôts d'argent, déposés en épitaxie sur un substrat monocristallin à partir d'une solution acidifiée de nitrate ou de perchlorate, croissent par un mécanisme bidimensionnel couche par couche. Si on augmente le pH, les ions OH^- inhibent l'interface. On assiste alors à un blocage des gradins de croissance et à la formation de germes tridimensionnels dont certains sont multimaclés. Dans le cas du nickel (réf. 18) le taux de recouvrement de l'interface en H^-_{ads} est régi par la compétition de vitesse de décharge des cations Ni^{++} et H^+. C'est aux faibles courants que l'inhibition est la plus prononcée et qu'apparaît la texture $[110]^A$.

Les premiers atomes déchargés sur un site de nucléation, constituent eux-mêmes à leur tour un site préférentiel de décharge tant qu'ils ne sont pas inhibés. Si le courant est limite par la diffusion radiale des cations métalliques, la densité locale de courant, étant une première approximation inversement proportionnelle au rayon du germe, va être extrêmement intense dans les premiers instants. Tout comme une surtension élevée, ces conditions très éloignées de l'équilibre sont favorables au développement d'édifices multimaclés de grandes dimensions.

REFERENCES

1   E. Budevski, Prog. Surf. Sci., 11, (1976) 71-116.
2   E. Budevski, dans ce volume.
3   R. Kaishev et B. Mutafchiev, Bull. Inst. Phys. Chem. (Sofia), 4 (1954) 105-108.
4   M. Fleischmann et H.R. Thirsk, Adv. Electrochemistry and Electrochem. Eng. Vol. 3 - edit. P. Delahay - Wiley N.Y. (1963) chap. 3 123-209.
5   G.A. Gunawardena, G.J. Hills et I. Montenegro, Electrochimica Acta 23 (1978) 693-697.
6   N.A. Pangarov, V. Velinov, Electrochimica Acta 11 (1966) 1753-1758.
7   C. Digard, G. Maurin et J. Robert, Met. Corrosion Ind. (1976) 255-263 et 320-331.
8   I. Epelboin, M. Froment et G. Maurin, Conférence 28ème réunion de l'I.S.E. - Varna (1977) 371-380.
9   C. Digard, G. Maurin et J. Robert, C.R. Acad. Sci., Paris 272 C (1973) 283-286.
10 C. Digard, G. Maurin et J. Robert, C.R. Acad. Sci. Paris 280 B (1975) 83-86.
11 F. Palmisano, E. Desimoni, L. Sabbatini et G. Toroi, J. Applied Electrochemistry 9 (1979) 517-525.
12 G. Maurin et D. Mercier, C.R. Acad. Sci. Paris 282 B (1976) 99-102.
13 D. Mercier et Diep The Hung.
    Scripta Met. 13 (1979) 11, à paraître.
14 M. Froment, G. Maurin et J. Thevenin, Met. Corrosion Ind. 536 (1970) 123-130.
15 J. Thevenin, J. Microscopie Spectroscopie 1 (1973) 7-12.
16 I. Epelboin, M. Froment et G. Maurin, Plating 56 (1969) 12 - 1356-1362.
17 J. Amblard, M. Froment, N. Spyrellis, Surface Technology 5 (1977) 205-234.
18 J. Amblard, I. Epelboin, M. Froment et G. Maurin, J. of Applied Electrochemistry 9 (1979), 2, 233-239.
19 N.A. Pangarov et N. TOMOV, Phys. Stat. Sol. 20 (1967) 371-376.
20 S. Ino et S. Ogawa, J. Phys. Soc. Japan 22 (1967) 1365-1374.
21 H. Sato et S. Shinozaki, J. Applied Phys. 41 (1970) 3165-3169.
22 J.G. Allpress et J.V. Sanders, Surface Sci. 7 (1967) 1-9.
23 E. Gillet et M. Gillet, Thin Solid Films 15 (1973) 249-257.
24 S. Ino, J. Phys. Soc. Japan 27 (1969) 941-953.
25 T. Komoda, J. Applied Phys. Japan 7 (1968) 27-35.
26 C.Y. Yang, M.J. Yacaman, K. Heinemann, J. Cryst. Growth 47 (1979), 177-186, 187-208, 274-282, 283-290.
27 M.R. Hoare et P. Pal, J. Cryst. Growth 17 (1972) 77.
28 A. Julg, M. Bourg, Surface Sci., 34 (1972) 705-716.
29 E. Gillet et M. Gillet, J. Cryst. Growth 13-14 (1972) 212-216.
30 C. Cachet, M. Froment, M. Keddam et R. Wiart, Electrochimica Acta, 21 (1976) 879-888 et 24 (1979) 713-722.

DISCUSSION

G. MAURIN

<u>Wynblatt</u> - The error of closure of ≈ 7° in multiply-twinned pentagonal crystallites will lead to very large strain energies at the crystallite sizes which you have observed. Have you checked whether the sub-boundaries and other defects also observed, are of high enough energy to account for the required strain energy ?

<u>Maurin</u> - S.E.M. observations of big decahedral or icoshedral M.T.P. silver crystallites (∅ ≈ 10µ) show grooves along edges and indicate that twin boundaries are very imperfect. In few cases, we observed real gaps. On small particles (∅ ≈ 300 A) we never saw any gap. In the case of (110) textured nickel electrodeposits, T.E.M. thin foils examinations confirm the imperfect nature of twin boundaries. Furthermore, grains contain numerous edge dislocations, forming sometimes sub-grain boundaries in (110) planes. We did not check if these defects have a sufficient energy to account for the strain energy due to the ≈ 1,5° distorsion of each individual part of pentagonal grains but we think that it is the case.

<u>Yacaman</u> - We have performed studies of multiple twinned particles produced by evaporation of a clean surface under ultra-high vacuum conditions. The results indicate that M.T.P. are not stable for sizes larger than about 200 A. On the other hand ab-initio X_α calculation indicate an even smaller stability size (∼ 20 A). That seems to be conflicting with your results that indicate a stability range much bigger. Would not your particles be stabilized by the presence of impurities into the M.T.P. matrix ?

<u>Maurin</u> - Nucleation by electrocrystallization cannot be performed in the absence of foreign atoms as it is possible in high vacuum evaporation technique. So, we cannot exclude the hypothesis that given impurities could act as precursors of pentagonal structures, as it has been proposed by K. Yagi and Col. (✱).

But, considering various experimental results, it seems to us that in our case the main effect of impurities consists in promoting on a limited number of non-inhibited sites, a strong flux and consequently a nucleation very far from the equilibrium.

(✱) K. Yagi, K. Tahayanagi, K. Kobayashi and G. Hondo. J. Crystal Growth <u>28</u> (1975) 117.

<u>Gillet</u> - Dans les systèmes concernant la croissances à partir de la phase vapeur, la migration des agrégats et leur coalescence jouent un rôle important. Lorsque cette coalescence a lieu, il est possible qu'elle conduise après restructuration à un agrégat de "structure pentagonale" "icosaédrique ou décaédrique". Pensez-vous que dans le cas de l'électrocristallisation, on puisse concevoir un phénomène de migration et coalescence dynamique ? Si oui, ces phénomènes pourraient-ils, dans votre cas, être à l'origine des structures multi-maclées ?

2°/ Vous avez mis en évidence des conditions d'inhibition des "structures pentagonales". Pouvez-vous relier ces conditions à des conditions sur les espèces adsorbées en surface qui pourraient jouer un rôle dans la <u>formation</u> ou la <u>stabilisation</u> des "structures pentagonales" ?

3°/ Il est possible que la formation et la croissance de ces structures pentagonales soient liées à leur cinétique de croissance. Dans le cas où elles se forment à partir de la phase vapeur elles sont favorisées par un flux incident important, c'est à dire une vitesse de croissance élevée. En est-il de même dans le cas de la croissance par électrocristallisation ?

<u>Maurin</u> - Nous ne disposons d'aucun résultat qui puisse faire penser que les cristallites multimaclés se forment par coalescence et restructuration de plusieurs particules. Par contre, comme nous l'avons dit dans les réponses ci-dessus, une cinétique de croissance très rapide est certainement très favorable à leur développement. Les adsorbats pourraient participer à leur stabilisation par modification de leur énergie superficielle. Enfin, l'inclusion d'impuretés est susceptible de provoquer des défauts cristallins qui permettent la poursuite de la croissance des édifices multimaclés jusqu'à des dimensions macroscopiques.

J. BOURDON (Editor)
Growth and Properties of Metal Clusters, pp. 115–123
© 1980 Elsevier Scientific Publishing Company — Printed in The Netherlands

ASPECTS THEORIQUES ET EXPERIMENTAUX DE LA NUCLEATION ET DE LA CROISSANCE BIDIMENSIONNELLE DES DEPOTS ELECTROLYTIQUES D'ARGENT

C. CACHET, M. FROMENT, M. KEDDAM, R. WIART
Groupe de Recherche n°4 du CNRS "Physique des Liquides et Electrochimie",
associé à l'Université P. & M. Curie, 4, place Jussieu, 75230 Paris Cedex 05.

La nucléation bidimensionnelle et la croissance couche par couche ont été observées lors de l'électrocristallisation de l'argent sur des électrodes monocristallines d'argent de haute perfection cristallographique [1,2]. Le but de cette communication est de décrire et de confronter à des données cinétiques et structurales un modèle d'électrocristallisation de l'argent basé sur l'hypothèse de monocouches générées successivement et dont la croissance suit une loi de vieillissement donnée.

I. BASES DU MODELE

Les germes bidimensionnels se forment au hasard dans le temps et sur la surface de l'électrode, à une vitesse moyenne déterminée par la fréquence de nucléation ν. Si la décharge des cations et leur incorporation au réseau métallique s'effectuent simultanément, les fronts de croissance se propagent à une vitesse v donnée par :

$$v = \frac{M J_o \eta}{\rho R T} \qquad (1)$$

où M est la masse atomique du métal, ρ sa densité, J_o la densité de courant d'échange, η la surtension, R la constante des gaz parfaits et T la température absolue. A cause de la coalescence et/ou de l'empoisonnement des gradins au cours de leur développement, les fronts de croissance auront une durée de vie τ limitée, leur croissance et leur extinction étant supposées déterminées par la loi f(t) de vieillissement. La figure 1 représente l'évolution d'un gradin, la distance r du front de croissance au centre de nucléation étant reliée à l'age t du gradin par

$$r = vt \qquad (2)$$

L'évolution de la longueur l d'un front de croissance est définie par f(t). Par exemple, en choisissant

$$f(t) = \frac{et}{\tau} e^{-t/\tau} \qquad (3)$$

on obtient l'évolution représentée sur la fig. 2.

Cette fonction f(t), qui décrit l'évolution d'une couche, est très voisine de celle calculée par FLEISCHMANN et THIRSK [3] en supposant la formation instantanée de plusieurs germes bidimensionnels qui au début croissent isolément et ensuite coalescent pour constituer une couche complète. L'approche adoptée dans [3] a permis une évaluation

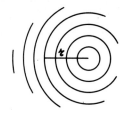

Fig. 1. Evolution d'un gradin

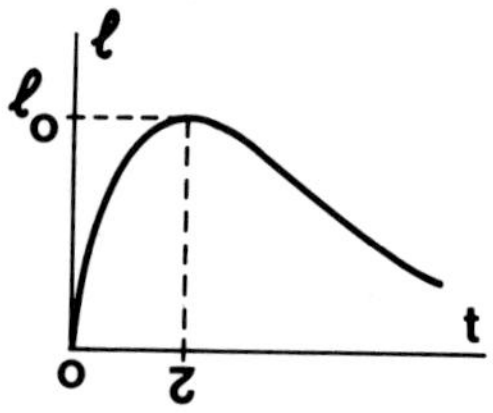

Fig. 2. Longueur d'un front de croissance en fonction de son âge.

numérique du courant [4] et de l'impédance d'électrode [5] à condition de considérer la contribution d'un grand nombre de couches successives. Par rapport à cette approche, notre hypothèse qui consiste à se donner a priori $f(t)$, présente l'avantage de pouvoir conduire aisément à une expression analytique du courant et de l'impédance. En effet, si les gradins ont tous la même hauteur h, la surface active sera définie, à un instant t', par la longueur active totale des fronts de croissance

$$L(t') = l_o \int_o^\infty f(r) \frac{\nu}{v} (t' - \frac{r}{v}) dr \qquad (4)$$

Dans cette relation, le terme $\frac{\nu}{v} (t' - \frac{r}{v}) dr$ représente le nombre de fronts de croissance qui, à l'instant t', sont dans la tranche d'âge (t,t+dt), avec dt = dr/v.

Le courant I est donné par :

$$I = \frac{J_o F \eta h L (v,\nu)}{R T} \qquad (5)$$

II. EXPRESSION DE L'IMPEDANCE D'ELECTRODE

Pour une petite perturbation de surtension

$$\Delta\eta = |\Delta\eta| e^{j\omega t} \qquad (6)$$

l'impédance Z est donnée par l'expression :

$$\frac{1}{Z} = \frac{1}{R_t} + (\frac{\partial I}{\partial L})_\eta \frac{\Delta L(v,\nu)}{\Delta\eta} \qquad (7)$$

où R_t est la résistance de transfert et où le dernier terme exprime la relaxation de L. Le calcul de ΔL, détaillé par ailleurs [6] donne :

$$\Delta L = l_o (\Delta\nu - \frac{\nu}{v} \Delta v) \int_o^\infty f(t) e^{-j\omega t} dt \qquad (8)$$

L'équation (8) révèle un processus de relaxation qui, provenant de la transformée de Fourier monolatère de f(t), fera intervenir la durée de vie τ des gradins et sera générallement caractérisé par une constante de temps distribuée.

D'après (1), Δv est en phase avec $\Delta\eta$:

$$\Delta v = \frac{M\,J_o}{\rho\,RT}\,\Delta\eta \tag{9}$$

Par contre la nucléation est en général retardée et nous écrirons :

$$\Delta\nu = \frac{d\nu}{d\eta}\,(\frac{\lambda}{1+j\omega\,\tau_n} + 1 - \lambda)\,\Delta\eta \tag{10}$$

où λ désigne la fraction des germes pour lesquels le temps τ_n s'écoule entre l'application de $\Delta\eta$ et le début de leur vieillissement. Ce retard à la nucléation sera à l'origine d'un effet inductif de constante de temps τ_n.

En supposant que la fréquence ν de nucléation croît linéairement avec η, le calcul de Z [6] aboutit à l'expression :

$$\frac{1}{Z} = \frac{1}{R_t}\,[1 + \frac{\lambda}{(1+j\omega\tau)^2}\,(\frac{1}{1+j\omega\tau_n} - 1)] \tag{11}$$

dans le cas d'une loi de vieillissement donnée par (3).

La figure 3 montre un exemple de diagramme d'impédance calculé d'après (11).

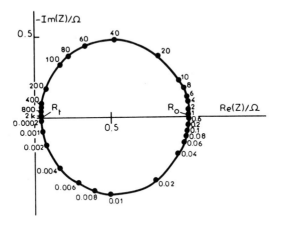

Fig. 3. Représentation dans le plan complexe de l'impédance calculée pour $R_t = 0,05\ \Omega$, $\lambda = 0,95$, $\tau = 10^{-4}$s et $\tau_n = 300$ s. La fréquence est indiquée en hertz.

Une distribution des constantes de temps τ et τ_n peut apparaître car les gradins ont des durées de vie τ diverses et la nucléation est issue de la formation en chaîne d'agrégats de tailles diverses. La figure 4 montre un exemple de diagramme d'impédance obtenu

118

en supposant une distribution de τ et de τ_n [6].

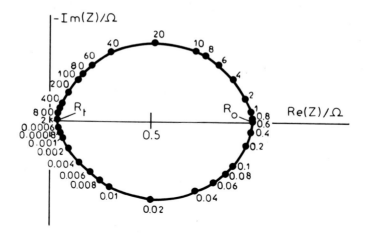

Fig. 4. Impédance calculée avec distribution de τ et τ_n autour des valeurs données fig. 3.

La résistance R_o, qui correspond à la taille du diagramme d'impédance, est telle que :

$$R_o I = \frac{\eta}{1 - \lambda} \tag{12}$$

où I représente la valeur stationnaire du courant correspondant à la surtension η. On notera que tant que $R_o \gg R_t$, le choix de la loi f(t) de vieillissement a peu d'influence sur les diagrammes d'impédance, car des diagrammes semblables à ceux des fig. 3 et 4 ont été obtenus [6] en prenant des expressions de f(t) différentes de (3).

III. COURBE DE POLARISATION CALCULEE

Afin de traduire une activation de la surface de l'électrode avec la surtension, on peut supposer que la longueur maximale l_o des fronts de croissance augmente linéairement avec η

$$l_o = \eta \frac{dl_o}{d\eta} \tag{13}$$

L'équation de la courbe courant-surtension est alors :

$$I = \frac{F J_o h \tau}{RT} \frac{dv}{d\eta} \frac{dl_o}{d\eta} \eta^3 \tag{14}$$

Une illustration de cette équation est donnée fig. 5.

IV. COURBE DE POLARISATION EXPERIMENTALE

La Fig. 6 montre un exemple de courbe courant-tension obtenue dans l'électrolyte Ag NO_3 1M + HNO_3 0,5M et avec une électrode à disque tournant suffisamment vite pour avoir

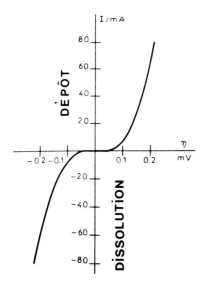

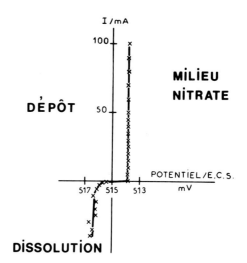

Fig. 5. Courbe de polarisation calculée.

Fig. 6. Courbe de polarisation obtenue en milieu nitrate acidifié avec une électrode d'aire 1,32 cm^2 tournant à 2600 tr/mn.

éliminé l'influence du transport de matière sur la courbe courant-tension. L'allure de cette courbe s'explique par un blocage de l'électrode à l'équilibre et une activation brutale de l'électrode dès que la surtension atteint 1 mV environ aussi bien anodiquement que cathodiquement.

V. DIAGRAMMES D'IMPEDANCE EXPERIMENTAUX

Les diagrammes d'impédance de la figure 7, obtenus avec un analyseur de fonction de transfert, ont la forme du diagramme théorique de la fig. 4. On constate que l'augmentation du courant se ramène à une diminution de R_o sans modification des constantes de temps qui demeurent distribuées. Cette situation est en accord avec l'équ. (12) lorsque η = cte et elle traduit une simple activation de l'électrode avec le courant. Des résultats analogues ont été obtenus avec des électrolytes enrichis en nitrate alcalin et pour diverses orientations du substrat monocristallin [7].

VI. ETAT DE SURFACE DES DEPOTS

L'observation au microscope électronique à balayage (M.E.B.) de dépôts préparés sur des substrats monocristallins d'orientation (100), (110) ou (111) préalablement polis chimiquement confirme le déblocage de l'électrode lorsque le courant augmente. Sur la fig. 8, on voit ainsi que le dépôt obtenu en milieu nitrate acidifié est localisé sur quelques pyramides à faible densité de courant (a) et se généralise à densité de courant plus élevée (b).

120

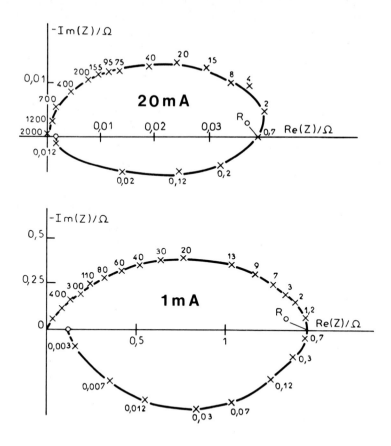

Fig. 7. Diagrammes d'impédance mesurés lors de l'électrocristallisation de l'argent pour deux valeurs du courant correspondant aux points A et B de la fig. 6. La fréquence est indiquée en hertz.

En milieu perchlorate acidifié (Ag ClO$_4$ 0,6 M + HClO$_4$ 0,7 M), la croissance couche par couche des dépôts est beaucoup plus nette [8] et la surface est formée de terrasses séparées par des marches de hauteur relativement importante (fig. 9).

VII. DECORATION DES GRADINS DE CROISSANCE

Une décoration des dépôts d'argent a été réalisée par dépôt chimique d'or dans une solution d'acide tétrachloroaurique [9]. L'observation de répliques extractives au microscope électronique à transmission (M.E.T.) permet alors de visualiser les gradins de croissance existant sur les terrasses obtenues en milieu perchlorate acidifié (fig. 9). Bien qu'aux premiers instants du dépôt il soit difficile d'obtenir une croissance régulière

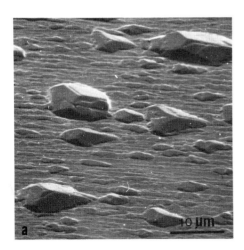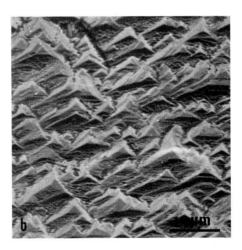

Fig. 8. Aspect au M.E.B. de dépôts préparés en milieu nitrate acidifié sur un monocristal d'orientation (111) et pour deux densités de courant : 1,5 mA/cm^2 (a) et 7,5 mA/cm^2 (b).

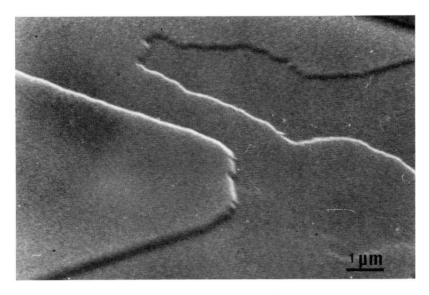

Fig. 9. Aspect au M.E.B. d'un dépôt préparé en milieu perchlorate acidifié sur un monocristal d'orientation (111) à la densité de courant 1,8 mA cm^{-2} après une impulsion galvanostatique (7,2 mA cm^{-2} pendant 5s).

et homogène, on observe, sur des dépôts de faible épaisseur (fig. 10a), des zones où les germes d'or s'alignent dans les directions denses de type [110] . Les gradins ainsi visualisés sont très nombreux et pour la plupart séparés par de faibles distances : moins de 10 nanomètres (nm).

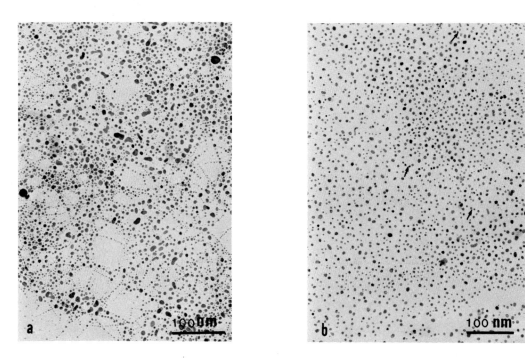

Fig. 10.   Décoration des gradins sur des dépôts d'argent préparés en milieu perchlorate acidifié à la densité de courant 8,5 mA cm^2. Epaisseur du dépôt : 5 nm (a), 2 µm (b).

A un stade plus avancé de la croissance du dépôt (fig. 10b) les interactions entre les gradins sont plus importantes, leur configuration devient plus compliquée et on ne distingue plus que quelques alignements sur de faibles distances.

VII.   CONCLUSIONS

Le modèle présenté de nucléation et croissance couche par couche constitue une explication raisonnable des résultats expérimentaux obtenus lors de l'électrocristallisation de l'argent. La confrontation du modèle aux résultats amène aux conclusions suivantes :

1 - La densité de courant de l'échange $Ag^+ + e \underset{\leftarrow}{\overset{\rightarrow}{}} Ag$ est très élevée, la résistance de transfert étant très faible et inaccessible aux mesures.

2 - L'électrode est en grande partie bloquée à l'équilibre et elle s'active avec le courant pour une faible surtension, sans qu'il y ait modification des constantes

τ et τ_n correspondant respectivement à la durée de vie des gradins et à un retard à la nucléation.

3 - De la valeur de τ et de la vitesse v de propagation des gradins, déduite de la relation $dv/d\eta \sim 1$ cm s^{-1} V^{-1} [2], on déduit que la nucléation est très fréquente et que les gradins avancent sur des distances faibles (quelques nm). La décoration de la surface des dépôts semble confirmer l'existence de nombreux gradins de croissance très rapprochés.

REFERENCES

[1] R. Kaischew et E. Budevski, Contemp. Phys. 8 (1967), 489.
[2] E. Budevski dans Prog. Surf. Membrane Sci., Academic Press, New York, 11, (1976), p 71.
[3] M. Fleischmann et H.R. Thirsk dans P. Delahay (Ed.) Advances in Electrochemistry and Electrochemical Engeneering, Vol. 3, Interscience, New-York, (1963) p 123.
[4] R.D. Armstrong et J.A. Harrison J. Electrochem. Soc. 116 (1969), 328.
[5] R.D. Armstrong et A.A. Metcalfe J. Electroanal. Chem. 71, (1976), 5.
[6] C. Cachet, I. Epelboin, M. Keddam et R. Wiart J. Electroanal. Chem. 100, (1979) 745.
[7] C. Cachet, M. Froment et R. Wiart Electrochim. Acta 24, (1979), 713.
[8] C. Cachet, M. Froment, M. Keddam et R. Wiart Electrochim. Acta, 21, (1976), 879.
[9] C. Cachet, M. Froment et R. Wiart J. Microscopie Spectroscopie Electroniques, 4 (1979) 565.

J. BOURDON (Editor)
Growth and Properties of Metal Clusters, pp. 125—127
© 1980 Elsevier Scientific Publishing Company — Printed in The Netherlands

INFLUENCE OF SULPHUR ADSORPTION
ON THE ELECTRODEPOSITION OF SILVER

R. Rousseau, N. Barbouth and J. Oudar.

Laboratoire de Physico-Chimie des Surfaces -
E.N.S.C.P - 11, rue Pierre et Marie Curie
75231 PARIS CEDEX 05

This study has been made on Ag (100) with various coverages of adsorbed sulphur. It has been recently published (1). The adsorption of sulphur was obtained by means of suited treatment in H_2S, H_2 mixtures. This treatment was carried out before the electrode immersion in the electrolytic cell. The tranfer between the treatment cell and the electrolytic cell was carried out in inert atmosphere (argon) to avoid atmospheric contamination. The electro deposition was conducted in $AgNO_3$ aqueous solution (5.10^{-3}M, PH 2,5).

The surface concentration of adsorbed sulphur was mesured by a radiochemical technique based on the use of ^{35}S by microscopical examination the following conclusions can be drawn :

1- At low sulphur concentrations ($\tau^* < \frac{1}{4}$), the surface is covered by a dilute phase of adsorbed sulphur. This phase has no significant effect on the silver deposition.

2- At mean sulphur concentrations ($\frac{1}{4} < \tau^* < \frac{1}{2}$) there occurs a phase separation in the adsorbed layer with surface equilibrium between a dilute phase ($\tau^* = \frac{1}{4}$) and a dense phase ($\tau^* = \frac{1}{2}$). Deposition of silver occurs only on the part of the surface covered by the dilute phase. In this manner islands or nuclei of the dense phase may be reverled.

3- For a near complete monolayer of sulphur disperse cristallites of silver are formed on structural defects of the adsorbed layer.

4- When bulk sulphide co-exist with near complete adsorbed layer electrodeposition of silver occurs preferentially on the nuclei of bulk sulphide. In general the presence of an adsorbed layer decreases the electrodeposition current. This study confirms the existence of a nucleation phenomenon in the growth of adsorbed layers. Such a phenomenon has been previously observed in many systems by L.E.E.D.

Similar effects related to electrodeposition inhibition have been observed for sulphur adsorbed on copper and chlorine adsorbed on copper. These effects occur up to a critical potential wich depends on the system. This phenomenon, wich affects simultaniously the morphology and the adherence of the deposit, seems very general. This may be due to species

---

* τ is the ratio between the density of adsorbed sulphur atoms and the density of metal atoms in the upper layer.

such as anions in the electrolytic solution wich can be adsorbed specifically on the electrode.

(1) R. Rousseau, P. Delescluse, F. Delamare, N. Barbouth et J. Oudar, Surface Technology $\underline{7}$ (1978) 91.

INFLUENCE DE L'ADSORPTION CHIMIQUE DU SOUFRE
SUR L'ELECTRODEPOSITION DE L'ARGENT

Cette étude a été réalisée sur une électrode d'argent (100) recouverte de quantités variables en soufre adsorbé. Elle a donné lieu à une publication récente (1).

L'adsorption du soufre était obtenue au moyen d'un traitement approprié au milieu $\frac{H_2S}{H_2}$ réalisée avant l'immersion de l'électrode dans la cellule électrolytique. Le transfert de l'appareil de traitement dans la cellule électrolytique était effectué sous atmosphère inerte (argon) de façon à éviter la contamination de la surface par l'air atmosphérique. L'électrocristallisation était réalisée dans une solution de nitrate d'argent (5.10^{-3}M à pH 2,5). La concentration en soufre adsorbé avant et après électrodéposition était mesurée par une méthode radiochimique basée sur l'utilisation du ^{35}S émetteur de rayonnement β. L'examen morphologique des dépôts en microscopie optique a permis de dégager les conclusions suivantes :

1- Pour de faibles concentrations en soufre ($\tau^* \leqslant \frac{1}{4}$) il se forme sur la surface une phase diluée en soufre adsorbé, dont l'influence sur l'électrodéposition de l'argent semble négligeable.

2- Pour des concentrations moyennes en soufre ($\frac{1}{4} < \tau^* < \frac{1}{2}$) la couche d'adsorption donne lieu à un phénomène de démixtion entre une phase diluée de composition $\tau^* = \frac{1}{4}$ et une phase dense de composition $\tau^* = \frac{1}{2}$. L'électrodéposition de l'argent s'effectue uniquement sur les régions de la surface occupées par la phase diluée. On peut ainsi mettre en évidence les îlots de la phase dense qui sont totalement exempts d'argent électrodéposé.

3- Lorsque la couche d'adsorption est quasi-complète, la formation de cristallites d'argent dispersés peut être associée à la présence de défauts structuraux dans la couche d'adsorption.

4- Lorsque le sulfure massif d'argent (Ag_4S) coexiste avec la couche d'adsorption quasi-complète, l'électrodéposition de l'argent s'effectue préférentiellement sur les germes de sulfure massif.

---

* τ est le rapport entre la densité des atomes de soufre adsorbé et la densité des atomes d'argent dans la couche la plus superficielle du métal.

127

D'une manière générale la présence d'une couche d'adsorption complète diminue le courant d'électrodéposition.

Cette étude confirme l'existence de phénomènes de germination et croissance dans la formation des couches d'adsorption. De tels phénomènes ont été observés au cours de nombreuses études réalisées au moyen de la diffraction des électrons lents. Des effets analogues d'inhibition de l'électrodéposition ont été également mis en évidence dans le cas du soufre adsorbé sur le cuivre et dans le cas du chlore adsorbé sur le cuivre. Il se font sentir jusqu'à un potentiel critique qui dépend du système étudié. Ce phénomène qui affecte simultanément la morphologie et l'adhérence des dépôts semble très général et peut en particulier être dû à des espèces présentes dans la solution (anions) et susceptibles de s'adsorber sur l'électrode.

———————

J. BOURDON (Editor)
Growth and Properties of Metal Clusters, pp. 129–136
© 1980 Elsevier Scientific Publishing Company — Printed in The Netherlands

ELECTRODEPOSITION OF METALS ON MOLECULAR CRYSTALS

Brian Thomas[+] and Frank Willig

Fritz-Haber-Institut der Max-Planck-Gesellschaft,

Faradayweg 4-6, D-1000 Berlin 33, Germany.

ABSTRACT

Electrodeposition of gold and silver on the surface of perylene and anthracene crystals has been studied. The injected holes resulting from the discharge of the metal ions ($AuCl_4^-$ or Ag^+) are removed by applying an electric field. The metal deposits are made up of conical shaped growth centres which deposit preferentially at dislocations. The contact properties of the gold film on anthracene and the silver film on perylene have been measured, and they show considerable improvement over those films produced by evaporation.

INTRODUCTION

The interface between metals and molecular crystals such as anthracene and perylene has been studied [1-6] by several workers with a view to understanding the exchange of electrons which occurs in these systems. The metal contacts were prepared by evaporation in high vacuum. In recent years it has become apparent, however, that the evaporation procedures do not yield an interface with reproducible behaviour, due to the influence of residual gas molecules, probably water, and mechanical damaging [2,5,6.]. In this paper we describe attempts to electrodeposit gold and silver onto anthracene and perylene, and report preliminary results for the contact properties of such deposits. The basis for believing that direct discharge of noble metal ions could occur at the surface of molecular crystals, by hole injection into the occupied valence band, can be explained in the following way: The standard free energy change, ΔG^0, for hole injection into the occupied valence band of a molecular crystal is defined as [7],

$$\Delta G^0 = I - E^0 - W_i \tag{1}$$

where I is the ionisation energy of the crystal, E^0 is the standard redox energy of the oxidised redox ion in the prevailing medium and W_i is a correction for interaction at the crystal surface. E^0 is expressed in energy units useing the gauge [8],

$$0 \ V \ (N.H.E.) \cong (4.5 \pm 0.1) \ eV$$

[+]Present address: Kodak Limited, Headstone Drive, Harrow, Middlesex HA1 4TY, England.

When the injected holes are removed from the crystal by applying an electric field across it, charge injection can be observed for ΔG^O values as endoergic as +0.8 eV [7]; this results from the spread of the electronic levels of the redox ions due to thermal fluctuations in solution. On the absolute scale the standard redox energy for the reaction [9],

$$AuCl_4^- + 3e \longrightarrow Au + 4Cl^-$$

is (0.99 + 4.5) eV = 5.49 eV, and for the reaction,

$$Ag^+ + e \longrightarrow Ag$$

is (0.8 + 4.5) eV = 5.3 eV. The above standard redox energies lie within 0.55 eV of the position of the valence band at the surface of a perylene crystal, 5.36 eV, and an anthracene crystal, 5.85 eV, in contact with an aqueous solution [10]. However, it is important to notice here that the above standard redox energies include the adsorption energy of the metal atom at the respective metal electrode, i.e. using the sublimation energy, 2.6 eV for the Ag atom and 3.16 eV for the Au atom. Clearly the adsorption energy of the metal atom would be expected to be smaller at organic crystals than at metal electrodes, and consequently the standard redox energies should be shifted to smaller values (reductive direction) at the surface of the organic crystals. However, hole injection currents have been observed in perylene and anthracene crystals due to the discharge of Ag^+ and $AuCl_4^-$ in aqueous solution [11]. The experimental results indicate a large adsorption energy of about 1.5 eV for the Ag atom, at least at a fraction of the ab surface of the aromatic hydrocarbon crystals. Therefore, it is feasible to produce metal-organic crystal contacts via electrodeposition. In this paper the growth characteristics of Ag and Au on these organic insulators, as well as the electric features of the electrodeposited metal-organic crystal interface, will be discussed.

EXPERIMENTAL

Plate-like crystals of anthracene and perylene (5-40μm thick) were prepared by recrystallisation of zone refined materials. A new crystal was used for each experiment. After determining the thickness with a "Lichtschnitt-Mikroscop" (Zeiss), the crystal was mounted over a hole (diameter 2mm) in a small plastic plate and contacted on one side with an inert salt solution (usually 0.1 M KCl), which was connected via a platinum wire and current measuring devices to the negative pole of the power supply. A platinum loop is placed $\approx$1 mm above the other side of the crystal, and is connected to the positive pole of the power supply (Fig. 1). The function of the applied voltage is purely to remove the injected holes from the crystal surface; the resistance of the crystal is so high that the voltage drop over the reaction distance is negligible and consequently has no effect on the electron transfer. Prior to dropping the charge injecting solution (2.4×10^{-1}, 2.4×10^{-2} M $HAuCl_4$ or 10^{-2} M $AgNO_3$) onto the surface of the crystal, a voltage is applied to the electrodes usually corresponding to a field strength of 10^5 V cm^{-1}, so that when a drop of solution is released from a pipette to drop through the

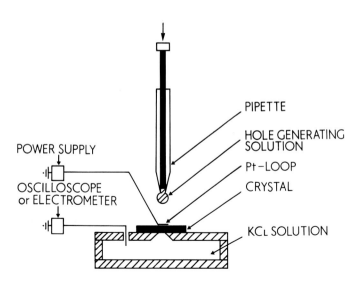

Fig 1. Experimental set-up for metal deposition on molecular crystals.

positive wire loop onto the surface of the crystal, the applied voltage is
switched across the crystal, thereby starting the experiment. This procedure
ensures that the crystal is never in contact with the hole injecting solution
in the absence of a voltage; this would lead to surface corrosion [12]. The
injection current was recorded as a function of time with either an oscillo-
scope (for short time measurements) or with an electrometer and chart recorder,
connected in series with the power supply. At the end of each experiment the
deposited metal was examined with an optical microscope.

To examine the contact properties of the deposited metal film (gold/anthra-
cene, silver/perylene), deposition was carried out until a large proportion of
the crystal surface was covered with metal; this was then gently rinsed with
distilled water to remove the hole injecting solution, and a small drop of
liquid silver solution was used to contact the edge of the deposit with the
positive electrode (in some cases the contact was made with 0.1 M HCl with
identical results). The hole injection from the gold or silver layer was
measured as a function of applied field strength and recorded via an electrometer on a chart recorder.

Solutions of $HAuCl_4$, $AgNO_3$ and KCl were made using triply distilled water
and Merck p.a. reagents.

RESULTS

Deposition Kinetics

Gold on Perylene: For both concentrations of $HAuCl_4$ solution, the hole injection current was sufficiently large to become diffusion controlled $\approx$100 ms
after contact formation, falling linearly with time$^{-\frac{1}{2}}$, Fig. 2a. In some cases,
Fig. 2b, the transient had an initial rising portion, a feature commonly observed for electrocrystallisation on metal substrates [13]; the rising portion
indicating the increasing peripheral area of the growing metal centres. The

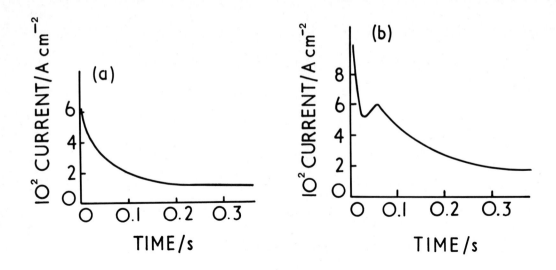

Fig. 2. Examples of the time dependence of the hole injection current in perylene after contact formation with 2.4×10^{-2} M $HAuCl_4$. Field strength, 1.5×10^5 V cm^{-1}.

magnitude of the injection currents (0.5 A cm^{-2} for 2.4×10^{-1} M $HAuCl_4$) were such that electrical breakdown of the perylene crystal usually occurred within 10 s of contact formation, and this made an investigation of the injection properties of the deposited gold after removal of the $HAuCl_4$, impossible. The purity of the deposited gold was investigated with X-ray emmission spectroscopy, which showed a complete lack of any chloride ion. Fig. 3 shows a typical deposit, where it can be seen to be made up of a large number of 3D growth centres as opposed to layers based on 2D planes. This type of growth behaviour is expected in systems where the deposited metal-metal interaction is stronger than the deposited metal-substrate interaction. It is also apparent that some decoration of surface features is taking place; a strip of the surface at the left of the picture has a higher density of gold islands and is framed by two even more densely decorated lines. This strip presumably corresponds to a different crystal plane incorporated into the ab plane crystal surface and is enclosed by two dislocation lines. The similarity in size between the centres suggests that all the nuclei are formed instantaneously. Decoration of screw dislocations in the crystal surface has also been observed [1].

Gold on Anthracene: The ionisation energy of anthracene is approximately 0.5 eV higher than that of perylene. This would be expected to result in a considerably lower rate of hole injection, and experimentally the initial injection current is about 10^{-5} that observed at perylene. The magnitude of the initial current was reproducible within a factor of 5, and remained constant for a period of time varying between 0.5s and several minutes, Fig. 4; this was followed by a rise in current which usually peaked and fell off to a diffu-

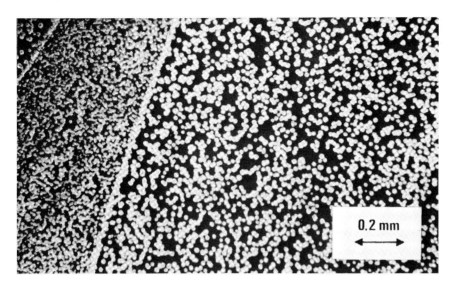

Fig. 3. Picture of electrochemically deposited gold islands on the surface of a perylene crystal (67 times magnification). Decoration effects can be seen on the left.

sion limited value. The slope of the rising portion of the current-time profile was related to the length of the initial current plateau, and microscopic investigation of many deposits in conjunction with their current-time profiles

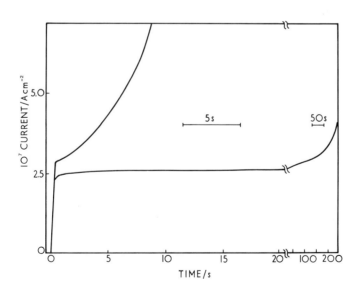

Fig. 4. Time dependence of the hole injection current in anthracene after contact formation with 2.4×10^{-2} M $HAuCl_4$ at an applied field strength of 10^5 V cm^{-1}.

permitted a qualitative correlation with the crystallisation process to be made;
A short initial plateau followed by a rapid increase in injection current was
always associated with a relatively high nucleation density on some part of the
crystal surface. On crystals showing a long initial plateau and subsequent
slow increase in injection current, there were no areas of the surface which
were specially favoured relative to others, and the nucleation density was
roughly the same over the whole surface of the crystal. Crystals from different batches tended to show widely different surface behaviour, although the
initial currents were very similar. The above information allows us to speculate about the mechanism of crystal growth; we assume that the initial plateau is caused by the discharge of gold ions over the whole surface of the
crystal to form isolated gold atoms on the crystal surface. Over the duration
of the plateau, no coalescence to form nuclei occurs. The ad-atoms are assumed to be mobile on the crystal surface and collisions would occur most
frequently in the area around surface faults, and here the nucleation probability would be high. Once nuclei are formed, these offer more favourable
sites for discharge than the crystal itself, and a positively charged nucleus
is assumed to release a hole more quickly into the valence band of the organic
crystal than an individual metal ion. The current would increase in proportion to the peripheral length of the growing centres. This mechanism
would explain why the initial plateau currents, at a given field strength,
were virtually independent of the anthracene crystal used, as isolated atom
deposition would occur over the whole surface of the crystal, and provided
that the dislocation density was not too high, one would expect little depend-
ency on the density of surface faults, as these would be small in comparison
to the total area of the crystal. When nucleation occurs however, this is
most likely to take place at surface dislocations and consequently their presence at this stage of the deposition is very important, explaining why the
rising portion of the current-time profile, after the initial plateau, is markedly dependent on the crystal used.

Silver on Perylene: The current-time behaviour in this system was similar
to that observed for gold growth on anthracene although the initial injection
currents were slightly lower, typically 7×10^{-8} A cm^{-2} for 10^{-2} M $AgNO_3$.
Again the deposit was in the form of islands.

Silver on Anthracene: This is the most energetically unfavourable of the
four systems studied and initial injection currents were lower than 10^{-10} A
cm^{-2}.

Contact Properties of the Deposited Metal
    The principle aim of this work as stated already was to produce metal-or-
ganic crystal contacts, with a view to comparing them with those produced by
evaporation techniques. A full report on this area of the work will be published elsewhere [14] , but results to date for the gold/anthracene and silver/

perylene contacts are very encouraging and the injection currents in the former case for example are 10^{-3} times higher than those observed with evaporated

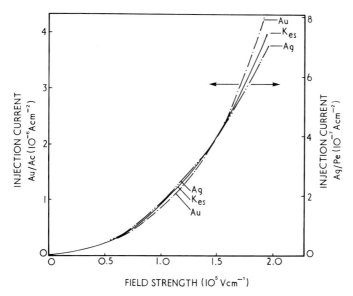

Fig. 5. Field strength dependencies of the hole injection currents for a silver film on perylene and a gold film on anthracene after removal of the metal ion containing solution. The theoretical curve, k_{es}, (see text) is also shown.

gold films [6]. In addition, in contrast to the behaviour of evaporated metal contacts, the field strength dependencies of the injection currents for the electrodeposited gold and silver films (after removal of the hole injecting solution), Fig. 5. fits the theoretical curve, $k_{es}(F)$ [15,16], which is the rate constant for the escape of the charge carriers from the interface between an insulator and a highly polarisable medium. The injection current is proportional to this rate constant k_{es}, since the concentration of holes at the crystal surface remains constant with rising applied electric filed. This is so since the majority of the generated holes recombine with electrons of the same energy in the metal contact and only a very small fraction can escape into the bulk of the organic crystal and contribute to the injection current.

ACKNOWLEDGEMENTS

   One of us (B.Thomas) is indebted to Kodak Limited, for financial support and to Professor H.Gerischer for hospitality. We are grateful to Herrn. K. Leder for crystal preparation.

REFERENCES

1. H.Baessler and G.Vaubel, Solid State Commun., 6 (1968) 97
2. J.Levinson, Z.Burshtein and A.Many, Mol. Cryst. Liquid Cryst., 26 (1974) 329
3. H.Kallmann, G.Vaubel and H.Baessler, phys. stat. sol. (b), 44 (1971) 813

4. H.J.Gaehrs and F.Willig, Chem. Phys. Letters, 32 (1975) 300.
5. H.J.Gaehrs and F.Willig, phys. stat. sol. (a), 27 (1975) 355.
6. B.Korsch, F.Willig, H.J.Gaehrs and B.Tesche, phys. stat. sol. (a) 33 (1976) 461
7. G.Scherer and F.Willig, J.Electroanal. Chem., 85 (1977) 77
8. R.M.Noyes, J. Amer. Chem. Soc., 84 (1962) 513. J.H.Baxendale, Radiation Res., Suppl. 4 (1964) 139. F.Lohmann, Z.Naturforsch., 22a (1967) 843
9. Handbook of Chemistry and Physics, 51st edition, Chemical Rubber Co., Cleveland, D-111.
10. F.Willig and G.Scherer, Chem. Phys. Letters, 53 (1978) 128.
11. F.Willig, B.Thomas and H.Gerischer, J.Electroanal. Chem., 100 (1979) 501
12. F.Willig, G.Scherer and W.Rothamel, Z.Naturforsch., 29a (1974) 131.
13. M.Fleischmann and H.R.Thirsk in P.Delahay (Ed), Adv. in Electrochem. and Electrochem. Eng., Volume 3, Interscience, New York 1963.
14. B.Thomas and F.Willig,. to be published.
15. F.Willig, Chem. Phys. Letters, 40 (1976) 331.
16. K.-P.Charle and F.Willig, Chem. Phys. Letters, 57 (1978) 253.

J. BOURDON (Editor)
Growth and Properties of Metal Clusters, pp. 137—149
© 1980 Elsevier Scientific Publishing Company — Printed in The Netherlands

RHODIUM RAFTS ON ALUMINA:
THEIR SIZE, STABILITY AND TOPOGRAPHY

D. J. C. Yates, L. L. Murrell and E. B. Prestridge

Corporate Research Laboratory
Exxon Research and Engineering, Linden, NJ USA

INTRODUCTION - The reality of atomic dispersion for supported metals has become more convincing with the passage of time, nevertheless many aspects of this highly dispersed state are still obscure, despite intensive work since 1960.

The first positive indications that atomic dispersion (in the sense that all metal atoms are in the surface) could be achieved and measured, are to be found in a series of papers on supported platinum [1-3], using hydrogen chemisorption as the diagnostic tool. This method received further impetus by a detailed study by Adams, Benesi, Curtis and Meisenheimer [4] in 1962. They studied the dispersion of Pt on silica by three independent methods--H_2 chemisorption, electron microscopy and X-ray diffraction line broadening. A comparison between H_2 chemisorption data and particle sizes measured by electron microscopy for Pt on alumina has been published by Wilson and Hall [5].

However, studies of metals in the atomically dispersed state and definitive information on the crystalline morphology of such systems are almost entirely lacking, although there have been numerous theoretical studies [6,7]. The only way in which direct information can be obtained on matter in the atomically dispersed state is by ultra-high resolution electron microscopy. Such studies were first published by Prestridge and Yates [8] who studied Rh on silica. The Rh atoms were found to be in the form of two-dimensional rafts, one atom thick. The Rh in the same catalysts had been shown earlier to be atomically dispersed by the H_2 and CO studies of Yates and Sinfelt [9].

Further information on well-dispersed Rh has now been obtained. The system has been investigated by three techniques: chemisorption, infrared spectroscopy and electron microscopy. We have shown that we can differentiate between various degrees of atomic dispersion. That is, a system which has a smaller raft size is in a very real sense more highly dispersed (i.e. lower mean metal-metal coordination) than another system which has a larger raft size. Both the above systems are atomically dispersed in the sense that all the metal atoms present can chemisorb a molecule from the gas phase. We propose to classify those systems containing only small rafts as ultra-dispersed. Such an ultra-dispersed system is defined as one that has a higher degree of dispersion than the minimum needed to achieve atomic dispersion.

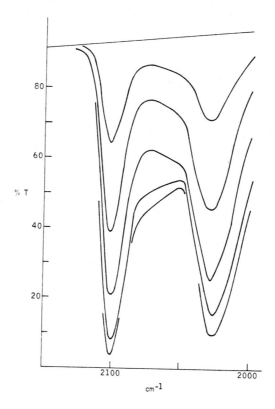

FIGURE 1. Sample of 1% Rh on alumina reduced at 200°C. Transmission at 2100 cm^{-1} before adding CO was 44%. The pressure of CO after the first four doses was zero. The pressure after the fifth dose was 0.15 cm.

EXPERIMENTAL - The support used was aluminum oxide C, (Degussa). A solution of $RhCl_3$ was added, using excess water, and stirred until adsorption took place. After filtering and air drying at 120°C, the catalyst was reduced in a high flow of H_2 at 200°C. Full details of the apparatus and procedure are given elsewhere [10].

RESULTS - A sample containing 1% Rh (thickness 15 mg/cm^2, weight 15 mg) was put in the cell and reduced for 1.5 hours at 200°C. From the pressures before and after adsorption, given in the legend of Figure 1, it will be seen that the first 4 doses were at coverages less than a monolayer. Saturation (or monolayer) coverage was reached with the fifth dose, with a final pressure of 0.15 cm. Many experiments have shown that no more CO is adsorbed once a pressure (after adsorption) of about 1 mm is reached. It is evident that two symmetrical bands dominate the spectrum at 2100 and 2025 cm^{-1}. Study of the high transmission region between these bands (i.e., approximately 2030-2080 cm^{-1} shows a change of slope occurring with increasing dosage at about 2075 cm^{-1}. This is also shown in the desorption studies of Figure 2. The desorption procedure is given elsewhere [10].

To show the effect of reduction temperature, another sample of 1% Rh was put in the cell and reduced for 1 hour at 480°C. The sample weighed 24 mg, and had a thickness of 19 mg/cm^2. Spectra obtained from this sample are shown in Figure 3. The strongest bands in Figure 3 have about 15% transmission, while the corresponding bands in Figure 1 had a transmission of only 3%. This relative decrease in intensity of the sample of Figure 3 occurred despite the fact that the thickness of the sample used in Figure 3 was 19 mg/cm^2 and that used in Figure 1 was 15 mg/cm^2. The other major difference is that the band at 2075 cm^{-1} which was only evident as a shoulder in the 200^{0}C reduced sample, is now clearly resolved at high coverage in the 480^{0}C reduced sample (see doses 4 to 6 in Figure 3). This 2075 cm^{-1} band is due to a species which is much more weakly held than that producing the bands at 2100 and 2025 cm^{-1}, as shown by desorption studies [10]. An interesting effect of adsorbed CO on the mobility of Rh atoms was observed and is shown in the spectra of Figure 4. A 1% Rh sample was reduced at 200^{0}C and a series of CO doses added to saturation. The spectra after the first of these doses (about 50% saturation) with initial pressure of 0.08 cm is shown in Figure 4 [1]. After evacuation of the cell at 25^{0}C for 90 min., H$_2$ was passed through the cell at 200 cm^3/min. and the sample re-reduced at 180^{0}C using the same procedure as for the first reduction. No adsorbed CO was present after this. After adding a dose of CO (initial pressure 0.085 cm) almost the same as that used in

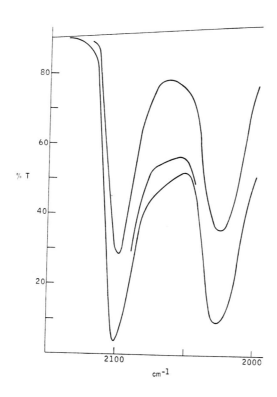

FIGURE 2. Desorption of CO from the sample used in Figure 1: Spectra shown are for: the fifth dose of CO (0.15 cm), after evacuation at 25°C for 80 min., and finally after evacuation at 100°C for 17 min. The top line is the spectra recorded before CO addition.

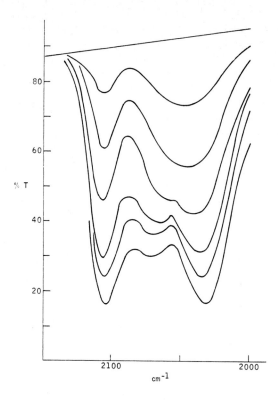

FIGURE 3. Sample of 1% Rh on alumina reduced at 480°C. The pressure of CO after the first five doses was zero. The pressure after the sixth dose was 0.08 cm.

Figure 4 [1] spectrum 4 [2] was obtained. Now a band at about 2055 cm^{-1} is present with significant intensity, in addition to the previously found bands. When the sample was reduced for the third time and CO adsorbed, the spectra shown in Figure 4 [3] was obtained. Now the 2055^{-1} band is stronger than the 2030 cm^{-1} band and the 2055 cm^{-1} band dominates the spectrum.

Table 1 contains the data obtained from the chemisorption of H_2 and CO. The data are given as H/M and CO/M. The main feature of this data is the existence of multiple CO adsorption on those samples showing predominantly the 2100 and 2030 cm^{-1} CO bands and its relative absence in samples showing predominantly the 2070 cm^{-1} CO bands.

Figure 6 shows the particle size distribution obtained by electron microscopy of the samples discharged from the infrared cell after CO spectra had been determined. The 1% Rh sample was that used in Figures 1 and 2, while the 10% Rh sample was that discussed elsewhere [10].

DISCUSSION - A classic study by Yang and Garland [11] some twenty years ago showed the existence of very complex infrared spectra of CO adsorbed on Rh. In general, except for minor frequency shifts, our spectra are in very close agreement with theirs. However, our motive in studying this system was not because we thought

141

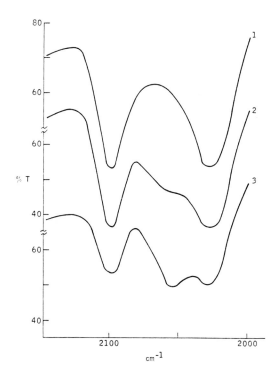

FIGURE 4. The effect of re-reduction on the spectra of CO adsorbed on 1% Rh on alumina.
Spectra: 1, after the first dose of CO added after the initial reduction at
200°C; 2, after the first dose of CO added after re-reduction at 180°C;
3, after the first dose of CO added after a second re-reduction at 180°C.

TABLE 1

Carbon Monoxide and Hydrogen Chemisorption
Data for Rhodium on Alumina

Rhodium Conc. (Wt%)	Reduction		H/M[a]	CO/M[b]
	Number per Sample	°C		
1	1st	200	1.16 (5)	-
	2nd	180	-	1.73 (5)
	3rd	180	-	1.19 (2)
1	1st	465	1.06 (2)	-
	2nd	450	-	1.46 (2)
	3rd	450	-	1.30 (1)

(a) Atoms of hydrogen adsorbed per Rh atom at 10 cm pressure.

(b) Molecules of carbon monoxide adsorbed per Rh atom at 10 cm pressure.

that there were significant deficiencies in their work, but that we thought useful information could be gained by investigating in a more detailed fashion the highly dispersed system exemplified by Rh on alumina. In addition, we hoped that we would derive synergistic information from a methodology combining infrared studies with chemisorption and electron microscopy.

For example, Yang and Garland, entirely on the basis of analogies with the spectrum of rhodium carbonyl chloride, suggested that the two band spectra of adsorbed CO had its origin in the symmetrical and antisymmetric modes of vibration of two CO molecules bonded to one Rh atom. If their assignment is correct, it should be capable of ready verification by chemisorption measurements, provided that the samples used in the two techniques are from the identical starting materials and reduced by identical procedures.

INFRARED DATA - Our initial experiments were conducted at low temperatures of reduction (200°C) and with a range of Rh concentrations. In the earlier work of Yang and Garland, they had only presented spectra on 2% Rh reduced at 200°C and of 8% Rh reduced at 400°C. It is unclear to us whether or not the effects they observed in going from 2% Rh to 8% Rh were due to a concentration effect, a temperature effect, or to some combination of these effects.

A sample containing 1% Rh reduced at 200°C gave a simple spectra when CO was added (Figure 1). Essentially, only two bands are observed and they are frequency invariant with coverage. At higher coverages there is evidently a very weak band present at about 2075 cm^{-1}. The latter band disappears entirely after a short evacuation at 100°C (Figure 2) showing those CO molecules with a frequency of 2100 and 2030 cm^{-1} are more strongly bound to Rh than those CO molecules having a frequency close to 2075 cm^{-1}.

For our 1% Rh samples reduced at 200°C (Figures 1 and 2), we find considerable similarity with the spectra shown by Yang and Garland for a 2% Rh sample reduced at 200°C. In our case the 2075 cm^{-1} band was very much weaker than they found and indeed in one case (Figure 11, Ref. 10) we have prepared a low temperature reduced sample that showed no band at 2075 cm^{-1}. We now inserted a new sample of 1% Rh in the cell and reduced it at 480°C for 1 hour. Figure 3 shows that the two frequency invariant bands at 2100 and 2030 cm^{-1} still dominate the spectrum, but that the band at about 2075 cm^{-1} is now present as a clearly resolved, although still overlapped, band. This higher temperature of reduction had no effect on the relative strengths of binding of the various CO species, as the desorption characteristics (Figure 5, Ref. 10) are essentially the same as those shown in Figure 2.

Finally, interesting spectroscopic evidence has been found of the effects of adsorbed CO inducing surface mobility of Rh during re-reduction. In all samples containing 1% Rh where the initial reduction of the sample was at 200°C, the two band CO spectra were invariably obtained. For the sample shown in Figure 4, we studied the effect of re-reduction (at 180°C) of a sample containing strongly held CO at the start of the reduction. On re-reduction the system is metastable in that a band at 2055 cm^{-1} associated with less well-dispersed Rh now becomes evident. A second re-reduction now produces a spectrum where the 2055 cm^{-1} band is dominant, while it was not present after the initial reduction. This striking effect shows the sample with adsorbed CO on the Rh goes through a surface reconstruction on re-reduction at 180°C. This mobility has been confirmed by chemisorption studies, as discussed later.

CHEMISORPTION DATA - Very few studies have been reported on the dispersion and chemisorption stoichiometry of Rh, either supported or unsupported. Following the original work of Yates and Sinfelt, [9] who studied both the unsupported Rh and silica-supported Rh, the most detailed work is that of Wanke and Dougharty [12], who used alumina as the support. With unsupported rhodium excellent agreement was found betwee areas determined by the physical adsorption of Ar and the chemisorption of H$_2$ [9]. As no infrared experiments could be done with unsupported Rh, no attempt was made to use the CO chemisorption data as a method of measuring the particle size.

For the silica-supported samples [9] the infrared spectra of adsorbed CO showed that the linear form predominated. Hence, we expressed our data as the ratio of CO molecules per rhodium atom (CO/M) and the corresponding value assuming one atom of hydrogen per metal atom (H/M). Table 1 of ref. 9 shows that for all catalysts except the one containing 0.1% Rh, the CO/M value was either equal to, or a little less than, the H/M values. In these circumstances, there is no evidence of multiple CO adsorption. On the contrary, mainly linear CO is present, with a significant number of bridged [(Rh)$_2$CO] species. The only exception to this [9] was the sample containing 0.1% Rh, where the H/M ratio was found to be close to unity while the CO/M ratio was 1.4.

The work of Wanke and Dougharty [12] showed that the situation with alumina-supported rhodium was much more complex. In particular, at Rh concentrations below 1%, the H/M ratio was significantly above 1 for 0.5, 0.1 and 0.02% Rh. No explanation was offered for these unexpected H/M ratios [12].

Table 1 shows our data for H/M and CO/M where the samples were reduced under conditions identical to those used in the infrared experiments. Because of the effects of surface mobility on re-reduction (Figure 4), a more detailed study than usual was done on chemisorption. The procedure was as follows. The initial reduction of a given sample of the 1% Rh sample was done at 200°C, the sample evacuated at 180°C and then a H$_2$ isotherm run after cooling to 25°C. The sample was re-reduced by flowing H$_2$ over it at room temperature, then heating to 180°C using the rate of rise of temperature and H$_2$ flow given in ref. 10. Then a CO isotherm was measured at 25°C. This was done five times for five separate samples taken from a master batch of the 1% Rh catalyst. The brackets after the H/M and CO/M values refer to the number of separate samples measured; the numerical value given is the average. Good experimental accuracy was achieved. For example, the five individual values giving the average H/M value of 1.16 are: 1.18, 1.14, 1.15, 1.10 and 1.23. For two of these samples the effect of re-reduction after a CO isotherm was studied by performing a second re-reduction. The CO/M was then found to be 1.19, a marked drop from the average value of 1.73 for the five samples studied after only one re-reduction. Reproducible data were also obtained with the CO isotherms, the individual values of 1.8, 1.65, 1.69, 1.75 and 1.77 giving the average of 1.73.

Reduction of a 1% Rh sample at 200°C leads to the following conclusions: as the H/M value is essentially unity, evidently all the Rh atoms in the sample are in the surface. The simplest way in which this can take place is by postulating an array of Rh clusters all one atom thick. Such two-dimensional rafts have been directly resolved in the electron microscope [8]. Evidently, the average number of atoms in each raft must be small, as high CO/M values were measured (1.73). It is unlikely, on elementary steric grounds, that the Rh atoms in the middle of large rafts (say 20 x 20 atoms) can adsorb more than one CO molecule per Rh atom. This interpretation is also in good agreement with the spectra shown in Figure 1.

For a series of 1% Rh samples reduced at 465°C (Table 1), it is interesting that atomic dispersion is still retained under these more severe conditions, as shown by the H/M ratio of 1.0 still being present. However, the CO/M is now found to be 1.46, which is most readily interpreted as an increase in the average number of Rh atoms in the two-dimensional rafts. Again, the infrared data in Figure 3 are in good agreement with this interpretation.

Based on the definitions given in the introduction, all of the 1% Rh samples on alumina listed in Table 1 show ultra-dispersion and are, of course, atomically dispersed in the conventional sense. Based on the above definition of ultra-dispersion, it is evident that the main effect of low temperature of reduction at the 1% Rh level is to increase markedly the extent of ultra-dispersion, as shown by the CO/M value of 1.73 versus the value of 1.46 after the more severe reduction.

CONCLUSIONS - The above considerations involving spectroscopy and chemisorption will now be brought into focus using one assumption: for two-dimensional rafts of Rh atoms, only edge or corner atoms can adsorb two CO molecules. All other Rh atoms in these rafts (the interior atoms) can only adsorb one CO molecule. Hence, we can readily construct the simple model of raft structure shown in Figure 5, based on the data of Prestridge and Yates [8] who measured a Rh-Rh spacing of 0.375 nm for two-dimensional Rh rafts. From this model we can also calculate the CO/M ratio for a given raft and measure its effective diameter from a scale diagram. Such a model should lead to the same conclusions from electron microscopy as from the CO chemisorption values, if our model is correct.

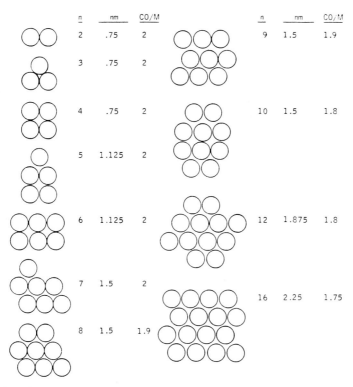

n	nm	CO/M
2	.75	2
3	.75	2
4	.75	2
5	1.125	2
6	1.125	2
7	1.5	2
8	1.5	1.9

n	nm	CO/M
9	1.5	1.9
10	1.5	1.8
12	1.875	1.8
16	2.25	1.75

FIGURE 5. Based on measured average packing spacing of Rh on SiO2 of 0.375 nm (E. B. Prestridge and D. J. C. Yates, Nature 234, 345 (1971))

Detailed electron microscope studies gave the particle size distributions as shown in Figure 6. The 1% Rh sample was that used to obtain the spectra shown in Figure 1, reduced at 200°C. The 10% Rh sample was reduced at 480°C. The photomicrographs of the 1% sample [10] showed only two-dimensional rafts. This is,

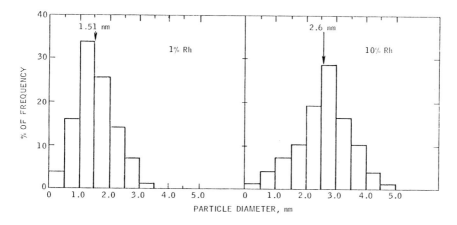

FIGURE 6. Particle size distribution for samples of 1% Rh reduced at 200°C (Figures 1 and 2) and for 10% Rh reduced at 480°C (Reference 10) determined by electron microscopy.

of course, in agreement with the H_2 chemisorption data given in Table 1, where five separate reductions showed that such samples were always atomically dispersed. The number average particle sizes of the rafts is 1.51 nm (see Figure 6) and particles were found in size ranges varying from 0.7 to 3.5 nm. For the 10% sample, large numbers of two-dimensional rafts were seen in the particle size range from 0.7 to 4.0 nm. Particles larger than this were all found to be more than one atom thick, i.e. they are normal three-dimensional entities that one considers as particles. In the size range between 2.0 and 4.0 nm, both rafts and three-dimensional particles were observed.

Figure 5 shows how the CO/M ratio varies with the number of atoms in a raft. For example, using this model one finds a CO/M of about 1.7 for a 20 atom raft, 1.6 for a 29 atom raft, falling to 1.5 for a 46 atom raft. With Rh on Al_2O_3 it proved to be more difficult than with Rh on SiO_2 to resolve individual atoms [8] so in this work we measured the diameter of the rafts, rather than count atoms directly. Hence, we constructed the plot shown in Figure 7 where CO/M is shown as a function of raft diameter for the two-dimensional Rh system.

The data of Figure 6 show a number average raft size of 1.51 nm, corresponding to the average size raft containing 7 to 10 atoms. It will be seen from Figure 5 that all of these rafts have the same size. From Figure 7, this would correspond to a CO/M value of 1.8. In other words the electron microscope data on the sample used for the CO spectra shown in Figure 1 predict that the sample would have a CO/M ratio of 1.8. Of course this cannot be measured accurately on a sample weighing some 0.015 gms, but the average of five separate chemisorption determinations using larger samples from the same batch of catalyst showed a CO/M ratio of 1.73 (Table 1). We consider that this is a very satisfactory agreement and that this system is the best defined example of an ultra-dispersed metal that we know of.

Finally, we should like to stress that this raft configuration is in excellent agreement with Yang and Garland [11] who state "It is believed that this 2% unsintered surface is highly irregular in structure with small groups of metal atoms essentially isolated from each other". For groups read rafts and this is exactly our configuration. This is in marked contrast with suggestions of recent workers [13,14] who have inferred from the frequency invariance of the bands of CO on Rh that the Rh atoms are isolated; furthermore they infer that Yang and Garland attributed the frequency invariance to isolated Rh atoms. It is evident from the particle size distribution shown in Figure 6, that very few, if any, of the Rh atoms in our catalyst can be isolated. The occurrence of isolated Rh atoms is also most unlikely, on general grounds, in view of what is known about the particle size distribution of many supported metal catalysts [15]. The cause of the frequency invariance must, therefore be sought elsewhere.

Two possibilities occur to us: either the Rh-Rh distances in the rafts are large enough to minimize lateral interactions, or the Rh atoms move on the support as a result of the adsorption of CO. In view of the drastic rearrangement shown in Figure 4, the "breathing" raft seems the most likely possibility to us. Only small increases in the Rh-Rh distances would be needed to stop lateral interactions.

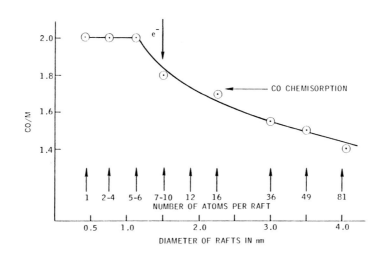

FIGURE 7. CO/M ratio for two-dimensional rhodium rafts as a function of their diameter.

REFERENCES

1. Spenadel, L. and Boudart, M., J. Phys. Chem. 64, 204 (1960).
2. Adler, S. F. and Keavney, J. J., J. Phys. Chem. 64, 208 (1960).
3. Gruber, H. L., J. Phys. Chem. 66, 48 (1962).
4. Adams, C. R., Benesi, H. A., Curtis, R. M. and Meisenheimer, R. G., J. Catal., 1, 336 (1962).
5. Wilson, G. R. and Hall, W. K., J. Catal. 17, 190 (1970).
6. van Hardeveld, R., and Hartog, F., Surf. Sci. 15, 189 (1969).
7. Anderson, J. R., "Structure of Metallic Catalysts", p. 244, Academic Press, New York, 1975.
8. Prestridge, E. B. and Yates, D. J. C., Nature 234, 345 (1971).
9. Yates, D. J. C. and Sinfelt, J. H., J. Catal. 8, 348 (1967).
10. Yates, D. J. C., Murrell, L. L. and Prestridge, E. B., J. Catal. 57, 41 (1979).
11. Yang, A. C. and Garland, C. W., J. Phys. Chem. 61, 1504 (1957).
12. Wanke, S. E. and Dougharty, N. A., J. Catal. 24, 367 (1972).
13. Yao, H. C. and Rothschild, W. G., J. Chem. Phys. 68, 4774, (1978).
14. Yates, J. T., Duncan, T. M., Worley, S. D. and Vaughan, R. W., J. Chem. Phys., 70, 1219, 1979.
15. Yates, D. J. C. and Prestridge, E. B., unpublished observations.

DISCUSSION

J.C. YATES, L.L. MURREL, E.B. PRESTRIDGE

Charcosset - What about a possible partial reoxidation of metallic rhodium during evacuation of hydrogen at the end of the reduction step, and before H_2 or CO chemisorption ?

Yates - If we had a problem with partial reoxidation of our Rh, we would readily detect CO_2 after adding CO. This we never did. In any case, we have measured the partial pressure of oxygen in our system using mass spectroscopy, and find it is lower than 10^{-10} Torr.

Basset - I would like to make comments with regard to your I.R. studies. We were able to observe the doublet at around 2100 cm^{-1} and 2030 cm^{-1} in various ways :

1 - Decomposition of $Rh_6(CO)_{16}$ on alumina. The decomposition of $Rh_6(CO)_{16}$ is followed by evolution of H_2 corresponding to the oxidation of Rh(0) by H^+ :

$$Rh_6(CO)_{16} + \overset{OH}{\underset{Al}{|}} \rightarrow 3\ H_2 + 6\ \overset{O}{\underset{Al}{|}}\!\!-\!\!Rh\!\!\overset{CO}{\underset{CO}{\diagup}} + 4\ CO$$

2 - Decomposition of $Rh_4(CO)_{12}$ on alumina - same bands.

3 - Adsorption of $[\,Rh\ \ CO)_2\ Cl\,]_2$ on alumina - same bands.

4 - Adsorption of CO on slightly reduced $RhCl_3$ adsorbed on alumina.

5 - Adsorption of CO on a Rh particle which has been previously oxidized by O_2.

I would like also to mention that H_2 can oxidatively add to Rh(I) to give $Rh(III)\!\!\overset{H}{\underset{H}{\diagdown}}$, CO can adsorb on Rh(I) to give $Rh(I)\,\overset{CO}{\underset{CO}{}}$.

Therefore I wonder if you could consider that your doublet is due to a $Rh(I)\!\!\overset{CO}{\underset{CO}{\diagdown}}$ species.

Yates - We would like to point out that the amount of hydrogen produced when a metal carbonyl is deposited on a support is extraordinarily dependant on such factors as : metal loading level, support pre-treatment conditions, and temperature of treatment of the supported metal carbonyl. We are reluctant to accept that a plus one oxidation state of rhodium is present over our wide range of metal concentrations (1-10 %) and reduction temperatures (200-480° C).

Furthermore, the two band spectrum of 1 % rhodium prepared from hydrated $RhCl_3$ is essentially independant of reduction temperature. A mild reduction at 200° C gives a CO doublet spectra, in the same positions as did a sample severely reduced at 480° C. Therefore, we believe that the morphology of the rhodium, and not the oxidation state to be the critical factor which controls the multiple bonding of CO to a single rhodium centre.

Although homogeneous rhodium complexes are known which oxidatively add hydrogen, for the systems discussed in our paper only one hydrogen atom per metal centre is chemisorbed. This is consistent with the chemisorption properties observed for unsupported rhodium metal. As shown in our paper, the intensity of the two band multiplet of CO can be dramatically reduced without changing the hydrogen chemisorption properties. It is this key observation which strongly suggests that morphological changes of the average raft size are controlling the extent of multiple CO chemisorption. Concerning the observance of the two band multiplet upon addition of oxygen to supported rhodium, we feel more work is required to establish that the two band CO multiplet then observed is as strongly bound to the rhodium cluster, as we have found for completely reduced rhodium systems.

Zecchina - The presence of a pair of I.R. bands with constant intensity ratio can be interpreted also in terms of three CO groups bonded to a single atom.
The solution of this problem is very relevant in order to confirm or reject your bidimensional cluster model. In fact if three CO groups are present on certain atoms, the overall CO coverage (figure 18) can be explained also in terms of tridimensional clusters where

edge atoms adsorb three CO, face atoms one CO and inner atoms no CO. Did you try to solve this problem by using ^{13}CO substitution ?

Yates - Yes, we have studied ^{12}CO - ^{13}CO exchange, and we have resolved all six bands involved in the three complexes :

$$Rh(^{13}CO)_2, \ Rh(^{12}CO)_2 \ and \ Rh^{12}CO, \ ^{13}CO.$$

This shows definitively that our adsorbed species is $Rh(CO)_2$.

Yacaman - What is the evidence that you have showing that the rafts have indeed a thickness of a monolyaer ?

Yates - This comes from consideration of our chemisorption data, which show that the H(atom) to Rh(atom) ratio is 1. For more details, see our paper in the Journal of Catalysis 57, 41, 1979.

Ehrlich - In your talk you suggested that CO becomes localized on a supported rhodium particle on the first collision. Could you summarize the experimental evidence for this ? Some interesting information about the efficiency of energy transfer to the support could emerge from this.

Yates   - This is basically an intuitive idea based on the very strong heat of adsorption of CO on our Rh (see detailed desorption data in J. Catal. 57, 41, 1979).

We have also indications along these lines from our new isotopic exchange experiments. For example, very rapid exchange is detected between pre-adsorbed pure ^{13}CO when small amounts of ^{12}CO are added. However, no further exchange takes place until the system is heated above room temperature. These experiments are still in progress.

Ruckenstein - The basic question is in what manner a given number of metal atoms organizes on a substrate. When this number is large enough they organize as a macroscopic particle on a substrate. When however their number is sufficiently small their equilibrium shape can be essentially different and we have shown (Ruckenstein and Lee, Surface Science, 1975) that there are conditions under which they can have a more planar shape, as detected experimentally by Dr Yates.

Yates - Thank you for your helpful comment.

Naccache - You suggest that the I.R. doublet observed when CO was adsorbed on raft rhodium is due to $Rh_{(0)}(CO)_2$ complexes. However it is well known that $Rh(I)(CO)_2$ complexes gave identical I.R. spectra with two I.R. bands at about the same frequencies as those you showed. Thus I think that to completely agree with your interpretation, it would be important to explain why Rh(I) and Rh(0) dicarbonyls should give identical I.R. spectra ?

Yates - Yes, I agree that this subject needs further study. Obviously, there are in a sense "bonds" formed between the Rh and the oxygen of the underlying Al_2O_3, but this does not necessarily convert the Rh to Rh(I) rather than Rh(0).

J. BOURDON (Editor)
Growth and Properties of Metal Clusters, pp. 151—164
© 1980 Elsevier Scientific Publishing Company — Printed in The Netherlands

APPLICATION DE LA RMN A L'ETUDE DE LA CHIMISORPTION DE L'HYDROGENE SUR PLATINE SUPPORTE

L.CH. de MENORVAL   ET   J.P. FRAISSARD
Laboratoire de Chimie des Surfaces, Université P. et M. Curie, Tour 55
4 Place Jussieu, 75230 Paris Cedex 05, France

ABSTRACT

L'étude par RMN de l'adsorption de l'hydrogène sur platine supporté a permis de mettre
en évidence par spectroscopie l'hydrogène fortement chimisorbé sur ce métal. Celui-ci peut
se trouver sous deux formes. L'une, indépendante de la nature du support et de la taille
des particules est liée au métal par liaison covalente ou métallique. La liaison Pt-H évolue avec le diamètre de la particule et le taux de recouvrement de la surface. La nature de
la seconde forme, essentiellement détectée sur le platine supporté sur silice, n'a pas encore été déterminée.

La structure électronique en surface d'un métal semble assez différente de celle en volume. En particulier, pour les métaux de transition, des pics de la densité d'états en fonction de l'énergie, près du milieu de la bande d , sont prévus par les calculs théoriques de
structure de bande (1) et sont observés par les méthodes de photoémission angulaire (2). De
même la densité d'états électronique au voisinage du niveau de Fermi doit être différente
de celle en volume et dépendre du site considéré de la surface. On s'attend à ce que cette
structure électronique en surface joue un rôle important dans les phénomènes de chimisorption et soit plus ou moins fortement modifiée par la présence d'adsorbats. Il est extrêmement important de disposer d'outils expérimentaux permettant d'étudier les liaisons adsor-
bat-substrat. Celles-ci dépendent des sites d'adsorption, et par conséquent, pour l'adsorption sur petites particules métalliques de la taille et de la forme de ces particules. Des
informations précises sur la forme et la nature des complexes adsorbés peuvent être obtenues par diverses techniques expérimentales. Citons par exemple la thermodésorption (3),
l'Infra Rouge (4), qui donne la perturbation des liaisons des complexes adsorbés par rapport
à la phase gazeuse, ou la RPE (5) dans le cas où il y a transfert de charge entre le solide
et la phase adsorbée. Pour l'instant seules les méthodes de photoémission angulaire permettent d'obtenir des informations sur les sites d'adsorption et la structure électronique des
liaisons ; ces études sont toutefois limitées au cas de substrats propres.

Nous nous sommes proposé d'utiliser les techniques de RMN pour l'étude des surfaces métalliques. Ces techniques ont été fort peu utilisées jusqu'ici, l'observation de la RMN ne
pouvant se faire que pour un nombre appréciable de noyaux ($\sim 10^{18}$ au moins). Elles ne sont
donc utilisables que pour des matériaux pour lesquels le rapport surface sur volume est élevé et qui sont loin en général de présenter des surfaces propres. C'est le cas des petites
particules métalliques supportées par des isolants, et utilisées comme catalyseurs. Les mé-

thodes de RMN peuvent donner des informations extrêmement fines sur la structure électronique, surtout lorsqu'elles peuvent être utilisées comme méthodes spectroscopiques, c'est à dire lorsque les déplacements des résonances (déplacement chimique pour les espèces adsorbées, déplacement de Knight pour les atomes du métal) sont suffisamment importants pour être résolus, et ainsi permettre de distinguer des sites ayant des environnements électroniques différents.

Nous avions envisagé de mener de front les expériences sur la RMN des adsorbats et du substrat métallique.

RMN DU SUBSTRAT METALLIQUE

Les premières prédictions théoriques relatives aux petites particules métalliques ont été faites par Kubo (6) qui a estimé les propriétés magnétiques et thermiques des particules isotropes de diamètre inférieur à 100 Å. Pour de telles particules et à la température 1 K il prévoyait des déviations relativement importantes par rapport au métal massif ; en particulier il était amené à distinguer les particules ayant un nombre pair ou impair d'électrons de conduction, les particules "impaires" devant être paramagnétiques à basse température. L'étude théorique a ensuite été affinée par GORKOV et ELIASHBERG (7) puis DENTON et coll (8). Les résultats théoriques de ces derniers relatifs à la susceptibilité de spin sont résumés sur la figure 1. La courbe B représente les "particules paires" pour lesquelles les spins sont appariés à la température T = 0 K, réduisant ainsi à zéro la susceptibilité et par conséquent le déplacement chimique $\underline{\delta}$ des noyaux métalliques. Par suite de la présence d'un électron célibataire, les "particules impaires" (courbe A) doivent suivre la loi de CURIE.

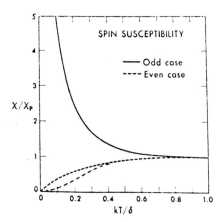

Fig. 1. Susceptibilité magnétique théorique des petites particules métalliques

Dans les métaux normaux cet effet quantique est atteint pour des particules de diamètre inférieur à 100 Å, à des températures $\leq$ 1,2 K. Pour les valeurs de KT supérieures à l'espace moyen entre les niveaux électroniques la susceptibilité pour les deux types de particules est égale à la valeur χ_p de Pauli.

KNIGHT et coll (9) on repris ces études précisant, à partir des résultats de Denton et coll (8), que le déplacement $\underline{\delta}$ des spins des noyaux des petites particules métalliques (relatif au métal massif δ_p) est :

$(\delta/\delta_p)_{pair}$ = 2,86 NKT/E_F pour les particules paires

(δ/δ_p)impair = 2 E_F/3 NKT   pour les particules impaires

Ces auteurs notent que la relaxation des spins nucléaires doit aussi être influencée par la taille des particules et la parité du nombre d'atomes qu'elles comprennent.

Les résultats concernant les petites particules d'aluminium ou de cuivre (9, 10) sont assez conformes aux prévisions précédentes mais ne permettent pas encore de conclusions systématiques. Par exemple la figure 2 reproduit le signal des noyaux [65]Cu de particules de cuivre de 100 Å détectés à 0,4 K et à 8,8 kG.

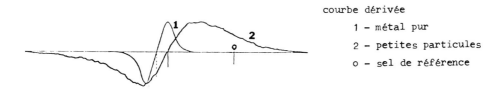

courbe dérivée

1 - métal pur

2 - petites particules

o - sel de référence

Fig. 2. Spectre RMN des petites particules de cuivre

On constate que le signal est moins déplacé et plus large que celui du métal. La diminution de δ est due au fait que les spins sont appariés dans les particules paires et la dissymétrie de la raie vers les champs faibles est attribuée aux particules impaires.

La figure 3 représente la variation de la susceptibilité χ en fonction de la température T pour quatre dimensions moyennes de particules. On constate que χ décroit avec T et que la valeur limite la plus faible correspond aux particules les plus petites. Elle n'est cependant pas nulle.

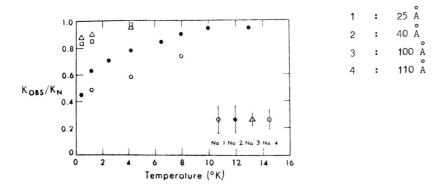

1 : 25 Å
2 : 40 Å
3 : 100 Å
4 : 110 Å

Fig. 3. Déplacement chimique pour des particules de cuivre de différentes dimensions

On doit remarquer qu'à une distribution détaillée de particules doit correspondre une distribution des valeurs de χ et du déplacement chimique δ. Ainsi le signal RMN doit

avoir une forme et une largeur qui dépendent de la distribution des dimensions. En particulier, à très basse température on devrait observer deux raies caractérisant des particules
paires et impaires.

Dans le cas de très petites particules, pour lesquelles tous les atomes sont pratiquement
en surface, on peut espérer une situation expérimentale suffisamment favorable pour mettre
en évidence l'influence des dimensions des particules à température ambiante, tout au moins
dans une première approche du problème. Par exemple Taupin et coll (11) ont étudié les petites plaquettes de Lithium composées de un ou deux plans atomiques ayant des dimensions voisines de 20 – 30 Å et formées lors de la forte irradiation aux neutrons, d'un cristal de LiF.
Dans ce cas la densité d'états devient faible et l'écart moyen entre deux niveaux électroniques est de 1/40 eV soit la valeur de KT à température ambiante. Ces auteurs ont effectivement détecté une raie non déplacée, attribuée aux particules paires. En outre ils pensent
que la raie des particules impaires n'a pu être détecté par suite de son élargissement en
fonction du nombre N d'atomes de chaque particule.

Les quelques références mentionnées ci-dessus montrent que la RMN des petites particules
a été détectée mais que les divers auteurs se sont essentiellement intéressés aux effets
quantiques observés lorsque la distance moyenne entre niveaux électroniques est supérieure
à KT.

Aucun effort n'a été développé à notre connaissance pour essayer d'observer la RMN des
atomes de surface, ou au moins pour détecter les changements éventuels du spectre de RMN
en présence d'adsorbats. En effet pour une surface libre on s'attend à des variations du déplacement de Knight (proportionnel à la densité d'états électroniques) en fonction du site
en surface. On peut espérer observer un spectre résolu si les petites particules ont des faces libres suffisamment bien définis. L'effet d'un substrat sur le spectre : déplacement de
raies, disparition de certaines d'entre elles, donnerait alors des informations précises sur
les sites d'adsorption, le transfert de charge entre adsorbat et substrat etc ... Ces expériences sont semblables à celles réalisées sur les alliages métalliques. Le groupe RMN
d'Orsay de l'Université Paris-Orsay par exemple est maintenant apte à observer des signaux
faibles dus aux sites proches voisins d'impuretés en faible concentration. Les raies correspondant à des concentrations en sites inférieures à 10^{-3} ont pu être étudiées en détail dans
des alliages de cuivre (12). La figure 4 représente le spectre du cuivre contenant 40 ppm de
manganèse ; celui-ci montre un nombre important de sites résolus et illustre la sensibilité
qui peut être atteinte. Cependant les énormes difficultés expérimentales rencontrées dans la
détection du platine ralentissent beaucoup l'étude entreprise directement sur le métal. Par
exemple les raies détectées caractéristiques du noir de platine commercial sont dissymétri-
ques et exclusivement larges. Les très grosses particules de platine supporté sur silice
($D \gg 200$ Å) donnent encore des signaux de 300 oe de large. Les très petites particules
sont quasi indétectables (même à 1,2 K) dans le cas de catalyseurs usuels (concentration inférieure à 10 %).

Signalons cependant une publication de I. YU et coll (13) sur ce sujet, dont les résultats
sont à notre avis assez surprenants. La largeur des signaux de Pt augmente quand le diamètre
D des particules diminue ; mais elle reste toujours très petite par rapport à nos mesures ;
par exemple elle n'est que de 7 oe pour $D \sim 33$ Å (Ho = 12 Koe). Ce déplacement chimique et
la quantité $T_1 T$ sont indépendants de D et ont la valeur du métal (respectivement −3,4 $\pm$
0,05 % et 29 $\pm$ m sec. K). Nous pensons que ceci est dû à la préparation des échantillons :

il s'agit de particules de platine de tailles différentes d'un échantillon à l'autre mais non supportées. Etant en contact, elles ne se comportent pas du point de vue magnétique comme des particules isolées et se rapprochent donc beaucoup du métal massif.

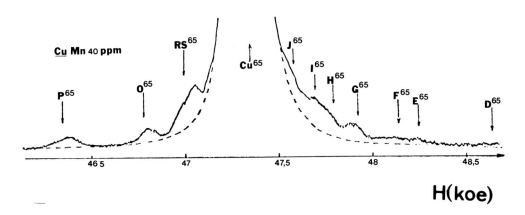

Fig. 4. Spectres RMN du cuivre dans une solution solide de Cu Mn Les diverses raies observées correspondent à diverses couches de voisins de l'impureté de Mn

RMN DE L'HYDROGENE CHIMISORBE

Devant les difficultés rencontrées dans l'étude directe de la surface du substrat métallique, nous avons entrepris parallèlement l'étude indirecte de celle-ci en utilisant comme sonde l'hydrogène chimisorbé qui présente les avantages suivants :
- sensibilité de détection du noyau ^{1}H
- utilisation possible pour tous les métaux

Enfin on peut espérer résoudre ausi le problème "éternel" de la nature de l'hydrogène adsorbé sur le métal.

Nous rapportons ici les résultats fragmentaires obtenus.

Préparation et traitement des échantillons

Les catalyseurs au platine supporté sur silice ou alumine sont préparés par imprégnation selon la méthode de Dorling et coll (14), puis réduits sous hydrogène à 500°C. Ceux sur zeolithe sont préparés selon la méthode de Gallezot et coll (15). Les tailles des particules métalliques ont été déterminées par microscopie électronique, chimisorption et R.X. Les Adsorptions d'hydrogène sont effectuées à 25°C après traitement des échantillons réduits à 300°C sous hydrogène puis 400°C sous vide.

Nous ignorons la méthode de préparation du catalyseur "européen" qui nous a été fourni.

Les caractéristiques des différents échantillons sont résumés Tableau 1.

Les expériences de RMN sont réalisées sur un spectromètre BRUKER CXP à pulses et transformées de Fourier (fréquence 96 MHz).

TABLEAU 1

Catalyseur	Support	Taille D des particules
10 % Pt / SiO$_2$	gel de silice Davison	200 Å
6 % Pt / SiO$_2$	{ gel de Silice Davison catalyseur EUROCAT	18 Å
4,8 % Pt / Al$_2$O$_3$	alumine Degussa	70 Å
2 % Pt / Al$_2$O$_3$	"	25 Å
14 % Pt / zeolithe Y	Na Y	10 Å

Résultats expérimentaux

Dans tout ce qui suit, on appellera recouvrement de la surface la quantité

$$\theta = \frac{H}{Pt_s} = \frac{\text{nombre d'atomes H chimisorbés}}{\text{nombre d'atomes de platine en surface}}$$

Pt/SiO$_2$ ($D \sim 200$ Å) . Pour un recouvrement $\underline{\theta}$ de la surface voisin de un, le spectre de l'hydrogène adsorbé est formé de 2 composantes déplacées vers les champs forts par rapport à la raie due aux groupes OH du support silice ; l'une très légèrement (raie 1, $\delta = -1$ ppm), l'autre beaucoup plus (raie 2, $\delta_2 = -46$ ppm).

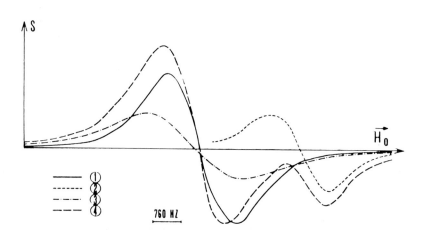

Fig. 5. Spectre de l'hydrogène adsorbé sur platine ($\theta \sim 1$)

  1 = espèce H$_1$ 2 = espèce H$_{(2)}$

  3 = OH de la silice   4 = spectre enregistré

En dehors de l'intensité des raies le spectre évolue peu en fonction du degré de recouvrement de la surface tant que celui-ci reste inférieur à 1. Mais δ_2 varie entre -46 ppm ($\theta \sim 1$) et -57 ppm ($\theta \ll 1$) correspondant à la limite de détection du signal.

 Ce premier résultat nous semble important car pour la première fois il a été possible de détecter par spectroscopie l'hydrogène chimisorbé de façon "irréversible" à température ambiante. L'étude de l'adsorption de certains gaz sur le platine contenant cet hydrogène "irréversible" a permis de montrer que ce dernier est actif dans de nombreuses réactions d'hydrogénation. Par exemple il est complètement éliminé de la surface du platine par adsorption d'oxygène ; l'eau formée est adsorbée, presque totalement par le support. De même cet hydrogène "irréversible" est totalement actif dans l'hydrogénation de l'éthylène. Ces résultats sont en accord avec ceux de nombreux auteurs qui ont utilisé l'influence de ces gaz O_2 (16) et C_2H_4 (17) pour doser l'hydrogène chimisorbé.

Signalons enfin que l'hydrogène "irréversible" est partiellement éliminé par l'adsorption de benzène. Ceci semble en contradiction avec les résultats de BASSET et coll (18) qui ont trouvé que l'hydrogène "irréversible" est sans action dans l'hydrogénation catalytique du benzène adsorbé.

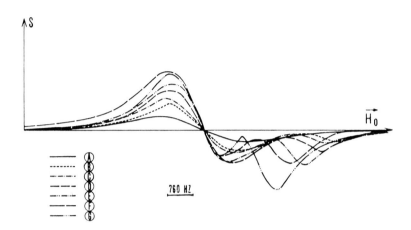

Fig. 6. Evolution du spectre avec la concentration en hydrogène. Spectre du support : A
Hydrogène adsorbé sous la pression   0,32 : E   2 torrs : F   49 torrs : G
Echantillon désorbé sous 10^{-4} torrs : 1 heure à 25°C : D
                                      12   "   "   "   : C
                                      2   "   " 48   : B

La figure 6 représente l'évolution du spectre quand le degré θ de recouvrement augmente en étant supérieur à un. La résolution du spectre en ces différentes composantes montre que la raie 1 n'évolue pas. Par contre la raie 2 se déplace vers les champs faibles quand la pression de gaz augmente.

<u>Influence de la nature du support et de la taille des particules</u>. Le tableau 2 et la figure 7 résument les résultats obtenus sur le nombre des composantes du spectre et la position δ_2 de la raie 2 en fonction de la taille D des particules et du recouvrement θ de la surface.

TABLEAU 2

Catalyseur	Diamètre D en Å des particules PT	Composantes du spectre
Pt / Y	10	raie 2
Pt / Al$_2$O$_3$	25	raie 2
Pt / Al$_2$O$_3$	70	raie 2 + raie 1 de très faible intensité quand θ est suffisant
Pt / Si O$_2$	18	raie 2 + raie 1 d'amplitude comparable
Pt / Si O$_2$	200	raie 2 + raie 1 " "
Ir / Al$_2$O$_2$	10	raie 2 + raie 1 de très faible intensité
Ir / Si O$_2$	10	raie 2 + raie 1 d'intensité comparable

158

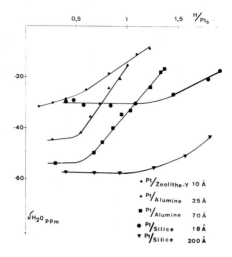

Fig. 7 a -

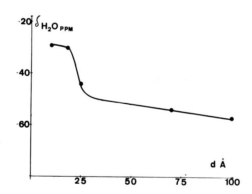

Fig. 7 b -

Fig. 7. Evolution du déplacement chimique de l'hydrogène chimisorbé

    a - en fonction du recouvrement de la surface de platine, pour différentes tailles des particules métalliques

    b - en fonction du diamètre des particules Pt, à très faible recouvrement

a) Quelle que soit la taille des particules de platine supporté <u>sur silice</u> et quel que soit le recouvrement θ le spectre de l'hydrogène chimisorbé présente les deux composantes 1 et 2 décrites précédemment. Au contraire, si le platine est supporté <u>sur alumine</u>, on ne détecte généralement que la raie 2 ; cependant dans le cas des grosses particules et pour des valeurs importantes de θ, la raie 1 peut être détectée mais reste toujours de très faible amplitude. Dans le cas de l'iridium supporté il semble que l'on retrouve cette influence du support sur l'intensité relative des deux raies RMN.

b) Pour les très faibles valeurs de θ, $\left|\delta_2\right|$ est d'autant plus important que le diamètre de la particule est grand. Mais cette variation monotone est irrégulière : elle est très faible pour $D \lesssim 20$ Å et $D \gtrsim 70$ Å ; par contre elle est assez brutale pour $20 < D < 70$ Å. Pour les très faibles recouvrements du platine, $\left|\delta_2\right|$ est indépendant de la nature (silice, alumine ou silice-alumine) du support ; en revanche l'évolution "apparente" $\delta = f(\theta)$ en dépend.

c) Pt / Al_2O_3 ou Pt / Y ; Sauf pour les très petites particules, la variation $\delta_2 = f(\theta)$ est la même quel que soit le diamètre D : $\left|\delta_2\right|$ reste sensiblement constante pour $0 < \theta < 0,6$ environ, puis décroît quand θ augmente davantage. Tout l'hydrogène adsorbé (mesuré volumétriquement) se trouvant sur le platine et sous forme de la seule espèce caractérisée par la raie 2, les valeurs $\theta = H / Pt_s$ portées en abcisse correspondent réellement au recouvrement de la surface de platine et les variations $\left|\delta_2\right| = f(\theta)$ sont <u>quantitativement vraies</u>. Dans le cas de l'échantillon Pt/Y comprenant des particules de 10 Å, il semble qu'il n'y ait pas de palier horizontal lorsque θ est petit. Cette abscence de palier peut montrer que la densité de spin négative sur H ne reste pas constante quand θ varie. Mais elle peut aussi être due au fait que l'échantillon comprend, en faible quantité, des particules de diamètre 20 et 25 Å.

d) Pt / SiO_2 ; l'évolution $\delta_2 = f(\theta)$ est qualitativement semblable à la précédente ; mais le palier horizontal s'étend apparemment sur un plus large domaine de <u>θ</u>. En fait ces courbes peuvent être quantitativement fausses. En effet le spectre RMN comprend deux raies ; même pour les valeurs moyennes de θ, celle qui est déplacée (raie 1) semble caractériser en partie de l'hydrogène se trouvant vraisemblablement sur le support ; donc le recouvrement θ réel sur le platine doit être plus petit que celui correspondant à la valeur calculée à partir des mesures volumétriques et indiqué en abcisse.

DISCUSSION

Rappelons tout d'abord les divers facteurs qui peuvent être la cause des déplacements chimiques observés. De façon générale on peut écrire que le déplacement θ d'une raie de résonance (mesuré par rapport à une référence diamagnétique) est :

$$\delta = \underset{>0}{\delta_{K(n)}} + \underset{\underset{\delta_{(S,d)} < 0}{\underbrace{\qquad\qquad}}}{\delta_S(n,t) + \delta_d(n,t)} + \underset{\underset{0}{\underbrace{\qquad}}}{\delta_{dia} + \delta_{\chi_v}}$$

δ_{χ_v} est dû à la différence de susceptibilité magnétique de l'échantillon et de la référence. Cependant, exceptionnellement dans le cas de systèmes hétérogènes, les déplacements ont été mesurés à l'aide d'une référence interne représentée par les groupes OH du support silice. On ne peut donc invoquer un tel effet.

δ_{dia} : les effets orbitaux ou diamagnétiques des électrons de conduction produisent des déplacements chimiques vers les champs forts. Ils sont cependant du même ordre de grandeur que les déplacements chimiques usuels (19) et peuvent donc être négligés dans ce cas.

δ_K : KNIGHT a montré que le signal RMN d'un noyau dans un métal est très déplacé par rapport au signal du même noyau dans un échantillon non magnétique. Ce déplacement est dû aux interactions magnétiques entre le noyau et les électrons de conduction. Si X_e est la contribution de ces derniers à la susceptibilité macroscopique volumique et N le nombre de noyaux par unité de volume, le déplacement de KNIGHT est égal à :

$$\frac{\Delta H}{H_o} = k . \frac{X_e}{N} \left\langle |\psi_M (0)|^2 \right\rangle$$

k dépend de la structure du métal,

$\left\langle |\psi_M (0)|^2 \right\rangle$ est la densité moyenne des électrons de conduction au niveau du noyau M ; donc dans un métal seuls les électrons de conduction $\underline{s}$ contribuent au déplacement de KNIGHT.

Ces déplacements de conduction peuvent avoir une densité non nulle au niveau des atomes H adsorbés sur le platine. Il doit en résulter pour ces atomes un déplacement chimique δ_K vers les champs faibles, donc opposé à celui observé par la raie 2 représentant une partie de l'hydrogène "irréversible".

δ_s, δ_d : il peut y avoir liaison platine-hydrogène par recouvrement liant des orbitales des électrons de conduction et des électrons 1S des atomes H. Par suite du principe de PAULI et de la corrélation électronique l'existence d'une telle liaison polarise les électrons 1s(H) de façon antiparallèle aux électrons de conduction. Il en résulte un déplacement opposé à δ_K, donc vers les champs forts.

Les électrons de conduction peuvent aussi avoir des interactions d'échange avec les électrons liants $\underline{d}$ des orbitales atomiques centrées sur Pt. La règle du couplage de HUND montre que les spins de ces électrons $\underline{d}$ doivent être polarisés parallèlement à ceux des électrons de conduction. Les électrons $\underline{d}$ transmettent cette polarisation de spin, changée de signe, aux atomes H par l'intermédiaire de la partie covalente de la liaison Pt-H. Dans ce cas le déplacement a lieu vers les champs forts.

En conclusion l'analyse précédente montre que l'amplitude et le signe du déplacement chimique dépendent d'une part de la contribution du déplacement δ_K de KNIGHT, d'autre part du mécanisme de polarisation responsable des déplacements négatifs.

Considérons en premier les spectres de l'hydrogène chimisorbé sur Pt/SiO_2. On pourrait tout d'abord supposer que ces raies ne sont pas indépendantes mais forment un doublet de type PAKE (20) dû aux interactions dipolaires nucléaires soit entre des atomes d'hydrogène adsorbés par paire, soit entre les atomes Pt et H. En outre, par suite d'interactions électroniques, ce doublet serait déplacé par rapport à la valeur de Ho. Cependant le calcul des interactions dipolaires montre que cette hypothèse ne peut être retenue.

Les deux raies enregistrées pourraient provenir du couplage spin-spin entre les noyaux Pt et H. Nous n'avons pas eu la possibilité de réaliser des expériences à différentes fréquences de résonance pour vérifier que la distance entre les deux raies n'est pas indépendante du champ appliqué. Cependant les plus fortes constantes du couplage J(Pt-H) mesurées pour les complexes dans lesquels un atome H est directement lié à l'atome de platine central (par exemple $\left[\text{PtH} \times \left(\text{PR}_3\right)_2\right]$ (21) sont de 1300 Hz, c'est à dire de l'ordre de grandeur de la largeur de chacune des deux composantes du spectre. En outre, dans ce cas, le spectre devraitcomporter trois raies, la troisième, située au milieu des précédentes, étant due aux atomes Pt, autres que ^{195}Pt (en abondance 1/3), qui ont un spin nucléaire nul.

La meilleure preuve de l'indépendance des deux raies enregistrées réside dans le fait que leurs intensités et leurs positions varient de façon indépendante en fonction de certains paramètres comme par exemple la pression d'hydrogène. En outre leur intensité dépend de la nature du support. Lorsque ce dernier contient de l'aluminium (Al_2O_3 ou zéolithe Y) l'intensité de la raie 1 est nulle sauf pour les valeurs de D et de θ importantes.

L'existence de ces deux composantes prouve donc que l'hydrogène peut être chimisorbé "irréversiblement" à température ambiante sous deux formes. En outre les échanges entre ces deux phases fortement chimisorbées (lorsqu'elles existent) sont très faibles à 25°C ; la fréquence d'échange est inférieure à la distance des raies exprimées en hertz c'est à dire inférieure à 5.10^3 Hz environ.

A partir de la position des raies que peut-on conclure quant à la nature de l'hydrogène chimisorbé ?

Le déplacement chimique δ_2 vers les champs forts caractérise une densité de spin électronique négative. La contribution due à la polarisation de spins 1S(H) antiparallèle au champ Ho est largement prédominante. Cette raie ne peut donc correspondre à une espèce ionique ; au contraire elle caractérise une liaison Platine-hydrogène de type covalent (en terme de liaison localisée) ou métallique (orbitale 1S (H) avec bandes $\underline{s}$ ou $\underline{d}$).

La raie 1, lorsqu'elle existe est plus difficile à expliquer. On peut émettre plusieurs hypothèses sur la nature de l'hydrogène ainsi représenté.

α - espèce ionique

β - espèce moléculaire peu perturbé électroniquement ; mais dans ce cas, l'hydrogène ne serait pas fortement lié au métal ; or une partie de cette raie "n'est pas réversible" avec la pression à température ambiante

- espèce localisée sur le support (spill-over). On peut faire la même remarque qu'en β En revanche la partie réversible de cette raie peut correspondre à cette dernière.

δ - autre phase d'hydrogène chimisorbée de façon covalente, pour laquelle le déplacement de Knight δ_K compense presque complètement les effets de polarisation des électrons liants.

Pour les faibles valeurs de θ le déplacement δ_2 semble caractéristique de chaque taille de particule et indépendante de la nature du support considéré. L'évolution de δ_2 avec le diamètre D traduit une diminution de la densité de spin électronique au niveau de l'hydrogène chimisorbé. Nous ne pouvons encore préciser la raison de cette variation. Cependant certains auteurs ont constaté un appauvrissement électronique (par rapport au métal) des petites particules de 10 Å supportées sur zéolithes (22). Un tel appauvrissement continu avec la diminution de D pourrait expliquer une telle évolution de δ_2. Signalons en outre que la variation brutale de ce déplacement vers 20-25 Å correspond aux valeurs de D pour lesquelles on observe des changements importants de l'effet catalytique.

D'autre part la longueur de palier, pour le même support Al_2O_3, semble diminuer avec D. Pour les grosses particules, celle-ci correspond à un recouvrement de 0,5 environ. Or la structure électronique du métal est $9,55/\underline{e}$ dans la bande Pt-d. On peut alors supposer que

162

ce palier correspond au remplissage, en premier, des trous $\underline{d}$. Dans cette hypothèse, l'existence de ce palier démontre que la densité de spin au niveau des noyaux H_d, et donc vraisemblablement la nature de la liaison correspondante Pt-H, sont indépendantes du taux de remplissage de la bande d.

Pour $\theta > 0,5$ la chimisorption se poursuivrait par l'intermédiaire des électrons $\underline{s}$. Cette dernière espèce H_s correspondrait alors théoriquement à un déplacement chimique $\delta_2(H_s)$ plus faible que $\delta_2(H_d)$. Cependant l'échange entre les atomes H_d et H_s étant très rapide, on ne détecte qu'une seule raie dont la position δ_2 dépend des valeurs $\delta_2(H_s)$ et $\delta_2(H_d)$ et des concentrations de ces espèces. Il est donc logique que δ_2 décroisse quand le recouvrement augmente en étant supérieur à $0,5$. On peut trouver une confirmation de l'interaction des atomes H avec les électrons de conductions $\underline{s}$ dans les résultats partiels sur la relaxation. En effet pour $\theta \sim 1$, T_1 varie linéairement avec $\frac{1}{T}$ dans le domaine $290 < T < 350\,K$ ($T_1 T = 9,37$ K. sec pour les particules de 25 Å). En se plaçant toujours dans l'hypothèse précédente, la diminution de la longueur du palier avec la taille D traduirait une variation parallèle du nombre de trous dans la bande $\underline{d}$. Pour les très petites particules, serait pratiquement saturée.

CONCLUSION

Les résultats de cette première étude RMN de la chimisorption de l'hydrogène sur platine supporté sont certes encore fragmentaires. On peut cependant en tirer les conclusions suivantes :

– Il est possible de mettre en évidence par spectroscopie l'hydrogène très fortement chimisorbé sur le métal (hydrogène "irréversible").

– L'hydrogène chimisorbé peut se trouver sous deux formes :

– L'une indépendante de la nature du support et de la taille des particules est liée au métal par liaison covalente ou métallique. La liaison Pt-H évolue avec le diamètre de la particule et avec le taux de recouvrement de la surface. Il semble que les niveaux $\underline{d}$ soient remplis les premiers.

– La seconde a été essentiellement détectée sur le platine supporté sur silice La nature n'a pas encore été déterminée.

Il semble donc que la RMN soit une méthode particulièrement intéressante pour l'étude des phases chimisorbées sur métaux.

REFERENCES

1 M.C. Desyonquères et F. Cyrot-Lackmann, J. Phys. F $\underline{5}$ (1975)1368, F $\underline{6}$ (1976)567

2 Noguera, Spanjaard, Jepsen, Ballu, Guillot, Lecante, Paigne, Petroff, Pinchaux, Thiry et Cinti, Phys. Rev. Letters $\underline{38}$ (1977)1171
   J. Lecante, 2 ème Ecole d'Eté Mediterranéenne, Florence, Juin 1977

3 Becker et Hartman, J. Chem. Phys. $\underline{57}$ (1953)157

4 L.H. Little, Infrared Spectra of Adsorbed Species, Academic Press, 1966

5 J.J. Rooney et R.I. Pink, Proc. Chem. Soc. 70 (1961)
   B.D. Flockhart, C. Naccache, J.A.N. Scott et R.C. Pink, Chem. Comm. 238 (1965)

6 R. Kubo, J. Phys. Soc. Jap. 17 (1962)975

7 L.P. Gorkov et G.M. Eliashberg, Sov. Phys. Jetp $\underline{21}$ (1965)940

8 R. Denton, B. Muhlchlegel et D.J. Scalapino, Phys. Rev. Lett. $\underline{26}$ (1971)707

9 W.D. Knight, J. Voc. Sci. Technol. $\underline{10}$ (sept.oct. 1973)
   P. Yee et W. D. Knight, Phys. Review B, $\underline{11}$ 3261 (1975)326

10 S. Kobayashi, T. Takahashin et W. Sasaky, J. Phys. Soc. Jap. Suppl. $\underline{31}$ (1971)1442 .
   J. Phys. Soc. Japan. Suppl. $\underline{32}$ (1972)1234

11 J. Charvolin, C. Froidevaux, C. Taupin et J.M. Winter, Solid State Commun. $\underline{4}$ (1966)357
   C. Taupin, J. Phys. Chem. Solids, $\underline{28}$ (1967)41

12 H. Alloul, Phys. Rev. Letters, $\underline{35}$ (1975)460
   H. Alloul, F. Nippert et H. Ishii, J. of Physics F, Métals. A paraître

13 I. Yu, A.A. Gibson, E.R. Hunt et W.P. Halperin
   A paraître

14 T. A. Dorling, B.W.J. Lynch et R.L. Moss, J. Catal. $\underline{20}$ (1971)190

15 P. Gallezot, A. Alarcon-Diaz, J.A. Dalmon, A.J. Renouprez et B. Imelik, J. Catal, $\underline{39}$ (1975)334

16 John E. Benton et M. Boudard, J. Catal. $\underline{4}$ (1965)704

17 G.C. Bond, Disc Farad. Soc. 200 (1966) et références citées

18 M. Primet, J.M. Basset, M.V. Mathieu et M. Prettre, J. Catal. $\underline{28}$ (1974)368

19 T.P. Dar et E.H. Sondheimer, Phil. Mag. $\underline{5}$ (1960)529

20 G.E. Pake, J. Chem. Phys. $\underline{16}$ (1948)327

21 J. Chatt, L.A. Duncanson et B. L. Shaw, Proc. Chem. Soc. 343 (1957)
   J. Chatt, Proc. Chem. Soc. 318 (1962)

22 M. Boudart, R.A. Dalla Betta et P. Gallezot, 6 ème Symposium Ibero-Americain de Catalyse, Rio de Janeiro, Aout 6-11, 1978

DISCUSSION

J.P. FRAISSARD, L.C. DE MENORVAL

<u>Martin</u> – On observe fréquemment la présence d'impuretés de carbone paramagnétique dans les catalyseurs à base de platine (en particulier, par R.P.E.). Quelle pourrait être l'incidence de telles impuretés sur les signaux de R.M.N. de l'hydrogène ?

<u>Fraissard</u> – S'il s'agit réellement d'impuretés (faible concentration) la présence de carbone entrainera un changement du temps de relaxation, mais n'aura qu'une influence négligeable sur le déplacement chimique, pour les systèmes étudiés.

J. BOURDON (Editor)
Growth and Properties of Metal Clusters, pp. 165—174
© 1980 Elsevier Scientific Publishing Company — Printed in The Netherlands

INTERACTION OF $Ni(CO)_4$, $Fe(CO)_5$, $Co_2(CO)_8$ WITH MgO AND FORMATION OF VERY SMALL METALLIC CLUSTERS.

E. GUGLIELMINOTTI, A. ZECCHINA, F. BOCCUZZI and E. BORELLO
Istituto di Chimica Fisica, Università di Torino, Torino (ITALY).

INTRODUCTION

The I.R. spectra of CO adsorbed on supported or evaporated metal particles show very broad bands in the 2100 - 1700 cm^{-1}, one order of magnitude broader than those of well defined carbonyl compounds. This fact is likely due to the large dispersion of the particle dimensions normally obtained by these methods (20 - 200 Å).

In fact particles of different sizes likely expose adsorbing sites of different nature, i.e. exhibit a large overall surface heterogeneity. Thus the I.R. spectra of CO adsorbed on dispersed metals allow an approximate description of the system in terms of few broad types of surface structures (i.e. linear and bridged forms).

In order to make the particle size dispersion more uniform and to reduce the dimensions, attempts have been made in recent years (ref. 1) to obtain the dispersed metal by decarbonylation of suitable metal carbonyl compounds deposited by impregnation on high area solids. The state of the final products however (dimensions, size dispersion, oxidation state) depends in a complicated way on the impregnation and decarbonylation conditions and on the hydroxyl content of supporting surface.

For these reasons in the present paper a method is described by which the impregnation of a high area support is carried out in conditions of total surface dehydration, absence of solvents and atmospheric gases.

EXPERIMENTAL

High area MgO samples (~ 200 m^2/g) have been obtained directly in the cells by decomposing under high vacuum at 523 K high purity $Mg(OH)_2$ as described in a previous paper (ref. 2). Total surface dehydration is achieved by subsequent outgassing at 1073 K under high vacuum conditions.

The pellet is then cooled down to room temperature under vacuum and the volatile $Ni(CO)_4$, $Fe(CO)_5$ and $Co_2(CO)_8$ carbonyls allowed to contact the surface.

After each dose the spectrum of adsorbed species (both I.R. and UV-VIS-Near Infrared diffuse reflectance) was carried out with a Beckman IR 12 and DK-2 spectrometers respectively.

RESULTS

The I.R. spectrum of increasing amounts of $Ni(CO)_4$ adsorbed on MgO is shown in fig. 1a (2150 - 1850 cm^{-1} range) and fig. 1b (1600 - 1000 cm^{-1} range).

It must be noticed that, due to the instability of $Ni(CO)_4$, CO is always present in the gaseous phase of this compound. After Ni(CO)$_4$ chemisorption bands are observed at ∿2100 (shoulder), 2085, 2072, 2025, 2010, 1990, 1975, 1930, 1915 cm^{-1} (fig. 1a) and at 1490 - 1462 and at 1060 - 1030 cm^{-1} (fig. 1b). Some minor component are observed in fig. 1b which will not be described in detail. We only recall that they (together with the shoulder at ∿2100 cm^{-1}) are due to CO adsorbed on MgO as discussed in detail in a previous paper (ref.2).

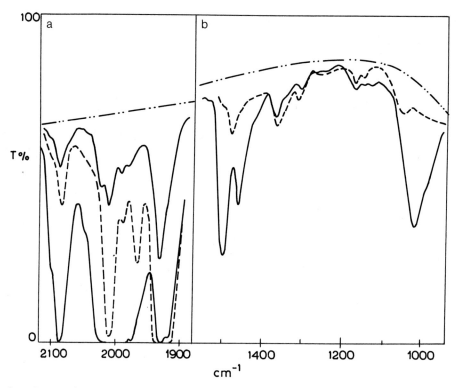

Fig. 1a,b.—Increasing amounts of Ni(CO)$_4$ adsorbed on MgO. --- Sample outgassed 30' at R.T.

By removal of the CO phase, the bands at 2085, 2072, 2025, 1990, 1975 and at 1490 - 62 and 1060 - 30 cm^{-1} disappear while bands at 2010, 1965 and 1930 - 1915 cm^{-1} grow in intensity (fig. 1, curve ---).

Reexposure to CO gas reverses the process as shown in detail in fig. 2. This figure refers to a sample onto which a smaller amount of Ni(CO)$_4$ has been chemisorbed, as this allows a better inspection of the behaviour of the bands in the high frequency range.

From Fig. 1 and 2 the following conclusions can be drawn: i) species responsible of the bands at 2085, 2072, 2025, 1990, 1975 and at 1490 - 62, 1060 - 30 cm^{-1} are stable only in the presence of CO in the gas phase; ii) species absorbing at 2010, 1965 and 1930 - 1915 cm^{-1} are favoured by low CO pressures; iii) interconversion between these species can be obtained by varying the CO pressure and this process is definitely activated as shown by its time dependence (see Fig. 2 --- and -.-.).

Degassing in high vacuum at 523 K causes the complete disappearance of all the carbonyl bands. The reexposure at this stage to CO gas is shown in Fig. 3.

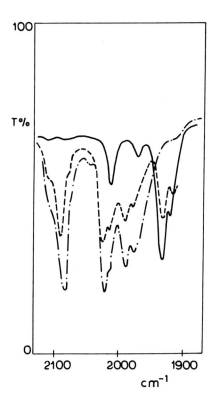

Fig. 2. ___ Ni(CO)$_4$ adsorbed and outgassed 30' at R.T.
--- Immediately after contact with 10 torr CO
-···-After 2 days.

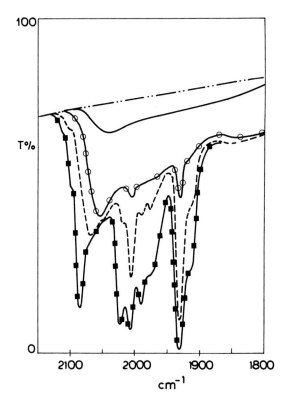

Fig. 3. -··-··- Background after Ni(CO)$_4$ adsorption at R.T. and 2^h desorption at 523 K.
After contact with CO: (___ 0,5, -o-o-2, -- 4 and ▬■▬■▬ 10 torr).

For low CO pressures and short contact time a broad structureless band centered at 2030 cm^{-1} with a large tail on the low frequency side is observed, similar to what observed for CO adsorbed on finely divided Nickel obtained in conventional ways (ref. 3). By increasing the CO pressure and or the contact time, narrow bands develope which are identical to those previously illustrated in fig. 1 - 2. The first bands to appear are those at 2010 - - 1930 cm^{-1}, whereas those at 2085, 2025, 1990 cm^{-1} are formed in the final stages of reaction.

Experiments similar to those illustrated in figs. 1 - 3 have been carried out in a reflectance cell and the results are illustrated in Fig. 4. The band at $\sim$25.000 cm^{-1} in Fig. 4a is formed upon contacting the surface with a Ni(CO)$_4$ dose roughly similar to that originating the most intense spectrum of Fig. 1.

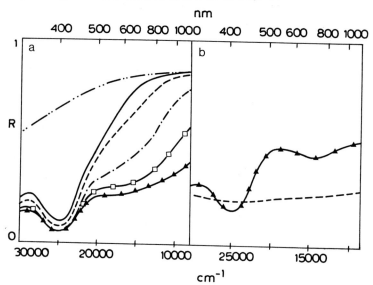

Fig. 4.   —··—··— MgO background
a) —— After contact with Ni(CO)$_4$
   After outgassing at R.T.: -- 20", -·- 1', -□— 5', -▲— 30'.
b) --- After outgassing 1^h at 523 K
   -▲— 10 torr CO adsorbed and spectrum recorded after 2 days.

By outgassing at room temperature (R.T.), the intensity of the band at 25.000 cm^{-1} increases; at the same time a broad absorption at $\sim$15.000 cm^{-1} gradually developes. Reexposure to CO at this stage nearly restores the initial spectrum.

The effect of outgassing at 523 K is shown in fig. 4b. The band at 25.000 cm^{-1} is drastically weakened, while a continuous, extremely broad and strong absorption in the 20.000 - 5000 cm^{-1} range becomes the most important feature of the spectrum.

Reexposure to CO after this treatment partially destroys the absorption in the 20.000 - 5000 cm^{-1} range and restores the band at 25.000 cm^{-1} (fig. 4b -▲-).

Fe(CO)$_5$. The adsorption of Fe(CO)$_5$ is illustrated in Fig. 5. Medium strong bands appear at 2080, 2020, 1995, 1967, 1930, 1900, 1875, 1845 cm^{-1} (fig. 5a) and at 1525 - 1481 and 1065 (broad) cm^{-1} (Fig. 5b) which are not weakened by R.T. outgassing.

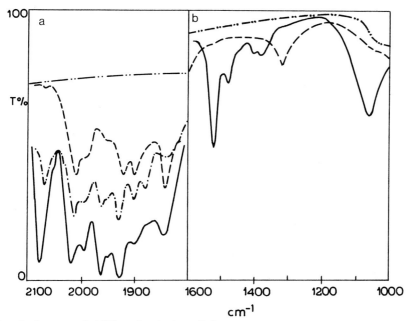

Fig. 5a,b. —— Fe(CO)₅ adsorbed on MgO
--- After outgassing 1ʰ at 353 K
-.-·After 20ʰ contact with 40 torr CO.

Outgassing at 353 K destroys the bands at 2080, 2020, 1967, 1930, and at 1525 - 1481, 1065 cm^{-1}, so showing that they are due to the same or very similar surface complexes. Moreover two bands at 1325 and 1660 cm^{-1} (partially shown in Fig. 5b) are formed which are due to carbonate-like species.

Exposure to CO only partially restores the initial spectrum, whereas the bands due to carbonate-like groups are not modified.

Complete decarbonylation is achieved at 473 K.

Exposure to CO after this treatment gives origin only to very weak carbonyl bands, so showing that the decarbonylation is irreversible. In this case parallel experiments have been carried out in the reflectance cell. The spectra, not reported for the sake of brevity, can be summarized as follows. After exposure to Fe(CO)₅ a weak band at ∿20.000 cm^{-1} is formed; in the following outgassing step at 353 - 473 K a broad intense absorption at 25.000 - 10.000 cm^{-1} is formed which is not destroyed by successive exposure to CO gas. This fact confirms that decarbonylation at 353 - 473 K is an irreversible process.

$Co_2(CO)_8$. By exposure of MgO to $Co_2(CO)_8$ the bands illustrated in Fig. 6 are formed. Contemporarily in the low frequency range, several bands are observed which are due to CO adsorbed on MgO. The effect of R.T. outgassing is to change the relative intensity of the high frequency components in an extremely complicated way. Exposure to CO after the R.T. outgassing step only partially restores the initial spectrum.

170

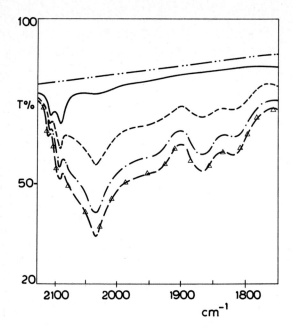

Fig. 6. $Co_2(CO)_8$ adsorbed on MgO at increasing amounts.

DISCUSSION

$\underline{Ni(CO)_4}$. The I.R. bands described in Figs. 1 - 3 are not due to weakly adsorbed molecular $Ni(CO)_4$, being their frequencies definitely different from that of the $Ni(CO)_4$ in the gas phase (2057 cm^{-1}).

We consider the bands reaching their maximum intensity in presence of CO gas (2085, 2072, 2025, 1990, 1975 and 1490-62, 1060-30 cm^{-1}) to be associated to carbonylic struc-tures $Ni_x(CO)_y$ (A species) with large y values.

Bands whose intensity grows when CO is pumped off and the previous species depleted (2010, 1965, 1930 - 15 cm^{-1}) are associated with subcarbonylic structures (B species) where the CO/Ni ratio is smaller.

The CO rich and the CO poor species A and B can be converted the ones into the others by admission or removal of CO at R.T. As shown by Fig. 4, B species are associated with electronic transition in the 25.000 - 15.000 cm^{-1} range, which is the typical range of the $\sigma \rightarrow \sigma^*$ transition in Ni-Ni bonds.

In particular the band at 25.000 cm^{-1} which grows upon short evacuation times, exactly corresponds to the frequency values found for dinickel or trinickel clusters obtained in cryogenic matrices (ref. 4).

As a consequence B species can be described in terms of low nuclearity clusters compounds where x $\geqslant$ 2. On the contrary species A, which do not show any electronic tran-sition at frequencies lower than 30.000 cm^{-1} should have a mononuclear nature (x = 1).

The transformation (upon CO abstraction) of the A species into the B ones can be de-scribed as an aggregation process where the loss of CO ligands is accompanied by inter-action of two subcarbonylic moietys and formation of Ni-Ni bond.

As far as the structure of A and B species is concerned the following considerations can be made.

CO rich mononuclear A species give rise to at least six bands in the I.R. (2085, 2025, 1990, 1975, 1490 - 62, 1060 - 30 cm^{-1}) two of them falling at extremely low frequencies for simple carbonylic or subcarbonylic species.

Uncommon structures must be invoked like the prototype one   originated by the strong interaction of a Ni(CO)$_4$ molecule with a Mg^{++}O^{--} surface ionic pair.

As this structure alone cannot justify all six I.R. bands, other species with similar structure must be at the same time present on the surface (for instance Ni(CO)$_3$), Ni(CO)$_2$ etc. subcarbonylic species interacting with other suitably placed c.u.s. Mg^{2+} and O^{2-} ions).

$$
\begin{array}{c}
CO\quad \overset{CO}{\underset{|}{}}\quad CO \\
\diagdown\;\;Ni\;\;\diagup \\
| \\
C \\
\diagup\;\;\diagdown \\
O^{-}\quad\quad O \\
\vdots \\
Mg^{+}
\end{array}
$$

On the basis of the presented data it is impossible to give a more detailed assignment.

B species are characterized by bands at 2010, 1965, 1930, 1915 cm^{-1}. Two of them (2010 - 1930 cm^{-1}) show a constant intensity ratio and hence are due to the same surface complex (B$_1$), whereas the others, which disappear last upon prolonged outgassing at 473 - 523 K, belong to other two different species (B$_2$ and B$_3$).

B$_1$ complexes, responsible of absorption at ~25.000 cm^{-1} are thought to be the smallest nuclearity complexes Ni$_2$(CO)$_y$ formed during the agglomeration process induced by the CO removal. On the basis of the observed frequencies, linear CO (absorbing at 2010 cm^{-1}) and bridged CO (absorbing at 1930 cm^{-1}) are likely present in constant ratio, as for example in the following structure:

$$
\begin{array}{c}
O \\
\|\\
C \\
\diagup\;\;\diagdown \\
OC - Ni \overline{\qquad} Ni - CO \\
\diagdown\;\;\diagup \\
C \\
\|\\
O
\end{array}
$$

B$_2$ complexes are evidenced upon further CO outgassing by the band at 1965 cm^{-1} and by the broad absorption at 20.000 - 15.000 cm^{-1}. Therefore it is inferred that they are originated by decarbonylation of B$_1$ species, the remaining CO groups being in bridging position.

The frequency values (1915 cm^{-1}) of the CO stretching in the B$_3$ species indicates that a tricentric bond like

$$
\begin{array}{c}
CO \\
|\\
Ni \\
\diagup\;\diagdown \\
Ni \overline{\qquad} Ni
\end{array}
$$

is probably present and as a consequence the B$_3$ species are thought to be aggregation products containing more than 2 metal atoms. The observed frequencies and structures of B$_2$ and B$_3$ complexes are very similar to those found by Hulse and Moskovits (ref. 5) for low-nuclearity Ni - CO clusters formed in cryogenic matrices.

After complete decarbonylation at higher temperatures, the samples exhibit a dark grey colour, which is an indication of further aggregation and formation of very small Ni crystallites. Reexposure to CO (Fig. 3) initially gives rise to weak and very broad bands typical of CO adsorbed on supported or evaporated Ni crystallites (ref. 3).

By increasing the CO pressure, the bands due to B$_1$, B$_2$, B$_3$ species appear again, followed, for higher CO pressures and contact times, by the bands of the A mononuclear species. As this process is accompanied by the partial destruction of the extremely broad absorption in all the visible region (Fig. 4b) likely associated with electronic transition of very small metal particles, it is concluded that CO adsorption causes the disgregation of Ni crystallites, leading ultimately to adsorbed mono and dinuclear complexes.

$Fe(CO)_5$. The spectrum obtained after $Fe(CO)_5$ adsorption is extremely complicated and very different with respect to that of the gaseous carbonyl ($\nu_{C=0}$ at 2035 and 2013 cm^{-1}): as a consequence a detailed assignment is at the present time impossible. As in the $Ni(CO)_4$ case, surface species can be roughly divided into two groups A and B depending on their behaviour towards CO. A species (bands at 2080, 2020, 1967, 1930 cm^{-1}) tend to disappear upon outgassing at 353 K and, like in the $Ni(CO)_4$ case, are characterized by very unusual bands in the low frequency region (1525 - 81, 1065 cm^{-1} broad) and the absence of any electronic transition at frequencies lower than 25.000 cm^{-1}. Hence, as in the previous case, their assignment to mononuclear carbonylic or subcarbonylic $Fe(CO)_y$ species interacting with MgO surface is strongly favoured.

B species (bands at 1995, 1900, 1875, 1845 cm^{-1}) are the most resistent to outgassing and can be partially converted into the A ones by successive CO adsorption (Fig. 5a: -··-): for example bands at 1845 cm^{-1}, probably due to CO bridged groups, decrease upon CO adsorption.

Hence their assignment to $Fe_x(CO)_y$, complexes were $x \geqslant 2$ is strongly favoured.

Moreover, the formation of carbonate groups after outgassing at 353 K and the strong weakening of carbonyls bands show that a prevailing oxidation process due to carbonyl groups disproportionation is beginning at this temperature, becoming faster at 473 K. In fact, reexposure to CO after a 473 K outgassing gives rise to very weak carbonyl bands: in this case oxidized Fe^{2+} ion can diffuse from the surface into the MgO bulk, the final product at higher temperatures being a FeO/MgO solid solution.

$Co_2(CO)_8$. Due to the larger experimental difficulties, only few data are available at the present time. However some considerations can be made, i.e.: i) by interaction of $Co_2(CO)_8$ with MgO, CO ligands are abstracted by the MgO matrix leading to adsorbed CO and to several carbonylic species whose relative concentration depends on the CO pressure; ii) the CO abstraction is accompanied by surface migration and agglomeration which can be partly reversed by exposure to CO; iii) no low-frequency bands similar to those observed for $Ni(CO)_4$ and $Fe(CO)_5$ are observed, in agreement with their assignment to mononuclear species.

CONCLUSIONS

We demonstrate that adsorption of simple carbonyls at R.T. in controlled condition of vacuum and support treatment can produce new polymetallic carbonyls with very few Me atoms.

But at higher temperatures (353 - 523 K) upon CO loss, the new carbonyl clusters can agglomerate (mainly in the Ni case) and/or the metal is oxidized by CO disproportionation (mainly in the Fe case). The experiments therefore demonstrate that it is very difficult to maintain highly dispersed metal clusters on MgO support due to strong interaction between adsorbed carbonyl and the MgO basic surface.

REFERENCES

1 a) R.F. Howe, D.E. Davidson and D.A. Whan, Trans. Faraday Soc.,I (1973) 1967.
   b) J.R. Anderson, P.S. Elmes, R.F. Howe and D.E. Mainwaring, J. Catalysis, 50 (1977) 508.
   c) D. Ballivet Tkatchenko and G. Couduriez, Inorg. Chem. 18 (1979) 558.
2 E. Guglielminotti, S. Coluccia, E. Garrone, L. Cerruti and A. Zecchina, Faraday Trans. I,
   75 (1979) 96.
3 a) A.M. Bradshow and J. Pritchard, Surface Sci., 17 (1969) 372.
   b) C.E. O'Neill and D.J. Yates, J. Phys. Chem., 65 (1961) 901.
4 M. Moskovits and J.H. Hulse, J. Chem. Phys., 66 (1977) 3988.
5 J.H. Hulse and M. Moskovits, Surface Sci., 57 (1976) 125.

174

DISCUSSION

E. GUGLIELMINOTTI, A. ZECCHINA, F. BOCCUZI, E. BORELLO

Basset - By adsorption of $Fe(CO)_5$ on alumina, magnesia, lanthanum oxide, zinc oxide, we observed a general behaviour : nucleophilic attack of OH^- groups on coordinated CO giving rise to the formation of anionic hydride species :

$$Fe(CO)_5 + M-OH \rightarrow [H\,Fe_3(CO)_{11}]^- \, [M-O]^+$$

Did you try to identify such anionic systems ?

Zecchina - We used MgO outgassed in vacuo at 800° C and in these conditions no -OH groups are present on the surface (no -OH stretching bands are detected by IR spectroscopy). Indeed, the 800° C outgassing temperature has been chosen in order to avoid the complications you have mentioned.

Bonzel - What is the assignment of the low frequency modes of the deposited Ni carbonyl (species I, frequencies at about 1500 and 1050 cm^{-1}) ? Can these still be viewed as CO stretching vibrations ?

The vibrational analysis of CO chemisorbed on stepped Ni(III) surface (Erley, Wagner and Ibach in Surface Science 1979) gives rise to a band at 1520 cm^{-1} which was identied as a CO stretching vibration due to molecules adsorbed at step sites. Such a low CO stretching frequency indicates severe bond weakening and hence a high probability for these CO molecules to dissociate.

Zecchina - The bands at ~ 1500 and 1050 cm^{-1} have a constant intensity ratio at all coverages, so they belong to the same (more than diatomic) surface species. This observation rules out a possible interpretation of the ~1500cm^{-1} band in terms of one CO bonded to a special site.

The bands at ~1500 cm^{-1} and 1050 cm^{-1} are associated to the carbonyl stretching bands at ~2080 and ~2030 cm^{-1}. We are so dealing with a surface species characterized by at least four IR active modes in the 2100 - 1000 cm^{-1}. The assignment can be only tentative and the structure

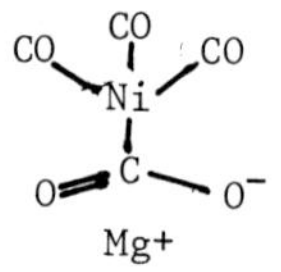

is favoured, as I said before. Alternative choices are possible so that a structure like

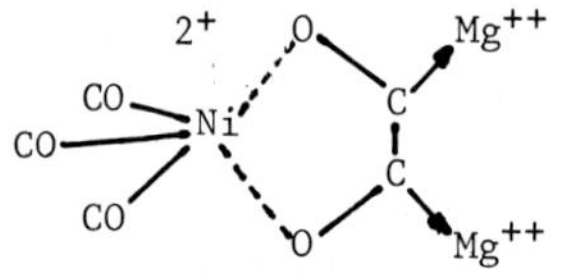

cannot be ruled out.

J. BOURDON (Editor)
Growth and Properties of Metal Clusters, pp. 175—183
© 1980 Elsevier Scientific Publishing Company — Printed in The Netherlands

ETUDE DE LA DISPERSION DE PLATINE SUR DES NOIRS DE CARBONE

P. EHRBURGER - Centre de Recherches sur la Physico-Chimie des Surfaces Solides
68200 Mulhouse

P.L. WALKER Jr - Department of Materials Science and Engineering, The Pennsylvania State
University, University Park, Pennsylvania 16802.

I. INTRODUCTION

L'usage de carbones comme supports de catalyseur présente un intérêt croissant pour de
nombreuses réactions. Ainsi les métaux précieux (platine, palladium, rhénium et ruthénium)
déposés sur des carbones servent à l'hydrogénation des oléfines et des dérivés aromatiques
nitrés. L'hydrodésulfuration des résidus pétroliers riches en impuretés métalliques s'effectue en présence de sulfures métalliques supportés sur des charbons actifs. En outre, le
carbone, de par sa bonne conductivité électrique, trouve des applications en électrocataly-
se. Cependant, l'étude de la dispersion de métaux sur des carbones n'a fait l'objet jusqu'à
présent que d'un nombre restreint de travaux et les modes de formation et de croissance des
particules métalliques restent encore mal connus (réfs. 1-3). Le but de ce travail est
d'étudier l'influence des propriétés de surface des carbones sur la dispersion et le frittage du platine.

D'une manière générale, la surface d'un carbone comporte principalement deux types de
plans cristallins, les plans de base et les faces prismatiques. Une surface de carbone com-
posée essentiellement de plans de base est dite homogène. C'est le cas de noirs de carbone
graphitisés. La présence simultanée de plans de base et de faces prismatiques confère à la
surface un caractère hétérogène. L'oxydation ménagée des noirs de carbone graphitisés permet d'accroître sensiblement l'hétérogénéité de leur surface. La réactivité des deux types
de plans cristallins est nettement différente et les interactions entre le solide divisé
et le support seront par conséquent fonction de la nature des faces cristallines en surface.

II. PARTIE EXPERIMENTALE

1. Carbone support

Le support de carbone utilisé est un noir au four Vulcan 3 (Société Cabot), purifié par
traitement sous chlore à 2 800°C pendant 1 heure puis sous argon. Le noir de carbone graphi-
tisé V3G est essentiellement non poreux. L'oxydation ménagée des échantillons de V3G a été
effectuée dans l'air sec à 500°C et à des pertes en poids variant entre 3,7 et 48,9 %.
L'un des échantillons, dénoté "V3G activé" a subi une gazéification dans l'air à une perte

176

en poids de 21,4 % suivie d'une oxydation dans l'acide nitrique concentré sous reflux pendant 24 heures.

Les surfaces spécifiques des carbones sont déterminées par adsorption d'azote à -196°C.

2. Dépôt du platine sur des noirs de carbone

Le dépôt du platine a été effectué selon la méthode d'imprégnation décrite par Bartholomew et al. (réf. 1). Le noir de carbone est mis en suspension dans une solution d'acide hexachloroplatinique dans un mélange 4/1 de benzène et d'éthanol absolu (50 cm^3 par gramme de carbone). Après évaporation sous azote et séchage à 70°C, l'échantillon est réduit par de l'hydrogène à 500°C pendant 10 heures.

3. Détermination de la surface spécifique et du diamètre des particules de platine

La surface spécifique du platine a été déterminée par la méthode de Benson et al. (réf. 4) qui consiste à adsorber à 20°C de l'hydrogène sur l'échantillon oxydé. La quantité d'hydrogène fixé à la surface des grains de platine est mesurée par volumétrie en présence de driérite pour retenir l'eau dégagée par la réaction (réf. 5).

Les échantillons ont été examinés par transmission sur des grilles autoperforées dans un microscope électronique JEM 100 B. En vue d'une étude statistique, deux mille particules de platine ont été mesurées pour chaque échantillon. Dans une publication antérieure, nous avons montré que la précision des mesures pour des particules de diamètre inférieur à 4 nm était meilleure que 1 nm (réf. 6). De ce fait, les intervalles de comptage des particules ont été fixés à 1 nm, à l'exception du premier qui correspond aux grains les plus petits (0 - 2 nm).

4. Frittage des particules de platine

Les échantillons ont été traités à 650 et 750°C sous un courant d'argon. Les principales impuretés contenues dans le gaz vecteur sont : N_2 < 40 ppm, O_2 < 5 ppm et H_2O < 5 ppm.

III. RESULTATS

1. Degré de dispersion du platine sur les noirs de carbone

Rappelons que le degré de dispersion est le rapport du nombre d'atomes de métal en surface sur le nombre total d'atomes du métal. Les surfaces spécifiques des supports carbonés et celles des particules de platine sont indiquées dans le tableau 1 pour une teneur en platine de 1 % en poids.

Le degré de dispersion du platine augmente très nettement par oxydation préalable du support carboné. L'accroissement de la surface spécifique du platine peut être dû à deux phénomènes liés à l'oxydation du carbone : d'une part, augmentation de la surface spécifique du support et d'autre part exaltation du caractère hétérogène du substrat. Afin

TABLEAU 1

Surfaces spécifiques et degré de dispersion du platine

Perte en poids du carbone (%)	Surface spécifique		Degré de dispersion du Pt (%)
	V3G (m^2/g)	Pt (m^2/g)	
0,0	56	41	16
3,7	67	45	17
8,0	70	47	18
21,4	87	69	26
48,9	110	145	55

d'étudier séparément ces deux effets, des échantillons de V3G initiaux et oxydés à 48,9 %
de perte en poids ont été imprégnés à différentes teneurs en platine. Les résultats sont
indiqués dans le tableau 2.

TABLEAU 2

Influence de la teneur en platine sur le degré de dispersion

Echantillon	Perte en poids (%)	Teneur en Pt		Degré de dispersion du Pt (%)
		% en poids	mg/m^2 V3G	
1	0	1,0	0,178	16
2	0	0,5	0,089	26
3	0	0,3	0,053	27
4	48,9	1,0	0,091	55
5	48,9	0,3	0,027	55

Dans le cas du support homogène, non oxydé, le degré de dispersion dépend fortement de la
teneur en platine entre 0,5 et 1 %. Cette influence est nettement moins prononcée lorsque
la surface de carbone est hétérogène. Il est à noter que les échantillons 2 et 4 qui correspondent respectivement à des substrats homogène et hétérogène ont des teneurs en platine
par unité de surface sensiblement équivalentes. La comparaison de leur degré de dispersion
respectif montre que l'introduction d'hétérogénéités à la surface du carbone a pour effet
d'accroître l'état de division du platine.

2. Distribution de la taille des particules de platine

L'influence de la nature du substrat sur la distribution de la taille des particules de
platine a été étudiée dans le cas de la surface homogène V3G et de la surface hétérogène
V3G activé (aire : 92 m^2/g). Les histogrammes correspondant aux diamètres des grains de
platine sur substrat V3G et V3G activé sont représentés sur la figure 1. Dans le cas du
substrat V3G initial, la distribution de la taille des particules est large et asymétrique,
quelques grains métalliques ayant des diamètres atteignant 15 nm.

L'analyse de la courbe de distribution montre qu'elle est de type logarithmonormale.
En effet, la probabilité cummulative de particules ayant un diamètre inférieur à une valeur
d donnée est une relation linéaire de log d sur un diagramme logarithmonormal (figure 2).
Les paramètres de la distribution logarithmonormale (diamètre géométrique moyen d_g et
écart quadratique moyen (σ_g) sont déterminés à partir des relations suivantes :

178

$$\text{Log } d_g = \Sigma \ n_i \ \text{Log } d_i / \Sigma \ n_i$$

$$\text{Log } \sigma_g = (\Sigma \ n_i \ \text{Log}(d_i/d_g)^2 / \Sigma \ n_i)^{1/2}$$

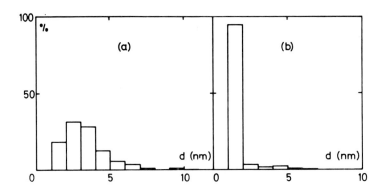

Fig. 1. Histogrammes de la taille des particules de platine après préparation à 500°C.
(a) sur support initial, (b) sur support activé.

Dans le cas du substrat V3G activé, la distribution de la taille des particules de platine est nettement plus étroite. En effet, plus de 90 % des particules ont un diamètre inférieur à 2 nm et la courbe de distribution est de type monodisperse.

Le diamètre arithmétique moyen $d_a = \Sigma \ n_i \ d_i \ / \ \Sigma \ n_i$ et le diamètre moyen de surface $d_s = \Sigma \ n_i \ d_i^3 \ / \ \Sigma \ n_i \ d_i^2$ peuvent être calculés à partir des histogrammes pour chaque échantillon. Par ailleurs, en supposant les particules de platine sphériques, il est possible de déterminer le diamètre moyen des grains de platine $\overline{d}$, d'après leur surface spécifique mesurée par adsorption d'hydrogène. Les valeurs des différents diamètres sont comparées dans le tableau 3.

TABLEAU 3

Diamètres moyens des particules de platine

Support	Diamètres (nm)			
	d_a	d_g	d_s	$\overline{d}$
V3G initial	3,6	3,3	7,3	6,6
V3G activé	1,6	—	2,5	1,7

Compte-tenu des incertitudes sur la détermination de la taille des particules par microscopie électronique, on peut considérer que l'accord entre les diamètres moyens d_s et $\overline{d}$ est satisfaisant.

3. Frittage des particules de platine

La distribution de la taille des particules n'est pas considérablement modifiée après traitement thermique sous argon à 650°C dans le cas du substrat homogène V3G. Cependant, une faible croissance des particules de platine est décelable après 48 h. de traitement à 750°C. Les distributions de la taille des grains de platine sont dans tous les cas de type logarithmonormal (fig. 2).

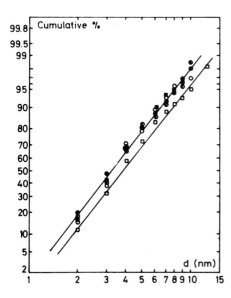

Fig. 2. Diagramme logarithmonormal. Droites de Henry correspondant aux particules de platine sur le substrat homogène V3G en fonction de la température de traitement : ●, initial (500°C) ; ◐, 24 h à 650°C ; ○, 48 h à 650°C ; ■, 8 h à 750°C ; □, 48 h à 750°C.

Le comportement des particules de platine déposées sur le support V3G activé est nettement différent lors des traitements thermiques. A titre de comparaison avec le substrat homogène V3G, les courbes de distribution des grains de platine sur V3G activé ont également été reportées sur un diagramme logarithmonormal (Fig. 3). Il apparaît que le pourcentage de particules de diamètre inférieur à 2 nm décroît très rapidement dès 650°C. Après traitement à 750°C pendant 48 h, la distribution de la taille des grains de platine suit une loi logarithmonormale comme l'indique la droite de Henry correspondante. Il est à noter qu'à ce stade, 22 % des particules détectées ont encore un diamètre inférieur à 2 nm. Les différents paramètres des courbes de distribution d_a, d_g et σ_g sont reportés dans le tableau 4 pour les échantillons étudiés. Dans le cas du support homogène, le diamètre moyen des particules métalliques n'augmente de manière sensible que pour des traitements à des températures de 750°C. Par contre, dans les mêmes conditions, le diamètre moyen des particules de platine s'accroît très nettement sur le substrat activé.

Au cours du frittage, le volume total du métal reste constant. Il est donc intéressant d'étudier les variations de la distribution en volume des particules de platine, notamment par le test de "self-preservation" (réf. 7). A cet effet, le rapport N_v/N_t est porté en fonction de la quantité $\eta = v_i N_t/\Phi$, les notations étant les suivantes:

180

N_v : nombre de particules de platine par unité de surface ayant un volume supérieur à v_i

N_t : nombre total de particules de platine par unité de surface

v_i : volume considéré

Φ : volume total des particules par unité de surface.

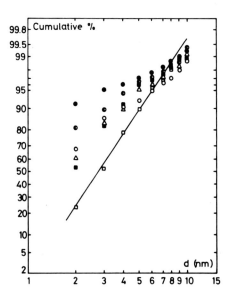

Fig. 3. Diagramme logarithmonormal. Distributions correspondant aux particules de platine sur le support V3G activé en fonction de la température de traitement :●, initial (500°C) ; ◖, 8 h à 650°C ; ○, 24 h à 650°C ; △, 48 h à 650°C ; ■, 8 h à 750°C ; □, 48 h à 750°C.

TABLEAU 4

Diamètres moyens (nm) et écart quadratique moyen des particules de platine après traitement thermique

Conditions de traitement	Support homogène			Support activé		
	d_a	d_g	σ_g	d_a	d_g	σ_g
initial 500°C	3,6	3,3	1,5	1,6	–	–
8 h à 650°C	3,8	3,3	1,6	2,0	–	–
24 h à 650°C	4,0	3,4	1,6	2,1	–	–
48 h à 650°C	3,9	3,3	1,7	2,3	–	–
8 h à 750°C	4,1	3,4	1,8	2,3	–	–
48 h à 750°C	4,5	3,8	1,7	3,2	2,8	1,6

Les courbes obtenues pour les différents échantillons sont représentées sur la figure 4. Dans le cas du substrat homogène, il apparaît un spectre de distribution unique à tous les échantillons. Les courbes de répartition sont par conséquent de type "self-preserving".

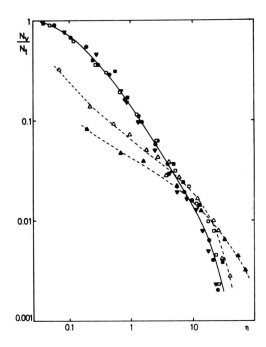

Fig. 4. Tests de "self-preservation" pour les particules de platine traitées dans différentes conditions. Support homogène V3G : ●, initial (500°C) ; ☐, 48 h à 650°C ; ■, 48 h à 750°C ; Support activé V3G : ▲, initial (500°C) ; △, 24 h à 650°C ; ▼, 48 h à 750°C.

Ce résultat n'est pas surprenant puisque toutes les distributions sont de type logarithmonormal avec un écart quadratique sensiblement constant.

Dans le cas du substrat hétérogène, les distributions ne sont pas de type "self-preserving", en début du frittage. Ce n'est qu'après un traitement thermique suffisant (48 h à 750°C) que la courbe de distribution se confond avec le spectre de répartition unique observé dans le cas du substrat homogène. Il apparaît par conséquent que la taille des particules de platine (diamètre moyen et courbe de répartition) est profondément modifiée au cours du frittage sur un substrat hétérogène.

IV. DISCUSSION

1. Mode de formation des particules de platine

(a) Support de carbone homogène. Les courbes de distribution de la taille des particules de platine sont logarithmonormales et n'évoluent pas sensiblement entre la température de réduction (500°C) et 650°C. Ce fait suggère que la distribution de la taille des particules s'est effectuée à une température plus basse, vraisemblablement au cours de la réduction de l'acide hexachloroplatinique. La courbe de répartition des agrégats d'acide chloroplatinique sur le carbone n'est pas connue. Cependant Flynn et al. (réf. 8) indiquent que l'acide chloroplatinique se dépose dans un état très dispersé sur l'alumine et que c'est pendant la réduction que l'agglomération des particules a lieu. Deux mécanismes principaux pour la croissance de particules déposées sur une surface ont été proposés récemment (réf. 9) : d'une part les particules se déplacent et coalescent après des collisions binaires, ou d'autre part, les particules croîssent par transport interparticulaire d'atomes ou de molécules (mûrissement d'Ostwald). Grandqvist et al. (réf. 10) ont montré que des distributions logarithmonormales suggèrent un mécanisme de croissance par diffusion et coalescence des particules. Par ailleurs, Ruckenstein et al. (réf. 11) ont établi que dans des conditions de croissance contrôlée par la diffusion des particules, les courbes de répartition en volume des grains sont de type "self-préserving" et peuvent être représentées par un spectre unique après frittage à température élevée. Par conséquent, on peut admettre que les agrégats d'acide chloroplatinique se déplacent et coalescent au cours de leur réduction sur la surface de carbone homogène et conduisent à une distribution logarithmonormale de la taille des particules de platine après traitement à 500°C.

(b) Support de carbone hétérogène. Il est connu que des hétérogénéités peuvent être introduites à la surface de noirs de carbone graphités lors de leur oxydation (réf. 12 et 13). L'accroissement du caractère hétérogène de la surface provient de la mise à nu de faces prismatiques consécutive à l'élargissement des défauts ponctuels dans les plans de base. La réactivité des faces prismatiques est généralement plus élevée que celle des plans de base. Il est vraisemblable d'admettre que les interactions des agrégats d'acide chloroplatinique avec les faces prismatiques sont plus fortes qu'avec celles des plans de base. De ce fait, lors de la réduction, les agrégats d'acide chloroplatinique restent plus fortement retenus à la surface et auront une tendance moindre à diffuser. Il s'en suit que la taille des particules de platine sera plus régulière et de diamètre plus faible après réduction à 500°C.

2. Frittage des particules de platine

Après un traitement thermique suffisant (en température et en durée), la courbe de répartition des particules est de type logarithmonormal quel que soit le substrat. Ces résultats suggèrent que dans les deux cas, le mécanisme de croissance s'effectue essentiellement par diffusion suivie de coalescence des particules. Récemment Wong et al (réf. 14) ont étudié par microscopie électronique le frittage de particules de platine déposées sur des paillettes de graphite. Ils ont ainsi pu montrer qu'à 830°C, sous une pression résiduelle d'oxygène de 1,1 10^{-5} Pa, la croissance s'effectue par migration des atomes de platine des petites vers les grosses particules. Cependant, pour une pression d'oxygène de 1,3 10^{-4} Pa, les particules de platine se déplacent à la surface du graphite. Compte-tenu de la pureté de l'argon utilisé dans notre cas, la pression partielle d'oxygène est de l'ordre de 0,5 Pa et est par conséquent largement suffisante pour permettre la croissance des particules par diffusion et coalescence.

Dans le cas du substrat hétérogène, les interactions entre les agrégats de platine et le carbone sont suffisamment fortes pour prévenir ou restreindre la mobilité des particules métalliques à 500°C. Cependant, pour des températures supérieures, le système constitué de particules de très petite taille devient instable, les interactions avec le support carbone devenant trop faible pour empêcher leur migration. Dans ces conditions, le système dispersé

tend vers une "distribution d'équilibre" de la taille des particules analogue à celle
observée sur un substrat homogène.

V. CONCLUSIONS

La dispersion de platine sur des carbones dépend considérablement de la nature de la
surface. Sur une surface de carbone graphitée et homogène, la taille des particules de
platine suit une distribution logarithmonormale, dès la température de préparation du
dépôt..Dans le cas d'un substrat carboné hétérogène, les particules de platine sont plus
petites et la distribution de leur diamètre de type monodisperse. Lors du frittage à
température élevée, la population des particules de platine tend vers une distribution
d'équilibre, indépendante du degré d'hétérogénéité de la surface de carbone.

REFERENCES

1 C.H. Bartholomew et M. Boudart, J. Catal. 25 (1972) 173-176.
2 D. Pope, W.L. Smith, M.J. Eastlake et R.L. Moss, J. Catal., 22 (1971) 72-83.
3 A.C.C. Tseung et L.L. Wong, J. Applied Electrochem., 2 (1972) 211-215.
4 J.E. Benson et M. Boudart, J. Catal., 4 (1965) 704-716.
5 P. Ehrburger, O.P. Mahajan et P.L. Walker Jr., J. Catal., 43 (1976) 61-67.
6 P. Ehrburger et P.L. Walker Jr., J. Catal., 55 (1978) 63-70.
7 D.L. Swift et S.K. Friedlander, J. Colloid Sci., 19 (1964) 621-647.
8 P.C. Flynn et S.E. Wanke, J. Catal., 37 (1975) 432-448.
9 P. Wynblatt et A. Tae-Moon dans G.C. Kuczynski : (Ed.), Sintering and Catalysis,
   Material Science Research, Plenum Press, New York 1975, Vol. 10, p 83.
10 C.G. Grandqvist et R.A. Buhrman, J. Catal., 42 (1976) 477-479.
11 E.R. Ruckenstein et B. Pulvermacher, J. Catal., 29 (1973) 224-245.
12 N.R. Laine, F.J. Vastola et P.L. Walker Jr., J. Phys. Chem., 67 (1963) 2030-2034.
13 D.W.L. Griffiths, W.J. Thomas et P.L. Walker Jr., Carbon 1 (1964) 515-524.
14 J. Wong, M. Flytzani-Stephanoponlos, M. Chen, T.E. Hutchinson et L.D. Schmidt,
   J. Vacuum Sci. Technol. 14 (1977) 452.

J. BOURDON (Editor)
Growth and Properties of Metal Clusters, pp. 185—192
© 1980 Elsevier Scientific Publishing Company — Printed in The Netherlands

STRUCTURE CRISTALLOGRAPHIQUE ET MORPHOLOGIE DES CRISTALLITES DE Pt ET DE Pd OBTENUS PAR
EVAPORATION THERMIQUE SOUS VIDE

par M. GILLET, A. RENOU et J.M. MIQUEL

Laboratoire de Microscopie Electronique - E.R.A. 545 : "Défauts dans les Phénomènes
d'Interface et de Microdéformations" - Université Aix-Marseille III, Centre de St-Jérôme,
Rue Henri Poincaré, 13397 Marseille Cedex 4

Des travaux récents ont signalé l'influence de la taille des agrégats sur les réactions
de surface comme par exemple ceux qui concernent l'adsorption de l'azote sur les particules
de Pd, Pt, Ni (1) ou des réactions catalytiques pour lesquelles la taille des catalyseurs
affecte soit la vitesse de réaction (2) soit la sélectivité (3). L'interprétation de ces
résultats nécessite la connaissance de la configuration des sites de surface et par
conséquent de la morphologie des agrégats en fonction de leur taille, c'est pourquoi nous
avons entrepris une étude de la morphologie de particules de Pt et de Pd préparées dans
des conditions particulières.

Les cristallites de Pt et de Pd préparés par condensation sous vide sur un support
amorphe à la température ambiante ne présentent pas en général de forme déterminée ;
cependant dans certaines conditions notamment lorsque les dépôts sont condensés sur un
support monocristallin isolant ou semi-conducteur chauffé, ils sont en épitaxie et leur
morphologie est caractéristique de la symétrie du support : tétraédrique sur un support
de symétrie hexagonale tel que MoS_2 ou mica, octaédrique dans le cas d'halogénure alcalin
comme NaCl ou KCl par exemple.

I. METHODE DE PREPARATION ET TECHNIQUE D'ETUDE DES DEPOTS

Les dépôts sont réalisés par évaporation thermique sous vide (10^{-8} torr) et condensés
sur un support dont la température varie entre 150 et 400°C ; la source chauffée par effet
Joule est constituée par un creuset en tungstène ; la vitesse de dépôt contrôlée au moyen
d'une microbalance à quartz est de l'ordre de 1 $\overset{o}{A}.s^{-1}$. Les supports utilisés sont des
clivages soit réalisés sous ultra-vide immédiatement avant le dépôt (NaCl, KCl), soit
clivés à l'air (mica, MoS_2). La taille des agrégats est comprise entre 15 et 200 $\overset{o}{A}$. Leur
morphologie et leur structure sont étudiées par microscopie et diffraction électroniques.
Les dépôts effectués sur NaCl ou KCl sont examinés par l'intermédiaire d'une réplique
transfert en carbone évaporé immédiatement après la formation du dépôt métallique. Ceux
qui sont réalisés sur MoS_2 ou mica sont étudiés directement sur leur support mince.

II. OBSERVATION DES AGREGATS FORMES SUR LES SUPPORTS DE MICA ET MoS_2

Les agrégats de Pt ou de Pd condensés sur mica ou MoS_2 à des températures comprises
entre 100 et 300°C ont en général une structure c.f.c. et une forme tétraédrique parfaite
qu'ils conservent jusqu'à une taille de 150 $\overset{o}{A}$ environ ; ils sont donc limités par des
plans (111) (fig. 1).

Ces agrégats sont en parfaite épitaxie sur le support tels que
(111) $\frac{Pd}{Pt}$ // (0001) MoS$_2$ et <110> $\frac{Pd}{Pt}$ // <11$\bar{2}$0> MoS$_2$ (fig. 2)

Lorsque la température du support et la taille des agrégats sont respectivement supérieures à 300°C et 150 Å, ces agrégats conservent une structure c.f.c. mais nous observons deux types de cristallites qui se distinguent par leur morphologie (fig. 3) ;

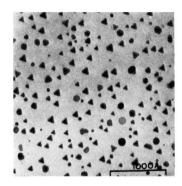 

fig. 1 : Agrégats de Pd/MoS$_2$
T$_S$ = 200°C
Diamètre moyen des agrégats :
                    100 Å.

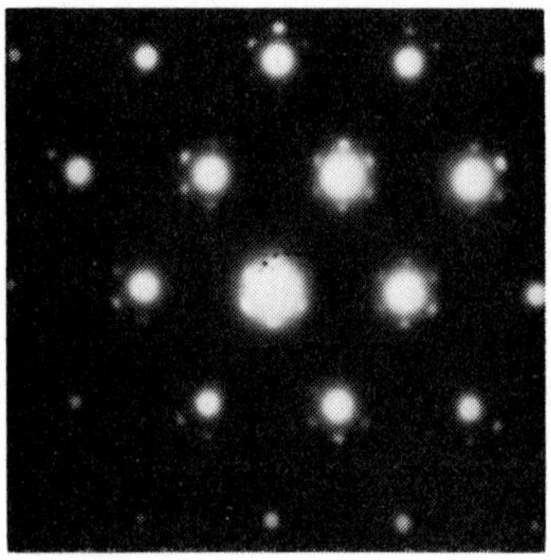

fig. 2 : Diagramme de diffraction électronique correspondant à la fig. 1.

fig. 3 : Agrégats de Pd/MoS$_2$
T$_S$ = 350°C, diamètre moyen
des agrégats tétraédriques T :
150 Å, des agrégats C: 170 Å.

les uns (T) conservent leur forme tétraédrique mais des troncatures (111) apparaissent à chaque sommet, les autres (C) ont une forme de calotte sphérique. Les observations en fond clair et en fond noir (4) révèlent que certaines particules tétraédriques ont même orientation épitaxique que celles de taille inférieure tandis que les autres particules (soit tétraédriques, soit en forme de calotte sphérique) sont désorientées azimutalement de R = ± 3° par rapport à l'orientation épitaxique parfaite. Il semble donc que jusqu'à une certaine taille, le phénomène d'épitaxie impose une morphologie. Cette taille dépend de la température du support. Au-delà de cette taille et pour une température donnée, les particules ont tendance à prendre une forme sphérique qui minimise leur énergie de surface.

III. OBSERVATION DES AGREGATS FORMES SUR UN SUPPORT D'HALOGENURE ALCALIN

L'observation en diffraction électronique des agrégats de Pt ou de Pd de taille comprise entre 25 et 40 Å préparés sur un clivage de NaCl porté à une température comprise entre 100 et 300°C montre que la plupart d'entre eux sont en orientation épitaxique (001) parallèle au support et qu'ils ont une structure c.f.c. parfaite sans défauts.

La micrographie fig. 4 représente l'image de plans réticulaires (200) d'un agrégat de platine (diamètre 25 Å) orienté sur NaCl tel que <110> Pt // <110> NaCl. Compte tenu de l'angle formé par les plans (200) avec les bords de l'agrégat soit 45°, nous en déduisons que celui-ci se présente sous forme d'une pyramide à base carrée reposant sur un plan (001) et limitée par quatre plans (111) (demi-octaèdre). De plus l'observation en haute résolution d'agrégats ayant subi une coalescence montre que celle-ci n'introduit pas de défauts dans les cristallites qui conservent leur forme octaédrique parfaite jusqu'à une taille de 35 Å environ. Lorsque les agrégats ont une taille supérieure à 50 Å environ,

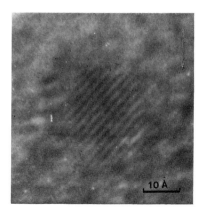

<u>fig. 4</u> : Image des plans réticulaires (200) d'agrégat de Pt formé sur un support de NaCl (001) : diamètre : 25 Å.

il est possible d'étudier leur morphologie par microscopie en fond noir en utilisant la technique du faisceau faible (5), technique qui permet de faire apparaître des franges d'égale épaisseur sur les cristallites.

La micrographie typique en fond clair (fig. 5a) et en fond noir correspondante (fig. 5b) obtenue avec cette technique en sélectionnant la réflexion $g_{2\vec{0}0}$ du diagramme de diffraction (fig. 5c) montrent que les cristallites conservent la forme soit demi-octaédrique soit pyramidale à base rectangulaire qu'ils avaient précédemment.

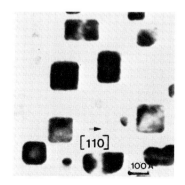

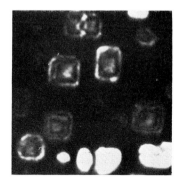

<u>fig. 5a</u> : Micrographie en fond clair Pd/NaCl - Diamètre moyen des agrégats : 120 Å.

<u>fig. 5b</u> : Micrographie en fond noir correspondant à la fig. 5a obtenue en sélectionnant la réflexion $g_{2\vec{0}0}$ de la fig. 5c.

<u>fig. 5c</u> : Diagramme de diffraction correspondant à la fig. 5a.

En général pour une taille inférieure à 120 Å environ ces cristallites ne montrent pas de troncatures importantes cependant leur diagramme de diffraction (fig. 5c) comporte des trainées de diffusion dans les directions (001) montrant ainsi qu'il doit exister de très petites troncatures (001) à la base de la pyramide.

Pour une taille supérieure à 150 Å environ, les franges d'égale épaisseur font apparaître des troncatures (001) au sommet de la pyramide et (110) sur deux arêtes opposées (fig. 6b) ; ces cristallites sont donc limités par quatre plans (111) et deux plans (110).

188

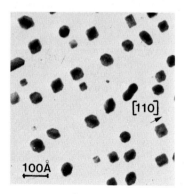

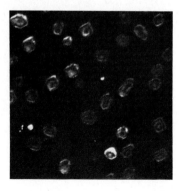

<u>fig. 6a</u> : Micrographie en fond clair
Pd/NaCl ; diamètre moyen des
agrégats : 200 Å.

<u>fig. 6b</u> : Micrographie en fond noir
correspondant à la fig. 6a obtenue en
sélectionnant la réflexion $g_{\vec{2}00}$ de la
fig. 5c.

En résumé, nous pouvons dire que les particules de Pt et de Pd de structure c.f.c.
présentent des caractéristiques morphologiques communes au cours de leur croissance mais
pour des tailles légèrement différentes, la forme généralement observée étant pour les
petites tailles celle d'un tétraèdre sur MoS_2 et d'un demi-octaèdre sur NaCl (001). Puis
les particules croissent et tendent à diminuer leur énergie de surface soit en prenant
une forme sphérique soit en faisant apparaître des troncatures sur les arêtes ; ces
troncatures généralement formées par des plans (110) présentent la particularité de
posséder un grand nombre de sites "B5" dont le rôle a déjà été signalé pour l'adsorption (6).

IV. OBSERVATION DES AGREGATS DE STRUCTURE DECAEDRIQUE OU ICOSAEDRIQUE

Dans certaines conditions de préparation (forte vitesse de dépôt, température du
support supérieure à 300°C), des agrégats de Pt ou de Pd présentent une structure et une
morphologie différentes de celles que nous venons d'étudier. Les contours de ces agrégats
sont soit pentagonaux, soit hexagonaux et leurs contrastes sont identiques à ceux que nous
avons déjà observés dans les agrégats d'or de structure dite "à symétrie pentagonale" (7).
Ces agrégats sont en effet caractérisés par des axes de symétrie d'ordre cinq. Par analogie
avec les agrégats d'or, nous dirons que ces particules de contour pentagonal ont une
structure décaédrique et celles de contour hexagonal une structure icosaédrique. La
figure 7 montre les contrastes les plus fréquemment observés d'une particule décaédrique
pour différentes inclinaisons par rapport au faisceau électronique.

Les particules de contour hexagonal apparaissent généralement avec un contraste dit
en "Croix de Malte" comme le montre la micrographie (fig. 8a). Ces différents contrastes
ont déjà fait l'objet d'interprétations (8) (9) (10).

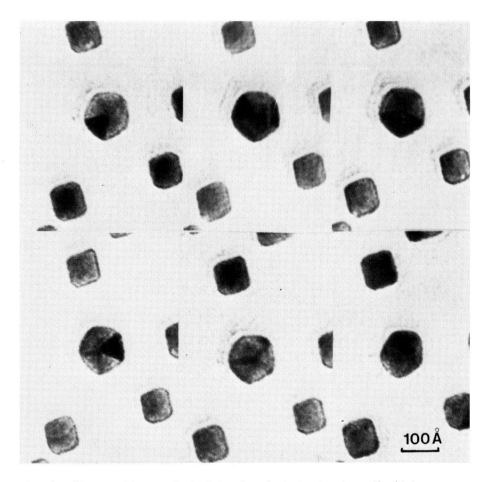

fig. 7 : Micrographies en fond clair d'agrégat de structure décaédrique correspondant à plusieurs inclinaisons (α) par rapport au faisceau électronique : diamètre de l'agrégat : 120 Å.

La présence de ces structures décaédrique ou icosaédrique se manifeste sur le diagramme de diffraction par des points supplémentaires sur l'anneau (111) en particulier sur le vecteur réciproque $g_{\vec{200}}$ correspondant aux réflexions dues aux cristallites d'orientation (001) (fig. 8b).

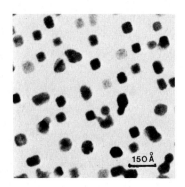

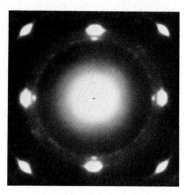

fig. 8a : Micrographie en fond clair Pt/NaCl, T_S = 300°C, diamètre moyen des agrégats : 40 Å, de la particule icosaédrique I = 60 Å.

fig. 8b : Diagramme de diffraction électronique correspondant à la micrographie fig. 8a.

Le tableau ci-après présente les principaux résultats concernant les observations des agrégats de structure à "symétrie d'ordre 5", réalisées sur un grand nombre d'expériences. Il apparaît que la proportion de ces agrégats aussi bien pour le Pt que pour le Pd est toujours faible. En ce sens nos résultats sont en accord avec ceux de Avery et al. (11) qui avaient déjà remarqué cette faible proportion dans le cas des particules de catalyseurs supportés.

Un certain nombre de conditions semblent favoriser la formation des agrégats de structure quinaire : ils sont principalement observés sur des clivages réalisés à l'air et lorsque les flux d'évaporation sont importants. D'autre part ces agrégats ont souvent une taille moyenne supérieure à celle des agrégats de structure c.f.c. obtenus dans les mêmes conditions (12). Ces remarques semblent indiquer que dans le domaine de taille considéré (40 - 100 Å) ces "structures pentagonales" résultent de coalescence entre agrégats. Ce mode de formation avait déjà été mis en évidence par des observations "in situ" sur des particules d'argent et d'or déposées sur MgO et MoS_2 (13).

Cependant le fait que l'on observe que très peu de particules de structure pentagonale ou icosaédrique pour des tailles supérieures à 25 Å ne signifie pas que de telles structures n'existent pas pour des tailles inférieures. Nous savons que pour l'or, ces "structures anormales" n'existent réellement que pour des tailles inférieures à 100 Å (14). Il est probable que leur stabilité ou pseudo-stabilité, pour des tailles allant jusqu'à 100 Å, soit due à leur très faible énergie de macle. Dans le cas du Pd et du Pt cette énergie de défaut d'empilement est grande comparativement à l'or, de telle sorte que des édifices atomiques de structures pentagonale ou icosaédriques peuvent rapidement devenir instables. L'observation des petits agrégats de taille inférieure à 15 Å, bien que difficile à réaliser, est actuellement en cours. Elle devrait permettre d'apporter une réponse à cette question.

Pression des gaz résiduels (torr)	Nature du dépôt	Nature du support	Flux d'évaporation at/cm²/s	Température du support (°C)	Structure anormale		Proportion d'agrégats de structure anormale	
					Pt	Pd	Pt	Pd
10^{-8}	Pt ou Pd	NaCl(001)$_{CA}$*	7×10^{13}	250 - 300	I + D*	D	5	4
			$1,4 \times 10^{14}$				5,5	3
			$5,4 \times 10^{14}$				6	3
		NaCl(001)$_{CV}$*	3×10^{14}	250 - 300	-	-	-	-
10^{-6}	Pt ou Pd	NaCl(001)$_{CA}$	$3,4 \times 10^{13}$	250 - 300	I + D	D	3	2
			10^{14}				5	4
			$1,1 \times 10^{14}$				7	5
			$1,5 \times 10^{14}$				8	4
10^{-6} ou 10^{-8}	Pt ou Pd	NaCl(111) in situ	10^{14}	300		D	3	1
		mica (CA)	"	350	D	D	4	<1
		MoS$_2$ (CA)	"	100 - 300			<1	<1

* CA : clivé à l'air   CV : clivé sous vide   I : icosaèdre   D : décaèdre

TABLEAU

192

REFERENCES

1 R. Van Hardeveld and A. Van Montfoort, Advances Catalysis, 22 (1975) 75.
2 M.J. Maat and L. Moscov, Proc. Intern. Congr. on Catalysis 3rd, (1965) 1276.
3 Y. Barron, G. Maire, D. Cornet, J.M. Muller and F.G. Gault
     a) J. Catal., 2 (1963) 152
     b) J. Catal., 5 (1966) 428.
4 M. Gillet and A. Renou, Thin Solid Films, 52 (1978) 23.
5 M.J. Yacaman and T. Ocañaz, Phys. Stat. Solidi (a), 42 (1977) 571.
6 R. Van Hardeveld and F. Hartog, Surface Science, 15 (1969) 189.
7 E. Gillet, Thèse de Doctorat d'Etat, Marseille 1969.
8 S. Ino, Journal of physical Society of Japan, 21 (1966) 346-62.
9 E. Gillet and M. Gillet, Thin Solid Films, 15 (1973) 249-57.
10 A. Renou, M. Gillet, M. Brieu and P. Larroque, Thin Solid Films, 44 (1977) 75-82.
11 N.R. Avery and J.V. Sanders, Journal of Catalysis, 18 (1970) 129.
12 A. Renou and M. Gillet, Thin Solid Films, 41 (1977) 15-28.
13 K. Yagi, K. Takayanagi, K. Kobayashi and G. Honjo, J. of Crystal Growth, 28 (1975) 117-24.
14 E. Gillet, A. Renou and M. Gillet, Thin Solid Films, 29 (1975) 217-22.

J. BOURDON (Editor)
Growth and Properties of Metal Clusters, pp. 193—199
© 1980 Elsevier Scientific Publishing Company — Printed in The Netherlands

PROPRIETES D'AGREGATS DE Ni° DANS LES ZEOLITHES NiX REDUITES PAR L'HYDROGENE ATOMIQUE.

D. Olivier, M. Richard, L. Bonneviot, M. Che. Laboratoire de Chimie des Solides. Université Paris VI.

I - INTRODUCTION

En catalyse hétérogène, afin d'augmenter la surface active, il est inté-ressant d'utiliser le nickel sous forme de particules de taille homogène et de diamètre le plus petit possible. Le métal dispersé est souvent obtenu en réduisant par H_2 les ions Ni^{2+} déposés par imprégnation sur un support oxyde inerte ou échangés dans des silicoaluminates tridimensionnels tels que les zéolithes.

L'utilisation de l'hydrogène comme agent réducteur implique la rupture de la liaison H-H. Celle-ci peut être effectuée de trois manières diffé-rentes:

1) thermique: c'est la méthode la plus utilisée. Les températures de réduction sont de l'ordre de 573 à 673 K. La taille des particules s'avère difficile à contrôler car plusieurs réactions se déroulent simultanément à la température de réduction: activation de l'hydrogène, réduction des ions en atomes, production d'eau, migration des ions et des atomes

2) catalytique: en présence de métaux dissociant l'hydrogène (Pt , Pd)[1] La température de réduction est de l'ordre de 573 K et cette méthode peut introduire de nouveaux sites actifs susceptibles de modifier les propriétés des particules de Ni°

3) photochimique: en utilisant le rayonnement UV d'une lampe à vapeur de mercure. Le rayonnement UV présente cependant l'inconvénient de produire des défauts (centres V et/ou F)en plus de la réduction des ions Ni^{2+}[20].

Pour obtenir des particules métalliques de faible diamètre et de taille homogène la réduction doit être réalisée à une température suffisamment basse pour éviter les phénomènes de migration des atomes qui forment des agrégats de diamètre croissant, et la dispersion des ions initiaux doit être la plus homogène possible. La première de ces conditions n'est pas réalisée dans les deux premières méthodes: par exemple il semble impossible dans le cas du nickel déposé sur silice d'obtenir des particules inférieures à 20 Å [2].

Le choix d'une matrice adéquate telle que les zéolithes améliore la dispersion des ions initiaux. En effet il a été possible d'obtenir des particules de 7 Å dans une zéolithe NiCeX [3], le taux de réduction atteint 85%, mais l'homogénéité de taille n'est pas parfaite puisque 85% des cris-tallites ont un diamètre de 7 Å et 15% un diamètre de 30 Å.

Dans ce travail nous proposons une nouvelle méthode de réduction: la réduction par l'hydrogène atomique, qui utilisée conjointement (ou séparément) avec un prétraitement de l'échantillon, permet de satisfaire les conditions de température de réduction et d'homodispersion des ions initiaux.

. Dans le cas des matrices zéolithiques un prétraitement par CO (3 heures à 373 K) favorise la migration des ions Ni^{2+} vers les supercages.

. Une décharge micro-onde produit à température ambiante des atomes d'hydrogène en dehors de la matrice que l'on désire réduire. Ces atomes d'hydrogène sont utilisés pour réduire les ions Ni^{2+} à des températures nettement plus basses (273 K) que celles utilisées avec H_2 activé thermiquement ou catalytiquement.

Ces procédés ont été testés sur deux séries d'échantillons conduisant par réduction par H_2 soit à une dispersion hétérogène des tailles des cristallites $(Ni_{31}X)(4)$ soit uniquement à des ions $Ni^{+}(Ni_{10}CaX)(5)$. Les particules métalliques obtenues ont été étudiées par résonance ferromagnétique (RFM) à température variable. Les applications de cette technique à l'étude des agrégats métalliques sont largement discutées.

II - PREPARATION DES ECHANTILLONS ET TECHNIQUES EXPERIMENTALES

Les échantillons sont préparés suivant les techniques d'échange classique, en solution aqueuse, à partir de la Faujasite sodique de type X fournie par la firme Union Carbide, Linde division.

L'analyse chimique des échantillons conduit aux formules : $Ni_{31}Na_{24}(SiO_2)_{106}(AlO_2)_{86}$ et $Ni_{10}Ca_{20}Na_{14}H_2(SiO_2)_{106}(AlO_2)_{86}$ appelés respectivement : $Ni_{31}X$ et $Ni_{10}CaX$.

Ces échantillons sont activés à 773 K, d'abord sous 100 Torr d'oxygène (3 heures) puis sous vide 10^{-5} Torr (une nuit) avant d'être réduits par l'hydrogène atomique à 273 K (4 heures). Activation et réduction sont effectuées dans une rampe sans graisse (Figure 1).

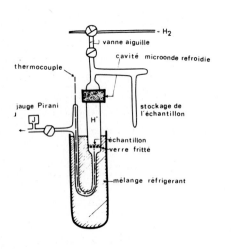

Fig.1. Réduction par H˙: réacteur

Le jet d'atomes d'hydrogène est obtenu à partir d'un jet de molécules $H_2(P_{H_2} \sim 1$ Torr) excité par une décharge micro-onde de 2450 MHz (Puissance = 200 W).

L'échantillon est maintenu à 273 K pendant la réduction. Les spectres RFM sont réalisés en bande X (9 GH_z) sur un spectromètre Varian CS-E-109 équipé d'une double cavité. Un accessoire de température variable permet d'enregistrer les spectres entre 77 K et 573 K. La puissance délivrée par le klystron n'affecte pas l'intensité et la largeur des raies RFM pour des valeurs de 2 à 10 mW. Dans ces conditions le facteur Q de la cavité ne varie pas en cours de résonance.

III - RESULTATS EXPERIMENTAUX

III$_1$. Réduction par l'hydrogène atomique

Le tableau I compare les taux de réduction et les tailles de particules
(mesurées par magnétisme statique (6)) des échantillons réduits soit par
l'hydrogène moléculaire à 573 K soit par l'hydrogène atomique à 273 K
après prétraitement par CO à 373 K.

TABLEAU I

Echantillon	Taux de réduction		Diamètre des particules	
	H$_2$ 573 K	H$^\bullet$ 273 K	H$_2$ 573 K	H$^\bullet$ 273 K
Ni$_{31}$X Ni$_{10}$CaX	0,190 (7) 0,076 (7)	0,600 1,000	15,60,100 Å Ni$^+$ (5) pas de Ni°	10 Å (6) 10 Å (6)

III$_2$. Etude par RFM des particules de nickel obtenues par réduction
par H°

L'application de la RFM à l'étude des petites particules métalliques est
récente (2,8-12) et l'interprétation des spectres souvent délicate.
L'analyse du spectre d'un échantillon totalement réduit en particules de
taille homogène égale à 10 Å (Ni$_{10}$CaX) permet non seulement de caractériser
les cristallites, mais aussi par comparaison avec les spectres de particules
soit hétérodispersées soit de plus gros diamètre, de tester les possibilités
de la RFM pour la caractérisation des particules métalliques.

III$_2$.$_1$. Forme des particules

La fréquence de résonance est déterminée non par le champ magnétique
appliqué mais par le champ effectif H$_{eff}$ qui dépend du champ démagnétisant
et d'un champ représentant soit les effets d'anisotropie magnétocristalline
soit les effets de tension (magnétostriction). Les effets d'anisotropie
magnétocristalline et de magnétostriction, sont dans le cas du nickel
négligeables au-dessus de 473 K (13a). La forme géométrique de l'échantillon influe sur le champ démagnétisant et cet effet de forme, indépendant de
la température, peut modifier énormément la fréquence de résonance (14).

Dans le cas d'un échantillon sphérique, le champ démagnétisant n'intervient plus et la résonance a lieu à g = 2,2 valeur du facteur g naturel
du Ni° (13b).

Supposons un échantillon contenant deux populations de particules de
Ni° sphériques de tailles différentes, chacune d'elle conduisant à un signal
RFM lorentzien: le spectre résultant, dû à la superposition de deux signaux
de largeur ΔH$_{pp}$ différente sera un signal symétrique et restera centré sur
g = 2,2. Au contraire si l'une des populations contient des particules de
forme anisotrope le signal résultant demeurera asymétrique au-dessus de
473 K. L'asymétrie des signaux peut être évaluée à partir du graphe obtenu
en portant l'amplitude normalisée (Y'/Y'$_{max}$) du signal dérivé à champ

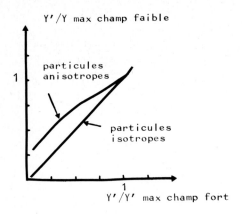

Fig.2. Caractérisation de la symétrie des signaux RFM au-dessus de 473 K

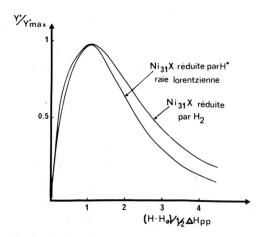

Fig.3. Forme des raies RFM des agrégats de Ni°

faible en fonction de l'amplitude normalisée du signal dérivé à champ fort; Y' est mesuré à des points équidistants du champ de résonance H_o pris à l'intersection du signal dérivé avec la ligne de base à champ fort (15). Ces points équidistants de H_o sont pris successivement égaux à: $(\Delta H_{pp}/2)$, 1,5 $(\Delta H_{pp}/2)$, 2 $(\Delta H_{pp}/2)$, 2,5 $(\Delta H_{pp}/2)$. Un signal symétrique apparaîtra sur ce graphique comme une droite de pente 1, tandis qu'une asymétrie au-dessus de 473 K traduira une anisotropie de forme des particules et conduira à une courbe ou à une droite de pente supérieure ou inférieure à 1 (Figure 2). Les signaux RFM des particules de 10 Å stabilisées dans $Ni_{10}CaX$ sont symétriques au-dessus de 473 K, g = 2,2: ces particules sont sphériques.

III$_{2.2}$. Superparamagnétisme

Le superparamagnétisme peut être mis en évidence par le tracé des courbes thermomagnétiques (2,16). Entre 300 K et 573 K, la courbe thermomagnétique des particules de 10 Å est une droite ce qui n'est pas le cas des particules soit plus grosses soit hétérodispersées (4).

Les particules de 10 Å ne possèdent pas d'aimantation rémanente.

Le superparamagnétisme est aussi confirmé par les mesures de magnétisme statique.

III$_{2.3}$. Homogénéité de taille: elle est caractérisée par trois données expérimentales déduites de l'analyse des spectres RFM.

Forme des raies: la forme des raies est déterminée suivant la méthode de Poole (17). Au-dessus de 473 K les particules sphériques, superparamagnétiques, conduisent à des raies purement lorentziennes si elles sont homodispersées. Toute hétérogénéité de taille se traduit par un élargissement par rapport au profil lorentzien théorique (Figure 3).

Largeur de raie. La décroissance linéaire de la largeur de raie (ΔH_{pp}), quand la température d'enregistrement croît, apparaît caractéristique de l'homogénéité de taille des petites particules métalliques: les échantillons

de taille hétérogène ne présentent pas de variation linéaire de ΔH_{pp} avec
la température (4).

Evolution des signaux à basse température (T < 300 K)

Les courbes RFM enregistrées entre 300 K et 77 K des échantillons homo-
dispersés sont asymétriques mais passent toutes par un même point (Figure 4).

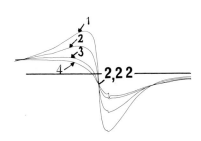

Ce point n'est pas situé sur la ligne
de base prise à champ élevé (15) et
il correspond à g = 2,2 valeur du
facteur g naturel du Ni°. Bien que la
signification physique de ce point
"isobestique" ne soit pas encore
élucidé, son existence apparaît comme
un critère d'homogénéité de taille.
De plus la mise en évidence de ce
point "isobestique" apparaît comme la
seule méthode pour mesurer la valeur
du facteur g des petites particules
métalliques dans le domaine de température où les effets d'anisotropie
magnétocristalline ou de magnétostriction rendent les raies asymétri-

Fig.4. Evolution des signaux RFM
des particules homodispersées :
la température d'enregistrement
décroît(dans le sens 1→4)tandis
que les autres paramètres d'enregistrement (gain, modulation, puissance) sont maintenus constants.

ques et augmentent la valeur apparente du facteur g (pris à l'intersection
avec la ligne de base).

III$_{2\,4}$. Taille des particules. Relation entre largeur de raie et taille de particule

Les interactions d'échange entraînent une diminution de la largeur des
raies RFM, tandis que les interactions dipole-dipole (magnétique) entraînent
un élargissement des signaux. Ces deux types d'interactions existent dans
les composés para et ferromagnétiques. Le premier étant plus intense dans
les ferromagnétiques que dans les paramagnétiques: le Ni° massique conduit
à des signaux FMR étroits (ΔH_{pp} = 400 G à 300 K). Dans le domaine des très
petites particules les interactions d'échange diminuent (18) et l'élargissement dipolaire est prédominant. Dans le cas de particules de Φ < 6 Å (4)
la largeur de raie atteint 8000 G à 300 K. Elle décroît brusquement jusqu'à
ΔH_{pp} = 862 G pour les particules de 7 Å stabilisées dans les zéolithes
NiCeX. Dans le domaine des particules superparamagnétiques de 10 à 60 Å,
la largeur de raie (à 300 K) décroît avec la taille des particules.
(Tableau II). Quand le diamètre dépasse 100 Å les signaux RFM deviennent
gaussiens et la largeur de raie augmente brusquement jusqu'à 2300 G. (19)

Asymétrie des raies à basse température

Parmi les échantillons étudiés, seules les particules de taille inférieure à 25 Å présentent à basse température un signal RFM dissymétrique
du côté des champs faibles. Cette dissymétrie augmente quand la température
et la taille des particules décroissent (Figure 5). L'anisotropie est

TABLEAU II

Taille des particules (Å)	Largeur de raie (G)
10	700
25	674
60	390

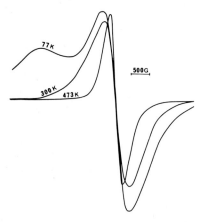

Fig.5. Ni$_{10}$CaX réduite par H·
Spectre RFM (Bande X)

considérable dans le cas des cristallites de 7 Å (NiCeX).

Plusieurs causes peuvent être à l'origine de cette anisotropie:

. anisotropie cristalline: elle
semble peu probable dans le cas
d'agrégats de 7 ou 10 Å qui ne contiennent que très peu d'atomes (13 pour
les particules de 7 Å).

. magnétostriction résultant des
effets de tension. L'asymétrie des
signaux RFM à basse température a été
observée dans le cas d'agrégats de
Ni°, de forme isotrope, de taille inférieure à 18 Å, déposés sur silice
(obtenus par réduction par H· (20)).

Il est probable que les effets de
contrainte du réseau sur ces particules sont inférieurs à ceux qui s'exer-
cent sur les particules de 25 Å incluses dans le réseau zéolithique
(NiPtX(3,4));pourtant dans le dernier cas l'anisotropie magnétique de basse
température n'a pas été observée. Dans le cas des particules sphériques de
7 Å (NiCeX (3)), 92% des atomes de Ni° sont en surface; on peut en particulier dans ce cas, envisager que l'anisotropie magnétique observée à basse
température provient de la déformation du réseau magnétique résultant de
tensions introduites par des différences de contraction thermique entre la
surface et le centre de la particule.

Dans le cas des petites particules de nickel (raies RFM lorentziennes
au-dessus de 473 K) l'anisotropie magnétique à basse température apparaît
comme une propriété intrinsèque caractéristique des très petits agrégats
métalliques, elle n'est pas due à des effets de contrainte du réseau.

III$_3$. CONCLUSIONS

Dans ce travail, sur l'exemple du nickel, nous avons montré que la
réduction par l'hydrogène atomique est une méthode assez puissante pour
réduire des cations en métal à température suffisamment basse pour
empêcher la migration et l'agglomération des atomes métalliques. Cette
méthode permet d'obtenir des très petites particules de taille homogène:

nous avons pu la généraliser à du Ni/SiO$_2$ et à des zéolithes au cuivre (20).

Nous avons confirmé que la RFM permet de caractériser l'isotropie de forme et le superparamagnétisme des petites particules métalliques.

Bien qu'il nous ait été impossible à partir des spectres RFM de mesurer la taille des particules, nous avons clarifié les relations existant entre la taille des particules, la largeur des raies et l'anisotropie magnétique à basse température.

Ce travail montre enfin que la RFM s'avère pratique et rapide pour caractériser sans ambiguité l'homogénéité de la dispersion.

REMERCIEMENTS

Les auteurs remercient Mlle M.F. Guilleux et M. G.A. Martin pour les mesures de magnétisme statique et pour avoir mis à notre disposition un échantillon contenant des particules de 7 Å (NiCeX).

REFERENCES

1 M.F. Guilleux, M. Kermarec et D. Delafosse, J. Chem. Comm., 102, 1977.
2 E.G. Derouane, A.J. Simoens, C. Collin, G.A. Martin, J.A. Dalmon et J.C. Vedrine, J. Cat., 52, 50, 1977.
3 M.F. Guilleux, D. Delafosse, G.A. Martin et J.A. Dalmon, J. Chem. Soc., Farad. Trans. I, 75, 165, 1979.
4 M. Che, M. Richard, D. Olivier, J. Chem. Soc., Farad. Trans I. Sous presse.
5 D. Olivier, M. Richard, M. Che, Chem. Phys. Letters, 60, 77, 1978.
6 M.F. Guilleux, G.A. Martin. Résultats non publiés.
7 M. Briend-Faure, M.F. Guilleux, J. Jeanjean, D. Delafosse, G. Djega Mariadassou, M. Tardy, Acta Phys. Chim. XXIV (1-2), 1978.
8 A.A. Slinkin, Russian. Chem. Review, 37, 643, 1968.
9 E.G. Derouane, A.J. Simoens, J.C. Vedrine, Chem. Phys. Letters, 52, 549, 1977.
10 R.S. de Biazi, T.C., Devezas, Physi 86-88 B, 1425, 1977.
11 J.L. Dormann, P. Gibart, G. Suran, C. Sella, Physi 86-88 B, 1431, 1977.
12 A.A. Andreev et P.W. Selvood, J. Cat., 8, 378, 1967.
13 A.Herpin, Théorie du Magnétisme, PUF, Paris 1968, a) p.370 b) p.437.
14 G.V. Skrotskii et L.V. Kurbatoo, Ferromagnetnyi Resonans, Gos Izd, Fiz mat Lit, Moscow 1961, p.38.
15 Schloeman, J. Phys. Chem. Sol, 6, 257, 1958
16 B.R. Loy et C.R. Nodding, J. Cat., 3, 1, 1964.
17 C.P. Poole, "Electron Spin Resonance, a comprehensive treatise on experimental techniques". J. Wiley, NY 1967, p.806.
18 M.I. Darby, Phys. 86-88 B, 1417, 1977.
19 P.A. Jacobs, H. Nys, J. Verdonck, E.G. Derouane, J.P. Gilson, A.J. Simoens J. Chem. Soc. Farad. Trans I, 75, 1979.
20 L. Bonneviot, D. Olivier, M. Che. Résultats non publiés.

J. BOURDON (Editor)
Growth and Properties of Metal Clusters, pp. 201—207
© 1980 Elsevier Scientific Publishing Company — Printed in The Netherlands

FERROMAGNETIC RESONANCE INVESTIGATION OF SUPPORTED NICKEL CATALYSTS : EFFECTS OF PARTICLE
SIZE, SHAPE, SUPPORT AND DEGREE OF REDUCTION.

A. SIMOENS and E.G. DEROUANE [a]

Facultés Universitaires Notre-Dame de la Paix, Namur (Belgium)

ABSTRACT

The effects of particle shape, particle size, particle-support interaction and incomplete
reduction or O_2-chemisorption on the FMR parameters have been investigated on various
supported nickel catalysts and analyzed by the FMR theory for polycrystalline samples in
the "independent grain approach". Samples without important size effect show the influence
of anisotropies on line-width, -shape and -position, while small particles seem sensitive
to a superparamagnetic decrease of apparent magnetic anisotropy. In some cases, the Curie
temperature is shown to vary with particle size.

INTRODUCTION

Ferromagnetic resonance (FMR) has been readily explored and reviewed in the case of
single crystals and films. Nevertheless few studies have been devoted to samples of great
catalytic interest, such as small supported metal particles.

The main purpose of this work is to apply the FMR method to gather new types of
information about the nickel particle state in supported catalysts. We try to answer
questions like : Are the particles spherical or not ? Are the very small particles
electronically different of massive nickel ? How do the particle and the support interact ?

In a first approach, different Ni samples without important size effect have been
studied. The purpose of this work is to elucidate the effects of supports. In a second
step, the size effect was investigated for nickel on silica and nickel bidispersed on
zeolites.

EXPERIMENTAL

The FMR measurements were performed from 150 K to 650 K using a Bruker B-ER-420 E.S.R.
spectrometer operating in the X-band at a microwave power of 13 mW, using 100- kHz field
modulation. Variable temperature was achieved by using the BST 100-700 X and BER-400 XHT
Bruker temperature control units. The technique used for electron spin resonance technique
is applicable to ferromagnetic resonance provided the cavity quality factor remains
constant when the spectrum is recorded.

---

[a] To whom queries concerning this paper should be sent.

The most important features of the investigated catalyst are summarized in table 1. They are reported in greater detail in previous papers (refs. 1-2-3).

TABLE 1

Sample	Ni content wt%	Reduction Temp.(K)	Degree of Reduct.(%)	Average Part. size (Range) (nm)		Curie Temp. (K)	
MgAl$_2$O$_4$-1400	12	1123	100	1408		631	
SiO$_2$-A -140	45	953	100	13.8(6-20)		631	
Al$_2$O$_3$-150	13	1130	97	14.6(6-20)		597	
SiO$_2$-53	15.8	923	106	53		625	
SiO$_2$-25	4.5	813	100	25		645	
SiO$_2$-53-0	15.8	923	78	53		610	
SiO$_2$-25-0	4.5	813	50	25		505	
SiO$_2$-24-0	4.5	793	65	24		570	
NiY-673	8.2	673	48	1.55	16.2	619	–
NiY-723	8.2	723	54	1.15	19.4	593	634
NiY-773	8.2	773	71	1.30	17.8	602	637
NiY-823	8.2	823	96	3.85	32.4	592	638
NiY-873	8.2	873	100	4.05	36.0	626	641

DISCUSSION

Ferromagnetic resonance applied to supported metallic particles

Ferromagnetic resonance absorption in nickel single crystals or films is characterized by a lorentzian type peak of about 300-400 Oe width and a g-factor value of 2.22. Anisotropies result in a peak shift. Moreover, the linewidth shows an increase with T above the Curie temperature, due to the paramagnetic-like behavior of the spins (ref. 4).

FMR on powdered type catalysts provides three parameters which can be used to characterize the ferromagnetic particles.

The FMR lineshape

From the theory for polycrystalline samples in the "independent grain approach" (refs. 5-6), the line-shape, - width and -position depend strongly on magnetic anisotropies. The type of anisotropy can be deduced from the variation of the linewidth with temperature, as (i) shape anisotropy is proportional to the spontaneous magnetization Ms, (ii) crystalline anisotropy is proportional to the magnetocrystalline anisotropy constant K$_1$, and (iii) magnetostrictive anisotropy to $\sigma\lambda$(σ : stress ; λ : magnetostriction constant).

The FMR intensity

It should be proportional to the amount of reduced metal as it is to the magnetization of the system. In most cases, it has to be obtained by double integration of the spectrum.

The Curie temperature (T_c)

It is derived from the variation of the FMR intensity with temperature. By plotting the square of the intensity vs. temperature, a straight line is obtained in the $0.9 < T/T_c < 1$ region (ref. 7) which allows an easy determination of T_c.

Very small particles are characterized by a superparamagnetic behavior. The magnetization vector of each crystallite is subject to a Brownian motion. The apparent magnetic susceptibility and anisotropy are decreased (refs. 8-9) provided the relaxation time of the magnetization τ_{sp}, is smaller than the measuring time (10^{-10} sec for FMR in the X-band). Since the lowest (estimated) value for τ_{sp} in nickel equals 10^{-10} sec, FMR is at the limit of detection of superparamagnetism. Anyway, the trend for small particles with very little anisotropy (even not superparamagnetic) consist in the decrease of the line distribution : the lineshape become lorentzian and the g value shift is decreased.

Samples without size effect

Three different catalysts (upper part table 1) were investigated whose mean particle size is above 10 nm.

At first glance, FMR doesn't detect major differences between the massive nickel on $MgAl_2O_4$ catalyst and the nickel on silica which was prepared from synthetic Ni(II) Antigorite (ref. 10). Both samples show the same Curie temperature as bulk nickel (631 K) and their linewidth ΔH (Fig. 1) vary roughly in the same way with temperature. The "Ms" component of the $\Delta H(T)$ curve indicates clearly a shape anisotropy. This is confirmed by electron microscopy as the particles appear to be elongated and hexagonally shaped. An epitaxial relationship between the metal particles and the support in the SiO_2-A case was evidenced by Dalmaï-Imelik et al. (ref. 11). Besides, sintering at 1123-1273 K of this last catalyst causes the disappearence of most of this "Ms" component in the $\Delta H(T)$ curve (fig. 1), and associatively the loss of the hexagonal shape of the particles as evidenced by electron microscopy. The magnetocrystalline anisotropy which must be present in all samples appears as an increase of the linewidth below $T/T_c = 0.4$.

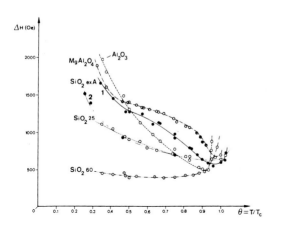

Fig. 1. Peak to peak linewidth dependence on temperature for various Ni catalysts. (SiO_2 ex Antigorite (1) before sintering and (2) after sintering at 1123-1173 K).

Although the nickel particle size distribution is quite similar on the silica and alumina supported catalysts, their magnetic properties are quite different. The Curie temperature of Al_2O_3-150 is shifted to lower values by about 35 K. A particle size effect must be excluded since the systems are similar. As in previous work (second part of this paper) we have to correlate the Tc shift with incomplete reduction of Ni. Moreover, the linewidth decreases continuously up to the Curie temperature ; this indicates the absence of shape anisotropy. Since the magnetocrystalline anisotropy vanishes at 400 K, this behavior accounts for the presence of magnetostrictive anisotropy with a stress value decreasing from about 10^9 dynes/cm^2 at low temperatures to less than 10^8 dynes/cm^2 at

600 K. It is tempting to conclude that some $NiAl_2O_4$ formed during the catalyst treatment is present as small inclusions in the Ni crystallites, accounting for the Tc shift and the stress anisotropy.

Size effect and Curie temperature

Carter et al.(ref. 12) concluded from magnetic data that the "electronic structure of supported nickel is different from that of bulk nickel". It was observed that, with decreasing particle size (down from massive to 1.2 nm Ni), the paramagnetic Curie temperature shifts from 638 to 547 K, while the paramagnetic magneton number decreases from 1.73 to 1.1.

The experiments are in clear contradiction with our work. FMR and Static Magnetization measurements on various nickel on silica catalysts (Table 1) show that the Curie temperature of small nickel particles does not decrease provided reduction is complete. However, incomplete reduction (SiO_2-53,24-0) or oxygen chemisorption (SiO_2-25-0) was found to shift the Curie point strongly towards lower temperature. For these last samples, we could establish a linear relationship between T_c and the average coordination number Z in the particle. Figure 2 shows the agreement between these experimental values and the equation

$$T_c = (631/12) < Z >$$

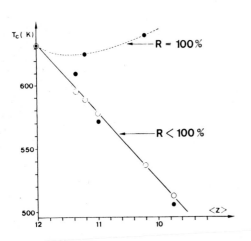

which was derived by assuming the same value of the Heisenberg exchange integral $<J>$ for small particles as for bulk metal. The fully reduced catalysts seem to fit a curve indicating an increase in $<J>$ with particle size decreasing. A tentative explanation for this is the contribution of surface atoms (which increases with dispersion) undergoing an effect of surface relaxation (or tension).

Fig.2. Curie temperature T_c dependence as a function of the average coordination number $<Z>$. (o) calculated values ; (●) experimental values (reproduced from reference 1 with permission from Academic Press).

A size effect on Curie temperature is observed in the case of nickel on zeolites. The bidispersed character of the particle size distribution was clearly established by chemical measurements (tpo - tpr), the appearance of two lines in the FMR spectra and the presence of two Curie temperatures ($T_c(1)$ and $T_c(2)$). Lower T_c values must be assigned to particles with lower degree of reduction, namely the nickel crystallites inside the zeolite . From the ratio of the slopes of the lines (Fig. 3) the fraction of external nickel in the total reduced nickel phase can be evaluated. This value is compared with those obtained by chemical measurements (Table 2). Good agreement exists between both data and confirms that superparamagnetism plays a minor role in these FMR experiments, as it does not decrease the apparent magnetization. The rather high and constant value of $T_c(2)$ demonstrates that the external particles are always completely reduced. Moreover a decrease of Curie temperature for internal nickel is observed when the reduction temperature is increased from 673 to 823 K. It is due to a partial oxidation (5-15%) at the particle-zeolite interface. Kinetic measurements for Ni, Ag and Cu lead to the same conclusions (ref. 13).

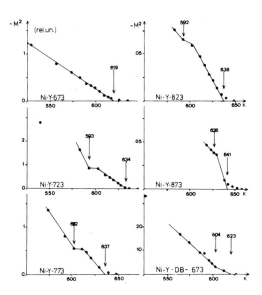

Fig. 3. Square of FMR intensity as a function of temperature for the NiY samples. (Reproduced from reference 3 with permission from the Chemical Society (London)).

Size effect and lineshape

For all samples listed in the second half of table 1, a rather narrow isotropic line is present with a lorentzian shape and a g-factor value close to 2.22. The line position remains nearly independent of temperature.

TABLE 2

Sample	$T_c(1)$ /K	$T_c(2)$ /K	% Ni (0) (fmr)[a]	(tpr)[b]
NiY-673	619	–	–	4
NiY-723	593	634	38	30
NiY-773	602	637	48	54
NiY-823	592	638	57	53
NiY-873	626	641	65	64.5

[a]Determined from the ratio of the slopes of M^2 vs T curves
[b]Determined from temperature programmed reduction measurements

For the NiY samples, ΔH ranges between 1200 Oe (at 150 K) and 800 Oe (at 550 K), while g equals 2.24. These facts indicate that a weak magnetostrictive anisotropy is present in these small particles, probably due to mechanical stresses. A broad gaussian line is found superimposed to the lorentzian line. The increase of intensity of the gaussian with reduction temperature, as compared to the chemical data, leads us to associate the broad line with the large particles outside the zeolite. The variation of linewidth and position occurs in parallel with spontaneous magnetization and indicates shape anisotropy (with a mean excentricity of 30%).

The comparison of the nickel on silica catalysts is rather instructive. We would expect smaller particles to be more superparamagnetic, as magnetocrystalline energy is proportional to the volume. In fact, no superparamagnetic decrease of linewidth is observed. The SiO_2-53 sample is characterized by a single lorentzian line whose width (400 Oe) and g-value (2.20) remain constant with temperature. On the other hand, the narrow line in the SiO_2-25 sample is obscured by a broad gaussian line characteristic of a strong anisotropy. The line-width increase with temperature and size decrease is related to internal stress anisotropy (due to surface tension) or/and surface magnetic anisotropy. Both anisotropies are proportional to the surface/volume ratio. Nevertheless we incline for the first possibility for the following reasons :

(i) the Curie temperature and the mean exchange integral are increasing with surface/volume ratio, and this was related to surface relaxation (tension)

(ii) this increase of $< J >$ vanishes when oxygen is chemisorbed. A similar disappearance of "stress release" upon oxygen adsorption has been observed elsewhere (ref. 14).

CONCLUSIONS

Line-width, -shape and -position depend mainly on magnetic anisotropies and are usefull to gather information about particle shape or stress anisotropies. Small particles are characterized by narrow lorentzian lines but some exceptions are found. Superparamagnetism seems to play a minor role.

The Curie temperatures equal the bulk value for completely reduced samples. In very small particles (down to 25 Å) this fact must be explained by an increase of the exchange integral and surface relaxation with decreasing particle diameter. Curie temperature decreases linearly with average coordination number after O_2-chemisorption or incomplete reduction.

ACKNOWLEDGMENTS

We wish to thank Haldor TOPSOE A/S (Lyngby, Denmark) for having supplied the Ni on $MgAl_2O_4$ and Ni on alumina catalysts. Thanks are also due to J.C. VEDRINE, G.A. MARTIN (CNRS, Villeurbanne) and P.A. JACOBS (K.U.L., Leuven) for partial characterization of the Ni on silica and Ni on zeolite catalysts.

REFERENCES

1 E.G. Derouane, A. Simoens, C. Colin, G.A. Martin, J.A. Dalmon and J.C. Védrine, J. Catal., 52 (1978) 50-58
2 E.G. Derouane, A. Simoens, J.C. Védrine, Chem. Phys. Lett., 52(1977)549-553.
3 P.A. Jacobs, H. Nijs, J. Verdonck, E.G. Derouane, J.-P. Gilson and A. Simoens, J. Chem. Soc., Faraday Trans. I, 75 (1979) 1196-1206
4 S. Bhagat and Rothstein, J. de Physique, 32(1971)777.
5 E. Schlömann, J. Phys. Chem. Solids, 6(1958)257.

6 Yu. Kotgukov and V. Abrosov, Sov. Phys. J., 15(1972)1.
7 S.V. Vonsovskii, Magnetism, J. Wiley, Chichester, 1974,pp.483-85 and 519.
8 L. Néel, Ann. Géophys., 5(1949)99-136.
9 J. Livingston and C. Bean, J. Appl. Phys., 30(1959)3185.
10 G. Dalmaï-Imelik and J.C. Bertolini, Compt. Rend. Acad. Sci.(Paris), 270C(1970)1079.
11 G. Dalmaï-Imelik, C. Leclerq and A. Maubert-Muguet, J. Solid State Chem., 16(1976)129.
12 J.L. Carter and J.H. Sinfelt, J. Phys. Chem., 70(1966)3003 ; J. Catal. 10(1968)134.
13 P.A. Jacobs, M. Tielen, J.P. Linart and J.B. Uytterhoeven, J.C.S. Faraday I, 72(1976)
   2793 ; J. Verdonck, P.A. Jacobs and J.B. Uytterhoeven, unpublished results.
14 S. Bagdonat, Ph.-D. Thesis (1973) ; M.M.P. Janssen, J. Appl. Phys., 41(1970)385.

J. BOURDON (Editor)
Growth and Properties of Metal Clusters, pp. 209—215
© 1980 Elsevier Scientific Publishing Company — Printed in The Netherlands

The Growth of Granular Tin and its Characterization by Mössbauer Effect

M. Pasternak
Department of Physics and Astronomy
Tel Aviv University, Ramat Aviv ISRAEL

Abstract

The atomic mean-square displacement (MSD) of granular tin was studied by the Mössbauer effect. Tin grains with a 45-$\mathring{A}$ average size embedded in an oxide matrix were produced by evaporating the metal in the presence of O_2. The lattice parameters and grain-size distribution were measured by electron microscopy. From the temperature variation of the MSD of the granular material, it was found that the $<\omega^{-2}>$ moment of the phonon spectrum increases by $(8\pm3)\%$ with respect to the bulk. These results, combined with data of the hyperfine constants and electron microscopy suggest a quasi-isolated grain whose frequency and electronic structure are barely altered and whose interaction with the surrounding oxide is negligible.

I. INTRODUCTION

During the last years we have been witness to significant scientific and technological efforts to produce and study microscopic granular material. Those efforts stem from the search towards physical phenomena at low dimensionalities and from obvious technological benefits for systems with large surface to volume ratio. Most of the interest was focused towards microscopic metal clusters with sizes less than $100\mathring{A}$ diameter, which are of course difficult to produce homogenously and furthermore to prevent coalescence at normal laboratory conditions. A frequently used technique is to use porous media in which grains are grown. Experiments by Novotny (ref. 1) with porous glass are typical. Although size distribution and structure of grains in the tens of Angstroms sizes can be measured by electron diffraction and microscopy, the nature of the surface atoms and the lattice dynamics of the grains can be studied only with methods that directly probe the atoms of the grain. This is important in order to reduce the "background" of the media holding the grains.

In this work we present the combined studies of [119]Sn Mössbauer Effect, electron micrography and electron diffraction performed in granular tins of $45\mathring{A}$ average size, embedded in tin oxide matrix.

II. EXPERIMENTAL PROCEDURES

1. Preparation of samples

The granular tin was prepared by condensing high-purity tin on an Al substrate at $85^{\circ}K$. Tin was evaporated at a rate of $30\mathring{A}/sec$ in an O_2 atmosphere at a pressure of 10^{-4} Torr. The presence of tin oxides inhibits the formation of large grains. In general, it was found that the above mentioned conditions were crucial for obtaining tin grains with diameters less than $70\mathring{A}$. Under these conditions the granular material remained stable with respect to coalescence even for a period as long as six months. When the substrate was held at ambient temperature, large grains of D̄=1000A were formed. With evaporation rate less than 20Å/sec, the metal was completely oxidized.

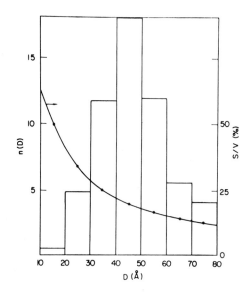

Fig. 1. Size-distribution histogram of a typical sample. The curve represents the surface-to-volume ratio dependence on grain size for Sn.

At each evaporation, three samples were *simultaneously* prepared: one for the ME measurements where the material was deposited over a large Al foil, the second for conductivity measurements and the third for electron microscopy measurements. The last two samples were rather thin films with 300-Å width and were formed under the same conditions as that for the ME measurements, by opening a special shutter for a short period of time during the evaporation. Altogether, three samples were used for each measurement.

2. Microstructure determination

Both the lattice parameters and the grain-size distribution were determined for the three samples. The lattice parameters were measured by recording several diffraction patterns with a JEM-7 electron microscope using a TlCl sample as a standard. The position of the lines were obtained by averaging over several patterns. It was found that the grains consist of β-Sn with lattice constants a = 5.82±0.01 Å and c = 2.16±0.01 Å which are the same within the experimental error as those for bulk Sn, as measured by Pearson (ref. 2) (a = 5.831 Å and c = 3.176 Å). The lines were substantially broadened which is characteristic of small micro-crystals. The broadening established the uncertainty in the lattice-constant parameters. No lines indicating the presence of crystalline SnO and SnO_2 could be found, suggesting that the oxides are in amorphous state. Recent diffraction measurements of granular Al (ref. 3) also have shown that the lattice spacing is not affected by the grain size down to 35-Å diameter.

The grain-size distribution was obtained by means of dark-field microscopy using a JEM 100B electron microscope. Taking a random portion of the sample, 140 grains were checked on the photographic plate. The results were plotted in histogram form. A typical histogram (sample No. 15) is shown in Fig. 1. Very similar histograms were obtained for the other two samples.

3. Mössbauer measurements

The Mössbauer spectra were recorded with a conventional spectrometer using a $BaSnO_3$ source. The absorbers containing 10 mg/cm^2 of material, were encapsulated in a lucite holder which was attached to an oven inside an evacuated chamber. Both the chamber and the source were immersed in liquid nitrogen. Measurements were performed at absorber temperatures above 78 °K.

III. DISCUSSION AND CONCLUSIONS

1. The nature of the grains and the oxide matrix

When metallic Sn is evaporated in an oxygen atmosphere under the conditions described above, the size of the grains of Sn formed is limited by the presence of oxygen and oxides formed simultaneously as the matrix for Sn grains. The tin oxides, namely SnO and SnO_2 will show themselves in the absorption spectrum. Whereas Sn and SnO_2 are characterized by single lines with different isomer shifts (i.s.), the SnO spectrum is composed of a doublet resulting from the quadrupole interaction at the [119]Sn nucleus. Typical spectra for various temperatures (sample No. 19) are shown in Fig. 2. The deduced parameters at 80 °K are given in Table I. The good quality of the fit suggests that no other oxidation states of Sn, apart from those mentioned, are present in the samples. *It is interesting to note that despite the extremely small dimensions of the grains, with an average of 1300 atoms/grain, no significant differences are observed in the i.s. or the linewidth between the bulk and granular samples.* The lack of appreciable broadening suggests that the symmetry around the Sn atoms is not altered as a result of possible penetration of surface defects. One might have expected that boundary conditions would affect the electronic structure of the grains. However we do not observe any change in the isomer shift, which is proportional to the s-electron density at the nucleus; we conclude that the electronic structure is unaffected by the smallness of the grains.

Another interesting observation concerns the calculation of the average number of oxide layers separating the grains. We assume from ionic-radii data that on the average the width of a layer is 2 Å. From the ME spectrum and knowledge of absolute f for the oxides and Sn metal we calculate, for sample 19, $Sn/(SnO+SnO_2)=3/2$. Thus, for a 45-Å particle we find approximately six layers of oxides between grains.

2. Lattice dynamics of surface and bulk atoms

Information concerning the lattice dynamics of the granular tin is contained primarily in the recoil-free fraction f of the absorbing nucleus. In principle, it is possible to obtain the absolute value of f by measuring the area under the absorption peak. From the relation

$$f=e^{-k^2 <x^2>}$$

(1)

the absolute value of the mean-square displacement $<x^2>$ is then obtained. However, in our

212

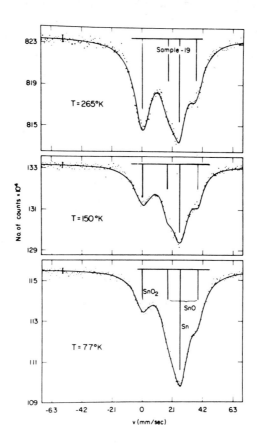

Fig. 2. Mössbauer absorption spectra of granular Sn (sample 19) at three different temperatures. The computer-fitted positions and relative intensities of the sample's constituents Sn, SnO, and SnO_2 are marked with vertical lines. The solid line through the experimental points is the least-squares-fitted spectrum.

TABLE 1

The isomer shift (i.s.),quadrupole splitting (q.s.) and linewidth (Γ)(in mm/sec) of the several constituents of sample 19 as well as of bulk Sn, at 80°K. The i.s. is with respect to a $BaSnO_3$ source at 80°K.

	Sn	SnO_2	SnO	Sn(bulk)
i.s.	2.69±0.03	0.025±0.02	2.82±0.03	2.59±0.01
q.s.	...	...	2.07±0.05	...
Γ	0.72±0.04	0.68±0.04	0.53±0.04	0.70±0.01

case, since the number of absorbing nuclei of each constituent is not known, this kind of information is unattainable. Nevertheless, one can measure the temperature dependence of the mean-square amplitude and within the high-temperature limit of the harmonic approximation one obtains from the slope of $<x^2(T)>$ the $<\omega^{-2}>$ moment of the phonon spectrum.

In the high-temperature region where $kT > \frac{1}{2}\hbar\omega_{max}$ one can expand the expression for $<x^2>$ in a series (Thirring expansion) where, to a good approximation, it will be linear with T, e.g.,

$$<x^2> = -2RkT<(\hbar\omega)^{-2}> \qquad (2)$$

or, in the Debye model,

$$<x^2> = -6RT/k\Theta^2, \qquad (3)$$

where R is the recoil energy of the absorbing γ ray and Θ is the Debye temperature. In fact, evidence for harmonic behavior of the grain will be the linear dependence of the effect on T on a logarithmic scale. In Fig. 3 we depict the temperature dependence of the area under the Sn absorption line. Within the error of measurements it is indeed linear. In Table II we give the average results of $<\omega^{-2}>$ and of Θ for the granular samples and for

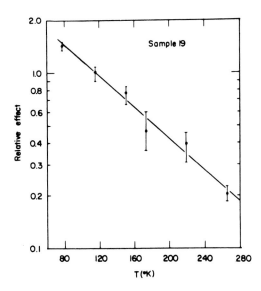

Fig. 3. Temperature dependence of the absorption peak of granular Sn. The straight line is a least-squares fit to the experimental points.

bulk tin. These results were obtained by a least-squares fit of the linear curve. Our results for bulk tin agree very well with those obtained by Hohenemser(ref.4). One immediately sees that there is an increase in $<\omega^{-2}>$ with respect to the bulk, which is beyond the experimental error, and is the same in all three samples. This result shows that there is indeed a change in the phonon spectrum as detected by this high-temperature probe.

We consider the possibility of change in Θ due to contraction or expansion of the grain's lattice. Within the uncertainty of our electron-diffraction measurements one can expect a deviation of 0.01 Å in the values of a and c. Making use of the Grüneisen relation, namely, $\Delta\Theta/\Theta = -\gamma\Delta V/V$, where γ is the Grüneisen constant, taken as 2 for Sn, and V is the grain's

214

TABLE II

Values of $<\omega^{-2}>$ calculated from the slope of $<x^2(T)>$ using a least-squares-fit program. The values of the errors were obtained from the computer. The Debye temperature Θ (see text) is proportional to $(<\omega^{-2}>)^{-\frac{1}{2}}$.

Sample No.	$<\omega^{-2}>(10^{-27}\text{sec}^2)$	($^\circ$K)
15	9.5±0.3	129±2
18	9.5±0.3	130±2
19	9.3±0.4	131±2
bulk	8.8±0.1	135±1

volume, we find that the change in Θ is of the order of 1.5%. This is much smaller than our observed change in Θ.

Let us assume that all the increase in $<\omega^{-2}>$ with respect to the bulk is due to surface effects only. Using a simple model we can then estimate values of the mean-square displacement at the surface. We assume each layer is characterized by its own $<x^2>$ and to simplify it even more we assume that the major influence due to the boundary conditions affects only the first layer of the grain whereas the inner atoms behave as in the bulk. Consequently the measured f_G for the grains can be considered the result of a weighted average of f_B of the inner-bulk atoms and of f_S of the surface atoms, as follows:

$$f_G = af_B + (1 - a)f_S, \tag{4}$$

where a is the fractional number of atoms inside the grain. The value of a can be estimated with the aid of the histogram as shown in Fig. 1. The surface to volume ratio $S/V(D)$ is calculated for each grain diameter D and the average value is found according to

$$<S/V>= \sum n(D)S/V(D), \tag{5}$$

where $n(D)$, the normalized size distribution values are taken from the histogram. We find for all three of our samples that $<S/V>=0.2$ or that 20% of the atoms are at the surface. From expressions (1) and (2) we calculate the values of f_G and f_B by using the values of $<\omega^{-2}>$ from Table II. By inserting them in expression (4) we can obtain the value of f_S and from it the "surface Debye temperature" Θ_S. These values were calculated for various temperatures; for 100 $^\circ$K, Θ_S = 114 $^\circ$K and for 200 $^\circ$K, Θ_S = 117 $^\circ$K. This result represents an increase on $<\omega^{-2}>$ of 37%, or $<x^2>_S/<x^2>_B = 1.4$. It should be emphasized that these calculations are based on the assumption of a perfect "bulk behavior" for layers beyond the first one. In reality, one might take into account the influence of the boundary effect in the second and probably the third layer. Unfortunately, there are no available calculations of mean-square displacements for grains. Nevertheless, it is interesting to compare our results with those obtained by Chen et al. (ref. 5) whose calculations were performed for a semi-infinite slab of NaCl, using a quasiharmonic approximation on 15 layers. The values of $<x^2>_S/<x^2>_B$ at 100 and 200 $^\circ$K were found to be 1.30 and 1.33, respectively, agreeing remarkably well with our results. One should bear in mind that for a grain, the surface-to-volume ratio is higher than in a thin slab, resulting in a further enhancement in the ratio of $<x^2>$. Another interesting calculation in Ref. 2 provides the values of the ratio of the second and third layer to bulk. At 300 $^\circ$K they are found to be 1.1 and

1.03, respectively. These results confirm our assumption that beyond the first layer the surface effects decrease rapidly.

The substantial increase of the $\langle x^2 \rangle_S$ as obtained from our experimental results suggests that the bonding of the grain to its surrounding matrix (trapped O_2 and oxides) is fairly weak. This conclusion, combined with the previously discussed findings of the isomer shift and electron diffraction, is consistent with a picture of an isolated grain that, apart from its first layer, is barely different from bulk material in its interatomic distances, lattice symmetry, electron structure, and vibrational frequencies.

REFERENCES

1 V. Novotny, P. P. Meincke, and J. H. P. Watson, Phys. Rev. Lett. 28, 901 (1972).
2 W. P. Pearson, *A Handbook of Lattice Spacings and Structures of Metals and Alloys* (Pergamon, Oxford, 1964/67).
3 G. Deutscher, H. Fenichel, M. Gershenson, E. Grünbaum, and Z. Ovadyahu, J. Low Temp. Phys. 10, 231 (1973).
4 C. Hohenemser, Phys. Rev. A 139, 185 (1965).
5 T. S. Chen, G. P. Alldredge, F. W. de Wette and R. E. Allen, Phys. Rev. B 6, 623 (1972).

J. BOURDON (Editor)
Growth and Properties of Metal Clusters, pp. 217—223
© 1980 Elsevier Scientific Publishing Company — Printed in The Netherlands

Optical Absorption of Matrix Isolated Li, Na, Si and Ge Clusters and Microcrystals

T. Welker, H. Schaber and T.P. Martin

Max-Planck-Institut für Festkörperforschung

Stuttgart, Fed. Rep. Germany

INTRODUCTION

Recently, there has been some progress made in stabilizing and identi-
fying metallic [1-6] and ionic [7] clusters isolated in solid rare gas
matrices. In particular, Schulze et al [2] have made a very careful study
of the Ag:Xe system and have identified aggregates containing up to 4 atoms.
Ozin and Huber [3] have extended this work by using an interesting photolytic method for aggregating isolated atoms in the matrix.

In the present paper the optical absorption spectra of matrix isolated
Li, Na, Si and Ge clusters and microcrystals are presented. A more complete
presentation will be published in refs. [4] and [8]. The alkali metals are
particularly suited to such a study because they have well defined surface
plasmon excitations in the crystalline state. This is important since, as
we shall see, the appearance of the surface plasmon absorption can be used
as a criterion to distinguish between molecules and microcrystals. In addition, the simple electronic structure of the alkali metals makes them amenable to relatively simple molecular orbital calculations.

A knowledge of the structure and electronic configurations of silicon
and germanium clusters should help us to better understand not only the
differences in the chemistry of carbon and silicon, but also the structure
of amorphous silicon and germanium. Si_2 has been the subject of several
earlier investigations [9-12]. These investigations were made difficult by
the low abundance of polyatomic species in silicon vapor.

METALS

A high temperature metal vapor is mixed with a rare gas and this mixture
is frozen onto a helium temperature, transparent substrate. The rare gas
matrix keeps the metal atoms separated without strongly interacting with
them. Metal clusters form when a relatively high concentration of metal vapor is mixed with the rare gas. This promotes cluster formation by surface

diffusion during growth of the matrix.

Figure 1 shows the absorption spectra of Li and Na in various states of aggregation. At the oven temperatures used in these experiments, the metal vapor consisted almost exclusively of atoms. If this atomic vapor is mixed with large amounts of rare gas, i.e. a metal to gas ratio of 1:1000, the metal atoms remain isolated from one another after the mixture is frozen onto a cold substrate. Therefore, the strong absorption in the top spectra of both figures corresponds to an s to p transition in metal atoms [13 - 17]. As the metal to rare gas concentration is increased to 1 % or more, new lines appear in the absorption spectra. These lines are due to metal clusters.

For increasing concentrations near 5 % (20 % in the case of Li) the cluster lines suddenly disappear and a single broad absorption band appears. This band is due to surface plasmon absorption characteristic of metal microcrystals [18]. That is, we have witnessed the transition from absorption by one electron transitions to absorption by a collective excitation. Increasing the concentrations of metal furhter, the frequencies of the plasmon absorption shifts to lower frequencies resulting in a slow transition to the optical properties of bulk metal.

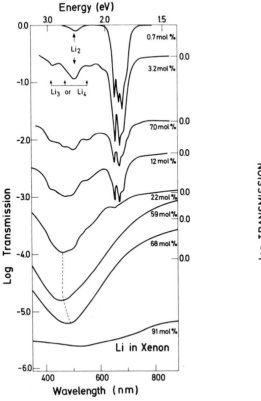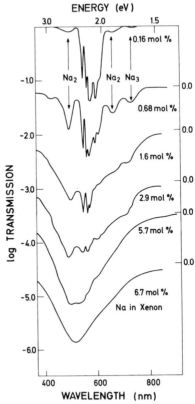

Fig. 1 Optical transmission of Li and Na in various stages of aggregation.

   In addition to the atomic absorption of Na between 550 and 600nm, at
least four new absorption lines appear when the Na concentration is raised
to 0.7%. In order to determine the concentration dependence of the intensity
of these lines, each line was fitted with a Gaussian and the integrated absorption, I, determined. The ratio of I to the total integrated absorption
strength I_{tot} is plotted in Fig. 2 for varying Na concentration. The relative
intensities of the monomer lines can be seen to decrease very slowly for concentrations below 1 %, while the relative intensities of the 495 and 658nm lines
rise linearly with slope equal to one on this double log plot.

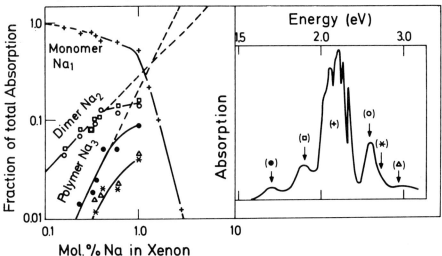

Fig. 2. Concentration dependence of the integrated optical absorption of
Na clusters in Xenon. The dotted lines have slope equal to one and two.

Since I_{tot} itself must depend linearly on concentration, this means that the
intensities of these two lines depend quadratically on the Na concentration.
Therefore, the 495 and 658nm lines must be assigned to dimer absorption. Similarly, the cubic concentration dependence of the 742nm line indicates absorption by trimer. The absorption line at 422 nm and the shoulder at 467nm
are observed in such a narrow range of concentrations that it is not possible
to assign them to a specific aggregate. This problem is somewhat simplified
through a study of the changes caused by irradiating the sample with mono-
chromatic light. If the frequency of the incident light corresponds to one
of the absorption lines of a cluster, this cluster is destroyed and all absorption lines belonging to this cluster diminish in intensity. This useful
effect, recently observed in Ag:Ar samples [5], is also present in matrix isolated alkali metal samples.

   Figure 3 shows the transmission spectra of a 0.7 mole % Na:Xe sample before and after it was irradiated for five minutes with about 1 mW of light
in the frequency interval indicated by the arrow. The dotted line shows the
absorption before irradiation, the solid line after irradiation. When the

220

frequency of the irradiating light corresponds to the long wavelength dimer line at
658 nm, both dimer lines decrease in intensity and monomer absorption increases, Fig.
3 (a). Therefore, the photolysis process
seems to be

$$Na_2 + h\omega = 2\ Na \qquad (1)$$

If the frequency of the irradiating light
is now switched on 480 nm, the intensity
of the trimer absorption at 742 also decreases. This seems to indicate that
there is also a weak trimer line near
480 nm. If now the sample is irradiated
in the monomer absorption region, the
monomer absorption decreases and the intensity of both dimer lines increases
Fig. 3 (d). These results can be explained by the two step process.

$$Na + h\omega = Na^* = Na + phonons$$
$$Na + Na = Na_2 \qquad (2)$$

that is, the light induces bulk diffusion
of the atoms, leading to the formation of
stable dimers. Finally,when these newly
formed dimers absorb light, the dissociate
back to atoms Fig. 3 (e)

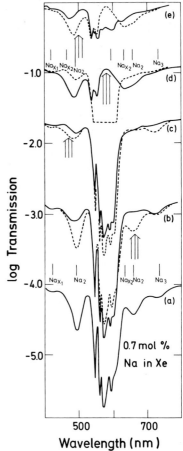

Fig.3. The optical trans-
mission of a sample composed of 0.7 mol % sodium in
xenon. The sample was suce-
sively irradiated by light
in the frequency range indicated by the arrows

SEMICONDUCTORS

   The vapor of silicon produced by electron beam evaporation is known to
contain from 1 to 2 % each of the species Si_2, Si_3 and Si_4 [19]. That is
even for low concentrations of Si in argon, absorption due to silicon cus-
ters should be observable. If the concentration is increased, the most important changes in the spectrum will be a decrease in the atomic silicon
absorption and a corresponding increase in the dimer absorption.

   In fact, these changes can be used to identify the Si and Si_2 absorption
lines. It is not possible to distinguish the Si_3 and Si_4 lines from one
another since their intensities are both expected to be only very weakly
dependent on concentration. The lines in the absorption spectrum shown

in Fig. 4 have been identified using these criteria. Notice that most of
the cluster lines have vibrational side bands. The vibrational structure of
the lower energy Si_2 absorption is particularly complicated.

The absorption due to germanium clusters was found to be much weaker
than that due to silicon clusters. This is not due to the fact that germanium vapor contains a smaller percentage of polyatomic species. A mass spectroscopic investigation has shown the vapors of germanium and silicon to be
quite similar [10]. Therefore, one must conclude that either the oscillator
strength for the dipole transitions in Ge is weak or, more likely, that
silicon has a greater tendency to form clusters in the argon matrix. Because of the weakness of the absorption lines in the Ge samples, the uncertainty in the concentration dependence of the relative intensities is even
greater than it is for Si. However, it does appear that the lines labelled
Ge_2 in Fig. 4 increase in relative intensity with increasing concentration
and the line labelled Ge has the reverse behaviour.

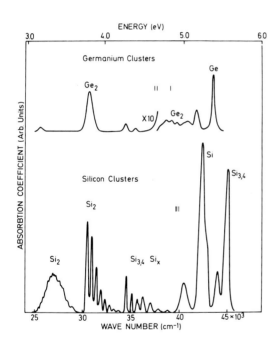

Fig. 4. Absorption coefficient
of Si and Ge atoms and clusters
isolated in a solid Ar Matrix

LCAO CALCULATION

The experimental results alone do not allow us to make a definite assignment of absorption lines to clusters of a given size and shape. Calculation
of the energy levels for various kinds of clusters should allow a more definite assignment. Our goals in making a calculation will be very modest. We
merely want to make plausible several trends which can be used in qualitative discussion of the experimental results. An appropriate simple calculational technique will be used, the Hückel method of molecular orbitals.

222

In using this semi-emperial LCAO procedure, we must assume an equilibrium configuration of atoms. This offers no problem of course for the dimer, but the trimer could be either linear or triangular. The tetramer could be either linear, square, rhombic or tetrahedral. Calculations were made for all of these configurations with the hope of eliminating some posibilities on rather general grounds.

The diagonal elements H_{ii} are approximated by the appropriate atomic ionization potential. The eight remaining parameters are fitted to the well known band structure of crystalline silicon. In fact, we have used the parameters of Pandry and Philips [21]. The calculation based on crystaline parameters correctly predicts that the ground state of the dimer is a triplet.

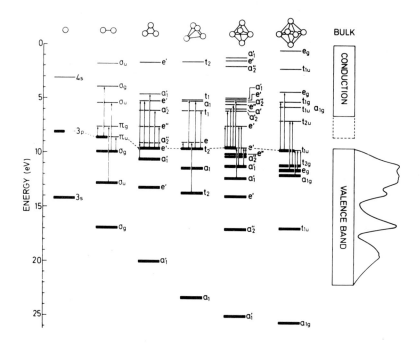

Fig. 5. Calculated electronic energy levels of Si clusters having the indicated sizes and shapes.

The trimer could be either an equilateral triangle with D_{3h} symmetry or a linear chain. Each atom in the triangle can form a bonding orbital with two neighbors. The end atoms of a chain can contribute at most one bonding orbital. Therefore, the lowest energy state of the triangel lies much lower than the corresponding state of the chain. In fact, one can make the generalization that as the average coordination number of a cluster increases, the energy levels of the cluster will span a larger interval.

As the number of atoms are increased in a linear chain the average coordination number increases from one to a maximum of only two. Therefore, more and more levels must be packed between two relatively constant energy limits. This results in a more or less continuous decrease of the dipole transition energies from the visible to the infrared. An important experiment result to keep in mind is that no cluster absorption lines were found at energies less than 3.0 eV. This places a severe contraint on the energy level schemes. In fact, it is possible to immediately eliminate the linear trimer and tetramer from further consideration since both are expected to have infrared absorption lines. On the other hand, in going from dimer to triangular trimer, to tetrahedral tetramer the coordination number goes from 1 to 2 to 3. The resulting large energy differences between bonding and antibonding levels and the high degree degeneracy in these symmetric clusters result in only a few high frequency absorption lines, in qualitative agreement with the experiment.

REFERENCES

1. M. Moskovits and J.E. Hulse, J. Chem. Phys. 67, 4271 (1977).
2. W. Schulze, H.U. Becker and H. Abe, Ber. Bunsenges, Phys. Chem. 82, 138 (1978).
3. C.A. Ozin and H. Huber, Inorg. Chemie 17, 155 (1978); 18, 1402 (1979).
4. T. Welker and T.P. Martin, J. Chem. Phys. 70, 5683 (1979).
5. M. Hofmann, S. Leutwyler and W. Schulze, Chem. Phys. 40, 145 (1979).
6. T. Welker, Ber. Bunsenges. Phys. Chem. 82, 40 (1978).
7. T.P. Martin, Phys. Rev. B 15, 4071 (1977); J. Chem. Phys. 69, 2036 (1978).
8. T.P. Martin and H. Schaber, Z. für Physik (in press).
9. A.E. Douglas, Can. J. Phys. 33, 801 (1955).
10. R.D. Verma, P.A. Warsop, Can. J. Phys. 41, 152 (1963).
11. W. Weltner, D. Mc Leod, J. Chem. Phys. 41, 235 (1964).
12. D.E. Milligan, M.E. Jacox, J. Chem. Phys. 52, 2594 (1970).
13. L. Brewer, B.A. King, J.L. Wang, B. Meyer and G.F. Moore, J. Chem. Phys. 49, 5209 (1968).
14. W. Schulze, D.M. Kolb and H. Gerischer, J. Chem. Soc. Faraday Trans. 2, 71, 1763 (1975).
15. L. Andrews and G.C. Pimentel, J. Chem. Phys. 47, 2905 (1967).
16. B. Meyer, J. Chem. Phys. 43, 2986 (1965).
17. D. Nagel and B. Sonntag, Paper 2.8, International Conference on Matrix Isolation Spectroscopy West Berlin (1977).
18. L. Genzel, T.P. Martin and U. Kreibig, Z. Physik B 21, 339 (1975).
19. H. Mell, M.H. Brodsky, Thin Solid Films 46. 299 (1977).
20. R.E. Honig, J. Chem. Phys. 21, 573 (1953).
21. K.C. Pandry, J.C. Phillips, Phys. Rev. B 13, 750 (1976).

J. BOURDON (Editor)
Growth and Properties of Metal Clusters, pp. 225—232
© 1980 Elsevier Scientific Publishing Company — Printed in The Netherlands

NEW TECHNIQUES FOR ELECTRON MICROSCOPY CHARACTERIZATION OF SMALL METAL
PARTICLES.

M. JOSE YACAMAN

INSTITUTO DE FISICA, UNAM, APARTADO POSTAL 20-364, MEXICO 20, D.F.

1. INTRODUCTION.

In modern catalysis science electron microscopy has been mainly used as an
auxiliary tool to obtain the size distributions of small metallic particles.
In most cases the imagining mode has been the standard brigth field ie;
images which are formed using the beam which do not suffer diffraction
neither in the particle or in the support. It has become increasedly appreciated in the recent years (ref. 1) that bright field images are extremely
limited and uninformative. On the other hand dark field techniques ie.
images which are formed using beams diffracted in either the particle or
the support, can yield a great deal of information about the shape and
cristallography of the particles (2-3). So far these techniques have been
applied only in a few cases of characterization of metal supported catalysts

In a previous work (ref. 4) we have demonstrated that a full characterization of the shape and crystallography for the case of platinum particles
supported on graphite can be obtained using dark field and micro-diffraction
techniques. In the present paper these studies are extended to the case of
Pt supported in γ -Al$_2$O$_3$ with the particles being in a very highly dispersed
state.

A new technique is described that allows the observation of small metal
clusters down to a diameter of 5 $\overset{\circ}{A}$.

2. THE TEM CONTRAST OF PARTICLES ON CRYSTALLINE SUBSTRATES

When a metal cluster supported on γ-Al$_2$O$_3$ is to be examined by electron microscopy several points have to be considered on understanding the contrast.
Firstly the support is, at least locally, single crystalline and since it is

226

thicker than the particles its orientation with respect to the electron beam
is quite important to determine the particle visibility. On the other hand
in supports of the type of γ -Al$_2$O$_3$ contrast due to porosity can mask the
particle visibility. A third problem is that in the diffraction pattern reflections of the γ -Al$_2$O$_3$ are close to reflections of the metal and when
forming a dark field image spots from the particle and from the support will
contribute to the contrast.

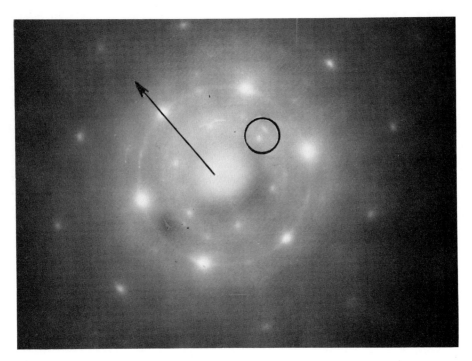

Figure 1. Diffraction pattern of a sample of Pt supported on γ -Al$_2$O$_3$.
           spots from Pt and Alumina are indicated.

These difficulties might be overcome by the following method. In figure 1
a typical diffraction pattern of Pt - γ Al$_2$O$_3$ is shown. Suppose that a dark
field image is made using the aperture located in the positions indicated
on the figure. Successive pictures can be obtained by keeping the aperture
on the same place but tilting the sample along an axis perpendicular to the
spots used to form the image as indicated in fig. 1. This operation will
produce images as the sequence shown in figure 2. The first image (Fig.2a))
corresponds to a standard bright field image which shows very little contrast from the particles. Fig. 2b) shows the corresponding dark field image

before tilting. Both the particles and the support are close to the Bragg condition and the image is dominated by the support (see next section). This picture on the other hand demonstrates that the observed γ -Al$_2$O$_3$ grain is single crystalline because it lightens up in the image and do not show dark areas. However in this image the particles are impossible to distinguish from the background. When a tilting of about 4° as been performed around the axis indicated in figure 1, the dark field image has the aspect shown in figure 2c). Now the background due to the support has entirely disappeared and the particles show up as bright spots without a well defined profile. The figure 2d) shows an image obtained at similar tilting conditions but at a much larger magnification. In this figure clusters of 5 Å diameter are clearly resolved. Confirmation that those spots correspond to metal cluster was provided by defocusing the image following the method proposed by Heinemann and Poppa (ref. 5). The spot corresponding to γ-Al$_2$O$_3$ was center-ed on the optical axis of the microscope and the spot corresponding to Pt was slightly out of the center. When defocussing the objective lens by about 1500 Å, the images corresponding to metal are displaced on the image and those corresponding to γ -Al$_2$O$_3$ remain undisplaced. In doing so the bright spots in fig. 2c) will be displaced and thus they should correspond to Pt clusters.

The figure 2d) shows for the first time the possibility of resolve extremely small clusters in a real catalyst using dark field methods. Those clusters will not be apparent on a standard bright field image.

3. THEORETICAL CONSIDERATIONS ON THE CONTRAST.

The findings of the previous section can be put on more firm theoretical ba-sis using the dynamical diffraction theory for bicrystals recently reported by Romeu et. al. (ref. 6). The diffraction situation which is set in this problem is schematically represented in figure 3.

The beams that contributed to the image are labeled (1) and (2) in the fi-gure 3. Beam (1) is that diffracted by the Pt particle and then transmitted by the support. The beam (2) on the other hand is that transmitted by the Pt and diffracted by the support. Beam (1) will give information mainly on

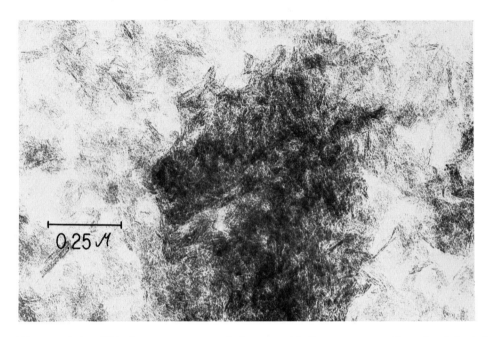

Figure 2a)   Tilting sequence of Pt - γ Al$_2$O$_3$ system.   Standard bright field
image.

the particles while beam (2) will give information mainly on the γ -Al$_2$O$_3$.
The best particle visibility will be obtained for a ratio of the intensities
of these two beams (I$_1$/I$_2$) considerable larger than one.   In figure
4 the ratio I$_1$/I$_2$ is plotted versus the tilting angle.   As can be seen near
the Bragg angle the ratio is <1 and the contrast is dominated by the substrate, corresponding to the case shown in fig. 2b).   However as the angle is
increased a dramatic change on the contrast is produced and the particles
are visible over the substrate as observed experimentally in figure 2c).

4.   ON THE PARTICLE SHAPE.
The profile of the particles appear not well defined.   When a tilting is
made thickness fringes are not observed on the particles even for very large

Figure 2b) Dark field image using the aperture in position indicated on
            the figure 1.

tilting angles. Recent calculations by Ocaña (8) shown that in those conditions an extinction distance of 10 Å is achieved. Since no fringes are
observed in the particles the only consistent explanation is that they are
very flat with a change of thickness less than 10 Å. Moreover, extra information can be obtained from the plots in figure 4. When the particle is
50 Å thick the contrast oscillates very strongly with the tilting angle.
The same situation is observed for a particle 20 Å **thick**. However for a
particle of 10 Å thick the contrast do not oscillate but always increases.
The thinner the particle, the less pronounced the change in the contrast.
In the experimental images we observed that particle contrast increases with
tilting but oscillations are not observed. That means that the thickness
of the particle should be of the order 10 Å or less. It is worth to

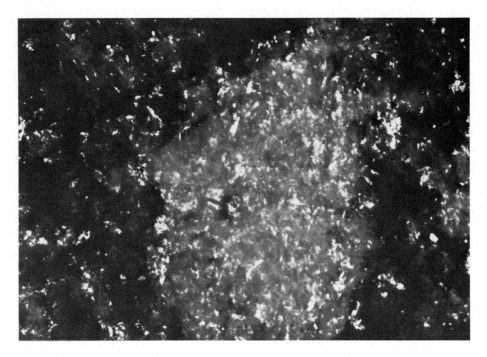

Figure 2c) Weak beam dark field image formed after tilting the sample.   The
            particles are now apparent.

mention that in the case of Pt on graphite (9) in which particles are thicker we have observed the oscillation effects predicted by figure 4.

All those findings suggest that the particles have the shape described by
Prestridge and Yates (ref. 10) as "rafts".Our experiments confirm the shape
proposed by those authors. Although it should be pointed out that our findings show particles more than one atom thick (with about 3 mono-layers) and
in that sense we use the word raft.

5.   CONCLUSIONS.

We have shown that weak beam dark field images can yield valuable information about the particle shape.

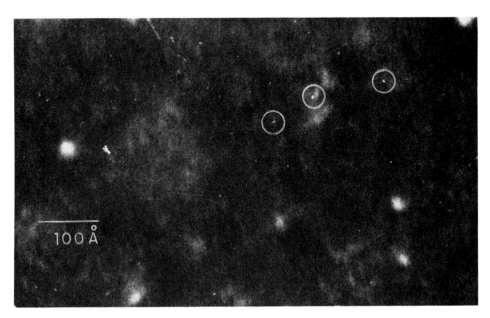

Figure 2d) Magnified portion of the figure 2c).   Encircled are par-
           ticles with a size of 5 Å.

We have described a technique that allows clusters down to 5 Å in diameter

to be observed. This technique should be very valuable in obtaining size

distributions that can be correlated with chemisorption data. By combining

this technique with thickness fringes and dynamical theory of diffraction

calculations we shown that the particle shape correspond to that described

as "rafts" in (ref. 10-11) but being about 3 layers thick. A detailled

discussion will be presented in a forthcoming publication.

The method described requires the use of a high resolution goniometer stage

and low contamination rate to allow a complete tilting sequence to be made.

The stability of the microscope to produce long exposure pictures is an

additional requirement.

232

FIGURE 3. Schematic representation of the beams used to form images of particles.

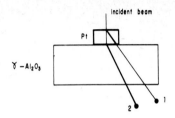

① = Diffracted (Pt) + Transmited (γ−Al₂O₃)
② = Transmited (Pt) + Diffracted (γ−Al₂O₃)

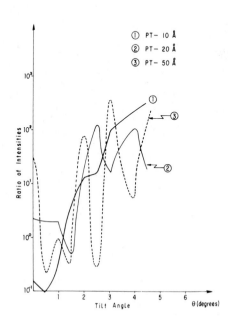

FIGURE 4. Many dynamical diffraction calculation of the intesities of the beams (1) (I_1) and (2) (I_2) as defined in figure 3. The thickness of the substrate is 500 Å in all cases. The thickness of the Pt particles is 10, 20 and 50 Å respectively.

REFERENCES

1. J.R. Anderson. The Structure of metal catalyst. Academic Press. New York (1975).
2. M. José Yacamán and T. Ocaña. Phys. Stat. Sol. a) 47, 571 (1977).
3. K. Heinemann, M. José Yacamán and H. Poppa. Phys. Stat. Sol. a)in press
4. M José Yacamán and J.M. Domínguez. Surface Science in press.
5. K. Heinemann and H. Poppa. Appl. Phys. Letters 20 (1972) 127.
6. D. Romeu, A. Gómez and M. José Yacamán. To be published.
7. G. Radi. Acta Cryst. A 26 (1970) 41.
8. T. Ocaña Z. Ph. D. Thesis. University of Mexico (UNAM) (1979).
9. M. José Yacamán and A. Gómez. To be published.
10. E.B. Prestridge and D.J.C. Yates. Nature (London) 234 (1971) 345.
11. D.J. Yates, L.L. Murrell and E.B. Prestidge. J. Of Catal. 57 (1979) 41.

J. BOURDON (Editor)
Growth and Properties of Metal Clusters, pp. 233—239
© 1980 Elsevier Scientific Publishing Company — Printed in The Netherlands

ASPECTS STRUCTURAUX DES COMPOSITES METAL-CARBONE CATALYTIQUE

M. AUDIER, M. COULON
Laboratoire d'Adsorption et Réaction de Gaz sur Solides - E.R.A. C.N.R.S.
n° 368 - Ecole Nationale Supérieure d'Electrochimie et d'Electrométallurgie
de Grenoble - BP 44 - Domaine Universitaire - 38401 - Saint Martin d'Hères -
France.

A. OBERLIN
Laboratoire Marcel Mathieu - E.R. n° 131 - Faculté des Sciences - 45045 -
Orléans La Source - France.

ABSTRACT

Metal-carbon composites have been produced by CO disproportionation on two
iron-cobalt alloys (Fe 49 %, Co 49 %, V 2 % and Fe 25 % Co 25 %). Between
400°C and 650°C, the carbon deposit induces an important fragmentation of the
metal-catalyst which is found after reaction under the form of cork-shaped
crystallites at one end of carbon filaments. By C.T.E.M. observations and
S.A.D. patterns performed on a goniometric stage we have been able to show
that for both alloy compositions, every crystallite presents a [100] axis
colinear with the filament axis. Thus the metal particles have their carbon
free surfaces exclusively composed of a (100) surface and are attached to
the carbon filament along high Miller index planes. CO disproportionation,
or any hydrocarbons decomposition which yields the some kind of products, is
an interesting way to obtain carbon-supported, crystallographically oriented,
metal or alloys catalysts.

INTRODUCTION

Il existe maintenant une littérature relativement importante concernant
les carbones filamentaires que l'on peut obtenir par dismutation de monoxyde
de carbone ou décomposition d'hydrocarbures au contact des métaux et alliages de la famille du fer. Une mise au point récente (ref. 1) présente un bi-
lan assez complet des connaissances actuelles et montre bien que l'on est
encore assez loin de la compréhension des phénomènes.

Il est frappant de constater que des morphologies de produits très voisines s'observent avec des carbones obtenus par réaction de gaz très divers
tels que le monoxyde de carbone, les alcanes, les alcènes, le benzène,
l'acétone et sur des métaux de natures très diverses, métaux purs ou alliages et sous des formes également très diverses telles que poudres, fils,

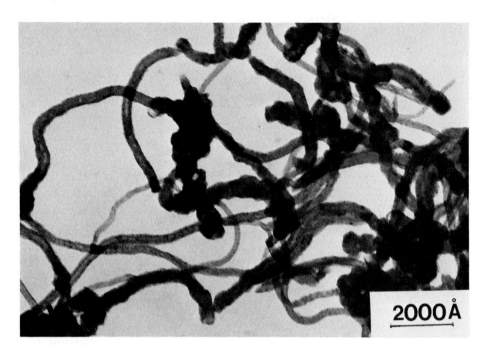

Fig. 1. Produit obtenu sur Fe49 Co49 V2

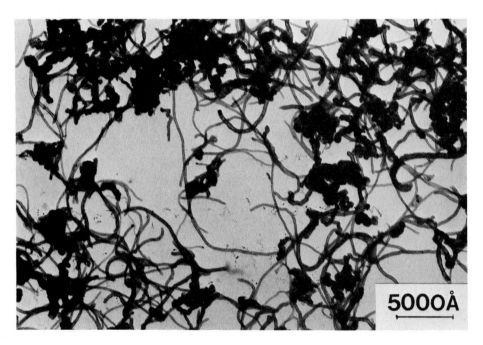

Fig. 2. Produit obtenu sur Fe25 Co 75.

235

feuilles ou plaques. Notamment la morphologie la plus courante est le carbone filamentaire qui est constitué par des tubes de carbone présentant à une de leur extrémité un cristallite métallique en forme de tronc de cône (Fig. 3). Ces cristallites métalliques, qui sont arrachés au catalyseur métallique par le phénomène de fragmentation ont des diamètres variant suivant la nature du métal et les conditions de dépôt de 50 à 1000 Å.

Comme les réactions de dépôt pourraient constituer un moyen de dispersion de métaux et d'alliages sur support de carbone, il nous a paru intéressant d'étudier des produits filamentaires obtenus par dismutation de monoxyde de carbone sur deux compositions d'alliages fer-cobalt. Le but de cette étude est de répondre aux deux questions suivantes :

- les tubules ont-ils la même composition et la même structure que l'alliage de départ ?

- compte-tenu de leur forme régulière, les cristallites présentent-ils une orientation cristallographique défini par rapport à l'axe des tubules ?

ELABORATION ET MORPHOLOGIE.

Les produits ont été fabriqués à 600°C par dismutation de monoxyde de carbone en faisant réagir un mélange contenant 75 % CO, 25 % CO_2 sur un lit traversé contenant le catalyseur métallique. Nous avons utilisé des limailles tamisées (taille des particules d'environ 100 μ) obtenues par meulage de deux lingôts d'alliages fer-cobalt, le Fe49 Co 49 V2 et le Fe25 Co75 (les

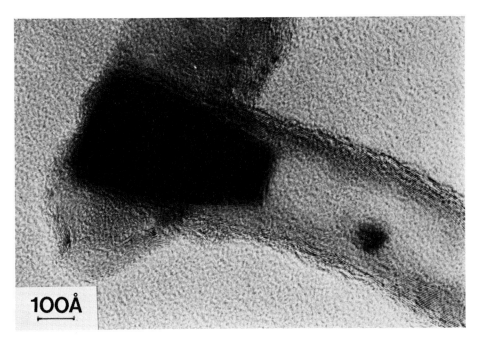

Fig. 3. Visualisation des couches aromatiques 00.2 au voisinage d'un cristallite métallique.

chiffres expriment les pourcentages pondéraux). La réaction de dépôt est interrompue lorsque le pourcentage de carbone dans le dépôt atteint 80 % en poids.

Les clichés de diffraction X montrent que le métal de structure cubique centrée dans les produits n'a pas subi de changement de structure et en particulier qu'aucun carbure n'est décelable.

Les produits observés en microscopie électronique en transmission, sont constitués exclusivement de carbone filamentaire (Figs. 1 et 2).

TEXTURE DU CARBONE FILAMENTAIRE.

La texture du carbone est déterminée par microscopie haute résolution avec visualisation des couches aromatiques 00.2. On observe que les filaments sont constitués de couches aromatiques disposées parallèlement à la surface du cône métallique et enroulées concentriquement à l'axe du tube (Fig. 3).

ORIENTATION CRISTALLOGRAPHIQUE DU CRISTALLITE METALLIQUE PAR RAPPORT A L'AXE DU TUBE DE CARBONE.

Cette orientation est déterminée en utilisant la platine porte-objet goniométrique à axe d'inclinaison fixe d'un microscope électronique à transmission (Philips EM 300). L'axe du tube est amené, par rotation et réglage en hauteur, confondu à l'axe d'inclinaison goniométrique (Fig. 4). On sélectionne ensuite à l'aide d'un petit diaphragme placé dans le plan image de la lentille objectif le cristallite et son tube de carbone à étudier en microdiffraction électronique (Fig. 5).

Le diagramme de microdiffraction comprend le diagramme de taches de la particule métallique superposé au diagramme du tube de carbone. Du fait de sa texture, ce dernier présente en particulier deux arcs 00.2 qui permettent de repérer avec une précision suffisante l'axe du tube sur le cliché de microdiffraction (Fig. 6). L'indexation des taches de diffraction du métal montre que le cristallite présente un axe <100> dans l'axe du tube. A titre de vérification on effectue une série de microdiffractions avec inclinaisons goniométriques différentes qui montre que les taches <100> dans l'axe du tube restent fixes alors que les autres taches apparaissent ou disparaissent (Fig. 7).

Ce travail a été fait, respectivement, sur cinq particules pour les deux alliages étudiés et a conduit systématiquement au même résultat. On peut donc raisonnablement affirmer que les faces planes des troncs de cônes métalliques, qui ne sont pas masquées par le carbone, sont des faces (100). La surface latérale des troncs de cônes sur laquelle est greffé le tube de carbone, qui n'apparaît jamais polyédrique, est constituée par une enveloppe de plans vicinaux de hauts indices de Miller.

CONCLUSION.

La dismutation de monoxyde de carbone au contact d'alliages fer-cobalt de structure cubique centrée permet d'obtenir des catalyseurs alliages - disper-

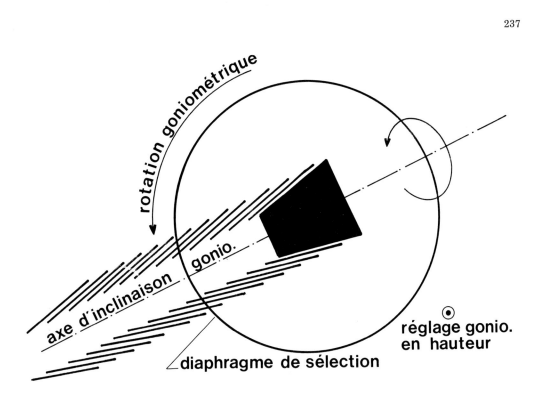

Fig. 4. Schéma des réglages goniométriques et du diaphragme de sélection sur
un cristallite en bout de tubule.

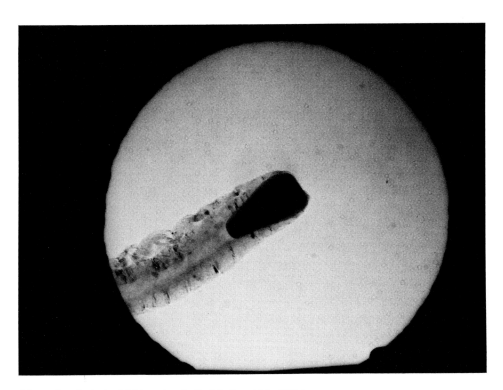

Fig. 5. Cristallite de FeCo75 (x 130 000)
diamètre du diaphragme de sélection : 15 μm
aire de la région sélectionnée : 0.25 μm^2

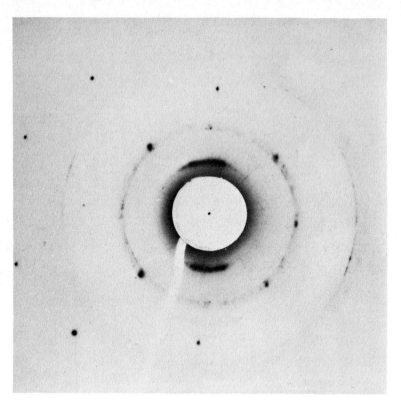

Fig. 6. Diagramme de microdiffraction électronique d'un cristallite de FeCo50 (structure C.C.) en bout de tubule. L'axe du tube de carbone est à π/2 des arcs de diffraction 00.2.

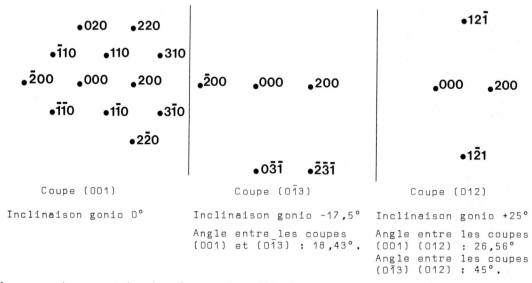

Il y a un bon accord entre les angles d'inclinaison gonio et ceux calculés à partir des coupes. Le cristallite possède un axe [100] dans l'axe du tube.

Fig. 7. Diagrammes de microdiffraction pour différentes inclinaisons goniométriques.

sés sur support de carbone - dont les particules métalliques présentent un seul type de face cristallographique. L'application qui est actuellement développée dans notre laboratoire est la catalyse d'hydrocondensation de CO. Ces produits permettent en effet d'entreprendre commodément des études d'effets de synergie des alliages contenant du fer, du nickel ou du cobalt, des études de l'influence de la taille des particules et de l'état de graphitation du support que l'on sait modifier en jouant sur les conditions de fabrication (ref. 2).

REFERENCES.
1 R.T.K. Baker, P.S. Harris, Chemistry and Physics of carbon Vol. 14 (1978)83
2 M. Audier, J. Guinot, M. Coulon, L. Bonnetain, A. Oberlin, Proceedings of
   the 14th Biennal Conference on Carbon Penn State University (1979) 119.

J. BOURDON (Editor)
Growth and Properties of Metal Clusters, pp. 241—254
© 1980 Elsevier Scientific Publishing Company — Printed in The Netherlands

ELECTRONIC AND CHEMISORPTIVE PROPERTIES OF CLUSTERS OF TRANSITION METALS

F. CYROT-LACKMANN, Groupe des Transitions de Phases, C.N.R.S., B.P. 166, 38042 Grenoble
           Cedex, France.

Catalytic properties of transition metals are related to chemisorptive ones. The aim of
this paper is to show the link between electronic structure of the surface and chemisorption.
In a first part, we show that the electronic properties of surfaces of transition metals
strongly depend on roughness and on the size and structure of the cluster. Striking modifications occur in the top of the band and resonant states are obtained in the local density
of states.

In a second part, we describe the influence on chemisorption of the local density of states on the active site. Examples are given : the large anisotropy of binding energy of transition adatoms on molybdenum and tungsten related to the appearance of resonant surface states ; the magnetic properties of nickel clusters and binding energies with hydrogen and oxygen.

1. INTRODUCTION

Catalytic properties of transition metals are related to their chemisorptive properties.
Indeed, it is well established that the catalytic fonction of surfaces is to reduce the activation energy of a reaction by temporarily forming chemical bonds with the adsorbing molecules (ref. 1). For instance, let us compare the bond energy Q_{AB} between two atoms A and B in
the molecule AB to the energy of the same bond when the molecule is chemically adsorbed on
the catalyst K. If the bond energy between the atom A and the catalyst K is denot Q_{AK}, to
break the bond AB into atoms adsorbed on K, one will need the energy

$$Q_{AB}^{K} = Q_{AB} - Q_{AK} - Q_{BK}$$

Thus the bond will be weakened on the catalyst if $Q_{AB} > Q_{AK} + Q_{BK}$. If $Q_{AB} < Q_{AK} + Q_{BK}$, the
A-B bond will be broken during adsorption. In principle, this scheme permits to calculate
the activation energy of a reaction through the energies Q_{AK} which will depend of course on
the other species adsorbed near A during the reaction. A zero order theory of the catalytic
reaction will be to replace these quantities by the bond Q_{AK}° of one atom A on the catalyst
without any other species on its surface. The energetics of heterogeneous catalysis is thus
simplified to the energetics of chemisorption.

In the process of chemisorption, when an adsorbate approaches the surface substrate, there is a broadening of its atomic levels due to the hydridization with the substrate electronic levels. Schematically, there are two limiting cases :

- for a weak adsorbate-metal interaction, the adsorbate keeps its atomic character and
its atomic level is slightly broadened forming a virtual bound state,

- for a strong adsorbate-metal interaction, the system adsorbate plus its neighbouring
surface atoms of the substrate behaves like a surface molecule coupled to the substrate. The
atomic level of the adsorbate will thus form two broadened states, a bonding and an antibonding one.

One expects that these two regimes will give different energetics of chimisorption, the second case leading to larger binding energies. But the strength of the interaction between the adsorbate and the substrate will not only depend on a direct overlap between the adsorbate and the lattice sites of the substrate directly connected but also on the band structure of the substrate due to an indirect interaction through the rest of the substrate. One has to take into account this second effect which is an essential one, and which explains the great variety of experimental results in chemisorption related in particular to the influence of the roughness of the substrate.

The ability of the surface to break some of the strong chemical bonds of the reactant molecules, such as H-H, C-H,..) depends on the surface considered for a particular catalyst. For example, it has been recently shown that there exist various active sites where chemical bond scission is easier (ref. 2). The structure and the chemical composition of the working catalyst is now investigated on the atomic scale, and kinks, steps, terraces,.. have been shown to have a different catalytic activity in many reactions. This shows that a Pauling type calculation of the bond energies is not sufficient. Indeed, the energy depends strongly on the electronic structure of the site on which the adatom sits.

To answer the main questions arising on catalysis concerning the specificity of a metal, its selectivity and its structure sensibility as a catalyst, we are led to first consider the local electronic structure of its surface and then its influence on the strength of the bond with the adsorbate.

2. ELECTRONIC STRUCTURE OF TRANSITION METAL CLUSTERS

Through the study of the electronic properties of transition metal clusters of various size and geometry, some questions of fundamental importance for the comprehension of chemisorption emerge. We are particularly interested in the following concepts :

- at what size does a cluster of metal atoms behave as a bulk metal ?

- what are the relations between the electronic properties of a possible active site for adsorption of a metal cluster and its geometry ?

- are we able to predict the stability of clusters when their size and atomic structures vary ?

2.1 Calculational procedure

The electronic structure of a transition metal is well described by a narrow d band with a high density of states within a broad sp band. Many of the peculiar properties of transition metals have been shown to be related to the d character of their valence states. One can thus reasonably neglect the sd hybridization, as a first approximation, when describing the electronic properties of surface and cluster transition metals. The small overlap between the d atomic orbitals leads naturally to study the d band in the tight binding approximation or LCAO where the wave functions $\psi_n(E)$ are developed in the atomic orbitals basis $\psi^\lambda(r-R_i)$, i.e. $\psi_n(E) = \sum_{\lambda,i} a_{i\lambda}(E_n) \psi^\lambda(r-R_i) = \sum_{\lambda,i} a_{i\lambda}(E_n) \psi^\lambda_i$ where λ indicates orbital degeneracy and R_i the lattice sites. It involves matrix elements between atomic orbitals and the lattice potential. They are thus of the type $\langle \psi^\lambda_i | V_1 | \psi^\mu_j \rangle$, either computed directly or obtained from interpolation schemes on band structure calculations. The usual approximation is to keep only the nearest neighbouring two center integrals.

As any molecular orbital theory, this approach is approximate and, therefore, its application is limited to a semiquantitative explanation of phenomena. But the use of physical concepts permits an useful insight understanding of several electronic properties (ref. 3).

This tight binding approach can be solved without difficulty for a bulk solid using the Bloch theorem, but for a cleaved crystal or a cluster the direct calculation of the eigenstates is practically impossible. One uses thus a moment's method with a continued fraction expansion so as to calculate directly the electronic density of states (D.S.) without having to know the eigenstates. This method is described in previous articles (refs. 4,5) and let us just recall briefly some of the main points.

The moment μ_p of order p of the D.S. n(E) writes :

$$\mu_p = \int_{-\infty}^{\infty} n(E) \, E^p \, dE = \text{Tr } H^p$$

as $n(E) = \sum_n \delta \, (E-E_n) = \text{Tr } \delta \, (E-H)$

where E_n are the eigenvalues of the hamiltonian H. Thus, if we expand the trace on the basis of the atomic orbitals, $\mu_p = \langle \psi_i^\lambda | H | \psi_j^\mu \rangle \text{---} \langle \psi_e^\mu | H | \psi_i^\lambda \rangle$. The calculation of moments involves then products of two center overlap integrals usually done by simulating the lattice on a computer. This leads to the knowledge of a finite number of moments ($\simeq$ 20-30) from which one has to reconstruct the best D.S. For that, one uses an expansion of the Hilbert transform G(z) of the D.S. (or Green's function) in a continued fraction, i.e.

$$G(z) = \int_{-\infty}^{\infty} \frac{n(E)}{z-E} \, dE = \cfrac{1}{z-a_1-\cfrac{b_1}{z-a_2-\cfrac{b_2}{\ddots}}}$$

with a_n, $b_n = f(\mu_0, \mu_1, \ldots \mu_{2n})$

The continued fraction coefficients are converging well to their asymptotic values, so that one can get the essential features of the D.S. (width, band limits, shape..).

The method allows also to compute not only the total D.S. but also the local densities of states (L.D.S.) on a site i, $n_i(E)$

$$n_i(E) = \sum_{\lambda, r} |a_{i\lambda}(E_n)|^2 \, \delta \, (E-E_n)$$

These L.D.S. are sensitive to the localization of the electronic states near the site i and give information on the spatial distribution of electrons in the various orbitals.

2.2 Results for semi-infinite transition metals

One can resume the detailed results obtained for various cleavage planes and various crystallographic structures in the following way (ref. 6).

 - For a dense cleavage plane (i.e. (111) for an FCC lattice, (110) for a BCC one), the L.D.S. on the surface behaves like the bulk DOS (Fig. 1a).

 - For a non dense cleavage plane such as the (110) for a FCC lattice or the (100) for a BCC lattice, it exists a virtual bound state peak in the middle of the band. This peak is due to the resonance of the surface atoms interacting weakly with the bulk ones (ref.7). There is correlatively a weakening in the shape of the L.D.S. at the top of the band (Fig. 1b).

 - When one enters in the crystal, the L.D.S. tend to have a behaviour similar to the bulk one.

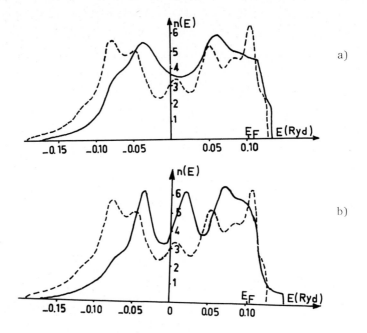

Fig. 1. LDS on the surface of nickel compared with the bulk one (broken curve)
a) (111) plane ; b) (100) plane.

These features of the LDS on surfaces exist for all the transition metals and have been observed by spectroscopy. They lead to a slight increase in the asphericity of the charge density of the d electrons when going from a bulk to a surface site giving indications on the possible adsorption sites.

In the case of stepped surfaces, there exist also extra virtual bound states on the LDS of the edge atoms. Spin orbit coupling may play an important role in that case (ref. 8).

2.3 Results for Ni clusters

We have studied Ni clusters between 13 atoms and 2089 atoms, of different geometries, icosahedra, cubooctahedra, truncated octahedra (refs. 9,10). The comparison between the properties of icosahedron and cubooctahedron clusters are particularly interesting, as they have the same total number of atoms but a different symmetry. Indeed, the cubooctahedron is formed by shells of close packed FCC atoms and the icosahedron is obtained through a distortion leading to a five fold symmetry. Their respective compactness if 0.74 and 0.688, the BCC being 0.680.

Experimentally one has observed transition metal clusters of five fold symmetry for small size with usually a contracted lattice parameter, these clusters making a phase transition towards an FCC lattice when the size is increased (refs. 11-13). These clusters, widely used in catalysis, have surely chemisorptive properties related to the peculiar role played by those surface atoms which are not located within low index planes with a high coordination number. Indeed these atoms might possibly act as active centers in adsorption (ref. 2). It is a situation similar to stepped surfaces, but enhanced in clusters by a high rate of surfaces to bulk atoms, which varies for example from 0.92 for a 13 atom cluster to 0.31 for a 2057 cluster.

Some of our results are presented in Figs. 2 and 3. They show the following trends for the LDS :

- a width for the icosahedron band smaller than the cubooctahedron one,
- an opening of a through in the center of the icosahedron band, related to its weak compactness. It is a characteristic which reminds some of the band structure of BCC lattice,
- depending on the nature of the surface sites and on the size and the geometry of the cluster, it appears or not some extra peak of resonant states in the middle of the LDS,
- the band features of clusters approach those of an infinite surface solid only for large clusters containing at least of the order of 1000 atoms, i.e. clusters of the order of 30 Å.

The total densities of states (ref. 10) show the same trends with a slight decrease in the band width when the size is decreased, and some change in the density of states on the top side. This could then induce some change in the magnetic properties of small clusters. This is reasonable, as for very small sizes, the cluster atoms will behave more like free atoms. This is confirmed by the few experimental results existing on the electronic properties or magnetic ones of transition metal clusters (refs. 14,15).

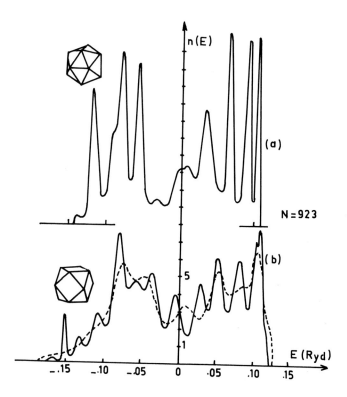

Fig. 2. Central atom LDS for a) icosahedra and b) cubooctahedra of 923 atoms (--- bulk fcc).

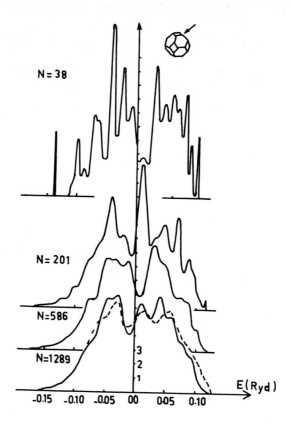

Fig. 3. LDS (—) on the edge between hexagonal and square faces for truncated octahedra of various sizes between 38 and 1289 atoms compared to the LDS (--) on the protruding edge of a 6(111) x (001) stepped surface which has the same nearest neighbour shell.

One can study also the relative stability of these clusters of various sizes by minimizing their cohesive energy as a function of the interatomic distance. One finds always a contraction for the lattice, larger for smaller clusters sizes, for example of the order of 10 % for a cluster of 13 atoms of Ni and 3 % for 147 atoms (diameter $\simeq$ 15 Å for Ni). This relaxation is the result of the balance between electronic and strain energy and leads to the relative stability of icosahedra with respect to FCC clusters for small sizes. This contraction is in agreement with recent results on Pt clusters using EXAFS (ref. 11).

3. ADSORPTION VERSUS ELECTRONIC STRUCTURE

Many attempts have been made to correlate the electronic factors of transition metals, such as their empty d orbitals, with their power to chemisorb, including for example the application of Pauling's valence bond theory or more recent quantum mechanical treatments of surfaces (ref. 16). But these approaches have some serious drawbacks, being generally qualitative models representing very roughly the complexity of the surfaces and of the chemisorptive bond.

However, any attempt at an understanding of adsorption must take into account the reality of the electronic structure of the surface of the catalyst. The important changes occurring in the electronic properties when going from the bulk to surfaces or to clusters, such as the extra resonant states, will affect the chemisorption process.

When an adsorbate approaches a metal surface, there is an hybridization of its discrete electronic levels with the band of the metal leading to a broadening in virtual or resonant states. The chemisorption is a quite localized phenomena due to a strong perturbation which affects primarily the atoms of the substrate where adsorption took place and their close environment. This explains why some approaches use a simulation of the substrate by a very small cluster which enables to apply sophisticated quantum chemistry models to the chemisorptive bond. But, as we have seen above, the electronic properties of surfaces or clusters of the size of catalysers, i.e. a few dozen atoms, have their own characteristics, depending on their geometrical pecularities, and are far from resembling the bulk or a very small cluster of a few atoms. One must then take into account in the description of adsorption, the main features of the electronic states of the surface substrate which have a determining influence as shown on the examples described below.

3.1 General description of the chemisorptive bond

When describing the adsorption of an atom A on a substrate, one can write the total hamiltonian as a sum of three terms

$H = H_a + H_m + H_c$

where H_a describes the free adsorbate characterized by an atomic level ε_a with z_a electrons, H_m the substrate characterized by its band structure, i.e. the LDS at the surface $n_s(E)$ and H_c the coupling between both.

This coupling can be characterized by the effective overlap B between the adsorbate and the Z_s corresponding atomic sites of the substrate and by the charge transfer occurring between the adsorbate and the substrate leading to a change in the atomic level $\varepsilon_a \rightarrow \varepsilon_a^*$ of the adsorbate.

One way of treating the chemisorptive bond is to use the closed analogy between ab-sorption and ad-sorption, i.e. between the alloy and the chemisorption problems. Indeed there appear similar effects depending on the strength of the coupling : a regime of weak coupling giving a virtual bound state on the adsorbate or the impurity, or a regime of strong coupling leading to molecular states.

The usual approaches are based on a one electron scheme, either a tight binding model or a Hartree Fock model hamiltonian of Anderson-Friedel type (ref. 17). These two approaches are very similar and differ only in the way of treating the charge transfer, i.e. of calculating ε_a^*.

In the tight binding model that we are using in the following of this paper, the charge transfer is calculated through the Friedel sum rule : the charge z_a brought by the adsorbate is equal to the charge variation induced on the substrate and the adsorbate when coupled. In fact, we are using a separate charge neutrality condition for the adsorbate and the substrate as experimentally the charge in work function indicates a neglectible charge transfer

(≈ 0.1 e$^-$). In the Hartree Fock treatment, the change in the position of the adsorbate level is due to the Coulomb repulsion U between two electrons, i.e. $\varepsilon_a^* = \varepsilon_a + U < n >$ where n is the number of electrons. But the values one can deduce for the charge transfer are quite important (≈ 1-2 e$^-$) and this approach seems to suffer from serious and unrealistic draw-backs.

The LDS on the adsorbate is given by an equation of similar type for both approaches

$$n_a(E) = \frac{\Gamma(E)}{|E - \varepsilon_a^* - \Omega(E)|^2 + \Gamma^2(E)}$$

with $\Omega(E) = \frac{1}{\pi} P \int \frac{\Gamma(E')}{E-E'} dE'$

$\Gamma(E) = \pi Z_s B^2 n_s(E)$ is the chemisorption function *. One finds easily on this expression for $n_a(E)$ the two limiting cases, virtual bound state regime or surface molecule regime depending on the strength of the coupling, i.e. of $\Gamma(E)$.

3.2 Strength of adsorption and surface states

The strength of the coupling will depend obviously on the effective overlap between the adsorbate and the corresponding substrate site, on its coordination number and also on its local density of states. This last term will be particularly important when there exist resonant surface states close to the Fermi level.

Let us illustrate briefly this effect by an example : the adsorption of 4d atoms on (110) and (100) Mo. The surface resonant states existing on (100) Mo induce a strong binding. A surface molecule limit is appropriate for the adsorption which results from a resonance between these surface states and the adsorbate levels. Contrary to this case, (110) Mo whose LDS behaves like the bulk, the adsorption retains an atomic character (Fig. 4). The occurrence of resonant surface states thus increases the strength of the coupling and induces consequently a large anisotropy of the binding energy (ref. 18). For example, one gets

$\dfrac{U_L(Mo/Mo(110))}{U_L(Mo/Mo(100))} \sim 0.56$, value which can be compared to 0.80 value given by a preliminary calculation where the effect of the band structure of the substrate was neglected. Nevertheless, the effect of the Coulomb correlation U which is quite important for these metals of the middle of the d series, could reduce this anisotropy.

---

* $n_s(E)$ represents the LDS at the surface only for simple adsorbate geometries, otherwise one has to consider the orbital group density of states.

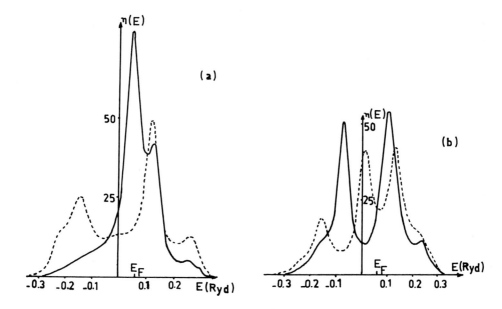

Fig. 4. The density of states of an Mo adatom (——) compared with the surface density of
states (---) of the clean substrate : a) Mo (110) ; b) Mo (100).

3.3 Adsorption and magnetism

The understanding of surface magnetic properties of transition metals or their change when
they participate in an adsorptive process still remains a challenging problem. However, magnetic techniques are often used to characterize the state of dispersion of supported metal
catalysts, and to throw some light on the intermediate states produced in the adsorption
process (ref. 19). Any model description of the adsorption process must then permit to explain these magnetic properties.

We will describe briefly two examples concerning the relative change in the magnetic properties of nickel when chemisorbing oxygen or hydrogen. One of the first question to ask is
whether the surface states occurring for non dense cleavage planes will affect the magnetic
properties of free nickel surfaces or clusters. We have been able to show that this is quite
unlikely using a rigid exchange splitting model i.e. the number of holes is not affected by
the roughness of the surface (ref. 8). Our conclusions are in agreement with the most recent
experiments, showing no noticeable change of the magnetic properties of surface nickel atoms
from those of the bulk (ref. 20).

When adsorbing a gas such as H_2, O_2, CO.. on a nickel substrate, there will be a broadening
of the adsorbate electronic levels and a displacement of the relative positions of the s and
d bands of the nickel. The very small charge transfer between the adsorbate and the substrate is shown by the small change in work function when adsorbing (ref. 21). These shifts
of the s and d bands will cause a reduction of the local density of states at the Fermi
level on the active sites of nickel for adsorption and on its first neighbours.

These conclusions are confirmed for example by a calculation for oxygen overlayers on Ni (100) (ref. 22). Experimentally chalcogen atoms are found to be in fourfold coordinated sites, forming p(2x2) or c(2x2) overlayer. Their distance to the substrate is rather well determined, and various spectroscopic investigations have also been performed. Our results show very similar trends in the change of the electronic structure of Ni (100) when adsorbing oxygen with various coverages (Fig. 5). There is a shift of the d band towards the negative energies and consequently a drastic reduction of the LDS at the Fermi level. A simple reasoning using the Stoner criterion relating the existence of ferromagnetism to a high value of the density of states at the Fermi level will thus lead to a demagnetization of the active sites of nickel. The results for a very low coverage ($\theta \to 0$) indicate thus that one atom of oxygen demagnetizes 4 atoms of nickel. For a p(2x2) oxygen overlayer ($\theta = 1/4$) the surface layer of nickel is likely to become non-magnetic. This is in agreement with experiments which have revealed a decrease of the saturation magnetization of Ni when adsorbing oxygen (ref. 23).

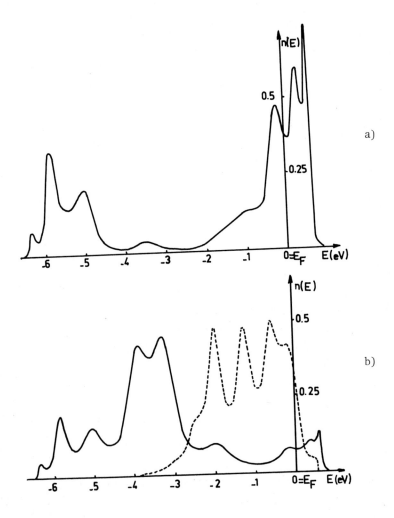

Fig. 5. c(2x2) adsorbed oxygen overlayer ($\theta = 1/2$) on Ni (100) ; a) LDS on the oxygen ; b) LDS on the first Ni (100) plane with an adsorbed c(2x2) oxygen overlayer compared with the clean surface (---).

Another case of interest is the relative change in the magnetic properties of nickel particles when chemisorbing hydrogen and the correlative difference in the absolute quantities of chemisorbed hydrogen atoms at saturation coverage which have been shown to depend on the surface structure (ref. 24) contrary to the initial heats of adsorption (ref. 21). The lowering of the magnetic moment μ of nickel per atom of chemisorbed hydrogen is higher when the surface is made of dense planes, i.e. $\Delta\mu/\mu$ varies between 1.4 and 0.75 when the surface roughness increases. The surface stoichiometry of chemisorbed hydrogen at saturation, i.e. the ratio of adsorbed hydrogen to the number of surface nickel atoms H/Ni_s varies in the opposite way, between 0.6 and 1.1 when the surface roughness increases. These features indicate the structure sensitivity of the hydrogen adsorption which can be explained by the difference in the electronic properties of surface nickel atoms with the roughness of the surface.

When H atoms are adsorbed, the s band will go up compared to the d band to achieve a $s^0 d^{10}$ configuration for active sites of nickel for adsorption instead of the usual $s^{0.6} d^{9.4}$ bulk ones. When the active sites have a dense geometry, such as that of the atoms of a (111) plane, the LDS is very similar to the bulk one (Fig. 1). Chemisorption of hydrogen will lower the density of states and thus decrease rapidly the magnetic moment. On the contrary, such as on non dense planes, kinks.., there exist resonant surface states in their LDS (Fig. 2). The density of states decreases more rapidly but extends to higher energies. This leads to the same number of holes or magnetic moment (Fig. 6) as for a dense plane as we mention earlier. Chemisorption of H will then decrease the magnetic moment less rapidly than in the case of a dense plane. In the same way, the maximum surface stoichiometry for hydrogen adsorption which will correspond to the complete filling of the d band will be larger than for a dense surface plane. Let us point out that in this model, the product $\Delta\mu/\mu$ x H/Ni_s remains constant, which is roughly verified by experiments (ref. 24).

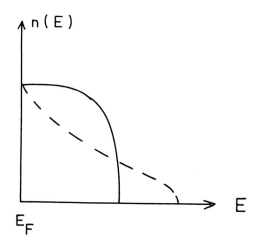

Fig. 6. Schematic top of the LDS of Ni surface atoms : —— dense surface --- non dense surface.

ACKNOWLEDGEMENTS

I would like to devote this paper to the memory of my colleague and friend Professor F. Gault from whom I benefited of so many stimulating discussions and who helped me to cast a glance on the field of catalysis.

REFERENCES

1 A.A. Balandin, Adv. in Catalysis 19 (1969).

2 G.A. Somorjai, Adv. in Catalysis 26 (1977) 1-68.

3 J. Friedel, The Physics of Metals, Ed. J.M. Ziman (1969) 340-408.

4 F. Cyrot-Lackmann, J. Physique C1 (1970) 67-74.

5 J.P. Gaspard and F. Cyrot-Lackmann, J. Phys. C 6 (1973) 3077-96.

6 M.C. Desjonquères and F. Cyrot-Lackmann, Surf. Sci. 53 (1975)429-442.

7 J. Friedel, J. Physique 37 (1976) 883-894.

8 M.C. Desjonquères and F. Cyrot-Lackmann, Solid St. Comm. 18 (1976) 1127-32 ; Solid St.

9 F. Cyrot-Lackmann, M.C. Desjonquères and M.B. Gordon, J. Physique 38 (1977) C2.

10 M.B. Gordon, F. Cyrot-Lackmann and M.C. Desjonquères, Surf. Sci. 80 (1978) 159-164.

11 B. Moraweck, G. Clugnet and A.J. Renonprez, Surf. Sci. (1979) to be published.

12 A. Renou and M. Gillet, Thin Solid Films 41 (1977) 15-28.

13 C. Solliard and Ph. Buffat, J. Physique 7 C2 (1977) 167-170.

14 S. Ladas, R.A. Dalla Betta and M. Boudart, J. of Catal. 53 (1978) 356-365.

15 W.D. Knight, J. Physique C2 (1977) 109-113.

16 A. Clark, The Chemisorptive Bond (1974) Academic Press.

17 S.K. Lyo and R. Gomer, Interactions on metal surfaces, Ed. by Gomer, Springer Verlag, (1975) 41-61.

18 M.C. Desjonquères and F. Cyrot-Lackmann, Solid St. Comm. 26 (1978) 271-274.

19 P.W. Selwood, Chemisorption and magnetization, Academic Press (1975).

20 E.G. Derouane, A. Simoens, C. Colin, G.A. Martin, J.A. Dalmon and J.C. Vedrine, J. Catal. 52 (1978) 50-58.

21 K. Christmann, O. Schober, G. Ertl and M. Neumann, J. Chem. Phys. 11 (1974) 4528-40.

22 M.C. Desjonquères and F. Cyrot-Lackmann, Surf. Sci. 80 (1979) 208-214.

23 J.A. Dalmon, G.A. Martin et B. Imelik "Thermochimie", Ed. CNRS n° 201 (1971) 593.

24 G.A. Martin, R. Dutarbe and J.A. Dalmon (1979) to be published.

DISCUSSION

F. CYROT-LACKMANN

Budevski - I would like to comment an experiment which we have done and which, in my opinion, very strongly supports the essential part of your contribution, namely the strong effect of surface structure on adsorption and catalysis :

On dislocation-free faces of silver single crystals in 6N AgNO$_3$ solutions, we have measured exchange current densities of the order of 0.06 A.cm^{-2}. On stepped surface produced by growth of crystal faces with screw-dislocations, we found an increase of the exchange current density proportional to step length and from this increase a value of the exchange current density in the vicinity of the step could be evaluated ranging in order of 200 A.cm^{-2}. This increase of the exchange current density of about four orders of magnitude, due simply to a step of atomic height, demonstrates how important the structure of the surface for catalytic effects can be !

Dadyburjor - In the work that I will present this afternoon (Ruckenstein and Dadyburjor, Paper n° 50, these Proceedings), we have hypothesized the presence of different types of adsorbed states even for simple molecules on "homogeneous" surfaces. Would it be possible to predict this phenomenon using your very elegant calculation scheme ?

Cyrot-Lackmann - It is possible to study various possibilities for the adsorbed states of simple molecules, such as those found for example in the adsorption of H on Ni, Pt in the work of ERTL et al. and to get their influence on the adsorption process. But, of course, a precise prediction of the possible presence of different types of adsorbed states is for the moment beyond the computation possibilities.

Ehrlich - It is very interesting that you can calculate absolute values of the binding energy of single metal atoms selfadsorbed on different crystal planes. However, comparison with experimental results is still desirable. Unfortunately, there are no valid experimental data available for such a comparison. Can you also calculate the binding energy of a metal atom at sites of different coordination on one and the same plane ? That would then yield the barrier to surface motion, a quantity which can be readily measured, and about which we already know a fair amount.

Cyrot-Lackmann - Yes, it is possible to do calculations of binding energy of a metal atom at sites of different coordination on one and the same plane. I agree : it will give information more easily comparable to the existing experimental data. We have already thought of that in particular while discussing with Prof. Dreschler's group in Marseille. It is simply a question of choice in our priorities due to the problem of appointing new scientists !

Kreibig - I have a question on the Ni clusters, which may be of importance to the experimentalist.
You found the energetic differences between icosahedral and fcc structures to be rather small. Can you compare these energy differences, perhaps, to thermal energy ? This size would be important for the possibility to observe both structures at same time.

Cyrot-Lackmann - We have indeed found differences between icosahedral and fcc structures of the order of thermal energy, i.e. ∼ 500 cal mol^{-1} , indicating that a coexistence of both structures is possible.

Renouprez - How do you explain that adsorption of O$_2$ and H$_2$ produce the same magnetic effect whereas the first adsorbate decreases the density of states near Fermi level and the other increases ?

Cyrot-Lackmann - I do not agree with the fact that adsorption of oxygen on Ni would decrease the density of states near the Fermi level, and that hydrogen would increase it. I think that both adsorptions would lead to a decrease of the density of states due to a charge in the electronic configuration of Ni, i.e. a filling of the d band.

Martin - There is a number of evidences, now particularly by UPS, that on transition metals, hydrogen adsorption causes a decrease of $N(E_F)$, except in the case of iron. This is in goods agreement with magnetic data and the Stoner criteria (the condition of ferromagnetism is that $N(E_F)$ is large), since H_2 adsorption decreases the magnetism of Ni and does not modify that of Fe.

Cyrot-Lackmann - I agree with what you said. Iron does not at all behave as nickel as it has 6 d electrons, and the Fermi level is close to the middle of the band.

Yacaman - The experimental evidence shows that icosahedral particles can exist up to a size of about 200 Å which is well above the limit that you show in your calculations. Could you comment on this please ?

Cyrot-Lackmann - There are two main points which can be raised with respect to this comment about experimental evidence :

1°/ The size at which particles undergo an icosahedral-fcc transition does depend on the metal considered. It is the same for our calculations which have been done only for nickel. Other metals would give other numbers for the critical size.

2°/ Our computation has been done for icosahedral and cuboctahedron particles. Other structures such as the truncated octahedron or dodecahedron could give also different numbers for this critical size. We have chosen to study the icosahedral and the cubo-octahedral structures because they have the same total number of atoms and that makes the comparison easier. Indeed cohesive energy is one of the most difficult quantity to calculate and, until now, no a priori determination of phase diagram of metals and alloys is available. The trends obtained in cohesive energy calculations have thus more meaning than the absolute numbers. Thus we think here that we have a critical size for nickel between 10 et 20 Å.

Maurin - Do you know if adsorption can modify the stability of a cluster and if, for example, hydrogen adsorption can stabilize pentagonal structures ?

Cyrot-Lackmann - No, I do not know of any calculation of that kind. I think this would be very interesting to try to study those clusters (stability, electronic properties) when adsorption occurs.

Martin - In catalysis, some investigators try to find analogies between properties of single crystals and of powders. You have shown an interesting transparency which illustrates the fact that the local density of states of surface atoms in small particles is similar to that of the corresponding atom in the half-infinite plane, only if the particle is sufficiently large. This implies that, to bridge the gap between single crystal and powder stydies, one needs to consider only properties of large metallic particles. Do you agree with this comment ?

Cyrot-Lackmann - Yes, but I think that the sizes at which particles will behave as single crystals are quite commonly used in powder studies i.e. sizes larger than ~ 30 Å.

J. BOURDON (Editor)
Growth and Properties of Metal Clusters, pp. 255—268
© 1980 Elsevier Scientific Publishing Company — Printed in The Netherlands

LE STATUT THEORIQUE DE LA METHODE DE HÜCKEL

André JULG

Laboratoire de Chimie Théorique - Université de Provence

Place Victor Hugo - 13331 MARSEILLE Cedex 3

SUMMARY

In spite of its empirical appearance, Hückel method, which is the simplest technique of the general molecular orbital method, can be deduced, taking into account certain hypothesis, from the rigorous self-consistent method. It is known that, in a Slater's atomic basis orthogonalized by means of the Löwdin procedure, the Hückel hypothesis (transferability of atom and bond parameters) are found, in so far as the orthogonality makes practically equal to zero all the bielectronic integrals except the coulomb integrals $\langle pp|r^{-1}|qq\rangle$. This condition, which is verified for the s and p-orbitals (alkaline metals or conjugated hydrocarbons), remains valid for the d-orbitals. Appropriately parametrized, Hückel method gives very satisfactory molecular orbitals and orbital energies, but the electron energy is bad. A corrected expression is given for the total energy (electron energy + nuclear repulsion). Simple relations between bond orders and internuclear distances allow to determinate the geometry of the system. A relation is proposed for alkaline-like-metals. The method can be applied to evaluate the transition energies. A reduction factor (~ 0.5) is absolutely necessary. The problem of monodeterminant approximation for the total wave function is discussed with respect to the size of the edifice.

I. INTRODUCTION

Bien que l'équation de Schrödinger relative à une molécule ne soit pas directement intégrable, le Chimiste Théoricien possède des méthodes capables d'obtenir les valeurs des diverses grandeurs observables avec une précision remarquable. Je pense par exemple à la méthode du champ self-consistent (S.C.F.) de Roothaan (réf. 1), complétée par interaction de configurations et développée avec des bases étendues. Malheureusement, la mise en oeuvre de cette méthode, d'une part, est très onéreuse et, d'autre part, se heurte à une impossibilité technique dès que la taille de l'édifice dépasse la dizaine d'atomes. On sait, de plus, l'intérêt toujours croissant porté, de nos jours, aux polymères, aux molécules d'intérêt biologique ainsi qu'aux édifices cristallins de taille finie mais contenant plusieurs centaines d'atomes. Aussi ne faut-il pas s'étonner si, à l'heure actuelle, malgré les moyens théoriques dont on dispose et malgré les performances sans cesse améliorées du calcul électronique, le théoricien, concurremment aux méthodes très élaborées réservées à des cas très particuliers —et aussi à des Laboratoires fortunés!—, continue à faire largement appel à des méthodes moins sophistiquées, de caractère plus ou moins empirique, comme la méthode de Hückel (réf. 2).

Initialement proposée pour l'étude des systèmes π des molécules conjuguées, cette méthode a été par la suite étendue à tous les électrons de valence (réf. 3). Cependant les résultats intéressants qu'elle permet d'obtenir ne peuvent faire oublier le caractère empirique des hypothèses simplificatrices sur lesquelles elle repose, et si elle est actuellement la méthode qui permet effectivement de traiter les plus gros édifices de taille finie, un examen théorique de sa structure mathématique est nécessaire, afin de savoir la qualité des résultats qu'elle obtient et son domaine exact d'application.

II. LE SCHEMA THEORIQUE DE LA METHODE

Comme souvent c'est le cas, pour étudier une question, l'ordre historique n'est pas le meilleur. Aussi présenterons nous la question à partir des données théoriques dont nous disposons à l'heure actuelle, plutôt que de raisonner comme le firent Hückel et ses continuateurs, il y a près d'un demi-siècle (réf. 2).

Nous travaillerons avec l'hamiltonien électronique non relativiste :

$$\hat{H}(1,2,\ldots n) = \sum_{\mu=1}^{n} \left[\hat{T}(\mu) + \hat{U}(\mu) \right] + \sum_{(\mu\nu)} r_{\mu\nu}^{-1} \tag{1}$$

où $\hat{T}(\mu)$ est l'opérateur énergie cinétique relatif à l'électron μ, $\hat{U}(\mu)$ l'opérateur énergie potentielle relatif à l'électron μ (attraction des noyaux ou des coeurs formés par les noyaux et les électrons des couches internes), et $r_{\mu\nu}^{-1}$, l'opérateur de répulsion coulombienne entre les électrons μ et ν. Les noyaux sont supposés immobiles.

Pour solution ψ de l'équation de Schrödinger

$$H\psi = E\psi \tag{2}$$

nous chercherons un produit antisymétrisé de fonctions monoélectroniques appelées *orbitales moléculaires* ϕ_i, associées à une des fonctions de spin α ou β. Dans la plupart des cas, ce sera un déterminant (fonction propre de S_z et S^2) :

$$\psi(1,2,\ldots n) = \frac{1}{\sqrt{n!}} \begin{vmatrix} \phi_1(1)\alpha(1) & \phi_1(1)\beta(1) & \cdots \\ \phi_1(2)\alpha(2) & \cdots & \cdots \\ \cdots & \cdots & \cdots \end{vmatrix} . \tag{3}$$

C'est le modèle de *Hartree-Fock*.

L'expression explicite des fonctions monoélectroniques $\phi_i(\mu)$ peut être obtenue, soit directement à partir de la théorie des groupes, comme pour les orbitales π du benzène ou dans les cristaux à cause de la périodicité (méthode dite *tight-binding*), soit en minimisant l'énergie électronique numériquement, comme le faisaient, vers 1930, Hartree, Slater ou Fock, ou algébriquement, en développant les ϕ_i sur une base de fonctions convenables.

Une solution usuelle en Chimie, et qui donne satisfaction pour les petites molécules, consiste à utiliser pour base de développement, un très petit nombre de fonctions qui sont les *orbitales atomiques* χ_p, utilisées dans la description des atomes isolés. C'est la méthode dite L.C.A.O. (linear combination of atomic orbitals) :

$$\phi_i = \sum_p c_{ip} \chi_p \qquad (4)$$

les coefficients c_{ip} ainsi introduits, étant déterminés par un calcul variationnel de façon à rendre l'énergie du système minimale. On voit donc, qu'en toute rigueur, nous ne cherchons pas à résoudre l'équation de Schrödinger (2), mais seulement à obtenir la meilleure solution satisfaisant aux conditions que nous avons imposées : la structure déterminantale (3) pour la fonction d'onde totale et la forme du développement des ϕ_i (4).

En ce qui concerne ce dernier point, il est bien évident que si les χ_r formaient une base complète, la seule approximation qui resterait, serait la structure déterminantale (3). Malheureusement, il n'est pas possible d'utiliser une base complète. Toutefois, l'expérience d'innombrables calculs effectués sur toutes sortes de molécules, a montré qu'on pouvait obtenir des résultats très convenables en utilisant des orbitales de Slater, c'est-à-dire de la forme :

$$\chi = f(r) \, Y(\theta,\phi) \qquad (5)$$

où $f(r)$ est une fonction radiale convenable et $Y(\theta,\phi)$ les harmoniques sphériques, et en se limitant aux orbitales des couches ou sous-couches utilisées dans la description la plus élémentaire des atomes isolés : *1s* pour H , *1s*, *2s*, *2p* pour C, N, O ... C'est ce qu'on appelle *la base minimale*. D'ailleurs, on peut même réduire le problème aux seuls électrons de valence dans le champ du *coeur* formé du noyau et des électrons décrits par les orbitales internes. Ainsi pour les éléments C, N, O ..., on se contentera des orbitales *2s*, *2p*, pour les métaux de transition de la première période (Cr, Fe, ...) des orbitales *4s*, *3d*, *4p*. C'est *la base subminimale*.

Bien entendu, cette façon de procéder n'interdit pas l'utilisation de bases plus étendues, qui donneront de meilleurs résultats et permettront d'atteindre la limite Hartree-Fock, donc la meilleure solution de structure déterminantale. La base minimale de Slater permet d'atteindre facilement 95% de l'énergie de Hartree-Fock. Etant donné le prix de revient rapidement prohibitif des calculs en bases étendues, dans la plupart des cas, on se contentera d'une base minimale ou même subminimale.

En ce qui concerne l'approximation déterminantale, on peut s'en affranchir en utilisant la méthode dite d'*interaction de configurations* qui consiste à construire les divers états ψ_i de structure déterminantale déduits des orbitales ϕ_i obtenues en minimisant l'énergie de l'état fondamental et à chercher pour solution, une combinaison linéaire de ces déterminants :

$$\psi = \sum_i C_i \, \psi_i \qquad (6)$$

les C_i étant déterminés de façon à minimiser l'énergie. Simple dans son principe, ce procédé se heurte à des difficultés matérielles difficiles à surmonter dès que la taille des édifices est tant soit peu élevée (quelques dizaines d'atomes). Toutefois, ici encore, si l'on ne s'intéresse qu'à l'état fondamental, le poids de la configuration la plus basse —celle de Hartree-Fock en l'occurrence— est tel qu'à elle seule, elle apporte plus de 98% de l'énergie électronique. De plus, les densités $|\psi|^2$ sont pratiquement les mêmes. De sorte que la base minimale ou subminimale et l'approximation déterminantale

258

peuvent être considérées comme un juste compromis entre la qualité des résultats d'une part et de leur prix de revient d'autre part. Valable pour des édifices de taille assez réduite, il n'est cependant pas évident que cette conclusion le reste pour des édifices infinis. Nous reviendrons plus loin sur cette question.

Les hypothèses sur la structure de la solution (3) et (4) étant choisies, la détermination pratique des orbitales moléculaires ϕ_i se fera d'une façon rigoureuse par exemple par la méthode dite du champ moléculaire *self-consistent* (S.C.F.) de Roothaan (réf. 1). Elle se ramène à la résolution d'un système :

$$\left\{ \sum_p C_{ip} (L_{pq} - e S_{pq}) = 0 \qquad (q) \right. \tag{7}$$

où les S_{pq} sont les intégrales de recouvrement $\langle \chi_p | \chi_q \rangle$ entre les orbitales atomiques de base χ_p et χ_q, et les L_{pq}, les éléments de la matrice énergie. Ces dernières dépendant des coefficients c_{ip}, le calcul se fera par itérations. Mais ceci est un détail technique que nous pouvons laisser de côté, supposant la cohérence atteinte.

La résolution de ce système exige la condition :

$$\text{dét.} |L_{pq} - e S_{pq}| = 0 \tag{8}$$

qui est appelée l'*équation séculaire* du système. Les racines e_i de cette équation, sont les énergies associées aux diverses orbitales ϕ_i.

Une amélioration technique importante due à Löwdin (réf. 4) consiste à remplacer les orbitales atomiques de base (χ), en général non orthogonales entre elles, par un jeu (χ') d'orbitales orthogonalisées, déduit du précédent par la transformation unitaire :

$$(\chi') = \mathcal{S}^{-1/2}(\chi) \tag{9}$$

où $\mathcal{S}$ est la matrice des intégrales de recouvrement S_{pq}. Au second ordre près, (9) permet d'écrire :

$$\chi'_p = \chi_p - \frac{1}{2} \sum_{k \neq p} S_{pk} \chi_k \tag{10}$$

L'équation séculaire (8) s'écrit alors :

$$\text{dét.} |L'_{pq} - e \delta_{pq}| = 0 \tag{11}$$

où δ_{pq} est le symbole de Kronecker.

Mais l'intérêt essentiel du choix de cette transformation réside dans le fait que, pratiquement, les diverses intégrales biélectroniques :

$$(pq,rs) = \langle \chi_p(\mu) \chi_q(\mu) r_{\mu\nu}^{-1} \chi_r(\nu) \chi_s(\nu) \rangle \tag{12}$$

qui apparaissent dans le calcul des L_{pq}, sont nulles ou tout à fait négligeables, dans la base orthogonalisée (9), sauf si $p = q$ et $r = s$, et que dans ce cas, elles sont pratiquement inaffectées par l'orthogonalisation. Ce qui revient à dire :

$$(p'q',r's') \sim (pq,rs)\, \delta_{pq}\, \delta_{rs} \qquad (13)$$

Le Tableau 1 donne quelques exemples de l'effet de l'orthogonalisation sur des intégrales portant sur divers types d'orbitales atomiques.

Tableau 1

Noyaux	Intégrales	O.A. non orthogonales	O.A. orthogonalisées
C-C	$(\pi_a\pi_a, \pi_b\pi_b)$	0,108 u.a.	0,104 u.a.
R=1,54 Å	$(\pi_a\pi_b, \pi_a\pi_b)$	0,013	0,000
	$(\pi_a\pi_a, \pi_a\pi_b)$	0,043	-0,003
Si-Si	$(s_a\pi_b, \pi_b\pi_b)$	0,136	0,002
R=2,25 Å	$(d_{z^2_a}s_b, s_b s_b)$	0,088	0,002
	$(d_{xy_a}\pi_b, \pi_b\pi_b)$	0,012	0,002
	$(d_{yz_a}d_{yz_b}, d_{yz_b}d_{y_b})$	0,054	-0,003

L'axe z est dirigé suivant la ligne des noyaux. $\pi = p_x$ ou p_y.

Il en résulte que le nombre d'intégrales qui s'introduisent dans les calculs est considérablement réduit, puisqu'il ne reste que les coulombiennes $(p^2,q^2)'$ et $(p^2,p^2)'$. En gros N^2 intégrales, au lieu de N^4, si l'on a N orbitales atomiques de base.

Mais il y a plus. Le fait de travailler dans la base de Löwdin entraîne, dans la mesure où la relation (13) est valable, que :

1) les éléments diagonaux L'_{pp} ne dépendent pratiquement que de la nature des orbitales χ_p et non du reste de l'édifice, (réf. 5)
2) les éléments non diagonaux correspondant à des orbitales χ_p et χ_q différentes, ne dépendent pratiquement que de la nature des orbitales χ_p et χ_q, et de leur position géométrique respective (réf. 5). En particulier, ces éléments sont nuls s'ils correspondent à des orbitales de Slater orthogonales par raison de symétrie (p. ex. : une orbitale s et une orbitale p portée par le même noyau, ou par un autre noyau, si l'axe de l'orbitale est perpendiculaire à la ligne des noyaux.

En d'autres termes, on voit que, connaissant la nature des orbitales et leur position dans l'espace, on peut directement écrire l'équation séculaire (11) et ainsi obtenir les orbitales moléculaires ϕ_i.

Et c'est là où nous retrouvons la méthode de Hückel qui précisément aboutit à une équation séculaire :

$$\det.|h_{pq} - e\,\delta_{pq}| = 0 \qquad (14)$$

correspondant à une base orthogonale et suppose que $h_{pp} = \alpha_p$ ne dépend que de χ_p et $h_{pq} = \beta_{pq}$ que des orbitales χ_p et χ_q.

En fait, dans la méthode de Hückel, l'équation séculaire (14) est obtenue à partir d'un hamiltonien simplifié, somme d'opérateurs monoélectroniques :

$$H = \sum_\mu h(\mu) \qquad (15)$$

Ecrivant que l'énergie de l'état fondamental

$$E = < \psi H \psi > \qquad (16)$$

est minimale, on aboutit à l'équation (14). Donc, bien que partant d'une expression approchée de l'hamiltonien, la méthode de Hückel retombe sur une équation séculaire correcte, les α_p et β_{pq} s'identifiant respectivement aux L'_{pp} et L'_{pq} de la théorie S.C.F. complète :

$$\alpha_p \sim L'_{pp}$$
$$\qquad\qquad (17)$$
$$\beta_{pq} \sim L'_{pq}$$

Mais, si les orbitales moléculaires données par la méthode de Hückel sont très voisines de celles données par la méthode S.C.F., il n'en sera pas de même pour l'énergie. Nous reviendrons sur ce point important.

III. UNE REMARQUE FONDAMENTALE

Prétextant que les orbitales atomiques de base χ_r ne sont pas orthogonales ($S_{pq} \neq \delta_{pq}$), très tôt, dès 1940 environ, on a cru améliorer la méthode primitive de Hückel, en introduisant le recouvrement entre les orbitales, donc à travailler avec l'équation séculaire :

$$\text{dét.} |h_{rs} - e\, S_{rs}| = 0 \qquad (18)$$

tout en gardant les mêmes hypothèses sur les α et les β.

Indépendamment des résultats que peut donner une telle modification apportée à la méthode originale, celle-ci constitue une erreur du point de vue théorique. En effet, les relations (17) que l'on continue à utiliser pour construire (18), ne sont valables que dans la base orthogonalisée de Löwdin. Il n'est donc pas permis de réintroduire le recouvrement entre les orbitales.

IV. DETERMINATION DES PARAMETRES α ET β

Dans la méthode initiale de Hückel, les termes α et β relatifs aux orbitales π étaient considérés comme des paramètres, ajustés les uns par rapport aux autres à partir de l'éthylène ou du benzène. Déterminés une fois pour toutes, ces paramètres permettaient de traiter une molécule conjuguée quelconque. On peut évidemment procéder de la même façon pour les divers paramètres α et β dont on peut avoir besoin. Toutefois, étant donné qu'ils s'identifient pratiquement avec les termes de l'équation séculaire (11) dans la base de Löwdin, on peut obtenir leur valeur d'une façon absolue, en prenant la moyenne des valeurs obtenues pour diverses molécules par la méthode S.C.F. . Mais, en fait, on peut procéder plus simplement.

Pour une orbitale simplement utilisée dans l'atome (orbitale $2s$ du lithium, $2p$ du carbone, ...) on peut montrer (réf. 5), en explicitant dans la base de Löwdin l'expression des L_{pp}, que :

$$\alpha \backsim - \frac{1}{2} \ (\ I \ + \ A \ ) \tag{19}$$

I et A étant respectivement l'énergie d'ionisation et l'affinité électronique de l'orbitale en question.

Cette formule appelle deux remarques :
1) α n'est pas égal à $- I$, comme on le prend souvent,
2) α est égal à l'opposé de l'électronégativité de l'orbitale, définie selon Mulliken.

En ce qui concerne les paramètres β_{pq}, le fait essentiel est que pratiquement, seuls les termes relatifs à des atomes voisins sont à retenir. Pour tous les autres couples (p-q), les β_{pq} sont négligeables.

Très tôt, dès 1938, cette rapide décroissance fut reconnue et diverses formules empiriques ont été proposées. Une des plus usuelles est la proportionalité aux intégrales de recouvrement (réf. 6) :

$$\beta_{pq} \backsim S_{pq} \tag{20}$$

Si cette formule simule d'une façon assez correcte la décroissance des $|\beta|$ avec la distance, elle peut paraître contenir une contradiction du fait que la méthode suppose les orbitales atomiques orthogonales. En réalité, il ne faut pas voir le moindre lien entre les β_{pq} relatifs aux orbitales orthogonalisées de Löwdin et les S_{pq} relatifs aux orbitales initiales. L'intégrale de recouvrement S_{pq} n'est utilisée ici que pour l'allure de sa décroissance avec la distance. D'ailleurs, une simple exponentielle convient aussi bien (réf. 7) :

$$\beta_{pq} \backsim e^{-kd_{pq}} \tag{21}$$

En fait, si l'on regarde les choses d'un peu plus près, on découvre que la décroissance en valeur absolue des β_{pq} n'est pas monotone. L'examen des valeurs L'_{pq} obtenues par la méthode S.C.F. aussi bien avec des orbitales $2p$ dans les molécules conjuguées (réf. 8) qu'avec les orbitales $2s$ du lithium dans des petites édifices Li_n (réf. 9), montre que, si pour les plus proches voisins (atomes liés au sens chimique), les β (qui sont négatifs) décroissent bien en valeur absolue avec la distance, pour les seconds voisins, les β sont très faibles, mais *positifs*. Ce changement de signe entraîne une répulsion entre atomes non voisins immédiats. Ce qui explique que, pour des édifices comme H_4, Li_4, Cu_4, où il n'y a pas de squelette σ sous-jacent comme dans les hydrocarbures conjugués (butadiène p. ex.), la forme la plus stable soit la forme linéaire (réf. 10).

A titre indicatif, voici un type de formule empirique qui simule assez bien la variation des β avec la distance $\underline{r}$ (réf. 11) :

$$\beta(r) = \beta_o \, e^{-Ar} \cos\left(\frac{\pi}{2}\frac{r}{R}\right) \tag{22}$$

β_o, A et R sont des constantes caractéristiques de la liaison. Au delà de r = 3R, on prendra β égal à zéro.

Si l'on ne dispose pas de valeurs S.C.F. pour ajuster les coefficients de la formule (22), on le fera à partir de l'énergie de dissociation de petites molécules (M_2 p. ex.) ou à partir de l'énergie de cohésion pour un métal. Ceci nous amène donc à examiner la question de l'évolution de l'énergie, que nous avons laissée jusqu'ici de côté.

V. EVALUATION DE L'ENERGIE

La théorie S.C.F. qui utilise l'hamiltonien exact (1) fournit l'énergie électronique totale sous la forme :

$$E_{S.C.F.} = \sum_i (e_i + I_i) \tag{23}$$

avec

$$I_i = <\phi_i|\hat{T} + \hat{U}|\phi_i> \tag{24}$$

Dans la méthode de Hückel qui utilise un hamiltonien simplifié (15), l'énergie électronique apparaît sous la forme plus simple :

$$E_H. = 2 \sum_i e_i \tag{25}$$

Les e_i de Hückel s'identifiant aux e_i de la méthode S.C.F. puisque les éléments L'_{pq} et h_{pq} sont pratiquement les mêmes, les énergies S.C.F. (23) et de Hückel (25) sont différentes.

Mais, de toutes façons, ce n'est pas l'énergie électronique qui conditionne la stabilité du système, mais l'énergie totale, somme de l'énergie électronique et de l'énergie de répulsion des noyaux (ou des coeurs) :

$$E_{tot.} = E_{élec.} + E_{rép.} \tag{26}$$

Les coeurs étant de symétrie sphérique, l'énergie de répulsion aura même expression que pour des noyaux ponctuels :

$$E_{rép.} = \sum_{PQ} \frac{z_P z_Q}{R_{PQ}} \tag{27}$$

z_P étant la charge du noyau ou du coeur P, et R_{PQ} la distance entre les noyaux ou les coeurs P et Q.

L'expression de l'énergie totale dans la méthode S.C.F. est assez compliquée. Toutefois, moyennant les mêmes approximations que celles faites pour établir les rela-

tions (17) dans la base de Löwdin, on peut mettre cette énergie sous une forme simple
(réf. 12) :

$$E_{tot.} = 2 \sum_i e_i + \frac{1}{4} \sum_{(pq)} \ell_{pq}^2 C_{pq} + \text{Cte} \tag{28}$$

$$\text{où } C_{pq} = (pp,qq) \tag{29}$$

et :

$$\ell_{pq} = 2 \sum_i c_{ip} c_{iq} \tag{30}$$

l'indice de liaison.

La constante est une somme de termes monocentriques, donc indépendante de la géométrie
du système :

$$- \frac{N}{4} C_{rr} \tag{31}$$

par exemple, dans le cas où le système est constitué de N atomes de même nature et
ne portant qu'une seule orbitale atomique. Cette constante est donc inessentielle pour
comparer la stabilité d'édifices isomères.

Les indices de liaison (30) sont inférieurs à l'unité. Ils diminuent d'autre part
rapidement en valeur absolue avec la distance entre les orbitales correspondantes. De
leurs côtés, les intégrales coulombiennes C_{pq} décroissent rapidement (en gros en $1/r$)
avec la distance. Il en résulte que pratiquement on peut se borner à n'introduire, dans
la sommation sur les couples (pq) de la formule (28), que les plus proches voisins.
Mais de toutes façons, la somme $\frac{1}{4} \sum_q \ell_{pq}^2 C_{pq}$ est faible devant $2 \sum_i e_i$ et est peu
sensible à la disposition des atomes dans l'espace, de sorte qu'on aboutit à cette
conclusion surprenante, à savoir qu'il vaut mieux se contenter de l'énergie électronique de Hückel pour représenter, à une constante près, l'énergie totale, que d'essayer
de raffiner en ajoutant à celle-ci, l'énergie de répulsion ! Ainsi s'explique que
pour obtenir des résultats satisfaisants, on doive ajouter à l'énergie électronique
calculée suivant une méthode de type Hückel, une énergie de répulsion des coeurs,
non pas en R^{-1} mais en exp.$(-KR)$ (réf. 13). Cette façon de procéder simule assez bien
en effet la décroissance du terme $\ell^2 C$, de décroissance plus rapide que R^{-1}.

VI. DETERMINATION DE LA GEOMETRIE DU SYSTEME

En principe, la géométrie du système correspond à la valeur minimale de l'énergie
totale. Mais la détermination de ce minimum est souvent très laborieuse, surtout
lorsque le système contient de nombreux noyaux. Aussi des moyens plus simples pour
obtenir la géométrie d'équilibre ont-ils été recherchés.

Dans les molécules conjuguées, la distance entre noyaux voisins se révèle comme
reliée à l'indice de liaison ℓ_{pq} correspondant, par une loi pratiquement linéaire
(réf. 14) :

$$d(\overset{\circ}{A}) = 1,52 - 0,19 \ell \tag{32}$$

par exemple, pour les hydrocarbures conjugués plans.

Connaissant la loi de variation des β en fonction de la distance, par itération, on aboutit à la géométrie d'équilibre (partant de β égaux, deux ou trois itérations suffisent en général).

Dans le cas des métaux où il n'y a pas de squelette σ sous-jacent comme dans les molécules conjuguées, une loi existe encore, mais elle est un peu plus compliquée. Par exemple, pour les métaux avec une seule orbitale s (alcalins, cuivre, argent) on a (réf. 15) :

$$r = R \, \frac{1 + 3,4\ell}{1 + 5,9\ell} \tag{33}$$

où $\underline{R}$ dépend du métal (4,10 Å pour Li, 5,00 pour Na, ...). $\underline{R}$ a la même signification que dans la relation (22).

VII. ENERGIE DE TRANSITION ELECTRONIQUE

Dans la méthode de Hückel, l'énergie mise en jeu dans une transition monoélectronique entre les orbitales ϕ_a et ϕ_b, d'énergies associées respectives e_a et e_b, s'écrit simplement :

$$^H E_{a \to b} = e_b - e_a \tag{34}$$

Dans la méthode S.C.F., l'expression est plus compliquée et on distingue le passage sur l'état singulet de celui sur le triplet :

$$^S E_{a \to b} = e_b - e_a - J_{ab} + 2K_{ab}$$

$$^T E_{a \to b} = e_b - e_a - J_{ab} \tag{35}$$

avec $J_{ab} = (\phi_a^2, \phi_b^2)$ et $K_{ab} = (\phi_a \phi_b, \phi_a \phi_b)$.

La formule (34) donne donc une valeur erronée, trop élevée à cause des termes J et K manquants. On peut cependant montrer que, pratiquement, l'énergie exacte peut être obtenue pour le singulet en corrigeant l'expression de Hückel par un facteur de l'ordre de 0,5 à 0,6, de sorte que qualitativement cette méthode donne des résultats corrects en ce qui concerne l'évolution des énergies de transition dans une famille donnée.

VIII. RETOUR SUR L'APPROXIMATION MONODETERMINANTALE

La méthode de Hückel, comme la méthode S.C.F., repose, ainsi que nous l'avons dit, sur l'approximation monodéterminantale pour la fonction d'onde totale (3). Valable pour des édifices de petite taille, nous nous sommes posés la question de savoir si elle continuait à l'être pour des systèmes très grands, infinis à la limite.

Sans prétendre donner une réponse définitive, nous avancerons deux points précis. D'une part, l'énergie de corrélation, c'est-à-dire ce qu'apporterait une interaction de configuration complète par rapport à la limite Hartree-Fock, dans un atome ou une molécule, augmente beaucoup moins vite que l'énergie électronique totale, de sorte qu'à la limite, pour un système infini, on peut considérer que la partie

principale de l'énergie est donnée par l'approximation déterminantale, c'est-à-dire
par le modèle Hartree-Fock.

D'autre part, nous avons nous-mêmes effectué un calcul explicite sur une chaîne
linéaire formée de $2n$ atomes alcalins (réf. 16).

L'énergie de corrélation, approximée par la formule de Brillouin :

$$\Delta E_{corr} = \sum_a \sum_b \frac{K_{ab}^2}{\Delta E_{a^2 \to b^2}} \tag{36}$$

où $\Delta E_{a^2 \to b^2}$ est l'énergie de transition biélectronique du niveau $\underline{a}$ initialement utilisé
deux fois dans l'état fondamental, vers le niveau $\underline{b}$ vide, est bornée supérieurement,
pour $\underline{n}$ grand, par $(Lgn)^2/n$. Comme l'énergie électronique varie en $\underline{n}$, le rapport

$$\frac{\Delta E_{corr.}}{|E_{él}|} < \left(\frac{Lgn}{n}\right)^2 \tag{37}$$

tend vers zéro, quand $n \to \infty$. Donc, le modèle de Hartree-Fock donne, même pour un
système infini, une valeur correcte de l'énergie électronique. Ce résultat, s'il est
général, comme le laisseraient penser ceux obtenus pour les atomes et les petites
molécules, est de la plus haute importance.

IX. CONCLUSION

En conclusion, nous voyons que, dans la mesure où l'orthogonalisation des orbitales atomiques de base permet de ne retenir que les intégrales coulombiennes, la
méthode de Hückel se présente comme une simulation de la méthode S.C.F. . Les hypothèses
d'apparence gratuite sur lesquelles, historiquement, s'est bâtie la méthode, sont
en réalité parfaitement légitimes puisqu'elles peuvent être retrouvées directement
dans un cadre mathématique très précis, celui de la base orthogonalisée de Löwdin.
Sous prétexte d'amélioration, il n'est donc pas possible de sortir de ce cadre, sous
peine de perdre tout support théorique et de verser dans le pur empirisme. Sans crainte,
nous pouvons donc appliquer la méthode de Hückel, mais, encore une fois, à condition
d'en respecter le schéma initial.

REFERENCES

1 C.C.J. Roothaan, Rev. Mod. Phys., *23*(1951)69-89.
2 E. Hückel, Z. Physik., *60*(1930)423-456 ; *70*(1931)204-286.
3 R. Hoffmann, J. Chem. Phys., *39*(1963)1397-1412.
4 P.O. Löwdin, J. Chem. Phys., *18*(1950)365-375.
5 A. Julg, Tetrahedron, *19*(1963)Suppl.2,25-42 ; voir aussi pour un exposé plus
   détaillé : A. Julg, Chimie Quantique Structurale et Eléments de Spectroscopie
   Office des Publications Universitaires d'Alger, Alger, 1978, p.236.
6 R.S. Mulliken, C.A. Rieke et W.G. Brown, J. Amer. Chem. Soc., *63*(1941)41-56.
7 R.S. Mulliken, J. Phys. Chem., *56*(1952)295-311.
8 A. Julg et al., Valeurs non publiées, obtenues pour une cinquantaine de
   molécules étudiées au Laboratoire entre 1960 et 1968.
9 B. Lévy, communication personnelle.
10 voir par exemple : D. Silver et R.M. Stevens, J. Chem. Phys., *59*(1973)3378-3394 ;
   F. Marinelli, A. Julg et G. Abbate, Surf. Sci., *59*(1976)319-324.
11 A. Julg, résultat original.

266

12 A. Julg, G. Del Re et V. Barone, Phil. Mag., *35*(1977)517-531.
13 voir par exemple : F. Cyrot-Lackmann, M.C. Desjonquères et M.B. Gordon, J. Phys., *38* C_2(1977)57-62.
14 voir par exemple : A. Julg, J. Chim. Phys., *65*(1968)541-548 ; A. Julg et O. Julg, Theoret. Chim. Acta, *22*(1971)353-360.
15 A. Julg, résultat original.
16 A. Julg, à paraître.

DISCUSSION

A. JULG

Boudeville - 1°/ Que pensez-vous de l'utilisation d'un potentiel (par exemple gaz rare : Lennard-Jones) pour étudier la suite croissante N = 1,2,3...12,13... du nombre d'atomes d'un petit cluster métallique ? En première approximation très grossière.

2°/ Pensez-vous que, grâce à l'utilisation de la bonne représentation de l'énergie totale par la méthode de Huckel + base orthogonale de Löwdin, on puisse avoir une bonne idée relative de la géométrie lors de la croissance de petits clusters ?

Julg - 1°/ Je pense qu'il faut absolument séparer le cas des interactions entre des atomes de gaz rares, de celui des atomes dans un métal. Dans le premier cas, on a affaire à des entités descriptibles en termes d'orbitales fortement localisées autour de chacun des noyaux, alors que dans le second cas, la délocalisation est complète. Entre deux atomes de gaz rares on peut utiliser un potentiel de type Lennard-Jones par exemple, l'énergie totale d'interaction est la somme des énergies d'interaction entre les divers couples d'atomes. En revanche dans un métal, l'énergie n'est pas la somme de telles énergies. Le système doit être considéré dans son ensemble.

2°/ Oui, nous avons en particulier fait de telles études sur des clusters $(Li)_n$: réseaux plans carrés ou rectangulaires (A. Julg, G. Del Re, V. Barone ; Phil. Mag.) une relaxation très nette apparaît. Un autre exemple (A. Julg, M. Bénard, M. Bourg, M. Gillet, E. Gillet, Phys. Rev.) montre que l'on peut estimer la taille à partir de laquelle un cluster de lithium adopte la structure bcc définitive du cristal massif (au dessous, ce sont les formes de symétrie d'ordre 5 qui sont les plus stables. La taille critique correspond à n $\sim 10^5$.

Cyrot-Lackmann - 1°/ Concernant l'énergie totale dans le modèle de Huckel, je pense que le terme répulsif est plus important que vous ne l'avez dit. C'est en effet un terme essentiel dans la cohésion, et si on le néglige, les constantes élastiques des métaux de transition sont négatives. Dans nos résultats sur la stabilité comparée de cuboocta-èdres et d'icosaèdres, ce terme joue aussi un rôle important.

2°/ Pour compléter cette question, je voudrais rappeler ici que dans l'étude des systèmes désordonnés (liquides, verres, ..), c'est la forme du potentiel répulsif qui fixe principalement les caractéristiques essentielles de la fonction de corrélation de paires d'atomes, donnée de base de leur structure atomique. Par contre, c'est la forme du terme attractif qui domine les propriétés électroniques. Il faut donc, selon la propriété physique que l'on étudie, porter une attention particulière à l'un ou l'autre terme composant l'énergie totale.

3°/ J'ai été très intéressée par la petite partie oscillante que vous trouvez dans le paramètre $\beta_\rho q$. Dans les métaux, à cause de la présence de la surface de Fermi, le potentiel interatomique présente un comportement oscillant de type :

$$\cos 2kFr/ r^3$$

Avez-vous comparé vos valeurs de R pour les métaux avec le terme oscillant qui proviendrait de la surface de Fermi ?

Julg - 1°/ Je me suis peut-être mal exprimé. Je n'ai pas voulu minimiser l'importance du terme répulsif. J'ai voulu dire : a) que l'énergie totale apparaît comme égale à l'énergie de Hückel, plus un terme qui n'est pas en R^{-1} ; b) que le terme de répulsion n'est pas très sensible à la différence de géométrie pour divers isomères, donc que le terme de Hückel suffit dans ces cas pour comparer la stabilité des divers isomères. Mais pour déterminer la géométrie de l'un d'eux, il faut travailler avec l'énergie totale. Naturellement, il en sera de même pour les constantes élastiques.

2°/ Je suis d'accord. Mais, il n'en reste pas moins qu'il faut faire attention même pour les propriétés strictement électroniques, que Hückel ne donne pas la bonne énergie électronique.

3°/ Non, je n'ai jamais envisagé la question. Mais je la retiens !

Renouprez - La méthode de Hückel est-elle bien adaptée pour décrire le sens des transferts électroniques et la valeur des charges portées par les atomes dans le cas de molécules organo-métalliques ?

Julg - La technique classique qui n'introduit dans l'équation séculaire que les termes non diagonaux relatifs à des atomes chimiquement liés, conduit à des charges électroniques incorrectes chaque fois que la molécule contient un ou plusieurs cycles impairs (ex : azulène). Pour rétablir la situation, il faut introduire des termes supplémentaires entre atomes non liés.

Dans votre cas, je pense que vous devriez pouvoir obtenir des résultats assez corrects, les transferts étant surtout conditionnés par les valeurs relatives des termes diagonaux, sauf bien entendu, si vous introduisez des cycles impairs.

J. BOURDON (Editor)
Growth and Properties of Metal Clusters, pp. 269—278
© 1980 Elsevier Scientific Publishing Company — Printed in The Netherlands

STRUCTURE ET PROPRIETES ELECTRONIQUES D'AGREGATS D'ATOMES DE CUIVRE. UNE
ETUDE LCAO-MO-SCF "AB INITIO".

C. Bachmann, J. Demuynck et A. Veillard

Université Louis Pasteur, Strasbourg (France)

I. INTRODUCTION

L'étude des structures géométrique et électronique des petits agrégats
métalliques "clusters métalliques" est importante pour plusieurs raisons :

1°) Les catalyseurs métalliques existent généralement sous la forme de
microcristallites dispersés, caractérisés par un rapport surface/volume
élevé [1]. Beaucoup d'effort est actuellement consacré à la recherche de la
corrélation entre la réactivité et la taille de tels catalyseurs.

2°) Un certain nombre de techniques expérimentales, en particulier la
technique de condensation en matrice inerte, permettent aujourd'hui la synthèse et l'observation d'agrégats comportant moins d'une dizaine d'atomes
[2-6].

3°) Une branche particulièrement féconde de la chimie organométallique
correspond à l'étude de composés organométalliques polynucléaires comportant de multiples liaisons métal-métal et généralement désignés par le terme
"clusters moléculaires". Plusieurs auteurs [7,8] ont souligné l'analogie
possible entre le rôle de ces clusters en catalyse homogène et celui des
agrégats métalliques en catalyse hétérogène.

Un certain nombre de travaux théoriques concernant l'étude de <u>petits</u>
agrégats (nous ne considérerons pas ici les études de particules relativement grosses, comportant plusieurs milliers d'atomes [9]) de métaux de transition ou de métaux nobles a été publié antérieurement.

Toutes ces études théoriques sont fondées sur l'emploi des méthodes semi-
empiriques de la chimie quantique. La méthode CNDO et la méthode EHT ont été
utilisées pour étudier les clusters de Ni, Cu, Pd, Ag et Au comportant jusqu'à 55 atomes [10-20]. Une étude des clusters M_8 et M_{13} (M = Ni, Cu, Pd et
Pt) a été faite en utilisant la méthode SCF-Xα-SW [21,22]. Cependant, les
conclusions de ces études semi-empiriques sont divergentes en ce qui concerne, par exemple, la rapidité avec laquelle les propriétés des agrégats con-
vergent, au cours de la nucléation, vers celles du métal massif. Les calculs
EHT et CNDO de Baetzold le conduisent à la conclusion que les clusters Ag_{55}
ont des propriétés très différentes de celles du métal cristallin [10,12]
alors que les calculs SCF-Xα de Messmer et Johnson suggèrent que le caractère du solide massif est déjà atteint pour des clusters de 13 atomes [21].

Nous présentons ici les résultats d'une étude "ab initio" des clusters
Cu_n avec n ⩽ 13. Dans ce travail, nous nous sommes efforcés de répondre aux

questions suivantes :

- quelles sont les structures géométriques les plus stables pour les différents agrégats considérés ?

- comment évoluent les propriétés de ces agrégats avec la croissance de leur taille ?

II. DÉTAIL DES CALCULS

Les calculs LCAO-MO-SCF "ab initio" ont été effectués avec le système de programmes Astérix [23,24]. Afin d'étudier l'influence possible de la base utilisée sur les résultats, nous avons répété les calculs relatifs à Cu_2 avec quatre bases différentes (Table 1) de fonctions gaussiennes contractées [25].

TABLE 1

Influence du choix de la base sur les résultats de Cu_2

Niveaux moléculaires	BSI	BSII	BSIII	BSIV
σ_g (4s)	-0.225 [a]	-0.223	-0.223	-0.221
σ_u	-0.461	-0.459	-0.469	-0.471
π_g	-0.470	-0.468	-0.478	-0.482
δ_u	-0.481	-0.479	-0.489	-0.491
δ_g	-0.487	-0.485	-0.494	-0.496
π_u	-0.501	-0.498	-0.506	-0.510
σ_g (3d)	-0.511	-0.508	-0.516	-0.519
distance Cu-Cu (Å)	2.34	2.333	2.327	2.41
énergie totale (u.a.)	-3271.0496	-3271.0851	-3271.6780	-3269.8680

a) les énergies d'orbitale sont exprimées en unités atomiques

La base BSI labellée (12,7,5/5,3,2) est une base mixte où les orbitales 3d et 4s sont décrites par deux fonctions (base double zeta), les autres orbitales étant décrites par une seule fonction (base minimale). Cette base a été utilisée pour l'étude des clusters n = 3-8. La base BSII (13,8,5/6,4,2) est une base double zeta pour les couches 3d et 4p, triple zeta pour la couche 4s et minimale pour les couches internes. La base BSIII est construite à partir de la base BSI à laquelle a été ajouté un jeu s, p, d de fonctions (excentrées) de polarisation. La base plus modeste BSIV (12,7,4/5,3,1) a été utilisée dans le calcul du cluster Cu_{13}. Plusieurs géométries ont été envisagées pour les clusters n = 3-8 et la distance interatomique Cu-Cu a été optimisée dans certains cas particuliers (Table 2). La valeur 2.40 Å a été adoptée dans les autres cas.

III. RESULTATS ET DISCUSSION

1°) Structure géométrique des agrégats Cu_n

Les résultats de la table 1 montrent que la distance optimum Cu-Cu est relativement sensible au choix de la base. Lorsque la qualité de celle-ci augmente, la distance diminue de 2.41 Å jusqu'à 2.33 Å. Nous estimons à 2.30 Å la valeur correspondant à la limite Hartree-Fock, la distance expérimentale étant égale à 2.22 Å [26]. Les calculs proches de la limite Hartree-Fock donnent généralement des longueurs de liaison très légèrement trop courtes [27]. L'anomalie rencontrée ici est probablement due à la présence dans la fonction d'onde exacte, de configurations du type $(4p_\sigma)^2$. Les résultats géométriques concernant les autres clusters n = 3-13 sont rapportés dans la table 2. On y voit que , pour n = 3 et 4, la structure linéaire est favorisée par rapport aux structures plus compactes mais que la situation s'inverse à partir de n = 5. Ce résultat infirme les conclusions des calculs EHT selon lesquels la structure linéaire demeure la structure la plus stable au niveau de nucléation n = 30 ou 50 [10,14]. Les données expérimentales concernant la structure des petits agrégats sont rares mais semblent confirmer les conclusions de nos calculs. Ag_3 est probablement linéaire puisqu'on n'observe qu'une seule bande Raman [28]. Le spectre ESR des espèces Ag_4^+ et Ag_4^{3+} est compatible avec l'existence de deux types d'atomes d'argent ce qui n'exclut pas la structure linéaire [29]. Les ions $Pb_5^=$ et Bi_5^{3+} ont une structure D_{3h} [30,31] et le cluster Ag_6 une structure octaédrique [32]. Schultze et collaborateurs [5] arrivent eux aussi à la conclusion qu'un changement de structure doit se produire pour Ag_n entre n = 4 et n = 5, en observant que l'énergie de la première bande d'absorption décroît de manière monotone de n = 2 à n = 4, présente une discontinuité pour n = 5 avant de décroître à nouveau de n = 5 à n = 6. Pour comprendre cette brusque tendance à la compacité, nous avons schématisé, dans la figure 1, le caractère liant ou antiliant des orbitales s occupées, dans le cas des deux structures les plus favorables (table 2) des agrégats n = 3, 4 et 5.

Si l'on compare les orbitales des systèmes linéaires avec leurs homologues des systèmes bi- ou tridimensionnels, on s'aperçoit que :

- les orbitales non liantes ou antiliantes sont systématiquement plus stables dans les systèmes linéaires que dans leurs homologues compacts. Ceci est dû au fait que, dans les systèmes linéaires, les orbitales possédant au moins un noeud contiennent aussi un certain nombre d'interactions liantes (exception faite pour n = 3) qui atténuent leur caractère antiliant. Cette constante favorise donc la structure linéaire et explique la contraction observée (table 2) pour la distance optimum Cu-Cu lorsque l'on passe, dans le cas de Cu_3 par exemple, de la structure D_{3h} à la structure linéaire. Ce phénomène de contraction a été souligné antérieurement par Baetzold [10] et par Anderson [18].

- les orbitales liantes sont, par contre, systématiquement plus stables dans les systèmes compacts que dans leurs homologues linéaires. Le nombre d'in-

TABLE 2

Principaux résultats obtenus pour Cu_n avec BSI et Cu-Cu = 2.40 Å

n	Structure		Etat fondamental et énergie (en u.a.)	Distance Cu-Cu optimisée (en Å)	Energie de cohésion par atome (en kcal/mole)	Potentiel d'ionisation (en eV)
2	$D_{\infty h}$		$^1\Sigma_g^+$ -3271.0493	2.343	9.7	5.7^a 6.1^b
3	$D_{\infty h}$		$^2\Sigma_u^+$ -4906.5753	2.35	10.0	5.4^a
	C_{2v}		$^2B_1$ -4906.5704			
	D_{3h}		$^2E'$ -4906.5700	2.41		
4	$D_{\infty h}$		$^1\Sigma_g^+$ -6542.1180		12.7	5.4^a 5.6^b
	D_{4h}		$^3A_{2g}$ -6542.1128	2.43		5.2^a
	Td		$^3T_1$ -6542.1016			
	D_{2d}	$\alpha = 150°$	$^3A_2$ -6542.1124			
		$\alpha = 120°$	$^3A_2$ -6542.1099			
5	$D_{\infty h}$		$^2\Sigma_g^+$ -8177.6437			
	D_{3h}		$^2E'$ -8177.6591		14.2	
	C_{4v}		$^4A_2$ -8177.6560			4.6^a
	D_{4h}		^2E_u -8177.6384			
8	O_h		$^1A_{1g}$ -13084.321	2.43	19.5	5.9^b
			-13079.537^c		11.5	
	D_{4d}		$^1A_1$ -13084.333		20.4	5.5^b
13	Cubooctaèdre		$^2T_{2g}$ -21254.314^c		14.6	

a   Calculé comme $E(Cu_n^+) - E(Cu_n)$; b   Calculé en utilisant le théorème de Koopman ; c   Calculées avec BSIV.

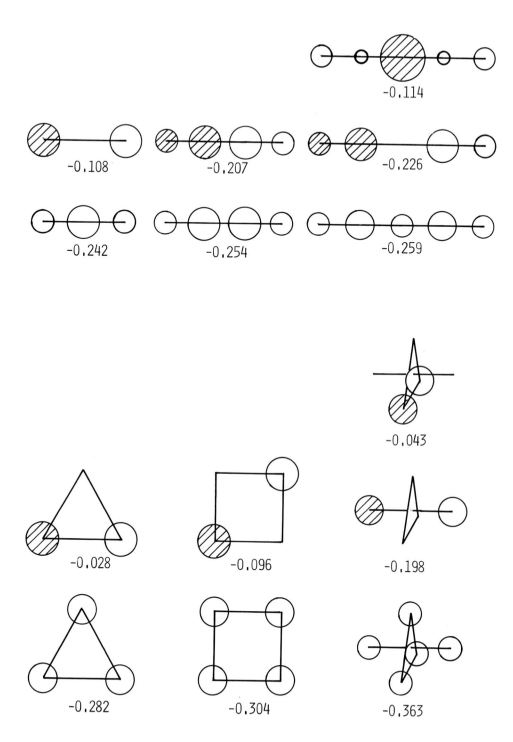

Figure 1. Description schématique et énergies (en u.a.) des dernières orbitales occupées dans Cu_3, Cu_4 et Cu_5 pour les structures linéaire et compacte.

274

teractions liantes qu'elles décrivent est en effet plus élevé dans une structure bi- ou tridimensionnelle que dans une structure linéaire. La figure 1
montre que ce deuxième facteur devient prépondérant à partir de n = 5 puisque neuf interactions stabilisantes apparaissent dans la structure D_{3h} contre seulement quatre dans la structure linéaire. L'importance de ce facteur
apparaît également lorsque l'on compare les énergies de l'orbitale liante,
pour les deux types de structure, dans la série Cu_3, Cu_4 et Cu_5, respectivement -0.24, -0.25 et -0.26 u.a. pour les systèmes linéaires et -0.28, -0.30
et -0.36 u.a. pour les systèmes compacts.

La distance interatomique Cu-Cu apparaît relativement peu sensible à la
taille de l'agrégat puisque nous avons obtenu la valeur de 2.43 Å dans le
cas de $Cu_4(D_{4h})$ comme dans le cas de $Cu_8(Oh)$. Notons que cette distance est
relativement éloignée de la valeur 2.56 Å qui caractérise le métal massif.

Goddard et collaborateurs [33] ont optimisé la distance Ni-Ni dans le
cluster Ni_{13} et obtiennent une valeur de 2.41 Å (la distance interatomique
dans le nickel cristallin est égale à 2.49 Å).

2°) Niveaux d'énergie et énergies de cohésion dans les agrégats Cu_n

Les niveaux d'énergie de Cu_2, présentés dans la table 1, apparaissent
pratiquement indépendants de la base utilisée et le niveau 4s est bien sépa-
ré des niveaux 3d quel que soit le calcul considéré. Ce résultat est très
différent de celui du calcul SCF-Xα-SW d'Ozin et Norman [34] où l'orbitale
4s apparaît localisée au milieu des niveaux 3d. Nous avons rapporté dans la
figure 2 les niveaux d'énergie 3d et 4s des agrégats Cu_3 - Cu_{13} dans leur
structure compacte. On peut y suivre la formation d'une bande relativement
étroite de niveaux 3d et d'une bande beaucoup plus large de niveaux 4s.
Pour Cu_8 les deux bandes sont nettement distinctes. Dans le cas de Cu_{13} les
deux bandes amorcent leur recouvrement et le niveau 4s le plus profond, de
symétrie a_{1g}, est pratiquement dégénéré avec les niveaux 3d les moins stables. Cette distribution des niveaux d'énergie est très différente de celle
du métal massif et nos résultats infirment les conclusions de Messmer et
Johnson [21] selon lesquels la bande d serait entièrement recouverte par la
bande sp, déjà au niveau de Cu_8. Les deux niveaux t_{2g} et e_g, qui sont représentés dans la figure 2 sous la bande d de Cu_{13}, décrivent l'interaction
liante entre les orbitales atomiques 3d de l'atome central et celles des
atomes périphériques. L'extra-stabilisation (0.02 u.a.) de ces deux niveaux
résulte du grand nombre d'interactions liantes présent dans la composition
de ces orbitales. Nous pensons que l'atome central du cuboctaèdre Cu_{13}
occupe une situation analogue à celle des atomes dans le métal massif. Ce
sont donc les deux niveaux profonds t_{2g} et e_g de Cu_{13} qui représentent l'origine de la bande d du métal massif alors que la bande d obtenue pour l'agrégat représente plutôt des états de surface du cuivre cristallin. Cette interprétation est tout à fait différente de celle de Messmer et Johnson qui
considèrent que la bande d de Cu_{13} est représentative du métal massif et

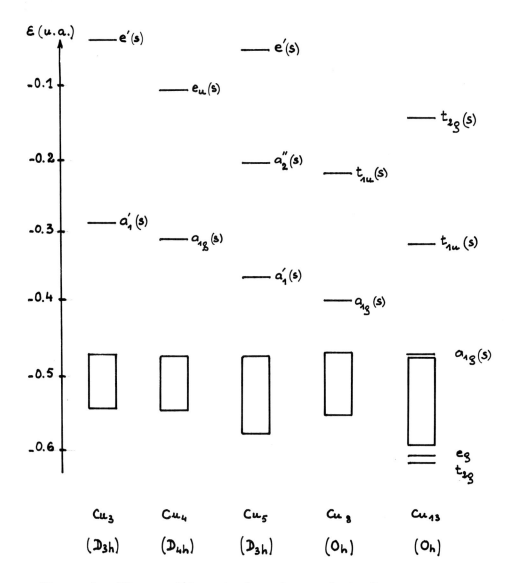

Figure 2. Niveaux d'énergie dans les agrégats Cu_n.

que le rôle particulier joué par les orbitales t_{2g} et e_g proviennent d'un arti-
fice de calcul [21]. Les résultats expérimentaux de Bradshaw [35] soutien-
nent les conclusions de notre étude en démontrant que les niveaux d'énergie
de particules (sensiblement plus grosses que celles envisagées dans notre
travail) de palladium demeurent très sensibles à la taille de celles-ci.

Les potentiels d'ionisation (P.I.), calculés dans ce travail (table 2) ne
permettent pas de dégager une corrélation quelconque entre la valeur de ces
P.I. et la taille des agrégats correspondants.

Les valeurs obtenues avoisinent 5 eV et sont remarquablement proches de

276

la valeur 4.7 eV, connue pour le cuivre massif.

L'énergie de cohésion des agrégats se présente, par contre, comme une fonction pratiquement linéaire du nombre d'atomes (table 2). De ce point de vue, les agrégats manifestent des propriétés différentes de celles du métal massif puisque la valeur 20 kcal/mole, calculée pour n = 8, est bien inférieure à l'énergie de cohésion du cuivre massif (80 kcal/mole), même si l'on tient compte du fait que l'approximation SCF sous-estime les énergies de liaison.

IV. CONCLUSION

Les agrégats d'atome de cuivre Cu_n (n = 2, 3, 4, 5, 8 et 13) ont été étudiés par la méthode LCAO-MO-SCF en incluant tous les électrons (calculs "ab initio"). L'ensemble des résultats obtenus pour ces agrégats (en particulier structure, énergie de liaison par atome et distribution des niveaux d'énergie électroniques) montre que ces petits agrégats possèdent une structure électronique originale, intermédiaire entre celle de la molécule diatomique et celle du métal massif.

REFERENCES

1 J.R. Anderson, "Structure of metallic catalysts", Academic Press, London, 1975.

2 M. Moskowits and J.E. Hulse, J. Chem. Phys., 1977, 66, 3988.

3 M. Moskowits and J.E. Hulse, J. Chem. Phys., 1977, 67, 4271.

4 G.A. Ozin and H. Huber, Inorg. Chem., 1978, 17, 155.

5 W. Schulze, H.U. Becker and H. Abe, Chem. Phys., 1978, 35, 177.

6 B.J. Garrison, N. Winograd and D.E. Harrison, J. Chem. Phys., 1978, 69, 1440.

7 E.L. Muetterties, Bull. Soc. Chim. Belg., 1975, 84, 959.

8 J.M. Basset and R. Ugo, dans "Aspects of homogeneous catalysis", R. Ugo ed., D. Reidel, Dordrecht, Netherlands, 1977, vol. 3, p. 137-183.

9 M.B. Gordon, Thèse de Doctorat de 3ème Cycle, Université Scientifique et Médicale de Grenoble, 1978.

10 R.G. Baetzold, J. Chem. Phys., 1971, 55, 4363.

11 D.J.M. Fassaert, H. Verbeek and A. Van der Avoird, Surface Sci., 1972, 29, 501.

12 R.G. Baetzold, J. Catalysis, 1973, 29, 129.

13 G. Blyholder, Surface Sci., 1974, 42, 249.

14 R.C. Baetzold and R.E. Mack, J. Chem. Phys., 1975, 62, 1513.

15 R.C. Baetzold, J. Phys. Chem., 1976, 80, 1504.

16 R.C. Baetzold, J. Chem. Phys., 1978, 68, 555.

17 A.B. Anderson and R. Hoffmann, J. Chem. Phys., 1974, 61, 4545.

18 A.B. Anderson, J. Chem. Phys., 1976, 64, 4046.

19 A.B. Anderson, J. Chem. Phys., 1978, 68, 1744.

20 J.D. Head and K.A.R. Mitchell, Mol. Phys., 1978, 35, 1681.

21 R.P. Messmer, S.K. Knudson, K.H. Johnson, J.B. Diamond and C.Y. Yang, Phys. Rev. B, 1976, 13, 1396.

22 N. Rösch and D. Menzel, Chem. Phys. Let., 1976, 13, 243.

23 M. Bénard, A. Dedieu, J. Demuynck, M-M. Rohmer, A. Strich and A. Veillard, "Asterix : a system of programs for the Univac 1110", unpublished work.

24 M. Bénard, J. Chim. Phys., 1976, p. 413.

25 B. Roos, A. Veillard and G. Vinot, Theoret. Chim. Acta, 1971, 20, 1.

26 N. Aslund, R.F. Barrow, W.G. Richards and D.N. Travis, Arkiv Fys., 1965, 30, 171.

27 Voir, par exemple : J.A. Pople, dans "Modern Theoretical Chemistry. Applications of electronic structure theory", H.F. Schaefer ed., Plenum Press, New-York, 1977, vol. 4, p. 1.

28 W.S. Schulze, H.V. Becker, R. Minkwitz and K. Manzel, Chem. Phys. Let., 1978, 55, 59.

29 R.S. Eachus and M.C.R. Symons, J. Chem. Soc. A, 1970, 1329.

30 J.D. Corbett and P.A. Edwards, J.C.S. Chem. Comm., 1975, 984.

31 R.C. Burns, R.J. Gillespie and W. Luk, Inorg. Chem., 1978, 17, 3596.

32 Y. Kim and K. Seff, J. Am. Chem. Soc., 1978, 100, 6989.

33 T.H. Upton and W.A. Goddard, J. Amer. Chem. Soc., 1978, 100, 5659, référence 16.

34 G.A. Ozin, H. Huber, D. McIntosh, S. Mitchell, J.G. Norman, Jr. and L. Noodleman, J. Am. Chem. Soc., 1979, 101, 3504.

35 R. Unwin and A.M. Bradshaw, Chem. Phys. Let., 1978, 58, 58.

DISCUSSION

C. BACHMANN, J. DEMUYNCK, A. VEILLARD

Gallezot - Les distances interatomiques dans les petits agrégats que vous considérez sont-elles contractées ou dilatées par rapport aux distances du métal massif ?

Demuynck - Les résultats expérimentaux concernant la structure des petits agrégats métalliques doivent être examinés de manière critique avant de les comparer aux calculs théoriques. En effet, les agrégats métalliques sont dans un environnement (support, atmosphère) qui peut perturber considérablement la structure théoriquement la plus stable.

Boudeville - Pensez-vous que la relative stabilité de l'icosaèdre par rapport au cuboctaèdre pourrait être due, conformément à ce que vous observez sur les petits clusters $N = 2,3,4$, à un plus grand nombre de liaisons liantes pour les orbitales liantes ($R_{tang} = a$) de l'icosaèdre par rapport au cuboctaèdre où certaines distances sont à $R_{tang} = a\sqrt{2}$

Je pense que comme avec "Ab Initio" où vous affectez à l'atome central les niveaux C_g et t_{2g} il est aussi possible de décomposer les mêmes niveaux pour les résultats X_α et ainsi de savoir s'ils correspondent à l'atome central ou non pour Cu_{13}.

Demuynck - C'est une explication possible que nous envisagerons très prochainement.

Salem - Il semble en fait que Messmer et K.H. Johnson soient d'accord avec vous sur l'origine des 2 niveaux discrets bas, à savoir l'atome central. Le désaccord semblerait porter sur l'amorce de la bande d, que vous attribuez à ces ceux niveaux inférieurs et qu'eux attribuent à la bande supérieure.

J. BOURDON (Editor)
Growth and Properties of Metal Clusters, pp. 279—288
© 1980 Elsevier Scientific Publishing Company — Printed in The Netherlands

A SCF-Xα-SW INVESTIGATION OF THE STEPPED Ni[m(100)x n(111)] SURFACE : A CLUSTER
APPROACH

R. HOOGEWIJS°, G. DALMAI°° and J. VENNIK°

° Laboratorium voor Kristallografie en Studie van de Vaste Stof,
  Rijksuniversiteit Gent, Krijgslaan 271, B-9000 Gent, Belgium.

°° Laboratoire de Surfaces et Interfaces, CNRS-ISEN, 3, rue François Baës,
   59046, Lille Cedex, France

ABSTRACT

Molecular SCF-Xα-SW cluster calculations are used to study the local density of
states at the central atom site on the protruding edge of a Ni_8 cluster in the configuration of a stepped Ni (100) surface. Comparison is made with the corresponding result
for a flat surface represented by a Ni_9 cluster. For the Ni_8 stepped surface cluster,
both a relaxed and a non-relaxed surface are considered. The adsorption of Na on Ni_8 is
briefly discussed

INTRODUCTION

A detailed knowledge of the electronic structure of the surface is necessary for the
understanding of the structure sensitivity of surface processes. Since the pioneering work
of Somorjai et al. [1] it is widely recognized that surface structural irregularities, such
as steps, kinks etc., may give rise to an increased activity for certain chemical reactions.
As a consequence, the influence of these irregularities on the electronic structure of the
surface has been the subject of a great number of papers within the last few years [e.g.
2-5]. Specific surface properties such as the surface electrostatic dipole moment [6],
the surface relaxation [7] and phonon dispersion [7,8] , which depend on, or are altered
by the presence of steps, have been studied extensively.

In applying cluster calculations in the study of the electronic structure of solids,
the question still remains which minimum cluster size is needed in order to demonstrate,
at least qualitatively a given bulk- or surface property. In the present work concerning
stepped surfaces, the minimum size is chosen in such a way that one of the "surface" atoms
has the correct nearest neighbour configuration. The cluster local density of states
(LDS) at this atom site is compared with tight binding results obtained by Cyrot-Lackmann
et al. [4] for the semi-infinite solid.

Clusters of respectively nine and eight Ni atoms are considered to represent the flat
Ni (100) and stepped Ni [m(100)x n(111)] surfaces respectively (for stepped surfaces
the nomenclature of Lang et al. [9] is used). Electronic densities of states have been
determined using the molecular orbital self-consistent field Xαscattered-wave cluster

method (SCF-Xα-SW) developed by Slater [10] and Johnson [11].

COMPUTATION METHOD

The configurations chosen for the Ni_9 and Ni_8 clusters are shown in fig 1.

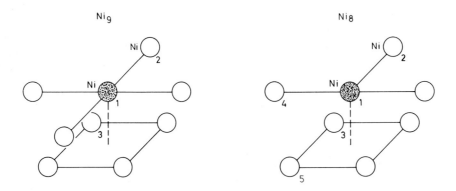

Fig. 1. Cluster configurations for flat (Ni_9) and stepped (Ni_8) Ni surfaces.
Four atoms are arranged in a simple square array, with, in the case of Ni_9, five atoms
symmetrically located in the layer above. In the Ni_8 case one of these five atoms is
missing in order to simulate a step on the (100) surface. The dotted atoms have all the
nearest neighbours of an atom in an ideal (100) surface, and those of a stepped [m(100)x
n(111)] surface in the Ni_9 and Ni_8 cluster respectively.

In the construction of the muffin-tin potential the touching sphere criterion was
used. The radius of the Ni spheres (2.355 a.u.) was chosen equal to about one-half of the
nearest neighbour distance in a bulk nickel crystal [12]. The exchange parameter used
(0.70896) is the one given by Schwarz [13]. For the stepped surface, a second set of
calculations has been carried out taking the atomic relaxation (an inward contraction
[7,14]) of the edge atoms into account; hereby the radius of the atoms was kept constant,
giving rise to a small overlap of the edge spheres with respect to the others.

For both the Ni_9 and the Ni_8 cluster, the secular determinant was formed using
partial waves up to l = 4 for the outer sphere region and l = 2 for the atomic spheres.
The dimension of the secular determinant was reduced by taking the cluster symmetry into
account ($\mathcal{C}_{4v}$ for Ni_9 and $\mathcal{C}_s$ for Ni_8). The energy levels have been classified according
to the irreducible representations of the respective symmetry point groups.

The adsorption of a sodium atom on the stepped surface has also been analysed. The
adatom has been placed in the three-fold co-ordinated site of the (111) plane of the
[m(100)x n(111)]surface. The adatom-nickel bond length has been taken equal to the corresponding experimental LEED value for adsorption of Na on a flat Ni (100) surface (5.3669
a.u.) [15].The radius of the sodium muffin-tin sphere has been chosen so as to satisfy the
touching sphere criterion. The exchange parameter α_{Na} has been put equal to c. 73 115 [13]

In the partial wave expansion s and p waves have been used for the adatom sphere.

RESULTS AND DISCUSSION

Ni$_9$-cluster : (local) densities of states

The density of occupied states profile of the Ni$_9$ cluster obtained from a nonself-consistent-field Xα scattered-wave calculation, i.e. from the zeroth iteration of the iterative self-consistent-field procedure, is represented in fig. 2a.

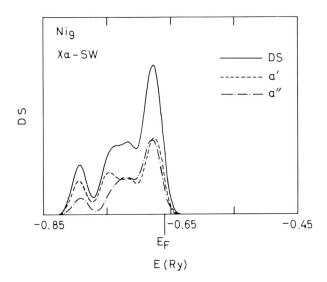

Fig. 2a. Non-self-consistent density of states for Ni$_9$.

For graphical purposes each discrete cluster energy level has been broadened by a normalized Gaussian with dispersion 0.01 Ry. For comparison with the Ni$_8$ cluster ($\mathcal{C}_s$ symmetry) the a'(a$_1$ +b$_1$ + 1/2 e) and a"(a$_2$ +b$_2$+1/2 e) contributions are also given. The Fermi level was taken to correspond to the highest occupied energy level. The general aspect of the spectrum closely resembles the corresponding non-self-consistent-field density of states curve of the related thirteen-atom cluster considered by Jones et al.[2]. There is a high density of d states close to the Fermi level and a "discrete" state at the high binding energy side slightly separated from the rest of the band. Jennings et al.[2] have related this "split-off" state to the corresponding feature appearing in the self-consistent-field thirteen-atom cubo-octahedral cluster result of Messmer et al.[16]

Apart from the inherent limitations of cluster calculations due to the limited size and to the restrictions imposed by the muffin-tin approach, the capability of representing a semi-infinite solid by a small cluster, to some degree depends on the self-consistency of the treatment [e.g. 17-18].

Figure 2b represents the density of occupied states of the Ni_9 cluster as obtained by iterating the potential to within 10^{-1} of self-consistency, keeping the cores frozen $(1s^2 2s^2 2p^6 3s^2 3p^6)$. The spectrum very closely resembles the self-consistent-field result obtained for the Ni_{13} cubo-octahedral cluster by Messmer et al. [16].

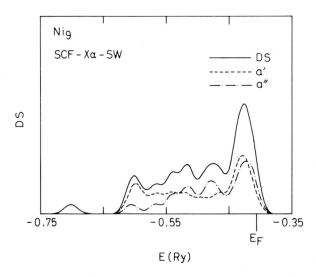

Fig. 2b. Self-consistent density of states for Ni_9.

These authors have attributed the split-off state to an increase of electronic charge at the central atom site of the cubo-octahedral cluster due to the greater potential well associated with this atom relative to the potentials of the so-called "surface" atoms. From an analysis of the valence charges within the different muffin-tin spheres for both the self-consistent and the non-self-consistent calculation, it follows that in the present case the split-off state can be associated with the charge transfer towards the dotted atom (atom 1) of fig. 1.

It is often interesting to define localized quantities which vary less strongly with cluster size than e.g. the total density of states. Such a quantity is the local density of states (LDS) which is obtained from weighting each molecular cluster eigenstate by the charge in the sphere surrounding the atom on which the total density is projected. Hereby the charge present in the iner sphere and outer sphere region has been redistributed among the atomic spheres in the same ratio as the calculated charges within the latter. The self-consistent LDS centered at atom 1 of the Ni_9 cluster is shown in fig. 3. Apart from the shift towards lower binding energies and the appearance of a distinct split-off state, the charge redistribution which occurred within the valence band is the most prominent feature. It is furthermore seen that the total band width increased with respect to the zeroth order treatment.

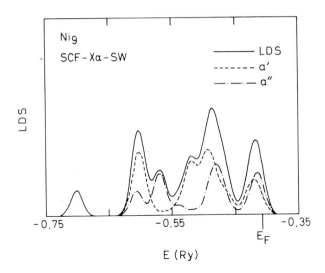

Fig. 3. Self-consistent local density of states at the central atom of the (100) "surface" of Ni_9.

The general aspect of the present self-consistent LDS closely resembles that of the (100) surface density of states as calculated by Desjonquères et al [19] using a tight binding moment method. In essence one obtains three intense peaks, of which the one near the middle of the band is the most striking feature in that it is not present in the bulk density of states and also not in the surface density of states of the more dense (111) plane [19]. The strong central peak has also been observed for the (100) surface density of states of other transition metals [see e.g. 20] and has been considered by Friedel [20] as being due to virtual bound d states on the surface atoms, broadened by interaction with the bulk of the metal.

Ni$_8$ -stepped surface cluster

It is interesting to notice that upon creation of a step (fig.4) at the atom

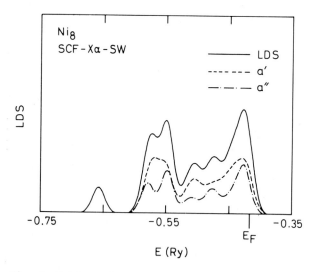

Fig. 4. Self-consistent local density of states at the central atom on the step edge of the non-relaxed Ni$_8$ "stepped surface" cluster.

1 site (the central atom on the protruding edge of the stepped surface cluster (fig. 1)), the central LDS peak mentioned above is much less pronounced than for the flat surface (fig. 3). An analogous result has been obtained by Cyrot-Lackmann et al.[4] for the LDS at the step edge of the Ni [6(111)x(001)] and Ni[9(111)x(01$\bar{1}$)]surfaces. The Ni case is different from e.g. the Pt case where a sharp surface virtual bound state is found in the density of states at the protruding edge of the stepped surface [3] .

Cyrot - Lackmann et al [4] also calculated the LDS at the most-central atom site on the edge between hexagonal and square faces of a series of cubo-octahedrae. The nearest neighbour environment of this central atom is identical to that of an atom on the protruding edge of a [m(100)x n111)] stepped surface. As far as the appearance of the central peak in the density of states is concerned, the calculations of Cyrot-Lackmann et al [4] have shown that depending on whether the number of atoms on an edge is odd or even, the central peak appears or disappears. Only for cubo-octahedrae of more than about 1000 atoms the oscillations have damped out and the residual LDS shows no central peak. The cluster that has been considered in the present work to represent the stepped surface is one with an odd number of atoms, i.e three atoms, on the edge between the (100) and (111) surfaces. This is precisely the condition whereby for the cubo-octahedrae the tight-binding moment method [4] gives rise to a central peak in the LDS. The fact that in the present SCF-Xα-SW calculation it is not present, supports the idea that its absence probably is not due to an artefact of the computation method, but could rather be related to an intrinsic physical property of the Ni stepped surface.

On the other hand, the split-off state at the high binding energy side can again be explained as being due to artefacts introduced by the deeper potential well present at the dotted atom site. This is manifested by the somewhat larger charge on this atom with respect to the others.

Considering the net charge on the central (dotted) atom, it follows that upon introduction of a step, the excess negative charge with respect to atoms of type 3 (fig. 1) is reduced. This is true for both the relaxed and unrelaxed case. Qualitatively, as far as the withdrawal of charge is concerned one thus observes the same trend as found for Pt, Au and W from workfunction measurements of Besocke et al.[6]. These authors state that edge atoms on Pt, Au and W stepped surfaces should carry a net positive charge of the order of 0.1 a.u.

In the present work calculations have also been carried out for a stepped surface cluster for which the atoms on the protruding edge have slightly been relaxed. The atomic relaxation that has been introduced here is the one calculated recently by Allan [14] for the Ni (311) surface (or the Ni [2(100)x(111)] stepped surface), i.e. an inward movement of the atoms on the protruding edge of 0.268 a.u. in the direction perpendicular to the (100) surface and 0.061 a.u. in the direction parallel to this surface. Although this atomic relaxation process has been shown to be important in the understanding of certain vibrational losses observed in high resolution electron loss spectroscopy [7] it has only a slight influence on the LDS on the central atom of the protruding edge; the relative contribution of s,p and d waves to the LDS does not change either.

Adsorption of Na on Ni

Preliminary results have been obtained for Na adsorbed on a stepped Ni surface. Calculations have been carried out for Na/Ni$_8$ using the cluster configuration described in section 2.

The main influence on the Ni-LDS of the adsorption of Na seems to be limited to a slight increase in intensity of the double peaked resonance situated at about -0.6 Ry (fig.4), and a more pronounced decrease of the resonance just below the Fermi level.

SUMMARY AND CONCLUSION

The present work on the electronic densities of states for small Ni clusters, is seen as a first step in a continuing study of chemisorption on flat and stepped surfaces. In this paper particular emphasis has been put on the influence of a step on the local density of states at the protruding edge of a Ni[m(100)x n(111)]surface. As compared to the flat surface, cluster calculations demonstrated the disappearance of a central peak in the self-consistent local density of states. This result is consistent with previous tight binding calculations of Cyrot-Lackmann et al [4] for semi-infinite stepped surfaces. More work is needed to understand the influence of this particular behaviour on the catalytic activity of Ni stepped surfaces.

It has been shown that, although important for the understanding of surface phonon phenomena [7], a relaxation of the edge atoms only slightly influences the LDS spectrum.

Concerning the use of the cluster model it has been stressed that both the fact to consider localized properties, i.e. LDS, and to treat the problem self-consistently, critically influence the numerical results. Whereas it is clear that the use of localized quantities is superior in discussing the properties of clusters of limited size, modelling an infinite or semi-infinite solid, this is less trivial for the self-consistency. Indeed, a self-consistent treatment might enhance effects due to coordinatively unsaturated "surface" atoms. As discussed in this paper and in accordance with Messmer et al [16] this indeed does seem to occur. However, one can expect that the latter only induce additional features in the LDS spectra that can easily be distinguished from the "bulk-like" features [16,21].

The present model calculations might serve as a basis for future work on adsorption systems, eventually using larger cluster sizes.

ACKNOWLEDGEMENTS

Stimulating discussions with Prof. Dr. W. Dekeyser are gratefully acknowledged. This work is part of a research scheme supported by CNRS-France under contract n° ATP-3900

REFERENCES

1 e.g. B. Lang, R.W. Joyner and G.A. Somorjai, Surface Sci. 30 (1972) 454;
  G.A Somorjai, R.W. Joyner and B. Lang, Proc. Roy. Soc. (London) A331 (1972) 335;
  S.L. Bernasek, W.J. Siekhaus and G.A. Somorjai, Phys. Rev. Lett. 30 (1973) 1202

2 G.S. Painter, P.J. Jennings and R.O. Jones; J. Phys. C. 8 (1975) L199
  R.O. Jones, P.J. Jennings and G.S. Painter, Surface Sci 53 (1975) 409;
  P.J. Jennings, G.S. Painter and R.O. Jones, Surface Sci 60 (1976) 255,

3 M.C. Desjonquères and F. Cyrot-Lackmann, Solid St Comm. 18 (1976) 1127

4. F. Cyrot-Lackmann, M.C. Desjonquères and M.B. Gordon, J. Physique 7, C2 (1977)

5 D.J.M. Fassaert and A. Van der Avoid, Surface Sci. 55 (1976) 313.

6 K. Besocke, B. Krahl-Urban and H. Wagner, Surface Sci. 68 (1977) 39.

7 G. Allan, Surface Sci 85 (1979) 37

8 H. Ibach and D. Bruchmann, Phys. Rev Lett 41 (1978) 958.

9. B. Lang, R.W. Joyner and G.A. Somorjai, Surface Sci 30 (1972) 440.

10 J.C. Slater, Adv Quantum Chem. 6 (1972) 1

11 K.H. Johnson, Adv. Quantum Chem. 7 (1973) 143.

12 C.S. Barrett, Structure of Metals, 2nd edn. McGraw-Hill, New York, 1952, p. 646.

13 K. Schwarz , Phys. Rev. B5 (1972) 2466

14 G. Allan, personal communication

15 - J.E. Demuth, D.W. Jepsen and P.M. Marcus, J. Phys. C8 (1975) L25.

16 - R.P. Messmer, S.K. Knudson, K.H. Johnson, J.B. Diamond and C.Y. Yang, Phys. Rev. B 13 (1976) 1396

17 - T.B. Grimley and E.E. Mola, J. Phys. C9 (1976) 3437

18 - H. Hjelmberg, Ph. D. Thesis, Göteborg (1978)

19 - M.C. Desjonquères and F. Cyrot-Lackmann, J. Phys. F5 (1975) 1368

20 - J. Friedel, J. Physique 37 (1976) 883

21 - K.H. Johnson, D.D. Vvedensky and R.P. Messmer, Phys. Rev. B19 (1979) 1519

288

DISCUSSION

R. HOOGEWIJS, G. DALMAI, J. VENNIK

Cyrot-Lackmann - The band width of bulk Ni is ∼ 4.5 eV. You find ∼ 2.7 eV. How do you explain the discrepancy if you believe that the cluster simulates the bulk.

Hoogewijs - We are aware of the fact that the clusters considered in the present work are too small to make possible a quantitative analysis. That the total band width is smaller than in bulk Ni, is a well-known finite cluster effect. It is believed however that small cluster models may be useful for a qualitative discussion of e.g. local densities of states.

Salem - In the Ni_9 cluster, have you looked at the s, d character of the split-off state ? Also at its symmetry ?

Hoogewijs - The a_1 levels are the only ones that contribute s-like charge to the predominantly d-like local density of states at the atom -1 site. Furthermore, upon self-consistency there is a general decrease of the s-part relative to the p(a_1 and e) and d(a_1,b_1,b_2,e) charge, apart from the $1a_1$ (the split-off state) and the $3a_1$ levels which show an even more distinct s-like character. The contribution of $3a_1$ to the local charge in the atom-1 sphere is small however.

Boudeville - Concernant le problème de la "réactivité" des atomes "mal entourés" : par exemple les atomes de nickel d'une marche, avez-vous de grandes différences dans le comportement des niveaux électroniques au cours du processus d'autocoherence sur ces atomes. C'est à dire une grande différence de comportement entre un atome "normalement protégé" et un atome de marche.

Hoogewijs - Les seuls atomes qui sont entourés par tous ses premiers voisins, par rapport au solide semi-infini, sont les atomes n° 1 (fig. 1). L'introduction d'une marche (Ni_8) ne donne pas lieu à des difficultés supplémentaires au cours du processus d'autocoherence. Les densités d'états locales sur des atomes, autres que les n° 1 n'ont pas été analysées en détail. Leur comportement au cours du processus d'autocoherence peut néanmoins être jugé par comparaison des densités d'états totales avec les densités d'états locales sur les atomes n° 1.

J. BOURDON (Editor)
Growth and Properties of Metal Clusters, pp. 289—302
© 1980 Elsevier Scientific Publishing Company — Printed in The Netherlands

THE CATALYTIC AND PHYSICAL PROPERTIES OF VACUUM-DEPOSITED METAL NUCLEI

by J. F. Hamilton

Research Laboratories, Eastman Kodak Company, Rochester, New York
14650

I.   INTRODUCTION

Vacuum deposits of metals in the monolayer and submonolayer thickness range consist of discrete clusters of small numbers of the metal atoms. When the condensation process is understood, it is possible to characterize the mean of the cluster size distribution and to vary this systematically by means of the total amount of metal deposited.

For this and other reasons, such deposits provide a convenient format for studies aimed at correlating catalytic activity with physical properties, as both are changed by particle size. A disadvantage for some experiments is the small amount of surface area compared with that provided by a modest volume of a conventional powder-supported catalyst. However, this disadvantage is frequently outweighed by the tractability of vacuum deposits for certain physical studies: they can be made with a relatively narrow size spread in a planar form ideally suited to transmission electron microscopy and to surface analysis techniques.

II.   PREVIOUS USES OF VACUUM DEPOSITS

Anderson and his colleagues [1] pioneered in the use of vacuum deposits in this coverage (size) range for the study of traditional catalyzed reactions. They compared the isomerization, hydrogenolysis, and dehydro-cyclization reactions of n-hexane and 2-methylpentane over "ultra-thin" vacuum deposits of nickel and platinum as opposed to continuous vacuum-deposited films of the same metals. They found very significant differences in the product distributions from the two types of catalysts. The upper limit of the particle-size distribution of their "ultra-thin" films was reported to be near 20 Å and the lower limit below the 8-Å limit of the electron-microscope determination. They did nothing more to characterize or study the effect of sizes smaller than these.

The most courageous attempts to be more quantitative about the smallest cluster sizes and their effects have come from photographic scientists, whose use of vacuum deposits to study the catalytic development reaction and analogs thereof dates back many years.

290

One of the earliest references to such an experiment is that of Estermann and Stern [2] in 1923, in which it was found that 1/13 monolayer of vacuum-deposited silver on glass was the minimum coverage which would initiate silver depositions from a Ag^+-hydroquinone physical developer.

Reinders and his associates [3,4] subsequently performed similar but more extensive experiments and found that much lower silver coverages— 1/1000 to 5/1000 monolayer—were effective.

These studies also included particle counts made from microscopical observations of deposits after limited development [5]. In dark field, the silver particles formed by development could be seen as bright spots and counted. With no experimental evidence about the condensation process, Reinders et al. confidently used a statistical model to predict how the cluster size distribution would depend on the metal coverage. They argued that the concentration of single atoms would increase as the first power of the coverage, pairs as the second power, triplets as the third power, etc. Their counts of developed particles showed a fourth-power dependence on the coverage, and they concluded that a cluster of four atoms was required for development. They could rationalize the absolute values of the particle counts with their model by assuming that growth occurred by atoms impinging on surface sites in direct contact with existing particles. It is interesting that the theoretical treatments of thin-film nucleation and growth which were developed in the intervening years [6] employed far different models which emphasized a high degree of surface mobility of atoms on the substrates. These models would have predicted much different size distributions and coverage dependence.

The Reinders studies also reported [4] a surprising effect which they called a reversal and discussed in relation to the photographic solarization effect. When the coverage of the vacuum-deposited silver was increased to 0.2 monolayer and beyond, the optical density of the developed sample decreased again, and in fact it was reported to be invisible. The authors allowed that at least part of this phenomenon could be attributed to an optical effect—reduced covering power of the developed silver, but they also speculated (with no experimental confirmation) that less developed silver was deposited on the high-coverage catalyst layer. They suggested that, when the surface density of catalyst nuclei was high, the development would quickly cause these to merge and form a continuous film, which they thought might be much less catalytic than a multiplicity of individual particles.

Both of these sets of experiments [2,3] included also studies of the enlargement of silver clusters by condensation of mercury and/or cadmium vapor. On a clean surface the adsorbed atoms from a cadmium vapor beam re-evaporate with a probability which can be unity, so that no cadmium is deposited [7]. If the surface is first "seeded" by deposition of a small amount of another metal, a film of cadmium is formed with high efficiency.

Mercury and zinc, the other closed-shell elements in the same column of the periodic table, exhibit the same behavior.

Estermann and Stern [2] found that the minimum silver coverage to nucleate cadmium deposition was the same as that for silver development, whereas Reinders and Hamburger [3] observed that the limit for cadmium nucleation was higher than that for silver development by a factor of 10 to 100.

A number of other studies of the nucleation of cadmium or zinc deposits by silver have been reported [8], and the phenomenon has been used commercially for producing zinc-coated paper for the construction of capacitors [9]. Minimum silver coverages of 1/100 to 1/1000 monolayer are confirmed. As the silver coverage is increased, both the optical density and the electrical conductivity of the resulting cadmium or zinc layer go through a maximum and decrease very markedly, and then show a second rise.

Kirstein et al. [10] used techniques similar to those described above, but studied palladium deposits rather than silver, on carbon substrates. They determined the minimum coverage for mercury vapor nucleation, for development by a Zsigmondy silver solution developer, and for the deposition from solution of palladium either by hydroxylamine or by bubbled hydrogen gas. Their results generally agreed with those of others for silver clusters, and they interpreted them to indicate a minimum active size of about four atoms.

Other photographic experiments employing vacuum-deposited silver include those of Evans, Hedges, and Mitchell [11], who deposited silver and other metals on silver halide sheet crystals and evaluated their activity for chemical development. They found the light sensitivity of the crystals was increased by a deposit of about 1/10 monolayer, but that almost the equivalent of a monolayer of incident silver was required for developability. They also found, however, that much of the silver diffused into the silver halide, either by direct or dissociative diffusion, and the residual surface silver was clearly less than a monolayer.

Behrndt [12] studied silver and gold evaporated onto TiO_2 substrates and amplified by a silver physical developer and by zinc deposition. She found that about 1/1000 monolayer of gold and slightly under 1/100 monolayer of silver could be detected by a silver physical developer. The minimum silver coverage for zinc deposition was about the same, but the gold was ineffective for this process.

Galashin, Senchenkov, and Chibisov [13] used rather heavier vacuum deposits of silver on carbon and a weak physical developer (reduction potential ∿ 55 mV). They found that particles less than about 40 Å were dissolved whereas larger ones grew rapidly.

In an elegant set of similar experiments, Konstantinov, Panov, and Malinowski [14] varied the reduction potential of the developer and observed the dependence of the transition size with potential. They analyzed their results by classical Gibbs-Thomson concepts to arrive at a value for the surface energy of the silver particles. They found that the energy was reduced from 920 to 400 ergs/cm^2 by a coating of gelatin over the particles but that the values were the same for both carbon and silver bromide substrates. Their results extrapolated to a minimum size of about 10 atoms for a developer potential of 200 mV in the presence of gelatin.

III. CURRENT EXPERIMENTS

The experiments I will discuss are extensions of these just described. There are improvements now in the experimental techniques, and much effort has gone into understanding the processes by which the metal vapor condenses into clusters [15]. This allows us to characterize the size distribution of the clusters with good confidence, and to vary the mean of the distribution systematically. Some different reactions have also been studied.

A major concern in the very early experiments of this type was devising a way to make accurate and reproducible deposits of known submonolayer coverage. This problem is easily solved in the present study by moving an aperture in the form of a narrow slot between the substrate to be coated and an atomic beam source emitting a known flux of the metal vapor. The flux is measured and controlled by a quartz-crystal microbalance.

The rate of evaporation, the aperture width, and the velocity with which it moves can be varied over wide ranges, and deposits with controlled coverages between about 10^{-4} monolayer and 100 or 1000 monolayers can easily be made. An electron micrograph of a deposit of about 0.2 monolayer of iridium is shown in Fig. 1.

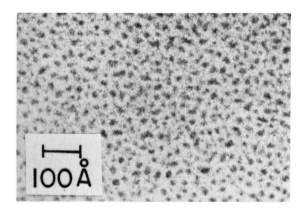

Fig. 1. An electron micrograph of iridium clusters on an amorphous carbon support film. The coverage, corrected for diffusion into the substrate, is about 0.2 monolayer.

It is convenient to use a shutter with a series of adjacent slots with different widths. This way a corresponding set of parallel strips of the deposit are formed, whose _relative_ coverage is controlled with high precision, considerably greater than it is possible to control the absolute coverage of any one deposit.

The substrates used have been inert vacuum-deposited films of either carbon, silicon dioxide, or aluminum oxide, usually deposited just before the metal, in the same pumping cycle. All deposits have been made at room temperature, at pressures in the 10^{-7} or 10^{-6} Torr range.

A number of metals have been examined, but most of the studies involve the noble metals of group IB (copper, silver, gold) and certain of the group VIII metals, namely nickel, palladium, platinum, rhodium, and iridium. During the condensation process there are quantitative differences among these metals and also the substrates, but qualitatively the basic features are common to all. Contrary to most of the recent theoretical treatments of thin-film formation, this process on these substrates at room temperature is amazingly similar to the early intuitive model of Reinders. There is virtually no lateral diffusion of adsorbed atoms, and the growth occurs entirely by direct impingement on existing clusters or immediately adjacent sites. The most significant new feature which we find is that there is a strong tendency for the incident atoms to diffuse into the bulk of the substrate, presumably along defect channels. Clusters nucleate only at certain specific but as yet undefined substrate sites, and the mass of metal in the surface clusters is less than that calculated from the incident flux by sometimes as much as an order of magnitude or two.

Except for the quantitative error, however, the dependence of the cluster-size distribution on coverage is the same as that used by Reinders et al.: the single atoms increase as the first power of the metal coverage, the dimers as the second power, the trimers as the third power, etc. Figure 2 shows graphs of these relationships.

The ability of the deposits to nucleate cadmium or zinc deposition from the vapor has proven to be very useful in the quantitative evaluation of the condensation process [15,17]. We have counted the number of zinc particles produced as a function of the silver or gold coverage, being careful to control the zinc coverage so as to avoid coalescence. We find that the number of zinc particles increases linearly with the coverage of the nucleating metal, indicating that single atoms of silver, gold, copper, and palladium are effective for this purpose. From these data, the parameters relating cluster concentrations to incident metal coverages can be evaluated.

To study the photographic development reaction [16], the deposits are immersed in physical-developer solutions for limited times. Counts of the density of developed particles are made by electron microscopy, and these

294

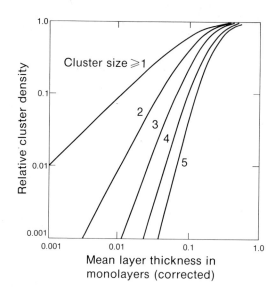

Fig. 2. Normalized plots
of log surface density of
clusters of i or more
atoms vs. log metal
coverage, corrected for
diffusion into the
substrate.

data are then compared with the theoretical size distributions to determine
the minimum cluster size which acts catalytically for this reaction.

One of the severe difficulties in an experiment of this type is the
tendency of silver or gold particles to aggregate. The aggregation is very
slow in vacuum, more rapid in room air, and highly accelerated if the
sample contacts water or an aqueous solution. Both cluster migration and
an Ostwald process seem to be involved to some extent. Aggregation was
restricted within useable limits only if the more insulating substrates
were used and the deposit was protected by a gelatin overlayer [16]. Our
experience is that the results of any investigation of silver or gold
clusters that neglects this concern must be regarded with some skepticism.
Other metals do not aggregate nearly as readily.

There is always some statistical scatter in count data such as these,
and therefore in order to make a confident fit to theory it is necessary to
collect counts over as large a range of values as possible. The lower
limit is set by the number of spontaneous or uncatalyzed particles that
form—the background or fog level. Silver physical developers are notor-
iously unstable, and our experience is that this poses a difficult problem.
We minimized this difficulty by using a form of solution physical development in which the silver ion concentration in solution is limited, but is
constantly replenished from the solid phase.

The upper limit to the unstable particle concentration is set by
overlap or merging of the particles, causing individual centers to become

indistinguishable. In this connection, the older studies which used light microscopy were at a distinct disadvantage, because in order to be resolved with confidence, the particles of developed silver had to be made much larger than they do for electron microscopy. Even so it is necessary that the reaction rate be uniform and under control, and that it be stopped at the proper time. In the format we have used, the reaction is diffusion controlled and apparently this is an advantage, because we can produce very uniform silver particles that are easily counted.

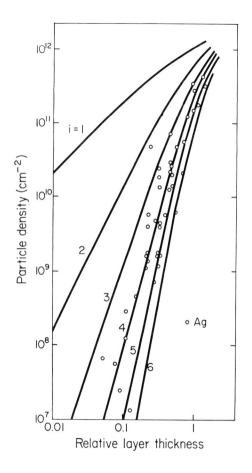

Fig. 3. Particle count data for physical development of silver clusters.

The data from the counts of silver developed on silver clusters are shown in Fig. 3. The lines in that figure are the same as those in Fig. 2, with the appropriate parameters for a silver deposit. The data fit best to the curve for i = 4, and we conclude that for these conditions, clusters of less than four atoms are not catalytic.

Similar data [16] for this same reaction but using a vacuum deposit of gold as the catalyst indicate that a pair of gold atoms has already acquired whatever property is necessary to be an active catalyst. This result is consistent with the indications from photographic results [18].

We have not observed the sort of loss in activity with further increase in coverage of the silver deposits which was reported in the Reinders studies. Perhaps it is true, as they implied, that this effect is not associated with the initiation of the reaction, but with its continuation once a continuous film has been formed.

We do, however, confirm that there is a maximum effective size for cadmium or zinc deposition, at least as judged by the optical density of the deposit. This is true for both silver and gold, as has been reported by others [8].

An analogous reaction we have studied [17,19] is the reduction of nickel ion from solution, a reaction known commercially as electroless plating [20]. Effective reducing agents include sodium hypophosphite and a variety of amine boranes, and the most effective catalysts are the platinum-group metals, particularly palladium. A paper by Yudelson [21] at this meeting describes a photographic system using a palladium salt as the photosensitive element and this reaction for amplification.

Dimethylamine borane is one of the more active reducing agents, and we have found that when this is used, nickel reduction is catalyzed by very small clusters—perhaps one or two atoms in size—of palladium, platinum, rhodium, or iridium.

For all of these metals except palladium, there is also an upper size limit to the catalytic activity [19,22]. This effect is shown for platinum in Fig. 4. As the particle size increases, the rate of the reaction, as measured by the increase of the optical density of the resulting nickel deposit, passes through a maximum for clusters in the ten- to fifty-atom range and drops thereafter. The particles become totally inactive at sizes greater than about 100 atoms. A similar upper size limit is noted for rhodium and iridium, at particle sizes decreasing in that order.

Here, then, is another instance in which small clusters have an activity in catalytic reactions which is far greater than the same amount of surface on the bulk metal. Many such instances are documented in the literature.

The important question remains to be answered: What is the cause of these size effects? What property is acquired as atoms combine to form clusters of two or three or four atoms (as the case may be) and is again lost (in some cases) after the cluster size reaches perhaps 50 or 100 atoms?

One possibility is that the electronic structure is undergoing a change with size, so that the bonding of reactants and products to the cluster changes. The details of the electronic changes as the first two metal atoms combine to form a dimer and then successive other atoms are added until finally the bulk-metal band structure evolves are of great

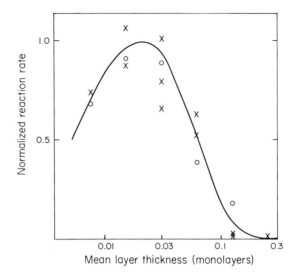

Fig. 4. Rate of reaction for nickel reduction vs platinum catalyst coverage.

fundamental importance. We have found that a combined program using quantum mechanical cluster calculations and photoemission spectroscopy can give some insight into this question.

The calculations [23] are done by my colleague Roger Baetzold, who has been applying these techniques to clusters of a variety of metals. He finds that for silver there is a pronounced oscillatory effect of most properties between sizes having odd or even numbers of atoms. In an odd-sized cluster the uppermost occupied electronic level is singly occupied. Bonding which involves the transfer of electronic charge to or from the cluster will in either case involve this same level. In an even-sized cluster, on the other hand, the uppermost occupied level is full, containing two electrons of opposite spin. An electron can be withdrawn from this level, but for injection of an electron, the next highest level must be involved. For this reason, the binding energy, the electron affinity, and the ionization potential all exhibit the odd-even oscillations. Experimental studies [24] of the abundance of oligomeric species in the vapor have resulted in reports of similar odd-even oscillations.

Conjectures have been made about an overall increase in electron affinity of silver cluster with size, as a possible explanation for the minimum effective size as a catalyst for photographic development [25]. There is no evidence for this from the calculations. If anything, the trend is in the opposite direction. It is not at all clear just what confers developability at a size of about four atoms.

The photoemission studies are part of a collaboration with Mason and co-workers [19,22,26]. Vacuum deposits are very well suited to such experiments using either UV or X-ray excitation. The results give a profile of the occupied density of states (DOS) function, as modified by differences in excitation cross section. The sensitivity of the method is such that data with good signal-to-noise characteristics can be collected within a fraction of an hour for deposits approaching monolayer coverage, and even the lowest coverages of interest may be studied by signal averaging overnight or over a weekend. Such studies confirm that the low-coverage deposits consist almost exclusively of isolated single atoms. The shape of the spectrum is in excellent agreement with the Gaussian-broadened state distribution derived from spectroscopic data taken from the atomic species, as shown for silver in Fig. 5.

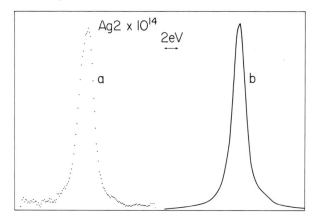

Fig. 5. Observed (a) and calculated (b) photoemission spectra of a silver deposit of principally single atoms.

As the coverage of the deposit is increased, the spectrum changes gradually, eventually becoming indistinguishable from that of a bulk-metal foil.

The most significant change for the noble metals is in the threshold of the photoemission signal, shown for silver in Fig. 6. This indicates that the high-energy edge—which is related to the ionization potential or the work function—moves toward the vacuum level by more than 4 eV between the atomic state and the bulk metal. We judge that the change begins to be apparent as soon as clusters of two or three atoms constitute a significant fraction of the deposit and is not complete until the mean cluster size is 100 or 200 atoms. This trend is predicted, though by a smaller amount, from the calculations. Because there is always a distribution of cluster sizes in the deposits used for experimental studies, there is little hope of being able to confirm the odd-even distinction with this type of investigation.

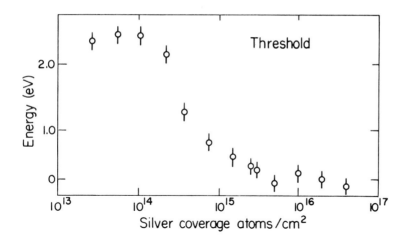

Fig. 6. Change in threshold energy of photoemission from silver deposits vs coverage.

Calculations and experimental data agree in indicating a significant difference between the behavior of the d bands of the noble metals silver and gold on the one hand and those of the platinum-group metals on the other. In silver and gold the d-electron levels lie well below the s levels and are not strongly involved in the bonding of the atoms. Therefore, both the centroid and the width of the d-electron levels are changed relatively little as the cluster size increases.

The Fermi level of the platinum-group metals, on the other hand, lies near the top of the d band. This band broadens significantly with cluster size in the platinum-group metals. Furthermore, in clusters of these atoms even as small as the dimer, a bonding s-type molecular orbital drops well below the d levels, giving the small clusters a $d^{n-1}s^{1}$ structure. In the bulk metals, there is less than one empty d state per atom. The accepted values are 0.4 for palladium and platinum and 0.1 for rhodium and iridium. High-resolution photoelectron spectra of platinum, rhodium, and iridium show a distinct steepening of the high-energy edges of the d bands over the coverage range corresponding to particle sizes of about 10 to 20 Å, as shown in Fig. 7 for platinum. We interpret this change as arising from the partial filling of the d electronic states.

The significant feature of this observation is that the size range over which the number of vacant d states decreases from one per atom to the smaller bulk value is just the range over which these metals lose their catalytic activity for nickel reduction. Furthermore, the particle size at which the change occurs increases in the order iridium, rhodium, platinum, as does also the density of d states at the Fermi level. Palladium, which has the highest DOS at the Fermi energy, is an active catalyst for this

300

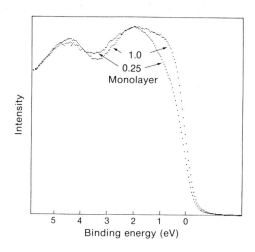

Fig. 7. High-resolution photoemission spectra of platinum below and above the coverage at which catalytic activity is lost.

reaction even in bulk form. Arguments for the importance of vacant d orbitals for chemisorption and catalysis have been presented before [27], but to our knowledge this is the first indication that particle-size effects are determined by this factor.

IV. SUMMARY

In summary, although it is clear that important questions dealing with the mechanism of cluster-size effects in catalysis remain unanswered, some insight has been gained by studies using submonolayer vacuum deposits. These preparations are useful in this regard because of the possibility of making direct comparisons between catalytic activity and electronic structure of the same material. Many other properties can also be investigated on deposits of this type, and their full potential as model systems is yet to be achieved.

REFERENCES

1. J.R. Anderson and R.J. MacDonald, J. Catal., 19 (1970) 227; J.R. Anderson, R.J. MacDonald, and Y. Shimoyama, ibid., 20 (1971) 147.
2. J. Estermann and O. Stern, Z. phys. Chem., 106 (1923) 399.
3. W. Reinders and L. Hamburger, Rec. Trav. Chim., 50 (1931) 3510.
4. W. Reinders and L. Hamburger, Z. Wiss. Photogr., 31 (1932) 32; ibid., 31 (1933) 265.
5. W. Reinders and R.W.P. DeVries, Rec. Trav. Chim., 56 (1957) 985.
6. For example, A.C. Zettlemoyer, Nucleation, Marcel-Dekker, New York, 1969.
7. I. Langmuir, Proc. Nat. Acad. Sci., Washington, 3 (1917) 14.

8. E. Traub, Z. Angew. Phys., 12 (1949) 545; E. Zehender, Optik, 4/5 (1950) 200; A.G. Kaspaul and E.E. Kaspaul, in Transactions of the Third National Vacuum Symposium of the American Vacuum Society, G.H. Bancroft, Ed., Macmillan, New York, 1963, p. 422; H.G. Wehe, in Electron and Ion Beam Science and Technology, 2, R. Bakish, Ed., American Inst. of Mining, Metallurgical and Petroleum Engineers, New York, 1966, p. 813; C. Chapon, C. Henry and B. Mutaftschiev, J. Cryst. Growth, 33 (1976) 291; C. Henry, C. Chapon, and B. Mutaftschiev, Thin Solid Films, 33 (1976) L1.

9. L. Holland, Vacuum Deposition of Thin Films, Wiley, New York, 1961, p. 252.

10. D. Kirstein, E. Kahrig, G. Dreyer, J. Erpenbeck, and Fr. Lange, Z. Wiss. Photogr., 61 (1967) 165, 171.

11. J.M. Hedges and J.W. Mitchell, Philos. Mag., 44 (1963) 357; T. Evans, J.M. Hedges, and J.W. Mitchell, J. Photogr. Sci., 3 (1955) 73; J.W. Mitchell, Die Photographische Empfindlichkeit, Helwich, Darmstadt, 1957; J. W. Mitchell, J. Phys. Chem., 66 (1962) 2359.

12. M.E. Behrndt, J. Vac. Sci. Technol., 8 (1971) 724.

13. E.A. Galashin, E.P. Senchenkov, and K.V. Chibisov, Dokl. Akad. Nauk. SSSR, 181 (1969) 124; E.A. Galashin and E.P. Senchenkov, Zh. Nauch. Prikl. Fotogr. Kinematogr., 16 (1971) 339.

14. I. Konstantinov, A. Panov, and J. Malinowski, J. Photogr. Sci., 21 (1973) 250; I. Konstantinov and J. Malinowski, ibid., 23 (1975) 1, 145.

15. J.F. Hamilton and P.C. Logel, Thin Solid Films, 16 (1973) 49; ibid., 23 (1974) 89; ibid., 29 (1975) L24; J. F. Hamilton, P.C. Logel, and R.C. Baetzold, ibid., 32 (1976) 233.

16. J.F. Hamilton and P.C. Logel, Photogr. Sci. Eng., 18 (1974) 507.

17. J.F. Hamilton and P.C. Logel, J. Catal., 29 (1973) 253.

18. T.H. James, The Theory of the Photographic Process, 4th ed., Macmillan, New York, 1977, Ch. 5.

19. M.G. Mason, J.F. Hamilton, S.T. Lee, B.F. Nellis, L.J. Gerenser, and P.C. Logel, Catalytic and Electronic Properties of Small Metal Clusters, J. Chem. Phys., in press.

20. E.B. Saubestre, Met. Finish., 60 (1962) No. 6, 67; No. 7, 49; No. 8, 45; No. 9, 59.

21. J.S. Yudelson, Heterogeneous Catalytic Considerations in Photographic Systems, paper, this conference.

22. M.G. Mason, L.J. Gerenser, and S.T. Lee, Phys. Rev. Lett., 39 (1977) 288.

23. R.C. Baetzold, Advan. Catal., 25 (1976) 1; J. Chem. Phys., 68 (1978) 555; J. Phys. Chem., 82 (1978) 738 and references therein.

24. G. Hortig and M. Müller, Z. Phys., 221 (1969) 119.

25. F. Trautweiler, Photogr. Sci. Eng., 12 (1968) 138; W. Jaenicke, J. Photogr. Sci., 20 (1972) 2.

26. M.G. Mason and R.C. Baetzold, J. Chem. Phys., 64 (1976) 271.

27. For example, A. Clark, The Chemisorptive Bond, Academic Press, New York, 1974.

DISCUSSION

J.F. HAMILTON

Harding - Your result that the energy of the lowest vacant molecular orbital increases with increasing size of cluster is contrary to the expectations of current photographic theory, as expressed in the energy level diagrams proposed by Trautweiller, Jaenicke and other authors. What are the implications of this for a model of sub-developable and developable silver centres ?

Hamilton - If the models on which Baetzold's calculations are based are adequate, and if the conditions of our XPS measurements are not altered by the reaction conditions (e.g. vacuum environment vs electrolyte, etc.) then we must look for some explanation for the onset of developability other than the change of energy levels. Malinowski's proposal in terms of Gibbs-Thomson concepts are one such possibility. But the reservations mentioned are strong enough that the conclusion is not very certain.

Mutaftschiev - 1°/ I wonder how can you determine the minimum size (1 atom) of silver clusters active for the cadmium condensation. Our experience on Cd condensation on small gold particles condensed on an NaCl substrate shows that this minimum size cannot be appreciated for three reasons : (i) there is not one to one correspondance between Au atoms sent onto the surface and observed Cd nuclei. The linear dependence between the number of the observed particles and the number of Au atoms (or the time by constant flux) is foreseen by all nucleation theories ; (ii) it is known that, when the Au atom flux is stopped, no single Au atom remains on the surface. Their life time is too small ; (iii) the number of particles visualized by the Cd is stongly dependent upon the Cd flux. This indicates that the cadmium does not condense on sitting gold clusters and even less on atoms.

2°/ During condensation of Au on NaCl substrate, one obtains also visible quantities of gold much smaller than the amount of gold sent onto the Surface. So we were also tempted to assume a diffusion of the gold atoms into the NaCl substrate.
The experiments showed however that if instead of fixing the gold particles by an evaporated carbon layer immediately after the gold condensation, we wait a certain time, the visible quantity of gold increase. For a waiting time of 10 sec, one sees about 10 % of the estimated amount of gold, since after some 30 min, all the gold is visible. We interpreted this by the formation, in the first moments of the condensation, of a great number of very small invisible particles, the migration and coalescence of which is relatively slow. Accordingly the size distribution of the gold particles is evoluating slowly and the final situation, when all the gold is visible is reached after 30 minutes only.

Hamilton - Your comments (i) and (ii) are based on the traditional models of nucleation, which probably are valid for Au on crystalline NaCl. I have given the evidence on which we have concluded that this does not apply for these amorphous substrates. As far as I am aware, most of these treatments (e.g. Zinsmeister, Venables, etc) predict a higher order dependence of the stable nucleus density on coverage in the early stages of condensation. (iii) If the Cd or Zn atom flux is too high, spontaneous nucleation can occur. Below that limit our results are consistent and do correlate with the Ag or Au coverage, as I have shown.

2°/ Your results are very interesting, but do not agree with ours. The substrates we use are themselves suitable supports for electron microscopy and it is not essential to cover the particles with another carbon film at all (though we have done this many times, in order to make comparisons such as yours). Deposits of Pt, Pd, Rh, and Ir left uncovered for more than a month are identical to those covered as quickly as possible, and those of Au and Ag remain unchanged for hours, after which coalescence can be detected. Our conclusions that most of the metal is missing from the particles is not based on a technique with freezes on unstable configuration.

I attribute most of the differences between our results and yours to the use of amorphons single crystal substrates, which in our experience are vastly different.

J. BOURDON (Editor)
Growth and Properties of Metal Clusters, pp. 303—320
© 1980 Elsevier Scientific Publishing Company — Printed in The Netherlands

FORMATION, STABILITY AND INITIATION OF DEVELOPMENT BY SMALL SILVER
CLUSTERS

J. Malinowski[+]

Central Laboratory of Photographic Processes,
Bulgarian Academy of Sciences, 1040 Sofia

I. INTRODUCTION

The most widely used photographic system nowadays is based on silver
halide emulsions. This is believed to be due to some specific properties
of the silver halides directly linked with the formation, stability, and
catalytic activity of small silver clusters.

On illumination, silver halides, like many other photosensitive substances, decompose to metal and the corresponding electronegative
component. In spite of many attempts however, until now a photographic
system based on some other photodecomposing metal compounds has not been
realized. This outstanding position of silver halides in photography
(predominantly the silver bromide) is due to their unique property to
form on exposure a developable latent image. It is now generally accepted
that the latent image is a cluster containing only a few silver atoms,
having some quite specific peculiarities:

First the operation of some very efficient concentration mechanism
makes it possible all or most of the few silver atoms formed on the
absorption of less than ten light quanta to form a single metal cluster
situated on the surface of the emulsion grain.

Second, this tiny metal cluster is surprisingly stable, does not undergo rehalogenation by the simultaneously evolved equivalent amount of
bromine, and remarkably well resists oxidation by ambient.

Third, this silver cluster, containing only a few silver atoms has the
outstanding catalytic activity to initiate the reduction in the developer
of the whole grain, thus allowing the developer to discriminate practically ideally exposed from unexposed grains.

It should be obvious therefore, that the unique position of silver
halides in photography has actually to be attributed to their ability to
form on exposure with exceptional efficiency small silver clusters of
atomic dimensions, which seem to have remarkable stability and catalytic
activity.

In the last several years much effort has been concentrated in our
Laboratory aiming to understand in some details the elementary stages of

the phenomena, forming as a whole the photographic process. It is the aim of this paper to review some of our investigations, trying to outline some results as well as to point out some new problems which seem to evolve.

II. THE PRIMARY PHOTOGRAPHIC PROCESS

The absorption of a light quantum of sufficient energy ($\sim$ 2-5 eV) leads to the formation of a pair of a photoexcited electron and a hole. The fate of the electron has been well established, and it is now known that it follows the mechanism suggested first by Gurney and Mott (ref. 1). The photoexcited electron is trapped, attracts a mobile silver ion interstitial and forms a silver atom. Deep electron traps seem to exist only on the surface.

We believe to have proved the operation of a fully symmetrical process for the elimination of the photoexcited hole. The hole is immediately trapped in the volume, incorporates a silver ion vacancy, forming thus a neutral, relatively stable hole-vacancy complex. This complex is chemically equivalent to bromine atom and is much less mobile than the electron. Thus one comes to what we have called the symmetrical scheme (ref. 2), illustrated in fig. 1.

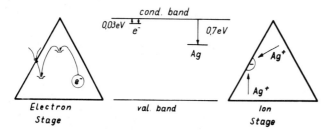

THE ELECTRON NEUTRALIZATION PROCESS
Shallow Bulk Traps Facilitate Concentration

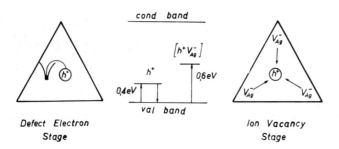

THE HOLE COMPLEMENTARY PROCESS
Deep Traps Prevent Recombination

Fig. 1. The symmetrical scheme of the photographic process.

As emphasized recently by Hamilton (ref. 3), due to surface space charge of silver halides, the enhanced concentration of silver ion interstitials in emulsion grains is always sufficient for the occurence of the ionic stage in the formation of silver atoms.

High concentration of silver ion interstitials automatically means low concentration of silver ion vacancies. Nevertheless, it has been established quite recently that the vacancies required for the neutralization of trapped holes are generated in situ (ref. 4). This provides a very fast channel for formation of bromine atoms in spite of the low concentration of the existing vacancies.

It should be admitted that these properties are actually quite specific peculiarities of silver halides, ensuring photodecomposition with the very high quantum yield of unity. An enhanced mobility of the metal atoms formed on illumination is necessary to provide an efficient coagulation of individual atoms into a single cluster catalytically active in the developer.

The Gurney and Mott theory originally aimed an explanation of the concentration of silver atoms at a single site of the grain surface. Curiously enough however, an attempt to describe in detail the formation of a speck of Ag_n by applying the consequent repetition of the elementary electron and ion stages meets serious difficulties (ref. 5-7). In addition to experimental observations, computer simulations made by Baetzold (ref. 8) indicate thermodynamic restrictions for the exact Gurney and Mott sequence of electronic and ionic events.

It should be stressed therefore, that the simple mechanism of Gurney and Mott (ref. 1), even as complemented to the symmetrical scheme (ref.2), is not in a position to explain the efficient formation on illumination of single metal cluster on the grain surface. The catalytic activity of the small silver cluster providing the discrimination of the developer also remains quite obscure (ref. 9).

III. CLUSTER FORMATION ON SURFACE SITES

I shall now review very briefly some observations on vacuum deposition of metal atoms on different substrates. This is a well studied technique, which does not seem in any way connected with the photographic process. Fig. 2 shows an electron micrograph of a NaCl crystal decorated by vacuum deposition of gold. In spite that gold atoms impinge the surface at random, the deposited material is seen to form clusters on distinct active sites. As seen in fig. 3, the mobility of gold atoms is obviously larger on AgBr, while it is still larger for silver on both substrates, becoming very significant on AgBr (ref. 10). These decoration processes by cluster formation have been very well interpreted by contemporary theories of phase formation as nucleation and growth phenomena. In all cases where a

Fig. 2. Surface defects on NaCl monocrystal decorated by vacuum deposition of Au.

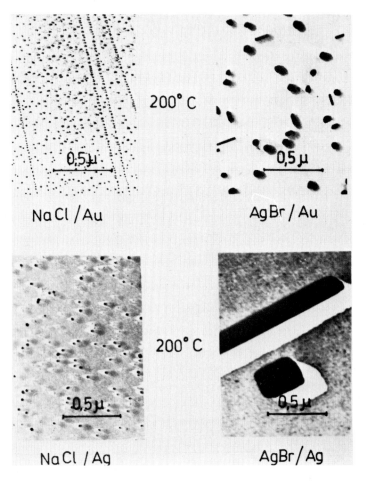

Fig. 3. Silver and gold clusters formed by vacuum deposition on NaCl and AgBr substrates (ref. 10).

calculation of the critical size of the stable cluster has been possible,
the result has always been that it contains only a few atoms, quite often
just two, coming surprisingly close to the smallest stable subimage
silver cluster, as established by Burton and Berg (ref. 11).

Recently Platikanova and Starbova from our Laboratory have obtained
very relevant electron micrographs for the decoration of evaporated AgBr
layers (ref. 12-13). Fig. 4 demonstrates unambiguously that different
sensitization procedures produce some active sites catalyzing efficiently
the nucleation of the deposited metal used for the decoration.

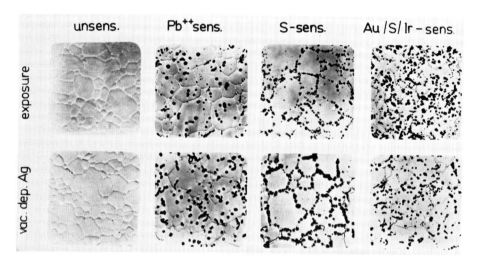

Fig. 4. Decoration of sensitivity specks on evaporated AgBr layers by
exposure to light or by vacuum deposition of Ag, followed by arrested
development. Different sensitization procedures give different
distribution of specks, identically decorated by either technique.

The distribution of these active sites is quite specific and typical for
the sensitization procedure used, but is practically independent of the
decoration technique (ref. 14). At present I shall leave aside the
exciting possibility demonstrated by Platikanova and Starbova to visualize
in the electron microscope sensitivity specks formed by different
sensitization procedures. I shall now stress the observation illustrated
in fig. 5 that active centers on the surface of evaporated silver bromide
layers can be equally well decorated by metal clusters formed by exposure
to light as well as by vacuum deposition of different metal atoms (ref.14).
This close similarity makes it quite difficult to avoid the hypothesis
that latent image formation is just another case of the general process of
cluster formation - nucleation and growth of a new phase. Following the
general requirements of thermodynamics, silver atoms coagulate to form
stable clusters - i.e. latent image specks. The only condition for the

occurence of this process is an enhanced mobility of the silver atoms on the grain surface.

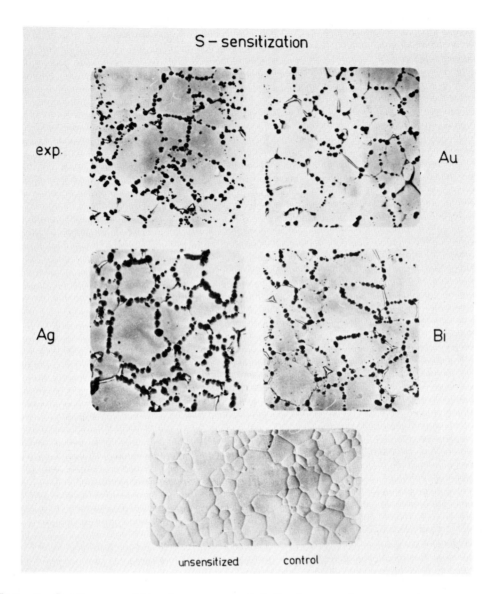

Fig. 5. Sulfur sensitized evaporated AgBr layers decorated by exposure or by vacuum deposition of Ag, Au, and Bi, followed by arrested development.

1. Surface Migration of Silver on AgBr Layers

The very high surface mobility of adsorbed metal atoms, convincingly demonstrated by Platikanova and Starbova, is a most outstanding property of silver bromide, very probably responsible for its unique position in photography. In this connection some further experiments are being now performed to elucidate the phenomenon (ref. 10, 15).

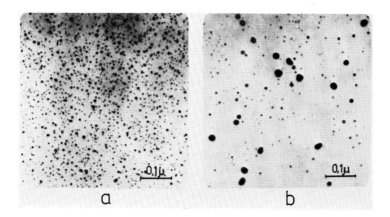

Fig. 6. Vacuum deposition of Ag on AgBr layers (no development).
a) sensitized; b) unsensitized.

The electron micrographs shown in fig. 6 compare the clusters obtained
by deposition of identical amounts of silver (now visible in the electron
microscope without intensification by arrested development) on unsensitized and sensitized AgBr layers. On the unsensitized surface silver
is seen to coagulate in widely scattered clusters demonstrating obvious
surface diffusion. Analogously to the case of invisible development
centers demonstrated by Platikanova and Starbova (ref. 12-13), the
sensitization procedure again increases substantially the number of active
coagulation sites, and much larger number of clusters, but smaller in
size, are now formed. It can be shown however that in spite of the very
dense population of Ag clusters, sensitization does not impair surface
mobility. Fig. 7 compares the experimentally observed growth of the metal
particles Δm_{ex} with material supply calculated as direct impingement from
the vapour flux Δm_{cal}. It is seen that especially at the early stages
$\Delta m_{ex}/\Delta m_{cal}$ is much larger than unity indicating that the metal particles
grow much faster than the material supply from direct impingements. The
large contribution of material supply via surface diffusion is obvious. As
seen, it is not likely to depend on the preparation of the AgBr layer, its
sensitization, the intensity of the metal beam, and the nature of the
deposited metal (ref. 15). High mobility of adsorbed metal atoms seems to
be an intrinsic property of silver bromide, very probably of utmost importance for the efficiency of the photographic process.

As summarized in Section III, quite extensive comparative study has
been carried out on two types of phenomena believed to be entirely
different - i. the decoration of surface defects by vacuum deposition of
metals and ii. the formation of latent image specks by illumination. The
first process - the vacuum decoration is known to be a typical phenomenon

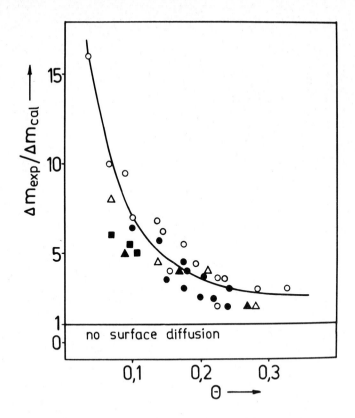

Fig. 7. Mode of growth of metal clusters on AgBr layers as dependent on the fractional coverage Θ : $\Delta m_{ex}/\Delta m_{cal}$ measures the contribution of material supply via surface diffusion. Different sets of points represent different treatment of the AgBr layers or different deposited metals.

of phase formation, while the second one is the essence of the photographic process. The AgBr films used as substrates in both cases have been subjected to sensitization procedures, known to increase substantially the photographic response of silver halides and believed to create the so called sensitivity specks. The striking similarity observed in the electron micrographs of the samples decorated either way, together with the established enhanced mobility of metal atoms on the silver bromide surface provide significant support to the assumption that the primary photographic process is a special case of the general process of phase formation.

IV. STABILITY OF SILVER CLUSTERS IN REDOX BUFFERS

The ability of a tiny silver cluster to induce complete discrimination between exposed and unexposed grains in the developer is currently considered to be another of the wonders of silver halide photography. In the last (1977) edition of "The Theory of the Photographic Process" Hamilton writes: "The mechanism of the catalytic effect involved in development is one of the most conspicuous unknowns of photographic science, although speculative proposals have been made" (ref. 9).

I shall now try to present arguments that the process of development is just a special case of another surface phenomenon - the heterogeneous phase nucleation and growth. It can be argued that the process of development also fits remarkably well into the frames of the theory of phase formation. To this aim I want to review briefly our work with Konstantinov on the stability of silver clusters in redox buffers (ref. 16-18). We believe to have provided an experimental evidence that development discrimination is nothing very different from the general process of phase formation.

Silver clusters were deposited on carbon or silver bromide substrate by evaporation in vacuum and then treated with a ferrous/ferric developer having a known ΔE value. Clusters smaller than some critical value were found to dissolve while the larger ones grew in the developer. Fig. 8 illustrates a minimum in the size distribution curve occuring after appropriate treatment in the developer. As shown this corresponds to the speck size r_0 which is exactly in equilibrium at a given ΔE value of the developer (ref. 16,17).

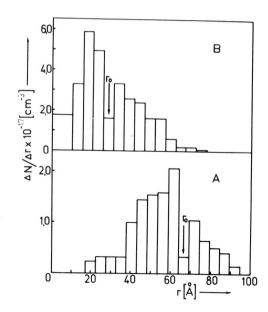

Fig. 8. Histograms of Ag clusters after treatment in a developer with buffered ΔE. The minimum indicates the critical r_0: smaller particles dissolve, larger grow spontaneously. A - without gelatin; B - overcoated with gelatin prior to development - the critical size decreases.

The results obtained, summarized in fig. 9, show that the stability and developability of small silver specks is described by the Gibbs-Thomson equation written in the form

$$E = 2 \sigma V_m / r_o F \qquad (1)$$

It is interesting to note that in the presence of gelatin the slope of the curve is considerably lowered, corresponding according to eq.(1) to a lowering of the specific surface energy σ. This has profound effect on the process of development since lower specific surface energy σ makes much smaller clusters stable and developable in the redox buffer(ref.17,18).

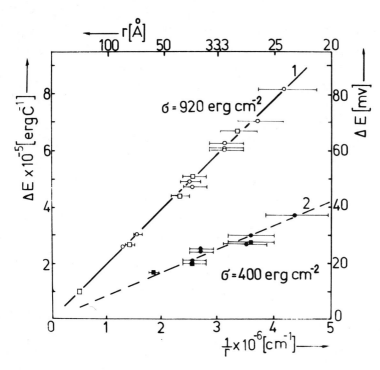

Fig. 9. Experimental check of Gibbs-Thomson eq.(1) relating the critical size r_o of silver clusters with stability in a developer with specified ΔE. The slope for samples overcoated with gelatin is smaller, indicating increased stability due to decreased specific surface energy σ.

V. THE PHOTOGRAPHIC PROCESS AS FORMATION OF A NEW PHASE

The experimental verification of Gibbs-Thomson equation as describing the stability and developability of latent image specks in ferrous/ferric developer is a very relevant result. As known, Gibbs-Thomson equation is the essence of the classical theory of nucleation and growth of a new phase. Based on the thermodynamic concepts, this theory operates with macroscopic magnitudes, such as specific surface energy σ, surface and bulk free energy, supersaturation, etc., which in the atomistic scale lack sound physical meaning.

The atomistic theory of phase formation developed in the last two decades should be free of these objections. Recent investigations show full continuity of the results obtained by the classical and the atomistic approaches (ref. 19, 20). Therefore, based on the classical theory - which is easier to follow, I shall attempt to draw some consequences. It should be assumed that the application of the atomistic theory yields identical results.

The formation of a cluster of a new phase is in principle connected with the surmounting of an energy barrier. It can be shown that the change of the Gibbs free energy of the system ΔG with the size of the cluster formed depends on the supersaturation $\Delta \mu$ as illustrated in fig. 10

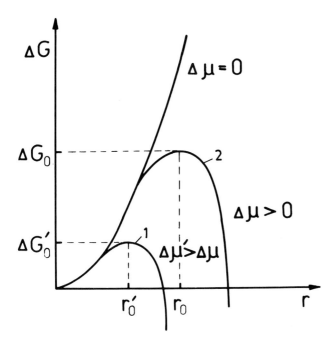

Fig. 10. The change of Gibbs' free energy ΔG with size r of the growing cluster. Nucleation possible only in supersaturated systems $(\Delta \mu > 0)$. Growth of clusters larger than the critical r_0 is spontaneous.

The heigth of the energy barrier represents the work of formation of the cluster with critical size $r = r_0$, the so-called nucleous for which the probability for growth of the cluster is 0,5.

The nucleation process is obviously possible only in a supersaturated phase, the size of the nucleous being in general inversely proportional to the supersaturation.

1. Latent Image Formation

I shall now make an attempt to describe the process of latent image formation from the standpoint of the theory of phase formation.

On exposure, according to the firmly established principle of Gurney and Mott, atoms of silver and bromine are first formed. A very relevant experimental fact, generally overlooked, is that the solubility of silver in silver bromide is negligible and orders of magnitude smaller that the solubility of bromine. In addition to that, it can be reasonably assumed that the emulsion grain is in contact with efficient bromine acceptors. Correspondingly the supersaturation for silver in the grain attains immediately significant values, providing thus substantial probability for the occurence of nucleation. Given enough light energy and material the silver cluster can now reach a developable size (curve 1 in fig. 10).

2. Discrimination in the Developer of Grains Containing Ag-Clusters

Now I would like to discuss in some detail the process of development. Following the classical work of Reinders (ref. 21) it has been now un-ambiguously established that the reduction of exposed silver bromide grains is possible only if the redox potential of the developer is more negative than the bulk silver potential (ref. 22). This is equivalent to the assumption that for the process of silver formation the developer maintains some supersaturation in the silver bromide grains. Although not as high as the supersaturation created on exposure, it should be sufficient to ensure the growth of pre-existing latent image specks under the condition that the latter exceed the corresponding critical size.

We have shown earlier that, without involving any speculative assumptions, these elementary considerations provide a very simple explanation of the hotly disputed developer discrimination of exposed and unexposed grains (ref. 18).

The reduction of a grain containing no latent image speck requires first the creation of a stable cluster. At the moderate supersaturation maintained by the developer, the surmounting of the energy barrier for phase formation is very improbable event, and the reduction is correspondingly a very slow process. The situation, however, is radically changed in the presence of a latent image center formed during exposure. If the size of the pre-existing silver cluster exceeds the critical r_0, the reduction process occurs without any energy restrictions and the process of development of exposed grains is spontaneous from the very beginning. Therefore, the latent image formation corresponds schematically to curve 1 in fig. 10 (higher supersaturation). At the critical size of two atoms the subimage is stable but undevelopable at the lower super-saturation maintained by the developer. This lower supersaturation, as represented schematically by curve 2, demands a nucleous larger than the subimage to initiate the process of reduction.

Our work establishing the validity of Gibbs-Thomson equation makes also possible some additional evaluations. Hillson (ref. 22) has shown that a developer with $\Delta E = 200$ mV is just capable of initiating the development of the latent image. As we have already pointed out (ref. 17,18), the extrapolation of the Gibbs-Thomson equation for this value of ΔE yields the very plausible value of 10 atoms for the size of the developable latent image.

According to the theory of phase formation the probability for growth of a cluster with size r different from the size r_0 of the critical nucleous can be exactly calculated. With our experimentally established value of $\sigma = 400$ erg/cm^2, for $\Delta\mu/zF = \Delta E = 200$ mV and r_0 calculated as a hemisphere containing 10 or 4 atoms respectively, one obtains the curves shown in fig. 11. The abrupt change of developability on the addition or substraction of only one silver atom to nuclei containing a few atoms is evident. Obviously any additional speculations to explain the abrupt change in developability, which has been intuitively assumed but never satisfactorily explained theoretically, seem now completely unnecessary.

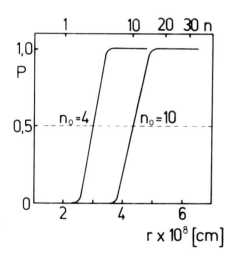

Fig. 11. The variation of the probability of development of Ag clusters with size r_0 (n_0) calculated according to the theory of phase formation.

VI. CONCLUSION

It is the aim of the present paper to provide evidence that the photographic process is not an exceptional sequence of peculiar reactions the occurence of which is entirely due to some extraordinary properties of silver halides. I believe to have shown that it is just another case of the general process of heterogeneous nucleation and growth of a new phase - the process of cluster formation, governed by the general laws of these rather complicated but nevertheless widely spread surface phenomena.

This rather simple approach leads immediately to some consequences which up to now are puzzles for the generally accepted scheme of the photographic process as suggested by Mott and Gurney (ref. 1). The theory of phase formation, based on the excess surface free energy of the newly formed nucleus, predicts the necessity to surmount first an energy barrier, building a stable but undevelopable two atom cluster - the subimage. On further exposure, given the mobility of silver atoms, it predicts the efficient coagulation of all silver atoms into a single surface cluster. It predicts further the spontaneous reduction in the developer of exposed grains containing a single speck of a few silver atoms. This provides a straightforward explanation of the efficient discrimination in the developer of grains which differ only by one or two absorbed quanta. Some extraordinary properties of gelatin as a carrier of the photosensitive entities is now seen to be closely linked with its ability to lower the specific surface energy. As a result specks of few atoms become completely stable and capable of inducing development discrimination.

The results obtained from the present analysis hint already some quite interesting and optimistic conclusions. The basic property of silver halides to form a developable latent image should not be regarded as a wonder. Any photosensitive compound decomposing with reasonable quantum efficiency should be able to build up centers catalytically active for a suitable process of development. The practical sensitivity attained should depend principally on two parameters:

The first one is the mobility of the decomposition product on the surface of the host entity, enabling the efficient coagulation into larger individual clusters. I am deeply convinced that the high mobility of silver atoms on the AgBr surface is the most outstanding property of the contemporary photographic system.

The second one is the nature of the development reaction used to intensify the clusters obtained via the primary photodecomposition process. In principle, any process of heterogeneous phase formation from a saturated system should be substantially accelerated by the presence of pre-existing surface centers, capable of serving as nuclei of the phase which is being precipitated.

REFERENCES

1 R.W.Gurney and N.F.Mott, Proc.Roy.Soc.(London), 164A (1938) 151.
2 J.Malinowski, Phot.Sci.Eng., 14(1970)112.
3 J.F.Hamilton, Phot.Sci.Eng., 18(1974)341.
4 V.Platikanova and J.Malinowski, phys.stat.sol.(a), 47(1978)683.
5 H.E.Spencer, L.E.Brady and J.F.Hamilton, J.Opt.Soc., 57(1967)1020.
6 H.E.Spencer, Phot.Sci.Eng., 11(1967)352.
7 E.Moisar, Intern. Congress on Photogr.Sci., Moscow (1970);
  Phot.Korr., 106(1970)149.
8 R.C.Baetzold, J.Solid State Chem., 6(1973)352; Phot.Sci.Eng.,17(1973)78.
9 J.F.Hamilton, in T.H.James (Ed.), The Theory of the Photographic
  Process, 4th edn., Macmillan, New York, 1977, p.111.
10 A.Panov, H.Haefke, M.Krohn, to be published.
11 P.C.Burton and W.F.Berg, Phot.J., 86B(1946)2; ibid. 88B(1948)84.
12 V.Platikanova and K.Starbova, Phot.Sci.Eng., 22(1978)6.
13 K.Starbova and V.Platikanova, submitted for publication in J.Signal AM.
14 K.Starbova and V.Platikanova, Phot.Sci.Eng., 23(1979)107.
15 A.Panov and J.Malinowski, Papers ICPS, Rochester 1978, p.89.
16 I.Konstantinov, A.Panov and J.Malinowski, J.Phot.Sci., 21(1973)25.
17 I.Konstantiniv and J.Malinowski, J.Phot.Sci., 23(1975)1.
18 I.Konstantinov and J.Malinowski, J.Phot.Sci., 23(1975)145.
19 B.Lewis, Thin Solid Films, 1(1967)85.
20 A.Milchev, S.Stoyanov and R.Kaischew, Thin Solid Films, 22(1974)267.
21 W.Reinders, J.Phys.Chem., 38(1934)783.
22 P.J.Hillson, J.Phot.Sci., 6(1958)97.

DISCUSSION

J. MALINOWSKI

Hoffmann - Just for a record, not everybody here is convinced that the latent image is necessarily a cluster of 4 silver atoms.

      One of the main points of your presentation is that the high efficiency of the photographic process is due to the high mobility of silver atoms on the AgBr surface ; consequently the Mott-Gurney concentration principle need not be invoked. How, then, does one explain internal latent image ?

Malinowski - There are two specific points which I would like to stress and to make clear.

      1°/ I do not exclude the operation of the Gurney and Mott principle. My main argument is that if one counts only on the Coulomb forces of attraction, the formation of a cluster of silver seems to meet unsurmountable difficulties. Therefore one has to take into consideration the operation of covalent forces which of course makes the exact Gurney and Mott principle irrelevant, or of secondary importance for the latent image formation.

      2°/ Internal latent image is observed as a rule along dislocations, slip or twin boundaries and other stacking faults. It should not be impossible to assume enhanced diffusion of Ag atoms along such lattice defects.

Marquardt - There are two experimental indications that the hole-vacancy complex is not an intrinsic defect in silver chloride or silver bromide. One is that photolytic silver is not formed in large zone-refined single crystals. The other is that the hole-vacancy complex should exhibit the characteristic ERS signal of atomic bromine (or chlorine) which has not been observed.

Malinowski - Photolytic silver is formed in large pure silver halide crystals if means are provided to remove the photolytic halogen produced simultaneously. If this is not the case rehalogenation occurs leading to apparent absence of photodecomposition (See for example P. Junod et al., Phot. Sci. Eng., $\underline{17}$, 205 (1973).

      It is in general difficult to observe ESR signals in Ag halides. The only well studied case is $Cu^+ \rightarrow Cu^{2+}$ but for not very well understood reasons its observation is also connected with difficulties (see for exemple R. Tucker, Phys. Rev., $\underline{112}$, 725 (1958), D. Burnham and F. Moser, ibid, $\underline{136}$, 744 (1964)).

      Obviously the failure to observe ESR signals does not prove that hole-vacancy complexes are not formed at least transitionally as intermediate species (see also Malinowski, Phot. Sci. Eng., $\underline{14}$, 112 (1970) ; J. Phot. Sci., $\underline{16}$, 57 (1968)).

Oudar - Did you have any explanation on the effect of sulphur on the sensitization process ? Is sulphur adsorbed on silver, or can we expect bulk silver sulphide formation ?

Malinowski - We do not have any indication to assume formation of silver sulphide in the bulk. I believe that silver sulphide builds up clusters which then catalyze the formation of developable silver specks by decreasing the energy barrier restricting their growth up to the critical size.

Levy - 1°/ It has been stated by colleagues from the field of catalysis, in particular Prof. Imelik, that they find differences in the properties of evaporated clusters as compared to in-situ generated clusters on the same substrate. Your experiments suggest that the differences in evaporated and photolytically produced clusters in Ag X are more similar. Would you care to comment on this ?

      2°/ The approach based on Gibbs-Thompson particle growth does not take into account in a manner that is obvious to me, the competitive kinetic steps which seem to be an intimate part of the cluster formation process, especially in the photolytic formation of silver clusters. I wonder if you could clarify this point for me.

3°/ Is there any theoritical reason why cluster formation according to the Gibbs-Thompson approach could not proceed with essentially the same conclusions regarding the size-stability relationships, if the process were proceeding using ionic species instead of neutral atoms ? I ask this question, partially because of the calculations of Sahyun, presented in the poster session of this meeting where he shows that over a range of Ag cluster sizes the positively charged cluster is more stable than the neutral cluster. This suggest that even in the case of evaporated Ag, there would be an equilibration and that cluster formation could proceed with ionic species. This is in fact some what supported by the work you reported in Rochester where you found that the ionic conductivity of AgX with a heavy deposit of Ag was larger than without the evaporated silver.

Malinowski - I shall try to answer your questions in the same sequence :

1°/ Our work does not indicate any special catalytic activity of silver specks in the process of development. It proves only that the stability and the growth of silver clusters in the developer (a redox buffer) follow simply the thermodynamic equation of Gibbs-Thomson. If this is assumed to be the case, there should be no reason to expect significant difference in the behaviour in the developer of silver clusters prepared in different ways.

2°/ The so-called classical theory of nucleation and growth of a new phase, although based on the thermodynamic equation of Gibbs-Thomson, is in fact a kinetic theory. This has been very well developed still in the thirties - see for example the classical book of M. Volmer - "Kinetik der Phasenbildung", Th. Steinkipf Verla, Dresden-Leipzig, 1939. So in fact if, as I tried to stress, a special case of this general theory is worked out to describe the phenomena occurring on illumination and development of silver bromide crystals, it should by necessity take inot consideration the kinetic factors which are obviously involved.

3°/ My answer to this question is similar to what I had offered to Dr Hoffmann. There are no reasons to object the formation of silver clusters in electronic and ionic steps - the classical visualization of Gurney and Mott. But a calculation based on the operation of Coulomb forces of attraction, due to the very high dielectric constant of AgBr, fails to explain the building up of a stable nucleus. One has obviously to take into account the operation of covalent forces binding eventually together the Ag atoms into a stable cluster. The actual mechanism of their arrival to the site of formation of the cluster should be irrelevant or at least of secondary importance.

Kreibig - In relation with the photosensitive silver glasses for which the development occurs at temperatures as higher as 500-600° C, are there any informations that the "magic" number of atoms of a critical nucleus may be changed at elevated temperatures ?

Malinowski - I do not feel in a position to speculate on the processes occurring in photosensitive glasses. This is an entirely different system which might have too little in common with the silver halide grain.

Yates - It is interesting that in catalytic chemistry, sulphur is a poison ; on the contrary for photographic systems, sulphur is the opposite ! Do you think that the action of sulphur in increasing the speed of photographic emulsions is due to the S forming Ag_2S, thus stopping the Ag recombining with the halogen, or in other words, stabilizing the latent image ? This might also be critical in the problem of reciprocity failure at low incident light levels.

Malinowski - There is evidence that Ag_2S acts as hole traps (Mitchell) but we are more inclined to describe its action as halogen acceptor - actually in the way you envisage its function (see for example J. Malinowski, Phot. Sci. Eng., 18, 363 (1974). In addition to that the well known affinity between silver and sulphur might help the binding of the separate silver atoms building up the critical nucleus.

Ehrlich - In your system, how sensitively does the size of the critical nucleus depend upon the actual value of the surface tension σ used ? Suppose that you inserted a value of σ 100 ergs/cm^2 larger than the quantity you derive from your experiments. Would the size of the critical nucleus still lie in a reasonable range ?

320

<u>Malinowski</u> - The critical size is quite sensitive to the value of σ , it is proportional to σ 3. Therefore the actual value of σ , in fact the binding energy between the silver atoms at the site of nucleation, should be expected to have a profound effect on the size of the critical nucleus.

<u>Moisar</u> - Same question as Ehrlich but only a complement.

J. BOURDON (Editor)
Growth and Properties of Metal Clusters, pp. 321—329
© 1980 Elsevier Scientific Publishing Company — Printed in The Netherlands

HETEROGENEOUS CATALYTIC CONSIDERATIONS IN PHOTOGRAPHIC SYSTEMS

J. S. Yudelson

Research Laboratories, Eastman Kodak Company, Rochester, New York 14650, USA

All photographic systems consist of the photogeneration of a latent-image species that can cause a subsequent reaction in which the latent-image boundaries are enlarged considerably. This enlargement is called the gain of the system.

Certain catalytic conditions must be satisfied for photographic systems with gain.

Photogeneration

$$P \xrightarrow{\;h\nu\;} C_n \qquad\qquad (1)$$

Amplification

$$A + \text{Redox Agent} \xrightarrow{\;C_n\;} Im \qquad\qquad (2)$$
(solid or solution)

In the above, P can be any photosensitive material that produces a product C_n that can catalyze the decomposition of material A to form the image Im. Redox reactions are generally involved here.

The catalytic condition for this set of reactions is that C_n be a catalyst for (2) and that the product Im be autocatalytic for (2). C_n is generally an aggregate of at least two atoms of a metallic element, and in an earlier talk, Jack Hamilton[1] has described his elegant experiments in which he determined the value of n for various metals.

The amplifying material can be the same as the photosensitive component. The silver halide photographic system falls into this category. Here the amplifying material is in the solid state, and the catalytic centers are imbedded, so to speak, in this solid. After decades of research, the path by which silver can reach the developing center in a silver halide crystal is still not known with certainty.[2]

Another class of systems utilize an amplification system consisting primarily of a kinetically stable solution of a metal salt and a reducing agent. These solutions are generally known as electroless plating baths. However, the photographic scientist for some strange reason prefers to call these physical developers.

Many light-sensitive catalyst precursors exist that can be coupled with these developers. First, there are materials that are photochemically reduced to the zero-valence state.

$$\left.\begin{array}{l} Ag^+ \\ (AgAu)^+ \\ Cu^+_2{}^+ \\ Pd^{2+} \end{array}\right] \quad \xrightarrow{\quad h\nu \quad} \quad \begin{array}{l} Ag \\ Ag\text{-}Au \\ Cu \\ Pd \end{array} \qquad \begin{array}{l} \underline{\lambda(\text{exposure})} \\ vis \\ vis \\ uv \\ uv \end{array} \qquad (3)$$

Next, there are many light-sensitive materials that are reduced to a lower valence state and which are used in conjunction with one of the elements shown in (3).

$$\left[\begin{array}{l} Fe \\ Co \\ Mo \\ W \\ Sn \end{array}\right]^{n+} \quad \xrightarrow{\quad h\nu \quad} \quad \left[\begin{array}{l} Fe \\ Co \\ Mo \\ W \\ Sn \end{array}\right]^{(n-1)+} \qquad \begin{array}{l} \underline{\lambda(\text{exposure})} \\ vis \\ vis \\ vis \\ vis \\ uv \end{array} \qquad (4)$$

A semiconductor such as TiO_2 can be used with an easily reducible ion such as Ag^+.[3] The amplifying systems are equally numerous. Table I lists those that can be used in the electroless plating mode. The metal salts are listed in order of increasing stability.

TABLE I

Amplification Systems

	Reducing Agent
Ag^+	Silver halide developing agents
Au^+	KBH_4
Cu^{2+}	Formaldehyde-tartrate
Ni^{2+}	NaH_2PO_2, $R_3N\text{-}BH_3$
Co^{2+}	NaH_2PO_2, $R_3N\text{-}BH_3$
Fe^{3+}	$R_3N\text{-}BH_3$
Sn^{2+}	$R_3N\text{-}BH_3$, $NaBH_4$
Cr^{3+}	$NaBH_4$

The limiting components in the various combinations of light-sensitive and amplification components are reducing agents. For nonsilver systems, alkaline formaldehyde-tartrate is specific for copper, leaving sodium hypophosphite and amine boranes for all the other elements in Table I. We will focus on the latter two materials.

The catalyzed decomposition of NaH_2PO_2 is postulated to form either atomic hydrogen or the hydride ion.[4,5] These then react with Ni^{2+}, H_2O, and possibly $H_2PO_2^-$ to give the following overall reaction.

$$Ni^{2+} + H_2PO_2^- \xrightarrow[H_2O]{Cat} Ni^0 + P + H_2PO_3^- + H_2 + H^+ \tag{5}$$

We have examined the interaction of various metals with tagged $NaH_2PO_2(P^{32}) + Ni^{2+}(Ni^{63})$. Table II lists the adsorption results with vacuum-deposited metals.[6]

TABLE II

Adsorption of Ni^{2+} and $H_2PO_2^-$ on Catalytic and Noncatalytic Metals

Metal	Catalyst	$[H_2PO_2]/[Metal]$	$[Ni^{2+}]/[Metal]$
Co	No	0.055	0
Bi	No	0.068	0
Pb	No	0.036	0
Pd	Yes	0.080	0

In all examples, the $H_2PO_2^-$ reacts very rapidly with the metal, and the adsorption reaction takes place almost immediately, whereas the Ni^{2+} does not react at all. The Ni^{2+} reacts only after the reducing agent has been adsorbed and presumably decomposed to form H or H^-.

Extrapolation of the results for $H_2PO_2^-$ to very low Pd coverages shows that in the limit, the specific adsorption of H_2PO_2/Pd is 1:1 (molar basis) (Fig. 1). A similar extrapolation for HPO_3^- shows a decrease to zero adsorption as the critical coverage for nickel plating is approached (Fig. 2).

Photographic systems involving mixed ferri-palladium oxalate[7] or potassium palladium oxalate[8] utilize the $Ni^{2+}-H_2PO_2^-$ amplification system. Both of these systems photolytically produce elemental Pd, although their mechanisms are quite different. We briefly discussed these two classes earlier. The characteristic curve relating image density with exposure for the potassium palladium oxalate film is shown in Fig. 3. Increased development time, which increases the concentration of Ni deposit because of the autocatalytic reaction, does not change the minimum exposure. Figure 4 shows the cross section of the developed film. The globular appearance of the developed Ni particles is characteristic of this type of development.

The reaction of another class of reducing agents - the amine boranes - with Pd resembles that of hypophosphite in that the reducing agent undergoes catalytic decomposition to form elemental boron. The overall reaction is:[9]

$$R_3N-BH_3 + Ni^{2+} \xrightarrow[H_2O]{Pd} Ni^0 + B^0 + H_2 + H_3BO_3 + R_3N \tag{6}$$

However, it differs from hypophosphite in that the boron formed in the initial step is autocatalytic towards the amine borane. Thus Lelental[10] has shown that boron is evidently autocatalytic towards the decomposition of amine boranes (Fig. 5). Noncatalysts such as bismuth do not cause any decomposition.

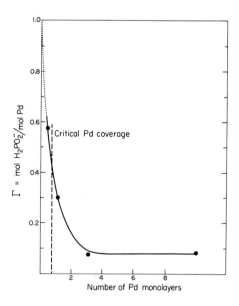

Fig. 1. Adsorption of $H_2{}^{32}PO_2$ on vacuum-evaporated Pd.

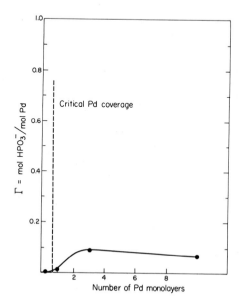

Fig. 2. Adsorption of $H^{32}PO_3$ on vacuum-evaporated Pd.

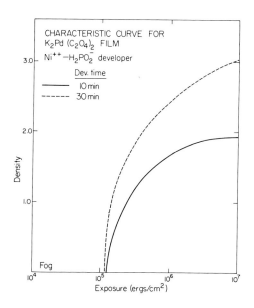

Fig. 3. Characteristic curve for $K_2Pd(C_2O_4)_2$ film developed in a Ni^{2+}-NaH_2PO_2 developer.

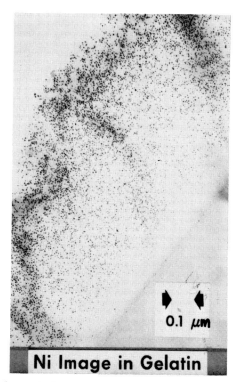

Fig. 4. Developed Ni particles in gelatin.

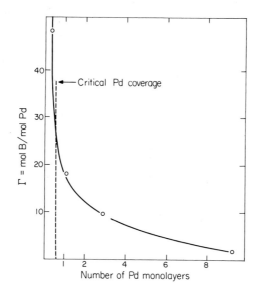

Fig. 5. Boron deposition on evaporated Pd, 10-min immersion in 1%
dimethylamine borane (Lelental).

Hamilton and Logel[11] have determined the critical size of Pd clusters
for B deposition and for Ni plating. Figure 6 shows that 2 Pd atoms will
catalyze the decomposition of the reducing agent, and a larger size is
required for Ni reduction onto the Pd-B center. It is not clear what
effect the B has on the catalytic activity of the amine borane.

The characteristic photographic curve is shown in Fig. 7. Here,
unlike the case of hypophosphite, there is a high fog level due to the
rapid reduction of the Pd salt by the amine borane.

The reducing agents used in the two systems described are both very
strong and both decompose to form a reducing species and a nonmetal. They
differ in the way they react with a metal catalyst such as Pd. Both give
rise to photographic systems that are slow compared to silver halide.

ACKNOWLEDGEMENTS

Many of the mechanistic results presented here are due to Mark
Lelental. The photographic evaluations were done by Barbara Nellis. I
thank them and the other members of the Solid State Photoscience Laboratory,
particularly Henry Gysling and Jack Hamilton, who have made these studies
possible.

327

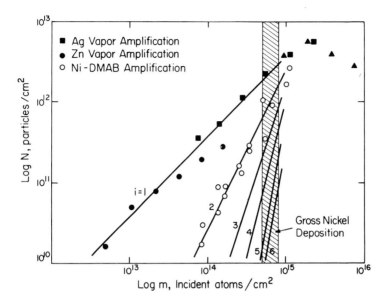

Fig. 6. Particle count data for physical development by Ni^{2+}-dimethylamine borane of Pd clusters (Hamilton and Logel).

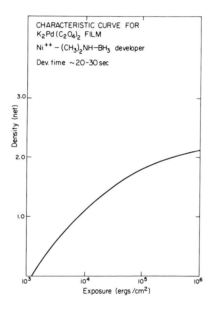

Fig. 7. Characteristic curve for K$_2$Pd(C$_2$O$_4$)$_2$ film developed in a Ni^{2+}-dimethylamine borane developer.

REFERENCES

1. J.F. Hamilton, "The Catalytic and Physical Properties of Vacuum-
    Deposited Metal Nuclei", these proceedings.
2. T.H. James, in T.H. James (Ed.), The Theory of the Photographic
    Process, 4th edn., Macmillan, New York, 1977, p. 377.
3. G. McLeod, SPSE Conference, Boston, June 1968.
4. R.M. Lukes, Plating 51(1964)969.
5. K.A. Holbrook, P. J. Twist, J. Chem. Soc. (1972)1865.
6. M. Lelental and J. Yudelson, unpublished work.
7. D.R. Callaby and M. Brotto, J. Photogr. Sci. 18(1970)8.
8. J.S. Yudelson and H.J. Gysling, US Patent 3,719,490.
9. G.O. Mallory, Plating 58(1971)319.
10. M. Lelental, J. Electrochem. Soc. 120(1973)1650.
11. J.F. Hamilton and P. Logel, J. Catal. 29(1973)253.

DISCUSSION

J.S. YUDELSON

<u>Harding</u> - What is the scope for using a fast silver halide emulsion with a non-silver amplification material, so that all the silver used can be recovered ?

<u>Yudelson</u> - The non-silver amplification systems require reducing agents that are much stronger than those used for silver halide. Thus, the non-silver amplification step would cause fogging at the silver halide.

<u>Levy</u> - Have you done any work with $SnCl_2$ in this connection ?

<u>Yudelson</u> - No. However Western Electric (Bell Lab.) have described a system for preparing printed circuits by a photo-oxidation of Sn^{++} followed by a nucleation step. The latter involves reduction of Pd^{++} by the unexposed Sn^{++}.

J. BOURDON (Editor)
Growth and Properties of Metal Clusters, pp. 331—343
© 1980 Elsevier Scientific Publishing Company — Printed in The Netherlands

FORMATION, PROPERTIES AND STABILITY OF LATENT IMAGE AS A METAL CLUSTER

E.Moisar and F.Granzer

AGFA-GEVAERT AG, Research Division, Leverkusen,

and J.W.Goethe-University, Dep. of Appl. Physics, Frankfurt (Germany)

1. Introduction

The photographic process in silver halides is described by the following steps:

a. Silver halides are photo semiconductors. Upon exposure with photons of an energy $\geqslant$ 2.6 eV (in AgBr) mobile electrons in the conduction band and mobile holes in the valence band are formed[+)]

$$Br_{lattice} \longrightarrow e^- + h^+ \tag{1}$$

b. The photo electrons react with mobile interstitial silver ions

$$e^- + Ag_i^+ \longrightarrow Ag \tag{2}$$

c. If reaction (2) is repeated n times, a silver cluster consisting of n Ag atoms is formed

$$n \cdot e^- + n \cdot Ag_i^+ \longrightarrow Ag_n \tag{3}$$

At least n absorbed photons are required to create a Ag_n cluster. Due to competing and reverse reactions such as recombination

$$e^- + h^+ \longrightarrow Br_{lattice} \tag{4}$$

actually more than n photons must be absorbed for Ag_n build-up.

d. If a silver cluster of about four silver atoms has been formed at the surface of the silver halide micro crystal, an essential property of the crystal has been changed drastically: The whole crystal consisting of appr. $10^8 \dots 10^9$ AgBr molecules becomes immediately reducible by the developer, which is the solution of an organic redox systems of sufficiently negative redox potential.

[+)] $Br_{lattice}$ is a bromine ion, not an atom, in a lattice position. Its negative charge is just compensated (except for surface sites) by the positive charge of adjacent silver ions. The hole h^+ is actually a bromine atom in the lattice. Its apparent charge (= positive hole) results from the uncompensated charge of the adjacent silver ions.

332

Without the presence of such a silver cluster which is called the latent image speck, the crystal will be reduced only after a very much longer time.

The latent image speck acts apparently as a catalyst for the development process.

e. The number of photons required for latent image speck formation is reduced greatly and may approach the optimum value of four, when at the surface of the micro crystal so-called sensitivity centres have been deposited. Such are e.g. clusters of several molecules of Ag_2S. While silver speck formation in an undoped AgBr crystal proceeds roughly at random and may occur at any site of the surface as well as in the interior (where it is absolutely useless for development), exposure of a crystal containing sensitivity centres leads to latent image formation exclusively at the site of these centres. This increases greatly the economy of silver formation.

The sensitivity centres seem to act as catalysts : They catalyze the formation of the latent image speck.

f. There exists a strong relation (c.f. fig. 1) between the location of sensitivity centres of the type mentioned above (Ag_2S e.g.) and the site, where latent image forms upon exposure (ref. 1-3).

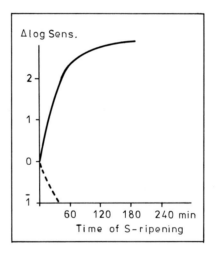

Fig. 1
Increase of surface speed (solid curve) and decrease of internal speed (dashed curve) after doping the crystal surface with Ag_2S. The abscissa is the doping (ripening) time. In a crystal doped at the surface latent image formation in the interior is greatly suppressed.

An increase of photographic sensitivity is also obtained, when the crystal is doped with very small silver clusters of a size - say, Ag_2 - which is still insufficient in order to induce development. Originally it was believed, that these so-called reduction specks are an entity halfways between nothing and a complete latent image speck. By capturing just two more (instead of four) electrons they could be enlarged to developable size Ag_4 :

$$Ag_2 + 2e^- + 2Ag_i^+ \longrightarrow Ag_4 \qquad (5)$$

This assumption prooved to be wrong since unlike Ag_2S clusters the small (Ag_2)-specks do not influence the random formation of latent image specks upon exposure (ref. 4, 5). There does not exist a strict topographic relation between the site of Ag_2 specks and the latent image (Fig. 2).

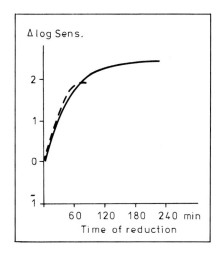

Fig. 2
Increase both of surface (solid curve) and internal speed (dashed curve) after doping the crystal surfaces with small silver specks. The abscissa is the time of reduction treatment. Reduction doping at the surface increases latent image formation generally.

It was found, that Ag_2 specks instead of trapping electrons captured holes and were destroyed (ref. 4-9):

$$Ag_2 + h^+ \longrightarrow Ag + Ag_i^+ + Br_{lattice} \qquad (6)$$

By capturing and eliminating holes they reduce the chance of recombination according to equ. (4). Thus more electrons will survive and become available for silver formation.

g. The Ag_2S sensitivity centres mentioned previously are formed during the
so-called chemical ripening by slow decomposition of trace amounts of
thiosulfate from the ambient phase, leading to Ag_2S deposits at the
crystal surface. With increasing time of ripening the photographic
sensitivity increases. Unfortunately, however, a second and very
unwelcome effect appears: An increasing number of the micro crystals
becomes spontaneously developable, i.e. without being exposed. This is
called fog.

It has been assumed, that something has happened to the sensitivity
centres during later stages of ripening. They might have grown to above
a critical size, they might have acquired a different structure or
composition. It is unknown, what has really happened, but apparently a
third kind of catalytic nuclei has been formed - the so-called fog
centres:

It is assumed, that alleged fog centres catalyze development.

2. The photographic process - an event of phase formation

The very brief description of relevant facts summarized in the preceding
paragraph has shown, that catalytic processes play an important role in
the reactions of the photographic process. The reactions taking place
during exposure, while a latent image speck is formed, or during
development are quite complex and not yet fully known. It is therefore
not surprising that only some effects, such as speed increase by Ag_2S
sensitivity centres (which act as electron traps) can be explained fairly
well, while others can not be. A considerable amount of further
investigations is still required before our knowledge of the reaction
details of the photographic process will approach completeness.

In the past years a different way of describing the photographic
process has been developed. It is an application of the general laws of
phase formation (ref. 10, 11). In principle, there is no question if
such a treatment is justified, since in photography actually a new phase
(silver) is either formed in a parent phase (the silver halide crystal)
or is supposed to grow (from the tiny latent image silver speck to the
large silver phase of a developed crystal). It is less certain, however,
if the exrapolation of the more macroscopic laws of phase formation down
to particle sizes of a few atoms still has a sound physical basis, even
if one never attempts to describe the fate of just one particle but the
time and number average of millions of them which are present in a square
millimetre of a photographic layer. What ever the case may be, the
results are surprising: With no additional assumptions the whole
photographic process can be described in a self-consistent manner and the
basic photographic effects can be understood immediately (ref. 12).

Phase formation requires a state of supersaturation. In a silver halide crystal during exposure photo electrons in large excess to the extremely low dark equilibrium concentration are formed. This is the source of supersaturation, because electrons are the minority component of the dissociation equilibrium

$$Ag \longrightarrow Ag_i^+ + e^- \qquad (7)$$

Thus, a crystal containing free electrons is at the same time supersaturated in respect to silver. It deposits as a new phase where by fluctuations the local supersaturation is particularly high, as has been convincingly shown by Ohachi (ref. 13), or where the formation energy has the lowest value. This takes place at condensation centres. The large effects caused by a nearly neglegible number of photo-induced charge carriers are not unique for silver halides. Fridkin (ref. 14) has observed phase transitions, shifts of the Curie temperature, in several other semiconductors due to exposure.

3. The action of sensitivity centres

A certain amount of Gibbs free energy ΔG, the nucleation energy, is required in order to create a semi-stable cluster of the new phase - a nucleus. Once a **particle** of this critical size exists, it can grow by lowering the free energy, provided the supersaturation persists. Smaller particles tend to decay for the same reason. This explains immediately, why very small silver specks (Ag_2 e.g.) do not grow during exposure, but react with holes which means decay according to equ. (6).

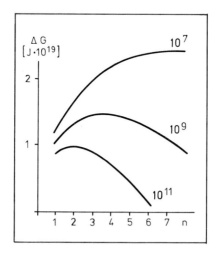

Fig. 3

Gibbs free energy vs. size of Ag_n clusters in the system AgBr/Ag calculated for different degrees of supersaturation c/c_∞ indicated at the curves.

The nucleation energy decreases with increasing supersaturation. Since there exists a reciprocal exponential dependence of the formation rate on the nucleation energy (ref. 15), at high supersaturations the nucleation rate is greatly accelerated. If foreign condensation centres are present, the formation energies are reduced (ref. 15). Homogeneous phase formation is then replaced by a heterogeneous nucleation event which proceeds much faster due to the lower formation energy (fig. 4).

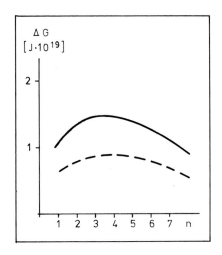

Fig. 4

Gibbs free energy vs. particle size for homogeneous (solid curve) and heterogeneous nucleation (dashed curve) at foreign condensation centres (c.f. ref. 15, 18).

This explains formally the action of **sensitivity** centres used in practice (e.g. Ag_2S): They lower the formation energy of latent image formation, they speed up silver nucleation. As silver deposition at these foreign condensation centres proceeds easier than anywhere else in the crystal, a topographic relation between them and the latent image must be expected. Since the nucleation energy is in fact an activation energy, the sensitivity centres can be immediately regarded as catalysts for latent image formation.

4. Development

Development, beginning at a latent image speck, as well as latent image formation depend on the presence of electrons. They are produced by exposure, as far as latent image formation is concerned, and they are transferred to the micro crystal in the case of development. In either case a state of supersaturation is thus created. The critical minimum size of a silver particle at which development, i.e. growth, starts, depends on the supersaturation and accordingly on the redox potential of

the developer. This has been prooved convincingly by the groups of
Hillson (ref. 16) and Malinowski (ref. 17). Furtermore they showed, that
the Gibbs-Thomson equation which is the thermodynamic basis of the
phase formation theory, is obviously valid down to particles of latent
image sizes. In fig. 5 the calculated plots of ΔG vs. silver particle
size in contact with developers of different

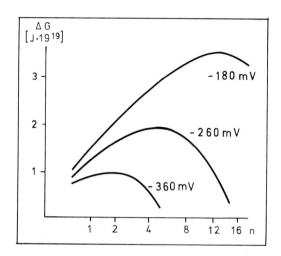

Fig. 5
Gibbs free energy of silver clusters vs. cluster size for developers of
different redox potentials which are indicated at the curves.

redox potentials are shown. The maxima of the curves correspond to
particles consisting of 2, 5, and 14 Ag atoms respectively. In the most
active developer particles as small as two atoms would be regarded as
latent image specks and could start to grow immediately without
requiring an activation energy, while in the least active developer the
minimum size for immediate growth would be as large as 14 Ag atoms.

5. Fog

5.1 Formation of fog at virgin AgBr crystals

In the absence of a sufficiently large silver (latent image) speck a
high nucleation energy has to be spent in order to form a silver
cluster. This activation energy is the barrier which separates the
crystal in the virgin state from a state where further growth could
proceed unrestrictedly. Evidently this nucleation, this random
formation of a silver cluster will be a comparatively slow process.
As soon as such a nucleus has been formed, its further growth will
proceed very fast since no or nearly no activation energy is required
any longer. It then follws that the total number of silver nuclei which

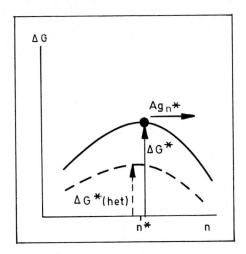

Fig. 6

On a virgin AgBr crystal surface nucleation energy ΔG^* ist required for
formation of speck Ag_n which then grows (develops) further. At a
sensitivity speck such as silver sulfide the smaller nucleation energy
ΔG^*- (het) leads to the same developable silver speck.

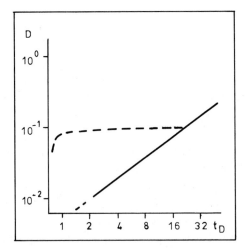

Fig. 7

Density of spontaneous fog (solide line) vs. time of development. In an
exposed area of the layer development of crystals bearing latent image
specks is completed very fast. The density of exposed layer areas
(above fog; dashed line) therefore remains nearly constant after a very
short initial rising time.

are formed in the developer and which lead to fog should increase
linearly with time. This can be seen from fig. 7 where the logarithm of
developed density (which is proportional to the number of developed
crystals) has been plotted as function of the logarithm of development
time. The slope is unity according to the predicted linear relation.
This process of silver formation takes place at the virgin crystal
faces. Since no particular foreign nucleation centres are involved the
probalility of forming a silver cluster at a crystal should increase
with the crystal size. With monodisperse AgBr cubes a linear relation
between the fraction of micro crystals which had become developable

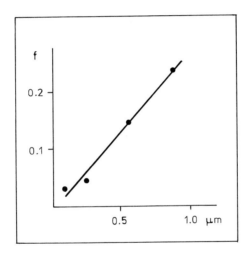

Fig. 8

Fraction f of AgBr crystals on which developable Ag clusters have been
formed vs. crystal size for constant time (32 min) of development.

(at which, hence, a silver cluster has been formed) and the crystal
edge length is observed experimentally (fig. 8). This result seems to
indicate, that nucleation takes place at the crystal edges and not at
the smooth (100) planes. This corresponds to the repeatedly abserved
higher reactivity of corners, edges and e.g. (111) and (110) planes as
compared to the less reactive (100) faces (ref. 20, 21).

5.2 Formation of fog at Ag₂S-doped AgBr crystal surfaces

Sensitivity centres such as Ag_2S increase photographic speed. This is
usually attributed to their ability to capture photo electrons which
then will react according to equ. (2) and (3). Recently with evaporated
AgBr layers it was shown, that a sensitivity increase could also be
obtained after doping with substances, which did not exhibit electron
trapping properties (ref. 22). So the more general, altough less
perceptual description of the action of such centres encloses the
statement that they generally facilitate silver nucleation or that they
decrease the formation energies. This happens during exposure, but it
could happen also in the reducing medium of the developer.

The increase in fog formation after doping the crystal surfaces with
Ag_2S can be seen from fig. 9. The rate of fog formation is faster as

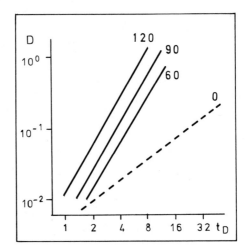

Fig. 9

Logarithm of fog density vs. logarithm of developing time of unexposed
AgBr layers, same as in Fig. 7. In addition to the virgin, undoped
crystals (curve 0) crystals after different doping with silver sulfide
(curves 60, 90, 120) are included.

compared to the undoped crystals and it increases with increasing amount
of doping. From the still relatively high activation energy it follows,
that there is still a nucleation process which leads to a silver cluster.
As soon as this is formed, rapid development starts. Oxidation, which
would destroy any silver clusters being possibly formed during doping due
to side reactions, leaves the rate of fog formation unchanged. Therefore
there is no reason to assume, that the cetres promoting fog are different
from the sensitivity centres.

341

6. Conclusion

The formation of silver due to exposure, the development of exposed silver halide crystals bearing a silver (latent image) speck, and the spontaneous, slow development of unexposed crystals (fog) have been treated as a phase formation process. Doping the crystals with sensitivity centres lowers the formation energies for latent image formation during exposure and also silver cluster formation (fog) at unexposed crystals in the developer. These processes can be regarded as heterogeneous nucleation events.

References

1. E.Moisar and S.Wagner, Ber.Bunsenges.physikal.Chem. 67 (1963) 356
2. R.Matejec and E.Moisar, Photogr.Sci.Eng. 12 (1968) 133
3. G.Junkers, E.Klein and E.Moisar, J. Photogr.Sci. 22 (1974) 174
4. E.Moisar, Photogr.Korresp. 106 (1970) 149
5. T.Tani, Photogr. Sci. Eng. 15 (1971) 28, 181
6. H.E.Spencer, Photogr.Sci.Eng. 11 (1967) 352
7. L.M.Kellogg, Photogr.Sci.Eng. 18 (1974) 378
8. E.Palm, F.Granzer, E.Moisar and D.Dautrich, J.Photogr.Sci.25 (1977) 19
9. D.Dautrich, F.Granzer, E.Moisar and E.Palm, J.Photogr.Sci.25 (1977) 169
10. E.Moisar, F.Granzer, D. Dautrich and E.Palm,J.Photogr.Sci.25 (1977) 12
11. J.Malinowski, Photogr.Sci.Eng. 23 (1979) 99
12. E.Moisar, F.Granzer, D.Dautrich and E.Palm, J.Photogr.Sci. (in press)
13. T.Ohachi and I.Taniguchi, Crystal Growth 1971, Proc. 3rd. Int.Conf. Crystal Growth (ed.R.A. Laudise, J.B.Mullin, B.Mutaftchiev), Amsterdam (1972) 191
14. V.M.Fridkin, J.E.T.P. Lett. 3 (1966) 252
15. A.C.Zettlemoyer (Ed.), Nucleation, New York (1969)
16. P.J.Hillson, J.Photogr.Sci. 22 (1974) 31
17. I.Konstantinov and J.Malinowski, J.Photogr.Sci. 23 (1975) 1, 145
18. S.Stoyanov and R.Kaishew, 28th Int.Sympos.Electrocryst.(Drushba, 1977), paper No. 20
19. E.Moisar, ICPS Rochester (1978)
20. E.Moisar, Ber.Bunsenges.physikal.Chem.72 (1968) 467
21. E.Moisar, J.Photogr.Sci. 14 (1966) 181
22. K.Starbova and V.Platikanova, Photogr.Sci.Eng. 23 (1979) 107

342

DISCUSSION

E. MOISAR, F. GRANZER

Wynblatt - There appears to be an inconsistency in the picture you presented. You state
that after photon exposure, Ag clusters consisting of 1, 2, 3, 4, etc ... atoms are present on the silver halide surface. Now, when you "develop" the system and produce new Ag
monomers on the surface, you claim that at this supersaturation the critical nucleus is
4 atoms in size. How is it possible for previously stable 2- and 3- atom clusters to become suddenly kinetically unstable when you inject additional monomers into the system ?

Moisar - The critical size below which clusters are unstable and tend to decay is a
thermodynamic property and depends largely on the level of supersaturation.If, how, and how fast
they really decay is governed by kinetics. In the dark e.g. an Ag_3 cluster in an AgBr crystal could decay only by $Ag_3 \rightarrow Ag_2 + Ag_i^+ + e^-$. If such a decay takes place the Ag_3 cluster
is supposed to inject one electron deliberately into the conduction band. Due to the very
low dark equilibrium concentration of electrons this process means a deliberate increase
in supersaturation. Such a process can never take place. This is the reason why small Ag
clusters are stable in the dark. During exposure there are always holes present which could
immediately consume the electron originating from the decay process. This also happens
in the developer when the system Ag/AgBr is brought in contact with the reversible redox
system, e.g. hydroquinone/quinone. The oxidized form acts as the consumer for electrons.
Therefore, very small silver clusters can decay without a kinetic barrier, provided
their size is smaller than the equilibrium size which is determined by the supersaturation (by the redox potential of the developer).

Levy - As we have shown in the paper we presented in the poster session, the results of
our kinetic analysis of photocharge decay during chemical ripening indicate that the major change occurring is a reduction in the rate of the second order component of the
process which we have associated with the recombination of a conduction band electron
with a trapped hole. In competition with this process is a pseudo first order process
leading to Ag cluster formation.

The conclusions based largely on arrested development followed by electron microscopy have been interpreted by you and others, il I understand correctly, in terms of the
building up of electron trapping centers due to chemical sensitization, since the region
where the chemical sensitizers forms coincides with the region where the silver forms.

Our conclusions are also compatible with the electron microscopy results. We conclude that the cluster forms at the site of the deposition of the chemical sensitizer
due to the reduction in rate of the competing second order process while the first order
process changes by only a small amount. This suggests that the hole trap distribution is
changing and not the elctron traps. Would you care to comment on this ?

Moisar - There are three alternative models for the action of sensitivity centres such
as Ag_2S : a) They are efficient electron traps. All reactions involving electrons, including silver cluster formation, will take place preferentially at the site of these
centres. This model is supported by the observed strict topographic relation Ag_2S
centre/latent image, and also by the decrease in electron life time (Kellogg) due to
presence of such traps.
b) They are for reasons not yet precisely known sites where the nucleation
energy of Ag cluster formation is reduced. It is not necessary that they trap electrons
like e.g. a multivalent cation by Coulombic forces. But, if they just generally speed
up and facilitate silver formation they quite naturally speed up also consumption of
electrons. Their influence on topography and, as I believe, electron life time should
be then the same as in model a). As fas as actual trapping properties are concerned
they could be also indifferent or even hole traps. Malinowski's experiments with very
different types of doping seem to support this concept of a phase formation process.
c) Your suggestion assumes hole capture. Everybody agrees with you, that this
would improve silver formation.

There remains the question, if Ag_2S traps holes under normal exposure conditions. A macroscopic Ag_2S phase has a rather high oxidation potential requiring a high hole concentration which could be hardly reached by normal exposure levels (a few photons per micro crystal). In analogy to the treatment of silver clusters of decreasing size presented here, with decreasing size of the Ag_2S phase down to a few molecules its reactivity should increase (Gibbs-Thomson). Thus the oxidation potential becomes more negative, and oxidation by holes could become possible even at comparatively low hole concentrations. If with decreasing size of Ag_2S specks they still maintain to act as nucleation centres they may very well have a dual function : they facilitate silver cluster formation (and thus electrons are consumed preferentially in their vicinity), and at the same time they consume holes and thus reduce recombination. I think this agrees quite well with your suggestion. I however believe, that hole capture alone would not change silver cluster topography.

J. BOURDON (Editor)
Growth and Properties of Metal Clusters, pp. 345—354
© 1980 Elsevier Scientific Publishing Company — Printed in The Netherlands

COMPUTER SIMULATION OF CLUSTER GROWTH ON SMALL CLOSED SURFACES

C.L. Marquardt, M.E. Gingerich, and J.W. Williams*

Naval Research Laboratory

Washington, D.C. 20375 (USA)

A number of potentially interesting processes involve the formation of clusters on small closed surfaces. One such process which has been the subject of recent experimental investigation is the photolytic formation of silver clusters on small (≈ 100 Å) silver-halide spheres in photochromic glasses [1]. Experimental results indicate that the dynamics of cluster growth depend on sphere radius in a manner which is not predicted from the simplest physical models. On the other hand, as models are made more realistic, calculational difficulties quickly become overwhelming. In order to obtain some insight as to how various physical parameters influence the cluster formation process we have employed a direct computer simulation based on a reasonably realistic model. In the present paper, we describe the model and the simulation method, and we present some results of the simulation which are related to the particle size dependence observed in photochromic glasses. We also indicate other problems to which this method might be applied.

I. MODEL

The process considered here is the flash photolysis of a small silver-halide sphere containing a bulk distribution of infinitely deep hole traps and very shallow electron traps. The light flash is regarded as a delta function in time so that at t = 0 our system contains a bulk distribution of deeply trapped holes (immobile) as well as shallow-trapped electrons and mobile silver ions. Eventually each electron either recombines with a trapped hole or contributes to the growth of the silver cluster. (For the present work we assume that on the surface of the sphere there is only one nucleation site around which a cluster can form.) Cluster growth occurs by alternate trapping of electrons and silver ions at the nucleation site, but the transit time for the electron is assumed to be negligibly small. Silver ions migrate to the growing cluster by bulk diffusion as well as by motion along the surface. The latter process is assumed to make the major contribution to cluster growth, so that motion of surface ions is the principal factor determining growth rate. Morphological rearrangement of the growing cluster is not included in this model. Thus the cluster, which grows primarily from mobile surface ions, tends to form as a monolayer, with some regions in which layer thickness is enhanced by trapping of bulk interstitials. Motion of the surface ions is assumed to be the random except for a screened Coulomb interaction with the cluster, and ion-ion-repulsion.

*NRL Junior Fellow

346

II. SIMULATION

We wish to observe the dynamics of silver cluster growth during the time following the light flash. To do so we simulate the motion of surface ions using a method analogous to Monte Carlo calculations of neutron trajectories in solids [2]. The problem is greatly simplified by replacing the spherical surface of the silver-halide particles by a square-planar surface with cyclic boundary conditions [3]. Motion of surface ions is then represented by "random" jumping between adjacent sites of a square lattice imposed upon this surface. The unit of time (clock period) is chosen so that the probability of any ion making two successive jumps during one clock period is vanishingly small. The subject of our simulation is illustrated in Figure 1. On the left we show the "surface" at t = 0; five percent of the lattice sites are occupied by randomly distributed walkers (mobile ions) shown as black dots, and a nucleation spot consisting of four adjacent lattice sites is shown as a shaded region. On the right we show the surface after a number of clock periods have elapsed, during which three of the walkers have formed a stable cluster shown as fully blackened squares. Figure 1 illustrates this process on a lattice containing 10^2 sites. Actual simulations use much larger lattices which typically contain $\simeq 10^4$ sites.

A block diagram of the simulation program is given in Figure 2. A number of parameters (such as lattice size, percent occupancy, etc.) are read-in to set up the problem. Walkers are then distributed on the lattice by considering their x and y coordinates to be independent random variables. A nucleation spot is established by designating one or more lattice sites upon which the jump probability per clock period is lower than it is on ordinary lattice sites.

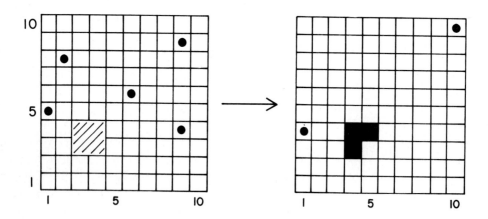

Fig. 1 Formation of a cluster by random walk on a square-planar surface with cyclic boundary conditions; illustrated for a 10 x 10 lattice with 5 % occupancy. Boundary conditons: if $U_j > 10$, replace U_j by $(U_j - 10)$; if $U_j < 1$, replace U_j by $(U_j + 10)$. Condition for a stable cluster: $N_S = 3$. Crosshatched region designates a nucleation spot for cluster formation; black dots indicate walkers. On the left - the surface at t = 0; on the right - the surface at some later time after the formation of a stable cluster.

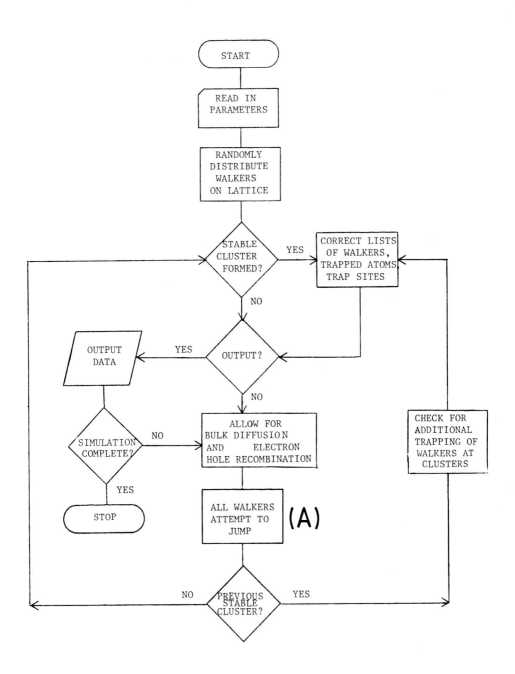

Fig. 2 Block diagram of the program used to simulate growth of a cluster on a surface of the type illustrated in Figure 1. One clock period is completed each time the program passes through Block (A). The subroutine used in Block (A) is outlined in Figure 3.

348

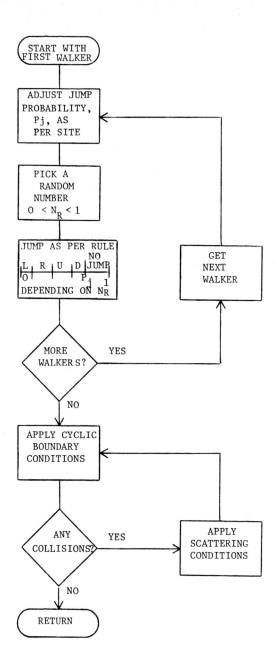

Fig. 3 Block diagram of the subroutine used to simulate the "random" motion of the
walkers during a single clock period.

During each clock period all walkers attempt to jump to adjacent lattice sites. The method of determining their trajectories is shown in Figure 3. Each jump is considered as an independent discrete random variable having five values: no jump, right, left, up and down. The probability of no jump is given by:

$$P_{no\ jump} = 1 - P_j$$

where P_j is the jump probability associated with the site from which the walker is attempting to jump. P_j may have either the "normal" value or the lowered value (both values entered as parameters of the program) depending on whether or not the walker experiences some additional weak binding to its present site. This lowering of the jump probability is assumed to occur not only when the walker is located on the nucleation spot but also whenever the walker is weakly bound in a cluster smaller than the critical size for stability (entered as parameter N_S). Jump probabilities to adjacent nearest neighbour sites are assumed to be of the form:

$$P_{\pm}(U) = (P_j/4)\ (1 \pm 4\alpha\,(U_o - U)/R^2)$$

where U is one cartesian coordinate of the walker on the lattice, subscript "+" or "-" indicates increase or decrease in the value of U, U_o is the corresponding coordinate of the nucleation site, R is the lattice distance to the nucleation site, and α is a parameter which scales the coulomb attraction. It is found that α and N_S influence the behaviour of the system primarily in the early stages of cluster formation but have little effect on subsequent growth of larger clusters.

An important feature of the present simulation is the assumption that within a clock period the order of events is inconsequential. Thus walkers are allowed to jump in an arbitrary order. Ion-ion repulsion between the walkers is subsequently taken into account by treating intersecting trajectories as elastic scattering events. Similarly bulk diffusion and electron-hole recombination are treated as independent processes. (See Fig. 2) Trajectories of electrons and bulk interstitials are not simulated. The electron density is assumed to decay exponentially by recombination in addition to its decay via cluster growth. At the beginning of each clock period the total number of shallow trapped electrons is decremented by the number which have recombined with holes. At the end of the clock period one electron is removed for each atom which has been added to a stable cluster. Bulk interstitials are only of interest if they reach the surface. At the beginning of each clock period we calculate the average number reaching the surface during the clock period and assume that they appear at randomly located sites.

Cluster growth occurs in the following manner. Ions reach the growing cluster either by surface migration or by bulk diffusion. Prior to the existence of a stable cluster a walker lands on a nucleation site, and his jump probability is thereby lowered as discussed above. This enhances the likelihood that a second walker will occupy one of the nearest neighbour sites before the first walker jumps off the nucleation site. When a second walker does occupy one of these nearest neighbour sites, then both walkers have lowered jump probabilities since they are members of a sub-stable cluster, etc. When the number of walkers in the growing cluster reaches N_S the cluster becomes stable, and the jump probability of all cluster members is reduced to zero. (They are no longer walkers.) Any walkers

350

which subsequently land on sites which are nearest neighbours to members of the stable cluster are permanently trapped and become members of that cluster. This scheme is equivalent to approximating the dependence of binding energy on cluster size by two steps, the break occuring at N_S.

The success of any Monte Carlo simulation depends on the availability of an efficient, high quality pseudo-random number generator. The present work utilized the vector random number generator "VRANF" which generates an array of 10^3 pseudo-random numbers, $0 < N_R < 1$ each time is called. (Each call requires about 21 μsec of computation time.) The output of this generator has been tested extensively for uniformity [4], and it is judged to be of extremely high quality except for minor deviations from uniformity in triplets. In the present work VRANF was "seeded" only at the beginning of each simulation. (Each seed determines a unique sequence of pseudo-random numbers.) Statistical "data" were generated by repeating each simulation using different values for the initial seed.

III. EXAMPLE

In flash photolysis of silver-halide photochromic glasses it is observed that for glasses containing the same total amount of silver halide, those containing smaller silver-halide particles darken faster. Specifically the darkening rate was found to vary inversely as some fractional power of the particle diameter [5]. Calculations from simple models involving only surface ions produced darkening rates which varied as higher powers of the particle diameter [6]. This suggested that a combination of bulk diffusion and surface ion motion may be required to fit the experimental results. We have used the simulation technique described above to study the manner in which the introduction of bulk diffusion influences the cluster growth rate and its dependence on particle size.

In our "computer experiments" we have assumed surface lattices having from 10^3 to 10^4 lattice points with fractional occupation of 2-5% and have ignored electron-hole recombination. We start the system with a superabundance of electrons at $t = 0$ and measure the time, T, required to form a cluster of N atoms. Normallized "data" from several simulations are displayed in Fig. 4 as a function of the parameter, δ_D, the average probability per unit area that a bulk interstitial will cross the surface within a clock period. N_o is the number of mobile ions initially present on the surface, and T_o is the value of T obtained as N/N_o approaches zero (very large surface or very small cluster). Three observations may be made regarding Fig. 4: (1) If δ_D and the fractional occupancy of the lattice are fixed, then for a given N, T always increases as the lattice size decreases. Thus if we wish to grow clusters of fixed size on two spheres having the same physical properties but different radii, the growth time will be longer for the smaller sphere. This is qualitatively the type of behaviour required to fit the experimental results on the photochromic glasses. (2) The dependence of growth time on particle size decreases as δ_D is increased. This tends to corroborate our assumption that the clusters are formed primarily by migration of surface ions, since the particle-size dependence (required to fit the experimental data) vanishes when the process is dominated by bulk diffusion. (3) The dependence of growth time on particle size also becomes negligible when the number of atoms in the cluster is only an insignificant fraction of the number of mobile ions initially on the surface.

In order to make actual comparisons with experimental results it is necessary to

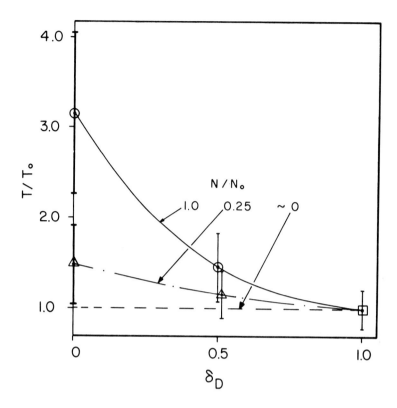

Fig. 4 Normalized "data" from computer simulation experiments designed to study the dependence of growth rate on particle size and bulk diffusion. Error bars indicate standard deviations obtained from groups of 10 simulations with different seeding of the random number generator. Symbols: N = number of atoms collected in the cluster, N_o = number of walkers initially on the surface, T = time required to collect N atoms, T_o = value of T for $N/N_o \sim 0$, δ_D = bulk diffusion parameter.

calculate the optical absorption of a system of spheres having small clusters on their surfaces [7]. This problem has not yet been treated satisfactorily, and for present discussion we will simply assume that the absorption per cluster is proportional to the number of atoms in the cluster. We further assume that the photoinduced optical absorption coefficient, α, grows linearly in time. Then for photochromic glasses containing equal amounts of silver halide, varying only in particle diameter, d, we find that

$$\frac{d\alpha}{dt} \sim d^{-3} [T(d)]^{-1}.$$

Since experimental data [1] indicate that $d\alpha/dt$ varies roughly as $d^{-1/2}$, we wish to determine the conditions under which our simulation could yield $T(d) \sim d^{-5/2}$. From Fig. 4 we see that the maximum size dependence occurs around $\delta_D = 0$, and that for $N/N_o \leq 1$, $T(d)$ varies at most as d^{-1} (in agreement with results of Ref. 6). In order to obtain stronger dependences of T on particle size we must consider $N/N_o > 1$. Since this corresponds to collecting in the cluster more silver than was originally available on the surface, the process must involve bulk diffusion ($\delta_D > 0$). One difficulty with the assumption of

$N/N_o > 1$ is that for reasonable densities of mobile surface ions and for one cluster growing on each sphere, we obtain clusters which are too large to exhibit the experimentally observed optical absorption spectra [1,7]. This difficulty can be avoided however by assuming that several non-interacting clusters grow on the surface of each particle, so that the N_o for each cluster is only a fraction of the N_o for the entire surface. Only in this way can we simultaneously make N/N_o large enough to obtain the correct size dependence of the growth rate, and make the final cluster sizes small enough to have the observed optical absorption spectra. Thus we suggest that in order to obtain agreement with the total body of experimental data, the growth process for silver clusters in the photochromic glasses studied in Ref. 1 must involve both the motion of surface ions and diffusion of bulk interstitials, and that a number of non-interacting clusters must grow simultaneously on each silver-halide particle.

IV COMMENTS

The above example is only one of many computer experiments which can be performed using the technique described here. This technique can readily be used to simulate other effects observed in the photochromic glass systems, such as dependence of darkening on excitation intensity and temperature. With minor modification, it can be applied to low level continuous excitation rather than pulsed excitation. With considerably more difficulty, it could also be extended to a surface having several nucleation sites. Since the minimum size of a stable cluster, N_S, enters as a parameter, simulations could provide an independent method of determining N_S.

It should be noted that the simulation method entails several intrinsic weaknesses. First we see that the error bars in Fig. 4 are quite large. They can be made "arbitrarily small" by increasing n, the number of computations per data point. The difficulty is that the error varies as $n^{-1/2}$ whereas the computation cost increases linearly with n. Another problem is that of uniquess. The fact that simulation based on a particular model agrees with experiment does not necessarily demonstrate that the model used in the simulation accurately represents the physical system. Finally the simulation contains a number of parameters to which it is difficult to assign meaningful numerical values. This makes it exceedingly difficult to use the simulation as part of a quantitative calculation. Nevertheless, simulation should be useful in determining the _manner_ in which the process of cluster formation depends on various physical properties of the system.

ACKNOWLEDGMENTS

We are most grateful to Dr. H.B. Rosenstock and to Dr. D.A. Nolan for discussions of this problem.

REFERENCES

[1] C.L. Marquardt and G. Gliemeroth, J. Appl. Phys. (July, 1979). See also references cited therein.
[2] See for example J.M. Hammersley and D.C. Handscomb, Monte Carlo Methods, Methuen, London (1964).
[3] H.B. Rosenstock (private communication).
[4] B.T. Caruthers and G.H. Herling, NRL Memorandum Report 3509, Naval Research Laboratory, Washington (1977); approved for public release, distribution unlimited.

[5] The reader should beware of imprecise terminology found in Ref. 1, which leads to confusion between darkening rate (optical absorption of the photochromic glass) and growth rate for an individual cluster.

[6] D.A. Nolan and C.L. Marquardt (unpublished); results are summarized in Ref. 1.

[7] D.A. Nolan, N.F. Borrelli and C.L. Marquardt, in Papers from the 1978 Int. Cong. of Photog. Science, pp. 83-85 (Society of Photographic Scientists and Engineers, Washington, 1978).

DISCUSSION

C.L. MARQUARDT, M.E. GINGERICH, J.W. WILLIAMS

<u>Belloni</u> - I wonder whether, whithin the time range of your observation, colloidal silver can be expected because it is probably not yet formed at that time. Did you try to observe optical absorption of the well-known precursor Ag_2^+ which presents a narrow band near 370 nm ?

<u>Marquardt</u> - The time scale in our experiments is of the order of several microseconds. This is qualitatively what one expects for formation of silver colloids. It is also in good agreement with recent measurements of time-resolved photoconductivity of emulsion grains, as presented in a poster paper by Levy and coworkers. We are not able to observe the growth of optical absorption at 370 nm since the matrix glass is highly absorbing at wavelength.

<u>Kreibig</u> - In your opinion what is the thickness of silver surface layer produced by the photolysis ?

<u>Marquardt</u> - By comparison of observed photoinduced optical absorption spectra with those calculated from a partial coverage model by Nolan and coworkers, we estimate the thickness to be on the order of 10 Å.

ION IMPLANTATION IN AgCl : SILVER CLUSTERS GROWING AND RELATION WITH THE PHOTOGRAPHIC
PROCESS

J.L. GISCLON, Ch. DIAINE[+], J. BERT, J.P. DUPIN, J. DUPUY

Département de Physique des Matériaux (associé au C.N.R.S.)

U.E.R. de Physique - Université Lyon I - FRANCE

+ U.E.R. de Pharmacie - Université Lyon I - FRANCE

ABSTRACT

Energetic ions implantation in AgCl thin films permits to confirm and precise the silver clusters characteristics, which grow after collisions under the beam.

We give the cluster distribution and concentration as well as the role of chlorine ions by mean of optical absorption measurements and back scattering ions analysis.

The light sensitivity variation permits to know the role played by silver ions in the photographic process.

RESUME

L'implantation d'ions énergétiques dans des couches minces d'AgCl permet de confirmer et de préciser les caractéristiques des amas d'argent se formant sous le faisceau à partir d'un mécanisme de collision.

Nous rendons compte par des mesures d'absorption optique et d'analyse d'ions rétrodiffusés, de la distribution des amas et de leur concentration ainsi que le rôle possible des ions Cl^-. La variation de la sensibilisation à la lumière rend compte du rôle joué par les ions Ag^+ dans le mécanisme photographique.

In some previous studies (1,2,3,4) we have shown by means of optical absorption, how to stress the changes appearing in a AgCl single crystal implanted with various energetic ions.

In particular, we have shown that the intrinsic Ag clusters formation can be explained by a mechanism which is strongly related to elastic collisions. Their properties and their stabilization are bound to a secondary mechanism such as ionization or chemical effect. However some problems have not been solved yet : these are essentially those related to the colloïds dispersion and the possible effect of the matrix Cl^- ions in some precise irradiation conditions.

In order to give precisions about the formation and properties of silver clusters we have studied the effects of energetic ions implantation in AgCl thin films. The choice of this material has been made for the following reasons :

- the Rutherford Back Scattering technique (R.B.S.) can easily be performed on thin films with a maximum efficiency

- from the optical point of view, the U.V. edge is shifted toward larger energies and lets appear electronic or internal transitions

- the sample thickness can easily be varied, thus involving a modification of the interaction ion-AgCl

- at last the specific properties of AgCl thin films are not quite different from the selective properties of this material inside glass matrixes or photographic emulsions.

I. THIN FILMS PROPERTIES

1. Preparation

The AgCl thin films on silica or carbon are obtained by thermal evaporation under 10^{-6}T vacuum. The tantalum crucible has been heated at 1200°C during 2 hours under vacuum before being filled by the spectra pure AgCl powder (Johnson Matthey).

The evaporations were made at the lowest possible temperature (550-600°C) for stoechiometry, in the dark, the silica or carbon pellet being constantly cooled at L.N.T.

The silica (optical quality) was used for optical measurements and carbon for R.B.S. . The thickness was checked during evaporation.

2. Characterization

The characterization is performed by R.B.S. . This technique (5) allows the identification of the sample elements, the calculation of the thickness of a film and its stoechiometry.

For instance, let us consider (Fig. 1) He^{+} ions with an incident energy E_o. Let $k_A^2 E_o$ be the He^{+} ions backscattered from the surface by the element A, and E_A be the He^{+} ions backscattered by element A (depth x).

In the case of 1 MeV alpha particles, the energies $k_A^2 E_o$ are given for various elements on table I.

C	Na	Cl	K	Rb	Ag
260	506	645	670	834	866 (keV)

Table I

Because of the He^{+} ions energy loss inside the target, the R.B.S. spectra are quite different whether they are performed on an AgCl single crystal or on a AgCl thin film (Fig. 2)

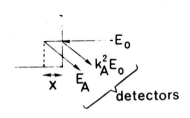

Figure 1

Typical arrangement of R.B.S experiment

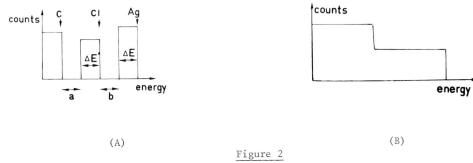

(A)   (B)

<u>Figure 2</u>

Typical R.B.S. spectrum of AgCl (2A) thin film ; (2B) single crystal

The implanted ions profile (for instance K, Rb, Na) will overlap these spectra. In the case of a single crystal these profiles will hardly be observable for two reasons : first the R.B.S. cross section is proportional to Z^2 and second, the profile will be superposed to an important background. However, in the case of the thin film, ΔE and $\Delta E'$ are proportional to the layer thickness so there exists "free spaces " a and b where the implanted ions profiles can easily be separated from the null background. In the case of Rb and Na, analyzed with 1 MeV He$^+$ ions, the maximum thickness to detect the implanted profile are respectively 300 Å and 1500 Å.

Figure 3 shows a 90 keV implanted sodium profile in a thin film. The ions are localized at a depth of 1100 Å . In the case fo 350 keV Ne$^+$ the theoretical penetration is 4400 Å, then this ion profile can't be detected.

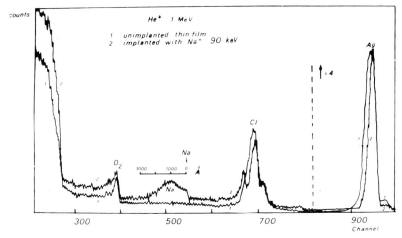

<u>Figure 3</u> : R.B.S. analysis of a Na$^+$ (90 keV) implanted in AgCl film

The maximum error obtained with R.B.S. is about 25 % on thickness and about 5 % on stoechiometry.

The minimum number of atoms which can be determined is about 10^{13} at/cm^2 . This number then lets us assume that our films have a good purity and are particularly free from iodine.

3. Optical properties

The single crystals and thin films absorption spectra show an important shifting of the U.V. edge from 3.1 eV to 6.2 eV at room temperature (Figure 4).

The coming out of a peak at 4.8 eV attributed to excitons (6) can be observed on the thin film spectra.

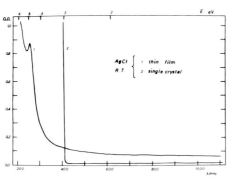

Figure 4 : optical absorption spectrum of pure silver chloride (1) thin film, (2) single crystal

II. ION IMPLANTATION INTO AgCl THIN FILMS AT L.N.T.

We give the main results obtained after Ne$^+$ (350 keV) implantation of various thickness AgCl thin films. The general features of implantation conditions are first examined and secondly the physical effects are analyzed in some details.

1. General character of mean energy (350 keV) light ions implantation

The energy losses appearing in the main processes occuring in this particular case have been calculated (7) (Figure 5) for one particle : these are correlated to :

- the nuclear interaction from direct collisions $(\frac{dE}{dx})_N$(8)

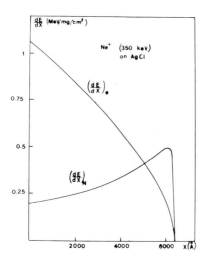

- the electronic interaction from binding electron excitation in the solid $(\frac{dE}{dx})_e$.
- the straggling of implanted ions.

It can be seen that opposite to single crystals, according to the thickness, a fraction of the total energy is dissipated in the film.

Figure 5 : nuclear and electronic energy losses of Ne$^+$ (350 keV) in AgCl as a function of penetration depth.

Figure 6 we have plotted the energy losses which are dissipated during collisions with the 2 different ions of the target for Ne^+ and Ar^+. The very important observed dissymetry for Ne^+ will certainly induce specific phenomena.

The Ne^+ repartition calculated profile (7b) is a gaussian curve with its axis at 4400 Å and its halfwidth at 1100 Å.

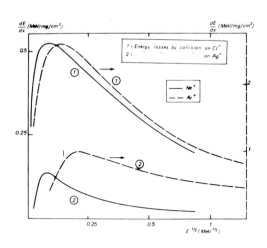

Figure 6 : nuclear energy losses dissipated on chlorine and silver for Ne^+ and Ar^+ as a function of $E^{1/2}$.

2. Optical properties changes after ion implantation

(a) The variation of optical absorption of AgCl thin films (1500 Å thickness) after implantation with 350 keV Ne^+ is given figure 7.

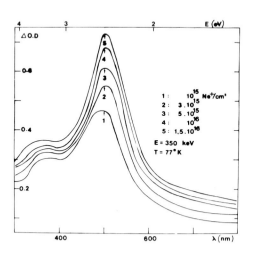

Figure 7: effect of Ne^+ (350 keV) implantation on the variation of the optical absorption of thin AgCl film

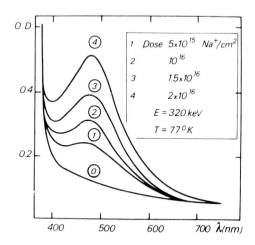

Figure 8 : Effect of Na^+ (320 keV) implantation on the optical absorption of single AgCl crystal

The analogy with the 2.65 eV band obtained with an "equivalent" ion i.e. Na^+ (figure 8) and with various implanted ions in a single AgCl crystal (4) proves that the *defect* which is responsible for this absorption is *not correlated to the type of the implanted ion*. We identified it as being *associated to silver clusters*.

In first approximation, *the size of these quite homogeneous clusters was found not far from 10 Å (2)*. The position (490-500 nm) and the half width (140 nm) obtained in this present work confirm the results obtained with Na^+ (3), (4) and proves the validity of our first analysis.

However, opposite to AgCl single crystals, one can notice a "satellite band" which would give *some more information about an important concentration effect*, according to Marton and Lemon (9).

If one makes an hypothesis on the cluster geometry one can deduce a filling factor (10) from the relative positions of these bands. This concentration phenomenon has already been mentionned in the case of implantation (11).

(b) Silver clusters dispersion

We have already shown that, in first *approximation, the cluster concentration is correlated to the collision energy losses of the particules into the AgCl matrix*. For a given energy ion, the energy fraction which is dissipated into a thin film is a function of its thickness. Figure 9 gives the optical density variation with the thickness of the film (for the same dose : 1.10^{16} Ne^+/cm^2).

From this result we can conclude that the *clusters are created along the whole particle path and that their concentration are in first approximation function of the collision dissipated energy*.

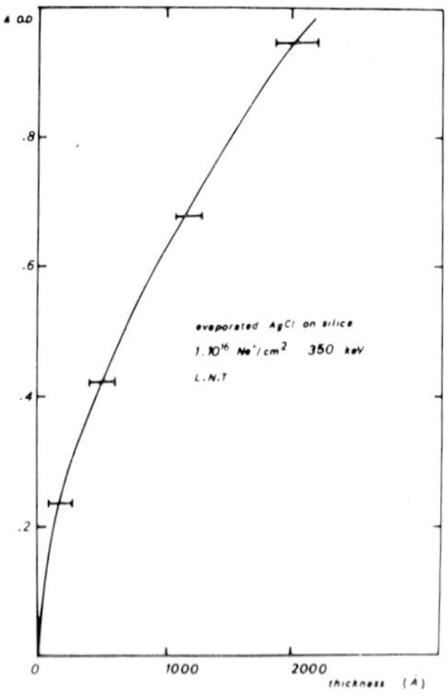

Figure 9 : thickness dependence of the optical absorption maximum of thin AgCl implanted film with the same flux conditions : E =350 keV, i=0,8 µA, d=1.10^{16} Ne^+/cm^2

(c) Modification of the matrix during implantation

The R.B.S. has permitted us to calculate. The film stoechiometry before and after implantation : *the stoechiometry variation becomes more important as the thickness increases*. The chlorine loss can rise to 20 % for a 2000 Å thickness.

3. Discussion

The thin film implantation results confirm and precise the characterization and formation of silver clusters created during implantation into AgCl.

The stoechiometry specific results and the shape of the collision efficiency as function of thickness are bound to some phenomena which we can try to explain.

The sputtering phenomenon can be carried out from the stoechiometry variation because it should not be dependent on thickness.

If one takes into account for the dissipated energy during collision by the 350 keV Ne$^+$, one obtain a Cl/Ag dissymetry which increases with the film thickness.

There results a chlorine substoechiometry variable with thickness and a change of the correlation cluster concentration/collision dissipated energy loss.

In the case of a single crystal this dissymetry is maximum but the chlorine ions being trapped into the matrix, there results an increase of the optical absorption background (4) comparable to that obained after chlorine dissolution in AgCl (12,13). In a thin film, collision can let chlorine diffuse out of the matrix, thus creating a rise of the background not so important as for single crystals. This is confirmed experimentally if we compare figure 7 and the equivalent results on a single crystal (4).

One can then foresee that an Ar$^+$ implantation with an equal flux will give different results for stoechimetry and efficiency beaause of the different proportions between the energy losses of this ion into the matrix (figure 6). The lack of background rise in optical absorption with 350 keV Ar$^+$ (4) oonfirms partially the role of chlorine ions.

III. APPLICATION TO THE PHOTOGRAPHIC PROCESS

The samples are illuminated with Hg high pressure light source, the beam being refocalised with silica lenses. Optical experiments are performed with a Cary 17 spectrophotometer.

1. Darkening of non irradiated film

The absorption band related to the photographic process is created by illumination. It is the same for thin films and for single crystals (figure 10). For a given illumination time, the optical density variation (Δ OD) increases with the sample thickness, being related to a more important mass. If one reduce the observed O.D. (at the maximum absorption) to the unit thickness one obtain a factor 10^3 between the thin film and the single crystal (table II).

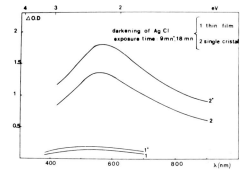

Figure 10 : darkening of AgCl in single crystal and thin film form,. after two different exposures time.

e Å (thickness)	Δ OD exposure time : 10 mn	Δ OD/e (film)
510	0.145	28400
1300	0.425	32600
3000	0.81	27000
Single crystal	1.8	15

Table II

This is in good agreement with the ionic carriers number given by Baetzold (14) for thin films.

2. Darkening of L.N.T. irradiated films with Ne$^+$ ions

The comparison (figure 11) of ΔOD (at the maximum absorption) showing the darkening of an irradiated film and of a non irradiated film, as function of the illumination time let appear an important difference. The irradiated films (Ne$^+$) is much less light sensitive than a new film. During Ne$^+$ irradiation, a certain number of Ag clusters appear (500 nm band) : a great number of Ag$^+$ ions are then no more usable for the photographic process.

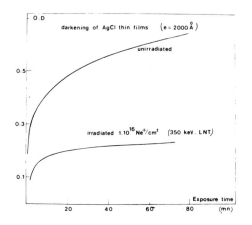

Figure 11 : variation of optical absorption maximum as a function of different light exposure time for an implanted and an unimplanted AgCl thin film.

In conclusion by means of implantation in AgCl thin layers we confirm the formation of silver clusters and their parameters such as size, distribution concentration as well as their formation mechanism . We analyze the possible role of Cl$^-$ ions and confirm the ionic mechanisum occuring during the photographic process. We can then think of the opposite effect to Ne$^+$ (350 keV) of an ionizing particle which would lead to an increase of the material sentivity.

REFERENCES

1 J.L. Gisclon, J.F. Jal, J. Dupuy, Rad. Effects, 34, 1977, p. 35
2 Ch. Diaine, J.L. Gisclon, J. Dupuy, Phys. Stat. Solidi, 87, 1978, 298
3 Ch..Diaine, J.L. Gisclon, J. Dupuy, to be published in Rad. Effects, 1039, 1979
4 Ch. Diaine, Thèse d'Etat (Sciences Pharmaceutiques) Lyon 1978
5 Nato Summer School "Material Characterization using ion beams" Corsica 1977,
   J.P. Thomas, A. Cachard Editors, Plenum Press
6 F. Moser, R. Akrenkiel, "The theory of the Photographic Process, 4th Ed. , T.H. James Ed.
   37, 1977
7 a) J. lindhard, N. Scharff, H.F. Schiøtt, Kgl. Danske. Vid. Selsk. Matt. Fys. Med. 33,
   14, 1963
   b) G.Dearneley, J.H. Freeman, R.S. Nelson, J. Stephen, Ion implantation, North Holland
   Publishing Company, 1973

8 L.C. Northcliffe, R. Shilling, Nuc. Data Tables, 7, 1970, 233
9 J.P. Marton, J.R. Lemon, J. Appl. Phys., 44, 1973, 3953
10 J. Davenas, Thèse d'Etat (Sciences Physiques) Lyon 1980 (to be published)
11 J.P. Dupin, Thèse de spécialité (physique des solides) Lyon 1976
12 F. Moser, J. Appl. Phys., 33, 1962, 343
13 J.L. Gisclon, Thèse de Spécialité (physique des solides) Lyon 1974
14 R.C. Baetzold, J. Phys. Chem. Sol. , 35, 1974, 89

J. BOURDON (Editor)
Growth and Properties of Metal Clusters, pp. 365—370
© 1980 Elsevier Scientific Publishing Company — Printed in The Netherlands

FORMATION AND PROPERTIES OF NUCLEI AS APPLIED TO THE PHOTOGRAPHIC PROCESS

AN ELECTROCHEMICAL MODEL

Arnold Hoffman

The Weizmann Institute of Science, Rehovot (Israel)

INTRODUCTION

The phenomenon of the latent-image has been extensively studied over the past century. The phenomenon is simple to describe and demonstrate: a silver halide grain exposed to light becomes more rapidly reduced to metallic silver by chemical reducing agents (developers) than an unexposed crystal. If a coating of these silver halide crystals is exposed to a light image and then the coating is immersed in a developer, image-wise development occurs and the result is a photograph.

It is apparent that in the predevelopment stage, the light absorbed by the silver halide crystal caused a change in the crystal, giving it the potential or latent ability to reproduce the image of the light as reduced silver when a developer is added; hence the term, latent-image.

The nature of the latent-image, i.e. the change in the silver halide crystal caused by light absorption, is not too clearly understood.

Conventional wisdowm describes the latent-image as a cluster of silver atoms on the surface of the crystal comprising a few atoms ($\sim$10) of silver formed by photoelectrons combining with silver ions of the crystal (1). This silver speck serves as a catalyst for development; e.g. in the electrochemical model of development, the silver speck formed by light acts as a metallic electrode, accepting electrons from the developer, forming more silver, thus initiating an auto-catalytic reaction (2). Thus, for a given residence time of silver halide grains in developer, T, the exposed grains are reduced to silver. The unexposed grains, not possessing this light produced metallic silver catalyst on the surface, do not undergo development in this time, T. The result is image-wise development.

This theory has been useful in rationalizing some of the observed phenomena, but it has limitations. Some of these limitations are:
1. No _quantitative_ theory has emerged that relates light exposure level and time of development to number of atoms of reduced silver (silver density).
2. A maximum in the dependence of speed on grain-size of a photographic emulsion is not easily explained by the conventional theory (3).
3. The remarkable effect of redox buffers which can shift H&D curves on the exposure axis without affecting their shape is very difficult to reconcile with the conventional picture of the latent image (4).

The purpose of this work is to describe an alternate hypothesis concerning the nature of the latent-image/development process. The basic premise of this model is that the latent-image is a _thermodynamic_ change in the silver halide crystal. This thermodynamic change has profound kinetic consequences when development occurs. In particular, the induction time for photographic (autocatalytic) development is shorter for the exposed crystal. There has been some questions as to the existence of an induction time, beyond such obvious delays in the development process as the swelling of layers and the arrival of reagent. Hillson (5) among others, has pointed out that there must be an induction period; otherwise there would be no significant difference between exposed and unexposed areas in the emulsion; i.e. there would be no photography.

<u>THEORY</u>

    <u>DEVELOPMENT</u>

The development process consists of two difference mechanisms of electron transfer from the developer to the AgBr grain.

<u>Phase I</u> - A kinetic reaction in which the rate reflects the product of the collision frequency (which in turn is proportional to the concentration of developer, (D^-), and cross-sectional area of the grain, S_{AgBr}) and collision efficiency (which is given by $e^{-\Delta V/kt}$ where ΔV = difference in energy level of conduction band of AgBr, and redox potential of developer). This is a slow reaction which is <u>not</u> sensitive to exposure. The rate of electron transfer, de^-/dt is,

$$de^-/dt = A \tag{1}$$

where A = constant

<u>Phase II</u> - An auto-catalytic reaction in which the developer-silver cluster - AgBr grain is involved in a corrosion process. The rate of silver development, dN/dt, is proportional to the surface area of the silver cluster. N is the number of silver atoms; the cluster is assumed to be spherical.

$$\frac{dN}{dt} \propto N^{2/3} \tag{2}$$

The theory considers that this auto-catalytic reaction, Phase II, can not be initiated until a threshold overpotential, η_T^K (6) corresponding to a critical surface area, $N_T^{2/3}$ (i.e. critical size cluster) is attained (7).

In the interim, electrons are transferred from the developer to the grain by the slow Phase I process, building up the size of the cluster to the threshold size. This time interval is the induction time, τ.

The equation that relates the induction time, τ, to potential, E, through the threshold overpotential, η_T^K is;

$$2\eta_T^K = E_D^o - E_g^o + \frac{RT}{\alpha nF} \ln \tau + B \tag{3}$$

where $\frac{RT}{\alpha nF}$ and B are constants and D and g refer to developer and silver hailide grain respectively. If the critical overpotential, η_T^K is constant, the induction time, τ, depends only on developer potential, E_D^o, and grain potential, E_g^o.

For a given exposure, E_D^o has been shown to be linear with $\ln \tau$ for several developers (8) consistent with equation 3. Hence, a developer with a greater tendency to give up an electron, (thereby increasing the driving force for electron transfer) requires a smaller silver cluster, and hence a smaller τ. Similarly, if the grain has a greater tendency to take an electron, (also increasing the driving force for electron transfer) a smaller cluster and hence a smaller induction period τ, would be required.

The change in the reduction potential of the grain, E_g^o, with exposure, p, is taken to be (9),

$$E_g^o = E^{o'} + \frac{RT}{F} \ln \frac{P}{P_u^*} \tag{4}$$

where $E_g^{o'}$, P_u^* = constants and $1 < p < p_u^*$
This equation, combined with the others characterizes the induction period as a function of exposure;

$$\tau = C \left(\frac{P_u^*}{p}\right)^\alpha \tag{5}$$

where C = parameter, containing electrokinetic and thermodynamic variables of the developer and silver halide couples.

∝ = transfer coefficient of developer.

Fig. 1, which is a plot of log τ vs. log p, shows that the equation is consistent with the experiment. Thus, the electrode kinetics of the developer (∝), plays a major role in determining the sensitivity of τ to exposure.

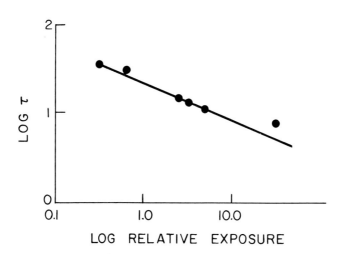

LOG RELATIVE EXPOSURE

Fig. 1. Plot of calculated and experimental curves of log τ vs. log exposure. The equation for hydroquinone developer is (8), $\tau = C(P_u^*/p)^{0.4}$ (line) Experimental results from J. Charkoudian, A. Ames and A. Hoffman, Phot.Sci. Eng. 17, (1973) 456. (points)

Combining equations (2) and (5) permits calculations of amount of silver (N_{Ag}) as a function of exposure and time. Fig. 2 show plots of this equation.

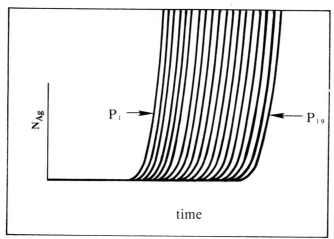

Fig. 2. Plot of amount of silver, N_{Ag} vs. development time, for a 1μ grain, $P_u^* = 8$, ∝ =0.2, and developer concentration of 4×10^{-1} M. Every increment in exposure, p, corressponds to ½ stop. Calculated from equations (2) and (5).

FIG. 3 is a plot of fraction of developed silver vs. log exposure for 45 sec. residence time of grain in developer, T, obtained from Fig. 2. Also plotted are some experimental curves. The agreement is good until the shoulder is approached. At this point statistics (of light, grain size) would have to be included to cause the calculated curve to round off like the experimental curves.

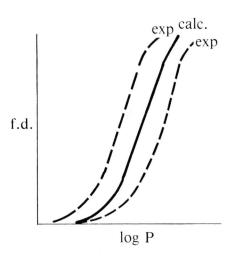

Fig. 3. Fraction of developed silver vs. log exposure. Data obtained from Fig. 2 for a development time, T = 45 sec. Experimental data and two solid curves presented by A. Ames, Phot. Sci. Eng., <u>17</u>, (1973) 154.

Redox Buffer/S$^=$ Sensitization

Reinders (6) has shown that the H & D curves of redox buffer equilibrated emulsions are shifted on the exposure axis, but the shape of the curves are essentially unchanged. It has been noted that this result cannot be simply explained by conventional latent-image theory (4). Since the parameter, P_u^*, is the number of oxidized vacancies in the grain, and is sensitive to redox buffers according to following equation:

$$P_u^* = D \frac{1}{(A_g+)} \frac{(F_e+3)}{(F_e+2)}$$

(6)

where D = constant
it can be seen that P_u^* will change proportional to ratio of F_e^{+3}/F_e^{+2}. To obtain the same development conditions (eqns. 4 & 5), P must change accordingly. This is in quantitative agreement with Reinder's results.

The effect of digestion time on the H & D curves of monodispersed emulsion grains also results in shifts on the exposure axis (to lower exposure) with little change in curve shape. Increased digestion time increases the amount of S$^=$ on/in the silver halide grain, which in turn decreases the number of vacancies (10). Thus, P_u^*, the number of oxidized vacancies decreases with increasing digestion time. To obtain the same development conditions (equations (4) and (5)) p, the exposure, will decrease accordingly, but as discussed below, fog will increase.

<u>FOG</u>

If every grain is considered to have a value of p equal to unity; i.e. if fog is the equivalent of having absorbed one photon/grain, then the equations show that for a large p_u^*, the result will be a low speed low fog response, and for a low value of p_u^*, the result will be a high speed, high fog response. This is to be compared with experimental observations on the effect of $S^=$ on speed and fog (11).

<u>LATENT-IMAGE</u>

The latent-image originates from exposed grains possesing a value of the ratio P/P_u^*, such that the induction period, τ, is less than the residence time of the grains in the developer, T: i.e

$$\tau_{unexp} > T > \tau_{exp}$$

<u>SPEED AND FOG VS. GRAIN SIZE</u>

The Phase I rate will increase with grain size, causing a decrease in τ; i.e. $\tau \propto S_{AgBr}^{-1}$.

It follows that for:

large grains: $\tau_{exp} < \tau_{unexp} < T$

small grains: $T < \tau_{exp} < \tau_{unexp}$.

moderate grain: $\tau_{exp} < T < \tau_{unexp}$.

Using a reasonable time T for moderate size grains will produce much fog in large grains and little density in small grains. Fig. 4 shows a comparison of calculated and experimental data.

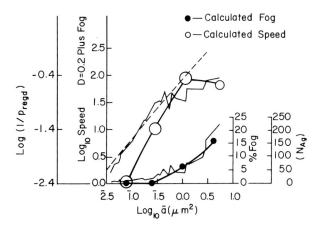

Fig. 4 Optimal speed and associated percentage fog versus mean grain projective area for silver-bromide emulsions. The exposures were to radiation of wave-length 430nm. Emulsions digested to optimum speed irrespective of fog (3). From G. C. Farnell, J.Phot.Sci., <u>17</u> (1969) 116. (N_{Ag}) fog vs. log S_{AgBr}; $p_u^* = 10$, $p=1$ (for a 1_μ grain), T = 7 sec. Dashed line denotes theoretical variation of speed assuming the conventional model (i.e. constant quantum sensitivity).

CONCLUSION

A theory has been formulated that considers the latent-image to be a thermodynamic change in the reduction potential of the grain, E_g^o, at exposures between the toe and the shoulder and predominantly a silver cluster at high exposures (i.e. beyond the shoulder, $p > p_u^*$).

In all cases, a critical cluster size is required to attain a critical overpotential for an auto-catalytic reduction in a given developing system. The time to attain this threshold value is the induction time, τ, and is exposure dependent. The grain can be said to have a latent-image if its value of τ, is significantly less then the residence time of the grain in the developer. The magnitude of τ is determined by both thermodynamic and electrokinetic constants of developer and grain, and the exposure of the grain to light.

REFERENCES

1. C.E.K. Mees and T. H. James, "The Theory of the Photographic Process", 3rd Ed., The MacMillan Co., N.Y. 1966, p.87.
2. Ref. (1), p. 338.
3. G. C. Farnell, J. Phot.Sci., 17 (1969) 116.
4. G. C. Farnell, J. Phot.Sci., 25 (1977) 125.
5. P. J. Hillson, J. Phot.Sci., 23 (1975) 237.
6. W. Reinders, J. Phys. Chem., 38 (1934) 783.
7. A. Hoffman, J. Charkoudian, and A. Ames, Phot. Sci. Eng., 18 (1974) 12. For a detailed treatment of corrosion see J.O.M. Bockris and A.N.N Reddy, "Modern Electro-Chemistry" Vol. 2, Plenum Press, N.Y.
8. R. G. Willis and R. N. Pontius, Phot.Sci. Eng., 14 (1970) 149.
9. A. Hoffman, J. Phot. Sci., 26 (1978) 124.
10. E. P. Honig and J. H. Th. Hengst, J. Colloid Interface. Sci., 29 (1969) 510.
11. Reference (1) p. 64.

J. BOURDON (Editor)
Growth and Properties of Metal Clusters, pp. 371—378
© 1980 Elsevier Scientific Publishing Company — Printed in The Netherlands

ABOUT A STRUCTURAL PHASE TRANSITION IN MINUTE GOLD PARTICLES EMBEDDED IN GLASS

U. Kreibig
Fachbereich 11 - Physik - der Universitaet des Saarlandes
D6600 Saarbruecken / Germany

The optical absorption of ensembles of Au particles with various mean sizes, prepared in photosensitive glass, was measured and Kramers Kronig analized to obtain the average dielectric constant of the particle material. By subtracting the size dependent 6s-electron contribution, the imaginary part of the dielectric constant due to interband transitions was separated around the low energy 5d - 6sp transition edge. A marked dependence of onset energy and slope of the edge on particle size was observed for particles smaller than about 4 nm. This size effect is attributed to a structural phase transition between a "cluster" state and bulk structure with a critical size of $\lesssim 1o^3$ atoms/particle, which has been postulated earlier from experiments on the temperature dependence of the optical absorption in such particle systems.

INTRODUCTION

The topics of interest of small particle physics may be subdivided into two main fields:
a) The investigation of "size effects" in solid particles of small size which are due to the geometrical limitation, i.e. the influence of the particle boundary.
b) The examination of atomic arrangements in particles which, because of their extremely small size, are rather molecule-like than solid state particles. Many model calculations have been performed (ref.1) but rather few experimental confirmations exist for this special state(ref.2), unless for molecules consisting of less than, say, 1o atoms which clearly show discrete electronic excitation spectra (for noble metals: ref.3).

The results of model calculations, though strongly depending on the state of approximation and on the kind of potentials, used, demonstrate that the most stable atomic arrangements of such clusters differ markedly from the lattice structure of the extended, bulky solid.

Complex structures with,e.g. linear or five fold symmetric or even irregular arrangements have been reported and ,also, regular lattice structures differently from those of the bulk (e.g. a fcc structure for Li clusters (ref.4) and a bcc structure for Au clusters (ref.5)).

All such structure changes are due to the atoms that form the cluster surface. As driving force their lower coordination number compared to the inner atoms may be considered. Hence, the atomic arrangement of a cluster appears as the result of a duel between these both groups of atoms, fought out by means of the interaction forces. While in extremely minute clusters most of the atoms are at the surface, the number of inner atoms surpasses that of the surface atoms with increasing particle size, and, eventually, in bulky solids the lattice structure is exclusively due to the former.

Then, the question arises about the transition from cluster to bulk lattice structures when the particle size is increased. Experimental hints have been obtained from matrix isolated clusters (refs.3,6) and from Au particles evaporated onto alkali halide surfaces which perform a bcc - fcc transition at particle sizes of about 5 nm (ref.5). Own recent experiments on the temperature dependence of the optical absorption of Au particles embedded in a glass matrix (ref.7) point to an almost abrupt transition (i.e. a well defined structural

372

phase transition) around a critical size of about $5 \cdot 10^2$ atoms/particle. Fig.1, taken from ref.7, shows this transition in the size dependence of $\Delta \varepsilon_2 = \varepsilon_2(300K) - \varepsilon_2(1.5K)$, ε_2 being the imaginary part of the average dielectric function $\varepsilon = \varepsilon_1 + i \cdot \varepsilon_2$ of the particle material.

Such optical experiments have been continued and further results, concerning the optical interband absorption edge will be reported in the following which confirm these findings.

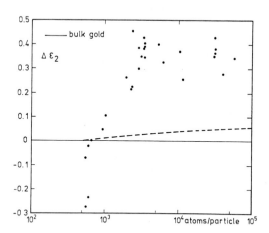

Fig.1: $\Delta \varepsilon_2 = \varepsilon_2(300K) - \varepsilon_2(1.5K)$ for Au particles at λ=510 nm (points) and for Ag particles at λ= 405 nm (dashed line), versus mean number N of atoms/particle.

The systems of Au particles to be investigated in these experiments, were prepared in photosensitive glasses (ref.8) of properly chosen compositions. These samples may be considered as model systems for photographic processes. Noble metal particles are produced in two steps: first, atomic nuclei are formed by UV irradiation, and, afterwards, the particles grow from these nuclei during an annealing process. So, number of particles and particle size can be varied independently(refs.8,12;a detailed description of particle production and of size determination in the glass:Au system will be published elsewhere).

Such particle systems stand out for high mechanical and thermal stability and for well defined single particle properties, like almost spherical shapes (Fig.2) and narrow size distributions (Fig.3).

Further features of these samples are:

a)extremely low filling factors (see Fig.2),whereby problems with interaction effects between neighboring particles and effective field effects are excluded which are, up to now, not yet solved satisfactorily (e.g. ref.9),

b) an extremely low growth process which may be interrupted repeatedly and ,thus, allows to perform experiments with one and the same particle sample, yet, with different particle sizes and

c) high temperatures (of about $500^{\circ}C$) during the growth process, whereby the lattice defect density in the particles is kept low (ref.10).

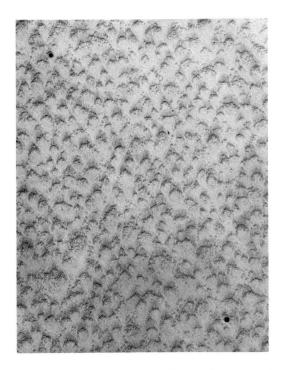

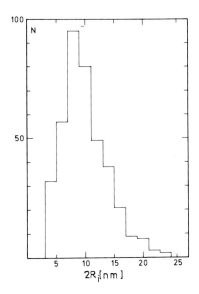

Fig.2. Two Au particles (2R=10nm) in the glass matrix. Particles were extracted from a freshly broken surface by a combined C-Pt-C double film technique.

Fig.3. Size distribution histogram of Au particles in a glass sample, as determined from electron micrographs.

RESULTS AND DISCUSSION

Optical absorption spectra at room temperature were recorded in the spectral region $0.5 \leqslant \hbar\omega \leqslant 4.0$ eV from Au particle samples with variing particle sizes. Special importance was attached to the early stages of particle growth. Fig.4 shows a sequence of spectra near the spherical dipole plasmon frequency, of one ensemble of Au particles with mean sizes increasing from 3 to 6 nm. With help of a Kramers Kronig analysis (ref.11) the average, complex dielectric constant $\varepsilon(\hbar\omega)$ of the particle material was evaluated from such spectra (Fig.5). A marked size dependence is observed, both, for ε_1 and ε_2. As has been shown, e.g., for Ag particles prepared analogously (ref.12), the main share of this size dependence is due to a size effect of the s-electrons (in the bulk acting as Drude conduction electrons) which can quantitatively be described by the continuum model of the "free path effect" and, also, as a quantum size effect by assuming that the electron energy bands split into discrete levels, in small particles.

This size effect is obvious in the spectra of Fig.6 which were computed with Mie's theory (ref.13), including electrical and magnetic multipoles up to the fifth.

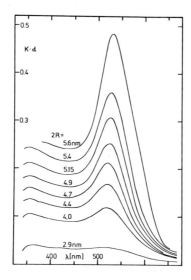

Fig.4.   Experimental absorption spectra of one (and the same) specimen of Au particles in glass with various mean diameters 2R.
K: absorption constant; d: sample thickness; λ : wavelength.

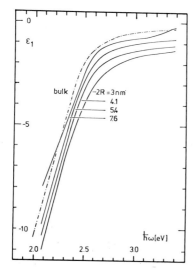 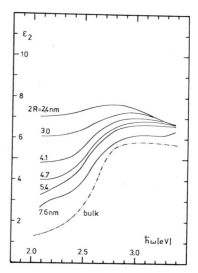

Fig.5. Spectra of the dielectric constant $\varepsilon = \varepsilon_1 + i\varepsilon_2$ of Au particles with various mean sizes 2R, as evaluated by Kramers Kronig analysis from experimental absorption spectra. The bulk spectra are taken from literature.

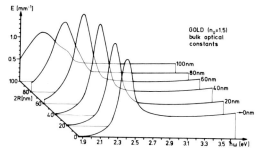
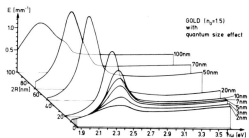

Fig.6. Extinction spectra of Au particles with various sizes 2R, as computed from Mie's theory using optical constants of literature without (left figure) and with (righthand figure) correction due to the 6s-electron size effect (ref.14). E: extinction constant; n_o: refractive index of the embedding matrix.

In the considered spectral region, the imaginary part of the dielectric response of gold stems from, both, electronic transitions within the 6s band and from interband transitions between the 5d band and the 6sp band (above Fermi level), the latter forming the low energy interband transition edge just above the energy of the particle dipole plasma resonance.

According to band calculations of bulk Au (ref.15), the interband transitions near the edge are direct ones around the symmetry point L in the Brillouin zone (with onset energy $\hbar\omega_2 = 2.4$ eV) and, with smaller intensity, around X (onset energy $\hbar\omega_1 = 1.7$ eV), as shown in Fig.7. The band edge in ε_2 has the form (refs.15,16):

$$\varepsilon_2^{\text{interband}}(\omega) = \begin{array}{l} A_1 \cdot \exp(\omega - \omega_1) \\ A_2 \cdot (\omega - \omega_2)^{1/2}/(\hbar\omega)^2 \end{array} \quad \text{for} \quad \begin{array}{l} 1.7 \le \hbar\omega \le 2.4 \text{ eV} \\ 2.4 \le \hbar\omega \le 3.3 \text{ eV} \end{array} \quad (1)$$

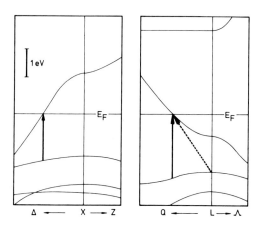

Fig.7. Two sections of the RAPW band structure calculation of ref.15 with the direct transitions $\hbar\omega_1$ and $\hbar\omega_2$ forming the low energy interband transition edge. E_F: Fermi energy.

376

Since the contributions of 6s band and interband transitions add up in the dielectric constant, $\varepsilon(\omega) = \varepsilon^{6s}(\omega) + \varepsilon^{interband}(\omega)$, the interband transition edge may be extracted from experimental $\varepsilon(\omega)$ - spectra by subtracting $\varepsilon^{6s}(\omega)$ which is a Drude dielectric constant including size effect. Preliminary results of this procedure have been published before (ref.7). Since then, about 8o samples have been investigated and analyzed to increase statistical accuracy.

Several spectra of $\varepsilon_2^{interband}$ are shown in Fig.8. For subtraction of the s-electron contribution the s-electron size effect was used in the formulation given by ref.14. A linear dependence of $(\varepsilon_2^{interband} \cdot (\hbar\omega)^2)^2$ on ω follows from eq.(1) for the region $2.4 \leq \hbar\omega \leq 3.3$ eV and, hence, this quantity was plotted in the figure.

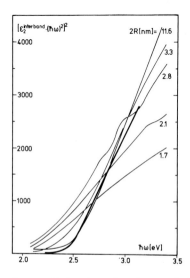

Fig.8. Size dependence of the interband transition edge in Au particles, as evaluated from experimental absorption spectra. 2R: mean particle diameter. Thick line: bulk Au, due to ref.16.

In fact, there is a such linear dependence for all particle diameters between 1.7 and 11.6 nm (i.e. about $2 \cdot 10^2$ to $6 \cdot 10^4$ atoms/particle), within the limits of accuracy, yet, position and slope vary markedly as the particle size is decreased. For large particles, the band edge coincides, both, in the value of the onset energy $\hbar\omega_2$ and in the slope with the band edge of bulk Au, as determined experimentally (ref.16). (It might be worth mentioning that no fit parameter is included in the evaluation.) With decreasing size, however, $\hbar\omega_2$ is shifted towards lower energies and the slope is diminished essentially.

Linear extrapolation yields 2.45 eV for $\hbar\omega_2$ of particles of about 10^5 atoms, and 2.o eV for particles of about 10^2 atoms. The latter value, however, should only be regarded as giving correctly the order of magnitude of the effect, since systematic errors may, for extremely small particles, arise from an inaccurate size determination which influences mainly the magnitude of the computed 6s-electron contribution, and from possibly occuring changes of total oscillator strength which is important for performing the Kramers Kronig analysis. Actually, the reason for these uncertainties is the lack of informations about details of the "cluster" state.

In contrast to the onset energy, the evaluated slope of the edge is rather insensitive to such details of the evaluation process. The reason is that the subtracted ε_2^{6s} is an only slowly variing function of ω, while $\varepsilon_2^{interband}$ varies strongly near the onset energy, and, hence, the absolute magnitude, but not the steepness is influenced by the precise choice of $\varepsilon_2^{6s}(\omega)$.

The differences of the quantity $(\varepsilon_2^{interband} \cdot (\hbar\omega)^2)$ at the energies $\hbar\omega = 3.3eV$ and $\hbar\omega = 2.4eV$, as a measure for the slope of the edge, are compiled in Fig. 9, as depending upon the inverse particle diameter. Despite a considerable scatter of the points, the decrease is obvious for particles with $2R \lesssim 3nm$. The slope is reduced for about 60% in the particle size interval $1.6 \lesssim 2R \lesssim 4$ nm (i.e. about $150 \lesssim N \lesssim 2500$ atoms/particle). For rating this decrease, its smearing out by the size distribution of the particles in each sample has to be considered (see, e.g., Fig. 3).

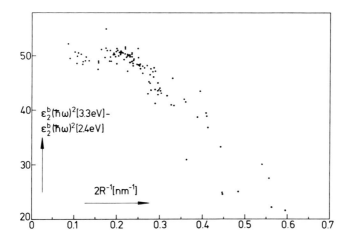

Fig.9. Steepness of the interband transition edge in Au particles versus the inverse mean particle diameter, as evaluated from experimental absorption spectra.

In the present state of knowledge, there is an ample field for speculations about the origin of this size effect. For a summary of several suppositions we may refer to a forthcoming paper. Here, we will rely upon the interpretation of the temperature dependence experiments, mentioned above (Fig.1), and attribute the abrupt change of the interband transition edge to a structural phase transition from a molecular "cluster" state of rather unknown structure to the lattice structure of bulk Au. The critical size of $\lesssim 10^3$ atoms/particle is in accordance with the value of $5 \cdot 10^2$, resulting from the temperature dependence experiments; its magnitude appears plausible in view of the picture, used above, of the duel between surface and inner atoms which decides for the actual structure of the particle, since, in that size region, both groups are of comparable numbers of combatants.

REFERENCES

1 I.I. Burton, J. Chem. Phys. 52 (197o) 345

R.C. Baetzold and R.E. Mack, J. Chem. Phys. 62 (1975) 1573

P.J. Jennings, G.S. Painter and R.O. Jones, Surface Sci. 6o (1976) 255

J.C. Barker, J. de Physique 38 C2 (1977) 37

D.M.P. Mingos, J. Chem. Soc. Dalton (1976) 1164

2 J. Farges, M.F. de Feraudy, B. Raoult and G. Torchet, J. de Physique 38 C2 (1977) 47

3 W. Schulze, D.M. Kolb and H. Gerischer, J. Chem. Soc. Faraday Trans. 71 (1975) 1763

T. Welker (T.P. Martin and L. Genzel) Dissertation, Max-Planck-Institut für Festkörper-forschung, Stuttgart (1978)

4 A. Julg, M. Bernard, M. Bourg, M. Gillet and E. Gillet, Phys. Rev. B 9 (1974) 3248

5 J. Klemke (and M. Harsdorff), Diploma work, University of Hamburg (1978)

6 T.P. Martin, Phys. Rev. B 15 (1977) 4o71

7 U. Kreibig, Sol. State Commun. 28 (1978) 767

J. de Physique 38 C2 (1977) 97

8 S.D. Stookey, Ind. Eng. Chem. 41 (1949) 856

J. Am Ceram. Soc. 32 (1949) 246

R.D. Maurer, J. Appl. Phys. 29 (1958) 1

U. Kreibig, Appl. Phys. 1o (1976) 255

9 L. Genzel and U. Kreibig, in preparation

1o U. Kreibig, Z. Physik B 31 (1978) 39

11 U. Kreibig, Z. Physik 234 (197o) 3o7

12 U. Kreibig, J. Phys. F: Metal Phys. 4 (1974) 999

13 G. Mie, Ann. Physik 25 (19o8) 377

14 L. Genzel, T.P. Martin and U. Kreibig, Z. Physik B21 (1975) 339

15 N.E. Christensen and B.O. Seraphin, Phys. Rev. B4 (1972) 3321

16 P. Winsemius, Proefschrift, University of Leiden (1973)

J. BOURDON (Editor)
Growth and Properties of Metal Clusters, pp. 379—385
© 1980 Elsevier Scientific Publishing Company — Printed in The Netherlands

ASPECTS OF BONDING IN SILVER CLUSTERS

M. R. V. SAHYUN

3M Company, St. Paul, Minnesota 55101 USA

The latent image in silver halide photography is usually thought to be a cluster of 4-10 silver atoms (refs. 1,2) and it is one of the most dramatically effective catalysts known to chemistry. Because it is small and not amenable to direct characterization by usual experimental methods, it has been the subject of several theoretical investigations (refs. 3-6). It is the purpose of this study to extend our previous methodology (ref. 5) in order to (a) refine the results; (b) provide some insight into the mechanism of latent image formation (cluster growth) in the silver halide crystal environment; and (c) establish a kinetic basis for the selectivity of the development reaction, i.e. the catalytic action of the cluster.

METHODS

The application of the extended Hückel method (ref. 7) to the calculation of the thermo-dynamic and spectroscopic characteristics of clusters of metal atoms having a symmetrically filled d shell has been described for clusters of up to 6 atoms (ref. 8), and the theoretical basis discussed (ref. 9). The calibration of the model for silver estimates the silver coulomb integral, α, as 4.25 eV, in accord with the average of the electron affinity and ionization potential of a gaseous silver atom (ref. 4), the experimentally based estimate of the level of the 5s electron in an isolated silver atom (presumably) in an interstitial position in silver bromide (ref. 10), and the work function of the bulk metal. The exchange integral, β, (and hence the overlap integral) is estimated on the assumption that each structure calculated (except Ag_2) is capable of yielding a cluster in vacuo with a stabilization energy, E_s, equal to that predicted from the empirical equation of Freund and Bauer (ref. 11),

$$E_s = nE_\infty (1 - n^{-0.25}) \tag{1}$$

where n is the number of atoms in the cluster and E_∞ is the lattice energy of the bulk metal, 2.62 eV. An experimental value (ref. 11a) is used for Ag_2. This procedure for calibrating the model supresses any tendency for it to reveal alternation in cluster properties with cluster size, as suggested by Baetzold (ref. 4). Shifts in molecular orbital energy levels on putting a positive or negative charge on the cluster are treated by the ω-method (ref. 5).

Interaction of the cluster with the silver bromide crystal lattice is assumed to involve two effects. The purely electronic effect results from the delocalization of positive charge into the cluster by coordination of lattice silver ions thereto as suggested by Jørgenson (ref. 12) and as realized in other structures in nature (ref. 13) and for silver clusters trapped in a zeolite matrix (ref. 14). It is estimated by the perturbational MO

method in terms of the splitting of the highest filled cluster MO energy level by interaction with the orbital representing a "dangling bond" at a silver ion associated with a
halide vacancy (ref. 15). The second effect presumes epitaxial growth of the cluster with
respect to the host crystal, and is included by adjusting the average bond length in the
cluster to correspond to the lattice spacing in silver bromide (275 pm). This bond
shortening produces an increase in overlap (hence in β), but also increases internuclear
repulsion, as estimated by application of a Morse function (ref. 15a), since this repulsion
is not explicitly treated in the extended Hückel method(ref. 7). It is always
destabilizing, but becomes progressively trivial for larger clusters. The net result of
these two effects is stabilizing only for all clusters of 5 or 6 atoms, and for Ag_4^-.

RESULTS--CLUSTER CALCULATIONS

Both in vacuo and in the crystal, three dimensional, defect octahedral cluster
geometries are found to be optimum, based on criteria of magnitude of overlap integral,
and bond length to bond order ratio (ref. 8). For Ag_4 the arachno geometry may be feasible
in vacuo, but epitaxiality drives the cluster to a square configuration in silver bromide;
it is impossible to conform a tetrahedral structure to the crystal geometry.

Owing to the calibration of the model with respect to empirical stabilization energies,
we expected to be able to predict electronic transitions without the use of a correction
factor (ref. 16). Comparison of calculated transition energies for clusters in vacuo with
the experimental observations of Ozin (ref. 17) and of Schulze and coworkers (ref. 18) on
clusters in noble gas matrices, as shown in Chart I, indicates reasonable agreement. The
somewhat shifted (owing to increased β as a result of epitaxy) predictions for clusters in
silver bromide can be compared to the observed optical absorption at 2.5 eV of clusters
produced in evaporated silver chloride layers by ion implantation (ref. 19), and the
emission observed at 2.3 eV thought to be associated with small silver clusters produced
by γ-irradiation of similar silver bromide layers (ref. 20).

CHART I

Spectroscopic Properties of Silver Clusters

n	Transition	$h\nu$ (in vacuo)	$h\nu$ (in AgBr)	$h\nu$ (observed)*
2	$\sigma-\sigma^*$	forbidden	forbidden	3.03, 3.10 eV
3	$\sigma-\sigma_2^*$	2.83 eV	3.05 eV	2.84, 2.94
4	$\sigma-\sigma_1^*$	2.47	---	2.55, 2.37
4	$n-\sigma_1^*$	---	2.86	---
5	$n-\sigma_1^*$	2.41	2.86	2.47, 2.36
6	$n-\sigma^*$	2.36	2.61	2.40, 2.43

*) Ref's (17,18)

RESULTS--LATENT IMAGE FORMATION

Mechanisms proposed for latent image growth include, in addition to schemes involving
atomic condensation (ref. 21), ones based on alternate accumulation of electrons and
interstitial silver ions. Those based on the original proposal of Gurney and Mott
(ref. 22) involve the intermediacy of negatively charged clusters, while those based on

the proposals of Mitchell (ref. 23) and Matejec (ref. 24) involve positively charged clusters. The critical steps in these pathways are illustrated in Chart II.

CHART II

Latent Image Formation Mechanisms

1) Gurney-Mott Mechanism

$$Ag_n^{\circ} + e^- \longrightarrow Ag_n^-$$

$$Ag_n^- + Ag_i^+ \longrightarrow Ag_{n+1}^{\circ}$$

2) Mitchell Mechanism

$$Ag_n^{\circ} + Ag_i^+ \longrightarrow Ag_{n+1}^+$$

$$Ag_{n+1}^+ + e^- \longrightarrow Ag_{n+1}^{\circ}$$

In Chart III is shown a thermodynamic cycle for estimating the exothermicity of addition of an interstitial silver ion to the growing, neutral silver cluster. (A similar cycle may be laid out for addition of the interstitial ion to a negatively charged cluster). It is assumed that the enthalpy for extracting the cluster from the crystal environment is equal but opposite in sign to the enthalpy for reinsertion of the incrementally larger cluster. This should be a good approximation for larger clusters, but crude at the lower end of the size scale. For $2 \leq n \leq 6$, in both cases, the net reaction is exothermic; the enthalpy becomes monotonically more negative, within the ± 1 eV accuracy of the calculation, to approach an asymptotically limiting value of ca -2.5 eV for the case of $n = 6$. Both illustrated reaction schemes are thus indicated to be equally feasible as regards the ionic step.

CHART III

Interstitial Silver Ion Complexation

1) $Ag_n^{\circ}(AgBr) \longrightarrow Ag_n^{\circ}(vac.)$ $\qquad\qquad \Delta H_1$

2) $AgBr \longrightarrow Ag^+(vac.) + \square^-$ $\qquad\qquad \Delta H_2 = 3.44$ eV

3) $Ag_n^{\circ}(vac.) + e^- + Ag^+(vac.) \longrightarrow Ag_{n+1}^{\circ}(vac.)$

$$\Delta H_3 = E_s(Ag_n^{\circ}) - E_s(Ag_{n+1}^{\circ}) - IP(Ag)$$

$$IP(Ag) = 7.50 \text{ eV}$$

4) $Ag_{n+1}^{\circ}(vac.) \longrightarrow Ag_{n+1}^{\circ}(AgBr)$ $\qquad -\Delta H_4 = \Delta H_1$

5) $Ag_{n+1}^{\circ}(AgBr) \longrightarrow e^-(vac.) + Ag_{n+1}^+(AgBr)$

$$\Delta H_5 = E_s(Ag_{n+1}^{\circ}) - E_s(Ag_{n+1}^+) - \alpha$$

$$\alpha = -4.25 \text{ eV}$$

$$\Sigma\Delta H = E_s(Ag_n^{\circ}) - E_s(Ag_{n+1}^+) + 0.19 \text{ eV}$$

Stability of the intermediates toward oxidation, and electron trapping ability were next explored. Energies of the highest filled cluster MO's in the silver bromide, E_{hf}, are shown relative to the silver coulomb integral in Chart IV. The silver bromide conduction and valence band edges are also indicated. (Note that on the basis of Koopman's theorem we are considering the electron affinity of, e.g., Ag_n° to be equivalent to E_{hf} of Ag_n^-). It is clear that Ag_2 does not trap electrons, consistent with Spencer's observation (ref. 25), recently elegantly confirmed by Moisar (ref. 20). Larger clusters, neutral or

382

positive, can trap electrons. All the clusters, on the other hand, can trap holes, again
consistent with the above cited work, and with Spencer's (ref. 25) and Tani's (ref. 26)
observations on reduction sensitization. The enlargement of Ag_2 to Ag_3 thus appears to be
uniquely critical in the process of latent image formation. Oxidation potentials for
reduction sensitization centers, as inferred by Leubner (ref. 27), and for minimum
developable latent image, as measured by Dähne (ref. 28) are also indicated on this scale;
the measured oxidation potentials are in reasonable agreement with the calculations, for
the identification of Ag_2 with the reduction sensitization centers and Ag_n or Ag_n^+ ($n \geq 4$)
with developable latent image.

Again it is not possible to distinguish generically between the Gurney-Mott and Mitchell
or Matejec mechanisms in terms of feasibility, except for the unique cases of n = 1 and 2,
where the Gurney-Mott pathway seems most unlikely, owing to the very high levels
corresponding to E_{hf} for Ag^- and Ag_2^-. It is thus possible that the exact pathway of cluster
growth beyond this point depends both on the relative frequency of electronic and ionic
events (controlled by exposure intensity and crystal doping, for example) and the detailed
crystallographic environment in which the cluster is growing.

CHART IV

Stability of Silver Clusters Toward Oxidation

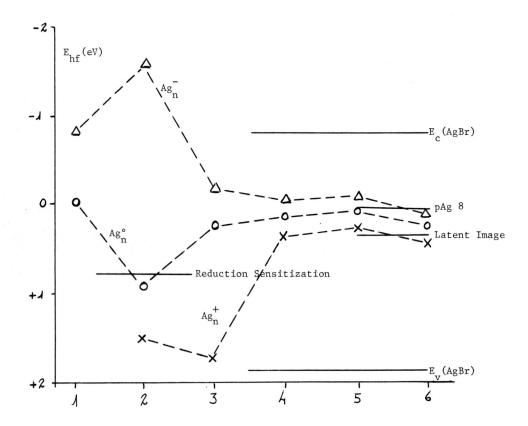

RESULTS--SELECTIVITY OF DEVELOPMENT

So far we have talked about thermodynamic considerations, but selectivity of development of exposed crystals is based on kinetic factors (ref. 29). The probability of electron transfer to clusters of varying size (hence to crystals bearing latent image comprising these clusters) can be estimated using a Marcus-Hush model in which only the cluster size dependent terms are evaluated. Variation of this probability with cluster size provides the basis for selectivity of development, provided the oxidation of developing agent is rate determining (refs. 30, 31). Accordingly (ref. 32), the rate constant for electron transfer, k, is given by

$$k = RT \ln - \Delta G* \tag{2}$$

where

$$\Delta G* = \tfrac{1}{2}(w_r + w_p + \Delta G° + \lambda/2) \tag{3}$$

in which w_r and w_p are work terms $\Delta G°$ is the free energy for the electron transfer reaction, and λ is the so-called reorganization energy. This last term includes both the molecular relaxation and environmental reorganization associated with the oxidation of the developing agent (assumed to be independent of the silver cluster size and formal charge), and the lattice and cluster reorganization occurring on electron transfer. The relative rate constant, k_n, independent of developing agent reduction potential, and based only on the cluster size dependent terms in the model thus becomes

$$k_n = RT \ln - \Delta G_n^* \tag{4}$$

where

$$\Delta G_n^* = \tfrac{1}{2}(\Delta G_n° + \lambda_n/2) \tag{5}$$

and

$$\Delta G_n° = -E_{1v}(Ag_n^+) \tag{6}$$

$$\lambda_n = E_s(Ag_n^+) - E_s(Ag_n°) - E_{hf}(Ag_n°) \tag{7}$$

for the case of a positively charged latent image, as assumed by Hamano (ref. 33) as well as by Mitchell (ref. 23). For the case of a crystal bearing no latent image, $\Delta G_n°$ may be set equal to $E_{red}(AgBr)$, -0.48 eV relative to α at pAg 8, and we choose λ_n to be the enthalpy of Frenkel defect formation, 1.27 eV, as uncatalyzed reduction presumably removes Ag^+ from an octahedral lattice site and deposits $Ag°$ at a tetrahedral interstitial site (ref. 31). A similar scheme can be established to estimate values of k_n for electron transfer to neutral clusters; the values of k_n for both cases, as functions of n, are shown in Chart V.

It appears that in the case of cationic latent image, these results require the formation of Ag_4 to be critical, consistent with conventional photographic wisdom (ref. 33a) which requires the latent image to be at least of this size; for the intermediacy of neutral clusters, formation of Ag_3 (as Ag_2^-) is shown to be critical, consistent with Budievski's identification of Ag_2 as the critical nucleus size in electrocrystallization of silver metal (ref. 34). The rate limiting step is however, much more rapid in the pathway involving cationic clusters, which analysis according to the scheme of Chart III has already shown to be exothemically formed in the silver bromide crystal environment from their neutral counterparts.

384

CHART V

n	$k_n(Ag_n^+)$	$k_n(Ag_n^o)$
0	---	$*5.0 \times 10^{-2}$
1	$*5.0 \times 10^{-2}$	4.0×10^{-14}
2	$3.9 \times 10^{+18}$	1.3×10^{-21}
3	$2.0 \times 10^{+6}$	4.2×10^{-3}
4	5.6×10^{-3}	8.2×10^{-3}
5	1.3×10^{-1}	3.1×10^{-3}
6	32	0.18
∞	83	83

Relative Probabilities for Electron Trasnfer (Marcus-Hush Model)

*) Unexposed crystal

We interpret these results in two ways: (a) the latent image is likely to be cationic and must be at least as large as produced by the action of four photons on the crystal: and (b) the formation of Ag_4 is also rate determining in fog formation. Thus the rate of catalyzed development (for large latent image) can be up to 10^4 times faster than the rate of uncatalyzed development (fog formation), as observed (ref. 29). It is furthermore obviously possible to form stable silver clusters smaller than the critical size, e.g. reduction sensitization centers produced by chemical treatment, controllably and without increasing the probability of reduction of the host crystal during development.

It is a shortcoming of this model that variation in selectivity with the chemical nature of the developing agent, as observed in the real world (ref. 34a), is unanticipated. The assumption of a purely anodically limited rate process is undoubtedly a gross over-simplification (ref. 31); furthermore, real developer formulations vary in silver halide solvent activity, hence the mix of "direct" (as treated here) and "solution physical" development likewise varies (refs. 31, 35).

The wide variation in k with n suggests that it should be possible to produce photographic emulsion-developer systems in which the individual grains could function as multi-level, instead of binary, detectors, thereby greatly increasing the formation capacity of a silver halide photograph (refs. 36, 37).

ACKNOWLEDGEMENT

The author greatly appreciates the opportunities for helpful and stimulating discussions with Dr. R. C. Baetzold and with Prof. Dr. W. Jaenicke.

REFERENCES

1   J. F. Hamilton and F. Urbach, in T. H. James (Ed.), Theory of the Photographic Process, 3rd edn., Macmillan, New York, 1966, p. 102.
2   J. Malinowski, Photogr. Sci. Eng. 23(1979)99.
3   F. Trautweiler, Photogr. Sci. Eng. 12(1968)138.
4   R. C. Baetzold, Photogr. Sci. Eng. 17(1973)78; 19(1975)11; Adv. Catal. 25(1976)1.
5   M. R. V. Sahyun, Photogr. Sci. Eng. 22(1978)317.
6   J. W. Mitchell, Photogr. Sci. Eng. 22(1978)1.
7   R. Hoffmann, J. Chem. Phys. 39(1963)1397.
8   M. R. V. Sahyun, J. Chem. Educ., in press.
9   A. B. Anderson, J. Chem. Phys. 68(1978)1744.
10 J. H. Webb, J. Opt. Soc. Amer. 40(1959)3.
11 H. Freund and S. H. Bauer, J. Phys. Chem. 81(1977)994.
11a J. Drowart and R. E. Honig, J. Chem. Phys. 25(1956)581.
12 C. K. Jørgenson, Chem. Phys. Letters 11(1971)387.

13   R. C. Rouse, J. Solid State Chem. 6(1973)86; H. G. von Schnering and
     K. G. Häusler, Rev. Chem. Miner. 13(1976)71.
14   Y. Kim and K. Seff, J. Amer. Chem. Soc. 99(1977)7055.
15   J. Pouradier, Sci. Ind. Phot. (2)30(1951)121.
15a P. M. Morse, Phys. Rev. 54(1929)57.
16   A. Julg, 32nd Int. Conf., "Metal Clusters", Scoiete de Chemie Physique,
     Villeurbanne, Sept. 1979., paper no. 42.
17   G. A. Ozin and H. Huber, Inorg. Chem. 17(1978)155.
18   W. Schulze, H. U. Becker and M. Abe, J. Chem. Phys. 35:(1978)177 Absorption
     spectrocopy of matrix isolated metal clusters and their analysis by the extended
     Hückel MO method have also been described by T. Welker and T. P. Martin, J. Chem.
     Phys. 70(1979)5683.
19   J. L. Gisclon, G. Diaine, J. P. Dupin, J. Bert and J. duPuy, 32nd Int. Conf., "Metal
     Clusters", Societe de Chemie Physique, Villeurbanne, Sept. 1979, paper no. 25.
20   E. Moisar, F. Granzer and E. Palm, J. Photogr. Sci., in press.
21   J. Malinowski, Photogr. Sci. Eng. 14(1970)112.
22   R. W. Gurney and N. F. Mott, Proc. Roy. Soc. (London) 164A(1938)151.
23   J. W. Mitchell, Photogr. Sci. Eng. 23(1979)1 and references cited therein.
24   R. Matejec, Naturwiss. 43(1956)175; Z. Physik. 148(1957)454.
25   H. E. Spencer, Photogr. Sci. Eng. 11(1967)352.
26   T. Tani, Photogr. Sci. Eng. 15(1971)28,181; 16(1972)35.
27   I. H. Leubner, Photogr. Sci. Eng. 22(1978)271.
28   S. Dähne, Z. wiss. Photogr. Photophys. Photochem. 59(1967)129.
29   T. H. James, Photo. Sci. Tech. (2)2 (1955)81; T. H. James and W. Vanselow, Photogr.
     Sci. Eng. 5(1961)21.
30   W. Jaenicke, Adv. Electrochem. and Electrochem. Eng. 10(1977)91.
31   M. R. V. Sahyun, Electrochim. Acta 23(1978)1101 and references cited therein.
32   R. A. Marcus, Electrochim. Acta 13 (1968)995 and references cited therein.
33   H. Hamano and G. Arai, J. Photogr. Sci. 27(1979)17.
33a B. E. Bayer and J. F. Hamilton, J. Opt. Soc. Amer. 55(1965)439,528.
34   E. Budievski, 32nd Int. Conf., "Metal Clusters", Societe de Chemie Physique,
     Villeurbanne, Sept. 1979, paper no. 5.
34a H. W. Atland, G. E. Smith, I. A. Olivares and S. W. Cowman, Photogr. Sci. Eng.
     23(1979)257.
35   T. H. James, J. Phys. Chem. 66(1962)2416.
36   R. Shaw, Photogr. Sci. Eng. 16(1972)192.
37   M. R. V. Sahyun, Photogr. Sci. Eng. 19(1975)38.

J. BOURDON (Editor)
Growth and Properties of Metal Clusters, pp. 387—391
© 1980 Elsevier Scientific Publishing Company — Printed in The Netherlands

BINDING ENERGIES, BOND-LENGTH CHANGES, AND BAND STRUCTURE FORMATION IN SMALL CLUSTERS

J.F. HAMILTON, G. APAI, S.T. LEE, and M.G. MASON
Research Laboratories, Eastman Kodak Company, Rochester, New-York 14650

ABSTRACT

Extended x-ray absorption fine structure (EXAFS) and photoemission measurements have been carried out on clusters ranging from isolated atoms to aggregates large enough to acquire bulk metal properties. EXAFS studies of copper show a substantial contraction of the nearest-neighbor Cu-Cu distance for small clusters. In addition, the onset of the K absorption edge shifts toward higher energy as the cluster size decreases. Variable energy photoemission spectra of gold clusters show the evolution of band structure with increasing cluster size.

INTRODUCTION

Supported small metal clusters frequently exhibit higher catalytic activity than is found in the bulk metal. The difference in electronic properties between clusters and bulk is thought to play an important role in this phenomenon. We have chosen x-ray absorption and photoemission (PES) spectroscopies to study copper and gold clusters supported on amorphous carbon substrates. The former technique has the capability to study interatomic distances of atoms in small clusters, whereas the latter is a powerful tool in studies of the occupied density of states. Cluster samples for EXAFS studies were prepared by evoporating multiple layers of carbon and metal onto 5000 Å polymer films, many of which were stacked together. For PES work, gold clusters were prepared in ultra-high vacuum, $< 1 \times 10^{-9}$ Torr, by evaporation onto amorphous carbon substrates which were cleaned by argon ion etching. In all studies, coverages were controlled by a quartz-crystal detector.

RESULTS

EXAFS measurements

The spectra obtained for copper (ref. 1) are shown in Fig. 1. Both the K-edge threshold and the fine structure change with cluster size. As shown in Fig. 2, the K-edge threshold remains identical with that of the bulk metal down to coverages of 8×10^{15} atoms/cm^2, corresponding to particle sizes of ~40-45 Å diameter. At our lowest coverage of ~ 8×10^{14} atoms/cm^2 there is an increase in the treshold energy

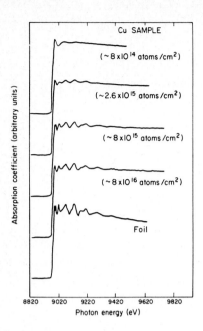

Fig. 1   EXAFS spectra of copper for a series of evaporated coverages and bulk foil. The bulk spectrum was recorded in the transmission mode. Cluster spectra were recorded by fluorescence detection.

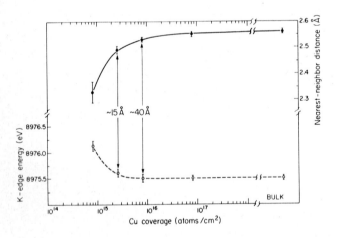

Fig. 2. Cu-Cu nearest-neighbor distance as a function of evaporated coverage (solid line). Relative change in the onset of the K-edge energy as a function of evaporated coverage (dashed line).

by ~0.7 eV. The changes in nearest-neighbor separations in the clusters exhibit similarities to the changes in the K-edge thresholds. The Cu-Cu neighbor distance remains constant for coverages above ~8x10^{15} atoms/cm^2, then shows a gradual contraction, with respect to the bulk value, of ~9% at the lowest coverage. At this coverage, the observed Cu-Cu distance is 2.33±0.04 Å compared to the bulk value of 2.56 Å. Experimentally, the bond length for gas-phase Cu$_2$ is 2.22 Å . Our results are for a distribution of cluster sizes, but compare favorably with distances expected for diatomics or slightly larger clusters. The observed changes in the K-edge threshold and bond lengths are a consequence of the evolution of electronic structure toward the bulk.

PES measurements

Low photon energy photoemission spectroscopy has been used to study the electronic structure of gold clusters (ref. 2) because of its spectral sensitivity to band structure effects in bulk polycrystalline materials. By studying the spectra of clusters as a function of photon energy. we followed the evolution of band structure with respect to cluster size. At coverages below 4x10^{14} atoms/cm^2 on amorphous carbon substrates, where gold exists predominately as single atom centers, the spectrum is a doublet with its splitting and intensity profile quantitatively reproduced by the free Au$^+$ (d^9 s^1) energy levels.

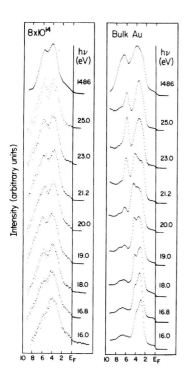

Fig. 3. Difference spectra, with carbon background subtracted, of gold clusters at 8x10^{14} atoms/cm^2 and bulk gold at various photon energies.

The splitting increases with cluster
size at all photon energies. A comparison of a low coverage with bulk metal is shown
in Fig. 3. In contrast to those of bulk gold, the spectra of the low coverage gold clusters
exhibit little variation with photon energy, indicating the absence of band modulation
effects. The spectra continue to change with coverage, but above $2x10^{15}$ atoms/cm^2 they
appear to resemble spectra for bulk gold. At this coverage the average radius of the gold
clusters is ~ 10 Å, corresponding to more than 100 atoms.

When the amorphous carbon substrates are heat treated before evaporations, dramatic
changes in the nucleation of gold occur. For low coverages of $3x10^{14}$ atoms/cm^2 on heat-
treated carbon (Fig. 4), the photoemission spectrum does not resemble that for single

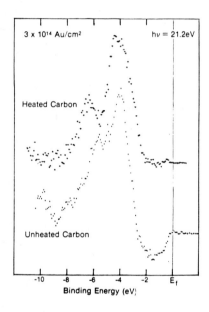

Fig. 4. Comparison of the effect of two differently prepared substrates on
the nucleation for a vey low gold coverage.

atoms as exemplified for the unheated carbon substrate. Peak separation is larger and
this intensity profile is different. At a coverage of $7x10^{14}$ atoms/cm^2 and much lower
coverages, the spectra of clusters on heat-treated graphite (Fig. 5) begin to acquire
characteristics similar to the bulk metal. Surface heat treatment prior to metal evaporation

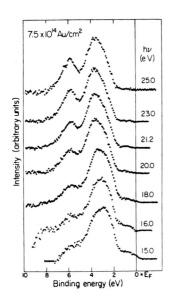

Fig. 5 Spectra of gold clusters at 7×10^{14} atoms/cm^2 on a heat-treated carbon substrate.

seems to have reduced the number of nucleation sites so that migration can occur to form clusters of larger dimensions.

ACKNOWLEDGMENTS

We wish to thank J. Stohr, R. Benbow, and Z. Hurych for their collaboration during various phases of the experiments.

REFERENCES

1 G. Apai, J.F. Hamilton, J. Stohr, and A. Thompson, Phys. Rev. Lett. 43(1979) 165.
2 S.T. Lee, G. Apai, M.G. Mason, R. Benbow, and Z. Hurych, to be published.

J. BOURDON (Editor)
Growth and Properties of Metal Clusters, pp. 393—397
© 1980 Elsevier Scientific Publishing Company — Printed in The Netherlands

KINETICS OF SILVER CLUSTER FORMATION IN SILVER HALIDE

B. LEVY, K.C. CHANG and F.P. CHEN
Polaroid Corporation, Cambridge, Mass., U.S.A.

A technique has recently been developed to measure the growth and decay of photocharge following the absorption of a pulse of light of ∼50 nanosecond duration (ref. 1). In silver halide photographic grains, silver cluster formation is a major means of relaxation of the induced photocharge. In these systems, the maximum photocharge is reached in less than 1 microsecond (usually ∼0.7 microseconds). The time for photocharge decay to half peak intensity ranges from ∼1-10 microseconds for room temperature determinations. The decay time has been found to depend on a variety of conditions such as composition, grain size and emulsion addenda.

The decay process is in general not adequately described by simple first or second order decay kinetics. A combination of first plus second kinetics as given in integrated form in equation (1) conforms well with the experimental data. This is shown in Fig. 1.

$$V = 1 / \left[\left(V_o^{-1} + k_2/k_1 \right) e^{k_1 t} - k_2/k_1 \right] \qquad (1)$$

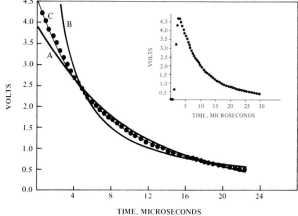

Fig. 1. Insert is the complete photocharge signal generated by a light pulse of ∼50 nanosecond duration at an intensity of 200 mw/cm². The main figure shows the computer fitting of the data points after the onset of the decay according to a) first order, b) second order, and c) first plus second order decay kinetics.

From measurements of photocharge decay of this type, it was possible to evaluate the first order, k_1, and the second order, k_2, decay constants for emulsion coatings which had undergone systematic variation in degree of reduction sensitization and chemical sensitization. Based on these determinations and on photographic evaluations of the same series of emulsion coatings, a mechanism was formulated involving k_1 and k_2 which explained the variation in photographic efficiency as a function of reduction or chemical sensitization. In this mechanism, k_1 is the rate constant for the reaction of a trapped photoelectron with an interstitial silver ion. The product of this reaction is in turn a trap for another photoelectron. A continuation of these processes lead to the formation of small, stable silver clusters (latent image centers) which serve as catalytic sites for further reduction of the silver halide grain during the development stage of photography. Competing with this process of silver cluster formation is the recombination of a photoelectron with a trapped photohole. The rate constant for this process is associated with the second order rate constant, k_2.

The build-up of photographic efficiency during chemical ripening with gold and sulfur sensitizers (see Fig. 2) has been shown to be associated with a decrease in the ratio of k_2/k_1. The major change is in k_2 with k_1 increasing slightly. This has led to the conclusion that chemical ripening with S and Au mainly changes the distribution of hole traps in a manner which allows the relatively unchanged first order rate process to utilize a larger fraction of the photoelectrons.

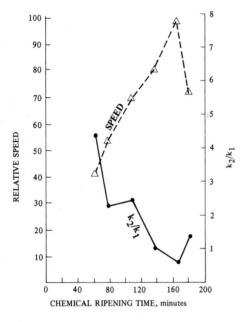

Fig. 2. Relationship between a) relative photographic speed, and b) k_2/k_1 ratio vs. chemical ripening time.

Reduction sensitization by addition of $AgNO_3$ to a melted emulsion prior to coating has yielded the results shown in Fig. 3. Here we see that log k_1 and log k_2 decreases linearly with decrease of the adjusted pAg of the emulsion prior to coating. This type of behavior has been interpreted in terms of alteration in the distribution of the energy levels of the electron traps. The traps deepen at the lower pAg. The decrease of both k_1 and k_2 is believed to be a consequence of the equilibria between trapped electrons and conduction band electrons - the equilibria shifting in favor of the trapped electrons as the energy levels of the traps become deeper. The link between k_1 and k_2 is through the concentration of conduction band electrons which appears in the mathematical expressions of both the first and second order decay processes. (For a more complete discussion, see ref. 1).

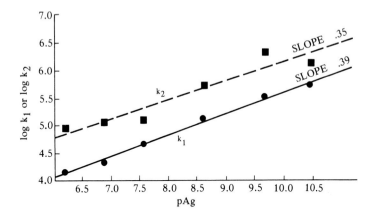

Fig. 3. Variation of a) log k_1 and b) log k_2 with pAg as derived from photocharge transients.

Based on this interpretation, we were led to conclude that lowering the pAg of the emulsion coating mix, which was found experimentally to cause a decrease in k_1 and k_2 along with an only moderate photographic speed increase, results in the formation of small silver clusters prior to exposure. Still more recent determinations consisting of measurements of dielectric loss as a function of frequency of an electric field applied to emulsion coatings, has shown that the ionic conductivity (f max) of the grains decrease as the pAg is lowered (see Fig. 4) (ref. 2). Photocharge decay measurements on the same emulsions also

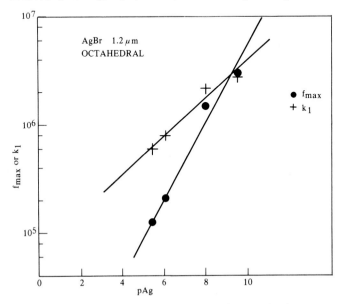

Fig. 4. a) Dielectric loss determination of ionic conductivity of emulsion grains (f max) vs. pAg and, b) k_1 vs. pAg.

show a decrease in k_1 as the pAg is lowered, in agreement with our earlier findings. It appears on the basis of these new results that the apparent value of k_1 decreases with lower pAg as a result of two processes;

    1) The activation energy for silver cluster growth increases as the trapped electron (possibly at the site of a silver cluster) becomes more stable at lower pAg.

and 2) The silver ion conductivity within a grain decreases as the pAg of the environment surrounding the grain increases.

    Photocharge measurements at considerably lower light intensities show a much more dramatic slowing down of the decay process than was obtained by the pAg adjustments described above (ref 3). An example is given in Fig. 5 for a 10 millisecond exposure at an intensity of 1 mw/cm^2 as compared to the 200 mw/cm^2 intensity of the 50 nanosecond exposure of Fig. 1. Decay of the signal after the light is off is in the order of milliseconds as compared to microseconds for the much higher intensity, shorter duration exposure used in Fig. 1. The three orders of magnitude longer decay time of Fig. 5 for the 10 millisecond exposure as compared to the nanosecond range exposure of Fig. 1 is believed to occur as a result of the more moderate rate of absorption of light quanta. Under these conditions, the ionic diffusion and reaction of an interstitial silver ion at the site of a trapped electron has time to take place and compete more effectively as a site for capture of the next photoelectron with the other processes involving, 1) less stable but more rapidly reacting electron traps requiring lower activation energy to combine with additional Ag_i^+ ions or, 2) with trapped holes in a second order recombination process. The net result is larger silver clusters at the lower light intensities. These exposure intensity effects manifest themselves photographically in the reduced efficiency of light utilization in image formation for high intensity exposures (high intensity reciprocity failure) (ref. 4). Earlier explanations offered in the literature for high intensity reciprocity failure usually invoke the concept of formation of smaller size and larger number of silver clusters at higher intensity exposures. The present paper reinforces this view by offering new experimental data based on the kinetics of the electronic and ionic processes taking place during and immediately after light exposure.

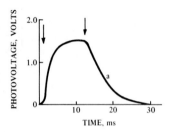

Fig. 5. Photovoltage for 10 millisecond exposure.($\downarrow$ indicates time at which shutter is fully open or closed.) Intensity is 1 mw/cm^2. Decay time after shutter is fully closed is in millisecond range.

REFERENCES

1 K.C. Chang, F.P. Chen and B. Levy, 1978. International Congress of Photographic Science, Rochester, N.Y., Aug. 20-26, 1978, p. 258.
2 F.P. Chen, K.C. Chang and B. Levy, 32nd Annual Conference, Society of Photographic Scientists and Engineers, Boston, Mass., May 13-17, 1979, Preprint Summaries, paper D4.
3 K.C. Chang, F.P. Chen and B. Levy, ibid., paper D6.
4 J.F. Hamilton, ch. 4 Sec. IIA in The Theory of the Photographic Process 4th ed. by T.H. James, Macmillan Publishing Co., Inc.

J. BOURDON (Editor)
Growth and Properties of Metal Clusters, pp. 399—413
© 1980 Elsevier Scientific Publishing Company — Printed in The Netherlands

MOLECULAR CLUSTERS : Models and Precursors for Metallic Catalysts.

G. MARTINO

Institut Français du Pétrole, Rueil-Malmaison, France.

INTRODUCTION.

Metals, skeletal or supported on carriers like oxides, zeolithes or charcoal are fairly good catalysts for a lot of reactions (ref. 1) and especially for hydrocarbon conversions (ref. 2). They are widely used in refining and in the petrochemical industry.

A lot of scientific work has been devoted to their preparation (ref. 3), their characterization (ref. 4) and to the study of the mecanisms of their interaction with reactants (ref. 2, 5, 6, 7) but, until now, numerous questions have remained. The nature of the active sites is not well defined regarding the number and the arrangement of the metallic atoms involved in ; the interaction between these metal atoms and reactants and the further development of the reaction is not yet clearly understood. The variation of specific activities from one metal to another and with the change of preparation conditions (ref. 8), the origin of bimetallic effects and support effects need further quantitative explanations.

Studies on clean surfaces, well defined monocristals are helpful for promoting of understanding in the field but for industrial people, small cristallites are more attractive because of, in general, their high activity per weight unit and also the drastic change in activity and selectivity often observed at very high dispersion. A good description of these well dispersed catalysts is difficult if not impossible now and it seems that a strong development of characterization technics will be helpful as well as a search for possible models and for new ways of preparing well defined supported small cristallites : the last two points will be considered here.

MOLECULAR CLUSTERS AS MODELS OF METALS.

During the last decade, homogeneous catalysis with defined complexes developed considerably and a great interest arose in comparing it with heterogeneous catalysis (ref. 20), but difficulties here are connected to the large differencies between mononuclear ligand surrounded catalysts and naked metallic clusters supposed to have collective properties. It was also found that metals were able to do reactions not performed by homogeneous complexes. A few years ago, most of the known molecular clusters had only a few atoms (ref. 21) and practically nothing was known on their catalytic properties.

Models have been developed for chemisorption and catalysis (ref. 9, 10, 11), bonding possibilities of individual atoms of a cluster have been estimated (ref. 12), small molecule interactions with clusters have been calculated (ref. 13), J.M. Basset and R. Ugo (ref. 14) compared the structural and electronic properties of molecular clusters and small particles   and E.L. Muetterties et Al. (ref. 15) recently examined all the aspects of the information or lack of it to obtain a good comparison between molecular clusters and surfaces.

Recent synthesis of numerous high nuclearity metal carbonyl clusters (ref. 22) probably promoted this new consideration of the possible modelling of well dispersed metals by molecular clusters (ref. 14, 15) even though that soluble cluster catalysis is just starting (ref. 23).

For models, to be satisfaying, they may be compared as far as number and arrangement of atoms, absorption properties, bond energies and kinetic aspects of reactivity are concerned. These different points will be illustrated for group VIII metal clusters and especially iron, nickel, rhodium and platinum because most of our catalytic work was done on these metals.

1. Number and arrangement of atoms.

All the people who have dealt with the problem, have pointed out the difficulties of such a comparison if one goes to a more quantitative analysis. Problems are connected to the poor knowledge we mostly have of metallic catalysts. As pointed out real catalysts are rather well dispersed and their geometry is often unknown ; surfaces are not well defined and Somorjai's (ref. 16) representation of big cristallites ($\sim$ 10 nm) with terrases, kinks, steps, adatoms may even be rather far from the situation of small cristallites with mean diameters of less than 1.5 nm which means that one will have clusters with less than 100 atoms. For platinum, for instance, in a fcc cristallite (ref. 17), the edge length, the number of surface atoms (dispersion) and the average coordination number of the atoms vary rapidly as the number of total atoms changes (figure 1).

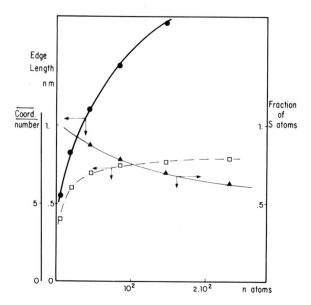

Fig. 1. Influence of the number of atoms on surface atoms, average coordination number, edge length for a cfc platinum cristallite (ref. 17).

The variations are much more important for cristallites of edge length less than 1 nm. From experimental determination and theoretical calculations, J.J. Burton (ref. 18) arrived to the following conclusions :

   ·- structure of microcristals are different of that of macroscopic material. Structure with icosahedron is thermodynamically preferred to a close packed one,

   - lattice parameters of small particles are smaller and melting temperatures are lower,

   - surfaces may have, primarily, triangular (111) faces.

Theses conclusions may be correct up to diameters of 2 nm which is the upper limit for calculations and close to the limit for experimental work. A good review of the experimental problems arizing with small metallic particles has been presented recently by R.F. Marzke (ref. 19).

Coordination chemists have prepared a lot of molecular clusters containing carbon monoxide as a ligand : this seems to be connected to the possibility of that ligand to withdraw electrons and so to stabilize low valence states. Tables I presents some clusters and shows that complexes with up to 15 metal atoms have been prepared ; this number of atoms correspond to that present in a fcc cristallite of about .75 nm and is of the size of some observed cristallites.

TABLE I

Fe - Ni - Rh - Pt Clusters (ref. 14, 22)

	$d\ M\_M$ nm x 10
Fe metal bulk	2.482
$Fe_2(CO)_9$	2.523
$Fe_3(CO)_{12}$	2.550 CO bridging 2.696 without CO bridging
$Fe_2(CO)_4Cp_2$	2.96
$[Fe_3(CO)_{11}H]^-$	2.577 H bridge 2.696 without H bridge
$[Fe_4(CO)_{13}]^{2-}$	2.59 CO bridging 2.50
$Fe_4Cp_4(CO)_4$	2.52
$Fe_5C(CO)_{15}$	2.60 base 2.55 base ≠ top
$[Fe_6(CO)_{13}]^{2-}$ $(\mu_2 CO)_3$	2.70

	$d\ M\_M$ nm x 10
	Platinum
Pt bulk	2.746
$[Pt_6(CO)_{12}]^{2-}$	2.66 3.04
$[Pt_9(CO)_{18}]^{2-}$	2.66 3.05
$[Pt_{15}(CO)_{30}]^{2-}$	2.66 3.08

TABLE I

Fe - Ni - Rh - Pt Clusters

	d M_M nm x 10	
Ni metal bulk	2.49	
$Ni_2 Cp_2 (CO)_2$	2.36	
$Ni_3 Cp_3 (CO)_2$	2.39	
$Ni_4 (CO)_6 L_2$	2.508	
$[Ni_3 (CO)_3 (\mu_2 CO)_3]_2^{2-}$	2.38 2.77	
$[Ni_6 (CO)_{12}]^{2-}$	2.36 2.81	
$[Ni_9 (CO)_{18}]^{2-}$	2.40 2.70	
Rh metal bulk	2.69	
$Rh_4 (CO)_{12}$	$\overline{2.75}$	
$Rh_6 (CO)_{16}$	$\overline{2.77}$	
$[Rh_6 (CO)_{15} C]^{2-}$	2.776 base / 2.817	base, base top
$[Rh_7 (CO)_{16}]^{3-}$	$\overline{2.76}$	
$[Rh_{12} (CO)_{30}]^{2-}$	$\overline{2.79}$ 2.68 2.81	between 2 octaedras (in octaedra)
$[Rh_{15} (CO)_{28} C_2]^-$	$\overline{2.87}$ 2.90 2.73 _ 3.33	
$[Rh_{13} (CO)_{24} H_3]^{2-}$	$\overline{2.80}$	

Bond lengths are rather close to bulk metal-metal distancies : differencies are due in part to the existence and the absence of CO bridging and to the presence of negative charges.

For the smaller clusters, different structure (tetrahedron, squarepyramid, trigonal bipyramid, and so on...) are possible but especially interesting are rhodium and platinum clusters with more than 10 atoms. Rhodium clusters with 13, 14, 15 atoms have been described by Chini et Al. (ref. 29) : $[Rh_{13} (CO)_{24} H_3]^{2-}$ has an hexagonal close packed cubooctahedron structure and the $[Rh_{14} (CO)_{25}]^{4-}$ is a body centered cubic incomplete dodecahedron (ref. 30). Cristal growth studies (ref. 18) indicate that a 13 atom cristallite could be a stable structure in an icosahedral form.

Platinum complexes (ref. 31) have a different structure and contain repeated trigonal prismatic stacking of metal triangles. They may, for instance, give an idea of two dimensionnal monolayer on a support.

As far as number of atoms, metal-metal distances are concerned, high nuclearity clusters seem to be fairly comparable to small cristallites.

2. Bonding energies. Adsorption properties.

Estimations of bonding energies for surface metal atoms have been made by Brewer
(ref. 24) ; they are of about 20 Kcal/mole per bonding electron for iron and nickel,
near to 27 for rhodium and of about 35 for platinum. Values presented (ref. 15 to 25)
for metal-metal bonds in clusters of iron and rhodium are quite in the same range.

For metals, the surface density may be related to their possibility to interact with
some molecules like CO or NO : both are useful because of their strong IR adsorption
and allow the measurement of low interactions. Results obtained (ref. 32) for CO adsorption
in different metal films, are represented in figure 2 ; two IR bonds are observed : one
located between 1900 and 2170 cm^{-1} is attributed to linear CO, the other, due to
bridging CO, is situated below 1900 cm^{-1}. It may be noticed that coadsorption of
trimethylamine shifts the band toward smaller wave numbers indicating a higher electron
transfer from the metal to the carbon monoxide. Similar results have been published
by Primet et Al. (ref. 33) ; they have shown that the IR adsorption of linear CO
adsorbed on supported platinum is shifted to lower wave numbers by the coadsorption of
electron donor molecules and to higher wave numbers by the presence of an electron
acceptor. Quite similar results have been published (ref. 26) concerning the
substitution of one CO by electron donating ligands in metal carbonyls.

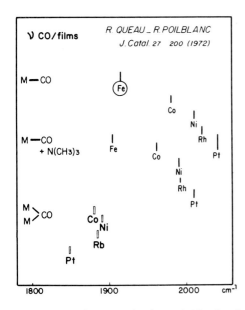

Fig. 2. IR characteristics of CO adsorbed on metal films.

As shown (ref. 18), small cristallites have stronger surface atoms interaction, this
could mean that CO adsorption might change with cristallite size. If there are no clear
results on CO, results published (ref. 27) on NO adsorbed on supported platinum
(figure 3) show that by cristallites give a higher back-donation.

404

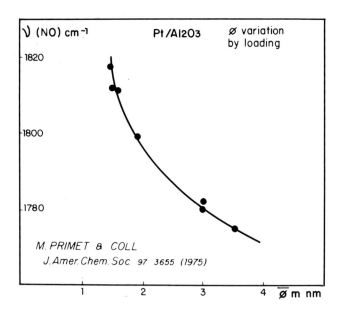

Fig. 3. NO frequencies as a function of mean particle diameter.

Chini's platinum clusters (ref. 31) are interesting regarding these last observations. As shown in figure 4, CO vibrations go to higher wave number as the number of platinum atoms is increased and γ_{CO} observed for 15 atoms are rather close to that observed on supported metals. Similar results are obtained on rhodium clusters when increasing the number of atoms but comparison is not as easy because of structural change.

Hydrocarbons or hydrogen adsorption is well known on solid catalysts ; it can be followed by magnetic measurements (ref. 28). Dissociative hydrogen adsorption generally occurs ; models may be the hydrido carbonyls presented before. For hydrocarbons, cyclopentadienyl carbonyls (ref. 34) may be one kind of a model, some more complex compounds containing bonded olefins or acetylenic compounds (ref. 21, 35) have also be described. Carbon containing clusters may be a representation of the carburization of metals in the presence of hydrocarbons. Even clusters with only hydrocarbon radicals and hydrogen have been isolated (ref. 36).

3. Kinetic aspects.

Possible ligand exchange and structural change in solution for molecular clusters are studied (ref. 15b) but it is probably to soon to get conclusions.

Nevertheless, it is interesting to point out that metals under reaction conditions are, usually covered by a monolayer of different radicals and that interaction is strong enough to reorganize the superficial structure (ref. 16), indicating that some metal-metal bonds may be broken and others formed.

Models of such a situation may be given by the interaction of DPA (diphenylacetylene) with iron carbonyls (figure 5), which leads to the formation of a new cluster after the transformation of the adsorbed ligands (ref. 37) to an other molecule.

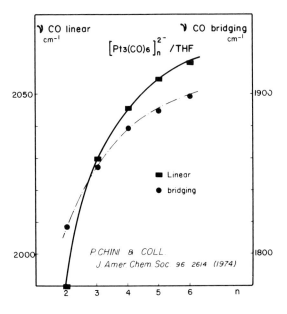

Fig. 4. Carbonyl frequencies in $\left[Pt_3 (CO)_6\right]_n^{2-}$

More experimental determination on ligand migration on clusters or of adsorbed molecules on surfaces are needed to get a better comparison in that field.

4. Conclusion.

Although a lot of more quantitative determinations are needed especially concerning the kinetics of ligand migration in both cluster and surface chemistry, molecular clusters can be helpful pictures of small metallic particles especially if one bears in mind that, under reaction conditions, reactant covered cristallites may be very close to molecular clusters. This is probably the reason why most accurate comparison will have to be made, and will be made in the field of carbon monoxide chemistry where cluster chemistry is now fairly advanced.

In the future, models of bimetallic catalysts may also be developed if additionnal heteronuclear complexes like these shown in table II, can be obtained.

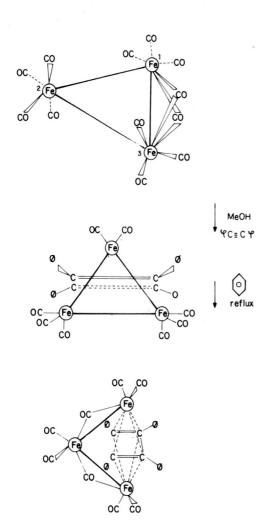

Fig. 5. Diphenylacetylene interaction with $Fe_3(CO)_{12}$ (ref. 37).

TABLE II   Bimetallic clusters   (38)

Clusters	Ref
FeNi$_2$(CO)$_3$ Cp$_2$ (C$_2$ Ph$_2$)	a
Fe$_2$Ni$_2$(CO)$_6$ Cp$_2$ (C$_2$ Ph$_2$)	a
Co$_2$Rh$_4$(CO)$_{16}$	b
[Mo$_2$Ni$_3$ (CO)$_{16}$]$^{2-}$	c
[W$_2$ Ni$_3$ (CO)$_{16}$]$^{2-}$	c

PRECURSORS OF SUPPORTED METALS.

Homogeneous catalysis gives rise to some problems with separation of products and catalysts which have been easily solved in heterogeneous catalysis. Molecular complexes have been anchored on oxides (ref. 39) but only recently molecular clusters have been used for that purpose ; table III shows most of the known results ; hydrogenations, dehydrocyclization, hydrogenolysis and carbon monoxide conversion are the reactions tested.

The goal, in most cases, was to obtain small metallic particles supported on silica or alumina, with a geometry as close as possible to that of the initial molecular cluster and to find out, if that special structure could have any particular catalytic property. Starting from a molecular cluster, the following steps have to be achieved : anchoring on the support, activation, characterization and catalytic testing. We are going to describe the results we have obtained for iron, nickel and finally platinum tin bimetallic clusters.

1. Monometallic clusters.

Anchoring of a molecular cluster on silica or alumina can be achieved by ligand exchange or by oxydative addition. Further activation to get bare metal must avoid transfer and sintering.

For iron clusters, we could not find any interaction with silica. During activation under helium, hydrogen or even with an hydrogen propylene mixture, iron carbonyl (Fe (CO)$_5$) was moving out of the support and we could not find any catalytic activity, even at 200 °C in hydrogenation reactions. This was a bit disappointing , nevertheless we went over to nickel clusters and we obtained a strong interaction between the compound and alkylaluminium treated silica or with silica

in the presence of oxygen. From different measurements, surface reaction may lead to the
distroying of the initial cluster.

TABLE III

SUPPORTED CLUSTER CATALYSIS [40]

CLUSTER	SUPPORT	REACTION	REF
$Rh_6(CO)_{16}$	Al_2O_3	–	a
$Ru_3(CO)_{12}$	SiO_2	OLEFIN HYDROGENATION & ISOMERIZATION	b
$Ni_2 Cp_2(CO)_2$	SiO_2	OLEFIN & AROMATIC HYDROGENATION	c
$[Pt_3(CO)_6]_n^{2-}$	Al_2O_3	DEHYDROCYCLISATION PARAFFIN ISOM	d
$NiCp_2$ DPA $NiCp_2(CO)_2$ $NiCp_3(CO)_2$	SiO_2	AROMATIC HYDROGEN HYDROGENOLYSIS	e
$Fe_2Cp_2(CO)_4$ $Fe_3(CO)_{12}$ $Fe_6 C(CO)_{12}$	SiO_2	HYDROGENATION HYDROFORMYLATION	f
Rh, Ir, Ru, Os Fe carbonyl chisters	Al_2O_3 or SiO_2	$CO + H_2$	g
$Rh_6(CO)_{16}$	La_2O_3 TiO_2 ZrO_2	$CO + H_2$	h
$Co_2 Rh_2(CO)_{12}$	SiO_2	HYDROGENOLYSIS	i
$Pt_3Sn_2Cl_6(NBD)_3$	Al_2O_3/Cl	HYDROGENATION DEHYDROCYCLIZATION CRACKING	j

It was noticed that without anchoring nickel, cristallites obtained were rather
big ($\emptyset > 5$ nm), only part of the nickel could be reduced and very low activities
were obtained.

With oxygen anchored complexes, high activities were reached. Hydroxyl groups
seem to be very important for activity and stability.

But, what seems to be the most important for the future of the use of clusters
as precursors is that, after reduction and evacuation, no hydrogen adsorption was
found at room temperature but the catalyst rapidly adsorbed hydrogen at high
temperature. Magnetic studies (ref. 40) indicated that during degazing, the nickel
was reoxidized (figure 6), generally, it was only partly reduced and the mean cristallite
size of reduced nickel may be estimated of 1.4 nm.

This may show that small cristallites on support are unstable in the absence of
any adsorbed radical, at least, adsorbed hydrogen is needed and that they undergo
a rapid oxydation even by surface hydroxyl groups. In addition, their characterization

is rather complicated and it does not seem easy to keep the initial cluster
structure.

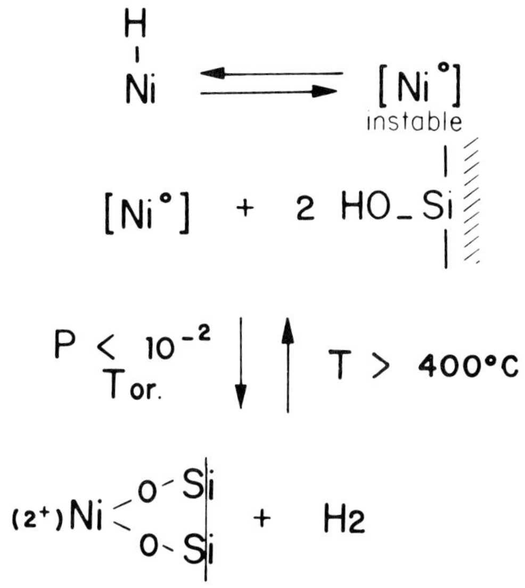

$$
\begin{array}{c}
\underset{|}{\overset{\text{H}}{\text{Ni}}} \;\rightleftarrows\; [\text{Ni}^{\circ}] \\
\text{instable}
\end{array}
$$

$$[\text{Ni}^{\circ}] \;+\; 2\; \text{HO}\!-\!\text{Si}$$

$$
\begin{array}{c}
P < 10^{-2} \;\downarrow\;\uparrow\; T > 400^{\circ}C \\
\text{Tor.}
\end{array}
$$

$$
(2^{+})\text{Ni} \underset{\text{O}-\text{Si}}{\overset{\text{O}-\text{Si}}{<}} \;+\; \text{H}_2
$$

Fig. 6. Nickel reoxidation by hydroxyl groups (ref. 40e)

The last conclusion may not be a general one because J.M. Basset et Al.
(ref. 41) were able to regenerate $Rh_6(CO)_{16}$ anchored on silica after all the carbon
monoxide had been removed.

Nevertheless, the oxygen anchored catalysts were found more active per nickel
atom, then normally prepared nickel catalysts but their selectivity for hydrogenolysis
of hydrocarbons was similar to that of classical nickel. Preparing naked metals on a
support from molecular clusters may be possible if one is able to prepare the clusters
surrounded with appropriate ligands and remove those ligands in smooth conditions. It
seems that Ozin's (ref. 42) cryophotoclustering may be a very interesting alternative.
Characterization also remains difficult. Nevertheless, high dispersion and high
activities can be obtained and the use of clusters seems to be promising for
hydrogen-carbon monoxide conversion especially if cristallites are trapped to avoid
migration. Synthesis of bimetallic catalysts may be another interesting
development in the future.

2. Bimetallics.

Bimetallic catalysts are especially used in catalytic reforming but, until now,
the initial interaction has not been clearly understood (ref. 43). We have tried
to find a bimetallic cluster containing platinum and an other metal from those used
in catalytic reforming and which did not contain any of the elements considered as

410

catalyst poisons. The only one meeting all these requirement was $Pt_3 Sn_2 Cl_6 (COD)_3$ described by R.V. Lindsey Jr et Al. (ref. 44). The use of norbornadiene and a slight modification of preparation conditions lead to orange-red cristals whose analysis, IR and NMR spectras, correspond to $Pt_3 Sn_2 Cl_6 (NBD)_3$. Its structure is probably comparable to that of the COD complex established by L.J. Gruggenberger (ref. 45).

This cluster has been anchored on prechlorinated alumina and treated with hydrogen. Microprobe scanning determinations indicate a non destructive anchoring, no cristallites could be detected by Electron Microscopy. Activity measurement compared to a commercial catalyst indicated 3 times higher activity for benzene hydrogenation and a similar initial dehydrocyclization activity.

These results show that bimetallic clusters can be rather good precursors for bimetallic catalysts. This field may be very interesting because the use of bimetallic clusters may allow the synthesis of bimetallic catalysts with controlled metal-metal ratio and may even give access to catalysts which cannot be prepared by classical methods.

CONCLUSION.

Molecular clusters are attractive compounds as precursors and models for small cristallites of mono or bimetallic catalysts, but to get more quantitative comparisons, we will still need a lot of work in surface chemistry, clusters synthesis and catalysis and also mathematic modeling of adsorption and catalysis.

In the future, to obtain a clear representation of catalysis by metals and to design and to prepare more effective catalysts, we shall need :

- improved knowledge of the nature and the mobility of adsorbed species,

- more data on the stability of naked metallic clusters and on the reactant induced mobility of metal atoms,

- synthesis of new high nuclearity clusters or of bimetallic clusters with ligands having properties similar to those of mineral carriers,

- development of homogeneous clusters catalysis perhaps by the preparation of coordinately unsaturated compounds (ref. 45).

REFERENCES.

1 G.C. Bond, Catalysis by metals, A.P. (1962).

2 J.E. Germain, Conversion of hydrocarbons, A.P. (1969).

3 B. Delmon, P.A. Jacobs and G. Poncelet, Scientific bases for the preparation of heterogeneous catalyst, Elsevier (1976).

4 J.R. Anderson, Structure of metallic catalysts, A.P. (1975).

5 J.R. Anderson, Metal skeletal reaction of hydrocarbons, Adv. in Catal., 23(1972)1-90 A.P.

6 J.H. Sinfelt, Specificity in catalytic hydrogenolysis by metals, Adv. in Catal. 23(1972)91-119 A.P.

7 M. Boudart, Catalysis by supported metals, Adv. in Catal. 20(1969)20-153 A.P.

8 M. Boudart, A. Aldag, J.F. Benson and N.A. Dongharty, J. Catal., 6(1966)92.

9 G.C. Bond, D.S.C. Far. Soc., 41(1966)200.

10 K.H. Johnson, R.P. Messmer, J. Vac. Sci. Technol., 11(1)(1974)236.

11 R. Ugo, Catal. Rev. 11(1975)225.

12a J.W. Lauher, J. Am. Chem. Soc., 100(1978)5305.

12b J.W. Lauher, J. Am. Chem. Soc., 101(1979)2604.

13 M.F. Charlot, O. Kahn, Surf. Science 81(1979)90 and ref. there in.

14 J.M. Basset, R. Ugo, Aspect of homogeneous catalysis III, Ed. R. Ugo, Milan (1978).

15a E.L. Muetterties, Bull. Soc. Chim. Belg., 84(1979)959.

15b E.L. Muetterties, T.N. Rhodin, E. Band, C.F. Burcker and W.R. Pretzer, Chem. Reviews
    79(2)(1979)91.

16 G.A. Somorjai, Catal. Rev. Sci. Eng., 18(2)(1978)173.

17 O.M. Poltorak, U.S. Broniu and A.N. Mitofayona, Proc. IVth Int. Conf. on catalysis,
    Moscou 2(1968)276.

18 J.J. Burton, Cat. Rev. Sci. Eng., 9(2)(1974)209.

19 R.F. Marzke, Cat. Rev. Sci. Eng., 19(1)(1979)43.

20 G. Martino, in catalysis heterogeneous and homogeneous, Ed. B. Delmon - G. James,
    Elsevier (1975).

21 R.D. Johnston, Adv. in Inorganic Chem and Radiochem., 13(1970)471 A.P.

22 P. Chini, G. Longoni, V.G. Albano, Adv. in Organomet. Chem., 14(1976)296 A.P.

23a J.B. Kerster and J.R. Shapley, J. Organomet. Chem. 85(1975)C 29.

23b R.C. Ryan, Ch. U. Pittmann Jr and J.P. O'Connor, J.A.C.S. 99(1977)1986.

23c C.G. Pierpont, G.F. Stuntz and J.R. Shapley, J.A.C.S. 100(1978)616.

23d P. Frediani, U. Matteoli, M. Bianchi, F. Piacenti and G. Menchi, J. Organomet.
    Chem. 150(1978)273.

23e M.G. Thomas, B.F. Beier and E.L. Muetterties, J.A.C.S. 98(1976)1296.

23f E.L. Muetterties, Pure and Appl. Chem., 50(1978)941.

23g G.D. Mercer, J. Shing Shu, T.B. Rauchfuss and D.M. Romdhill, J.A.C.S. 97(1975)1967.

24 L. Brewer, Science 161(1968)115.

25 L.S. Brown, J.A. Connor and H.A. Steinner, J. Chem. Soc. Faraday I 75(1975)699.

26a C.A. Tolman, J.A.C.S. 92(1970)2953.

26b G. Booth, J. Chatt and P. Chini, Chem. Comm. (1965)639.

27 M. Primet, J.M. Basset, E. Garbowsky and M.V. Mathieu, J.A.C.S. 97(1975)3655.

28 J.A. Dalmon, J.P. Candy and G.A. Martin, Proceed. 6th Int. Cong. Catalysis 2(1976)903.

29 V.G. Albano, A. Ceriotti, P. Chini, G. Ciani, S. Martinengo, W.M. Anker, J. Chem.
    Soc. Chem. Comm. (1975)859.

30 C.E. News, (April 3, 1979)21.

31 J.C. Calabrese, L.F. Dahl, P. Chini, G. Longoni and S. Martinengo, J. Amer. Chem. Soc.
    96(1974)2614.

32 R. Queau, R. Poilblanc, J. Catal. 27(1972)200.

33 M. Primet et Al., J. Catal. 29(1973)213.

34 E.O. Fischer and C. Palmy, Chem. Ber. 91(1958)1725.

35 O.S. Mills and B.W. Shaw, J. Organomet. Chem. 11(1968)595.

36 G. Huttner and H. Lorentz, Chem. Ber. 107(1974)996.

37 R.P. Dodge and V. Schomaker, J. Organomet. Chem. 3(1966)274.

38a J.F. Tilney-Bassett, J. Chem. Soc. (1963)4783.

38b F.G.A. Stone and S.H.H. Charton, Progress in coordination Chem. Ed. E. Caïs,
    Elsevier (1968).

38c J.K. Ruff, R.P. White and L.F. Dahl, J. Amer. Chem. Soc. 93(1971)2159.

39 Y.I. Ermakov, Cat. Rev. Sci. Eng. 13(1)(1976)77.

40a G.C. Smith et Al., Inorg. Chem. 14(1975)1419.

40b J. Robertson and G. Webb, Proc. Royal Chem. Soc. A 341(1974)383.

40c M. Ichikawa, J. Chem. Soc. Chem. Comm. (1976)26.

40d M. Ichikawa, J. Chem. Soc. Chem. Comm. (1975)1088.

40e P. Leroux, G. Martino and G. Martin, French-Soviet Catalyst Symposium, Tbilissi (1978).

40f P. Leroux, Thesis, Lyon (1977).

40g D. Commereuc, J.M. Basset et Al., to be published.

40h M. Ichikawa, Bull. Soc. Chim. Jap. 51(1978)2268.
                Bull. Soc. Chim. Jap. 51(1978)2273.

40i J.R. Anderson and D.E. Mainwaring, J. Catal. 35(1974)162.

40j N. Rosas and G. Martino, to be published.

41 J.L. Bilhou, V. Bilhou-Bonguol, W.F. Graydon, J.M. Basser, A.K. Smith, G.M. Zanderighi
    and R. Ugo, J. Organomet. Chem. 153(1978)73.

42a A.J. Lee Hanlan and G.A. Ozin, Inorg. Chem. 16(1977)2848.
                        Inorg. Chem. 16(1977)2857.

42b G.A. Ozin and W.J. Power, Inorg. Chem. 16(1977)2864.

43 H. Charcosset, Rev. Institut Fr. du Pétrole, XXXIV(2)(1979)239.

44 R.V. Lindsey Jr, G.W. Parshall and J.G. Stolberg, Inorg. Chem. 5(1966)109.

45 L.J. Guggenberger, J. Chem. Soc. Chem. Comm. (1968)512.

DISCUSSION

G. MARTINO

Figueras - Ne pensez-vous pas que la taille minimum qu'on peut avoir avec un métal donné est surtout limitée par la stabilité de la particule (elle même déterminée par l'énergie de formation du réseau métallique) ? Y a-t-il un exemple de comparaison d'activités, calculées pour un atome de métal superficiel, qui permette de dire que les petites particules ainsi formées sont effectivement plus actives que celles qu'on peut produire par une méthode classique ?

Martino - La taille minimum dépend du métal, du support et de l'atmosphère présente au dessus de la particule métallique. Ce que nous avons observé est qu'en l'absence d'hydrogène, il y a réoxydation et pour le nickel sur silice, formation de silicate de surface. D'après nos calculs (thèse de P. Leroux, Lyon 1977), les petites particules obtenues semblent plus actives en hydrogénation du benzène. Mais, il est possible que la surface métallique soit sous-estimée, vu les difficultés rencontrées pour la déterminer.

Salem - Lors d'un calcul d'approche d'un cluster par une molécule, pensez-vous qu'on représente la "réalité" de la catalyse mieux en laissant les autres atomes du cluster nus, ou en leur adjoignant des ligands ?

Martino - Il me semble que les clusters moléculaires, entourés de ligands, sont plus proches de l'état d'un catalyseur réel. En effet, ce dernier est généralement utilisé sous pression de réactifs et la surface dans ce cas, est pratiquement totalement recouverte de radicaux hydrocarbonés ou d'hydrogène par exemple. Le cluster du rhodium (Rh_{15}) entouré de CO est certainement assez proche d'espèces catalytiques réelles (voir réf. 30).

Che - You said that you could obtain high dispersions using metal clusters. Are they actually higher than those obtained by conventional methods, other things being equal. Did you check that ?

Martino - Yes, the dispersion were higher than those obtained by conventional methods, which lead to cristallites of about 25 to 30 Å.

Basset - Bien entendu un cluster moléculaire peut être la source de petites particules. Mais, il existe un certain nombre de travaux qui essayent d'utiliser les clusters moléculaires sous une forme moléculaire pour réaliser des cycles catalytiques par exemple réaction du gaz à l'eau, etc ...

Martino - Tout à fait d'accord.

Mirodatos - Vous avez montré l'effet stabilisant de l'hydrogène sur une surface de nickel bien dispersée, dérivée de clusters. Avez-vous constaté une diminution de cette dispersion pendant/ou à l'issue d'une réaction entrainant la consommation de cet hydrogène ? (par exemple, l'hydrogénation du benzène).

Martino - Si on enlève l'hydrogène aux petites entités de nickel présentes, on a formation de silicate de surface et par conséquent, la réduction ultérieure est aussi difficile que celle de produits obtenus par imprégnation et conduit, de ce fait, à un frittage.

J. BOURDON (Editor)
Growth and Properties of Metal Clusters, pp. 415—420
© 1980 Elsevier Scientific Publishing Company — Printed in The Netherlands

ELECTRON DEFICIENCY IN PLATINUM CLUSTERS SUPPORTED ON Y-ZEOLITES

R.S. Weber and M. Boudart

Department of Chemical Engineering, Stanford University
Stanford, California 94305

and P. Gallezot

Institut de Recherches sur la Catalyse, 2 avenue Albert Einstein
Villeurbanne Cedex 69626, France

Abstract

Electron deficiency in 1 nm clusters of Pt supported on Y type zeolites has been
substantiated by O_2 chemisorption studies and Extended X-ray Absorption Fine Structure
(EXAFS) spectroscopy. For the samples studied, the electron deficiency is thought to be
due to zeolite acidity and not to intrinsic effects of cluster size.

Résumé

Le défaut d'électrons des clusters de platine mesurant un nanomètre déposés sur une
zéolite de type Y a été établi suite à une étude par chimisorption d'oxygène et par
Spectroscopie d'Absorption des Rayons X par des Structures Fines (EXAFS). De l'examen
des échantillons, il apparaît que le défaut d'électrons serait dû à l'acidité de la
zéolite et non pas à l'effet de la dimension du cluster.

Platinum clusters encaged in Y type zeolites comprise an appropriate system to study
the effects of particle size and support interaction on a supported metal catalyst
(ref. 1). Even at high metal loading, clusters in a narrow size range around 1 nm can
be obtained by special preparative techniques. Additionally, the acidity of the zeolite
can be controlled by varying its charge compensating cations. Enhanced catalytic activity
(refs. 2-4) and resistance to sulfur poisoning (refs. 5,6) were observed for platinum
clusters encaged in acidic Y zeolites, and originally attributed to an electron deficient
character of the metal. Evidence from infra-red, X-ray photo-electron, and X-ray
absorption spectroscopies (refs. 6-9) has been obtained in support of this premise. However, it has been difficult to evaluate the relative importance of cluster size and support
effects on the properties of the metal. Here we attempt to establish that the acidity of
the carrier can be a major factor responsible for the electron deficiency observed in Pt
clusters supported on acidic Y zeolites.

The procedure for obtaining well-dispersed samples of PtY was first detailed by Dalla-
Betta and Boudart (ref. 2) and by Kubo et al. (ref. 10). Platinum is introduced into
the zeolite by ion-exchange with a water solution of $Pt(NH_3)_4Cl_2$. Sufficient amounts

416

have been used to give metal loadings between 0.4 and 14% by weight. The ammine complex
is decomposed by careful calcination in flowing O_2. Either evacuation or purging with He
at elevated temperature precedes reduction of the Pt(II) ions with H_2. In most cases
the charge compensating cation in the zeolite was exchanged before introduction of the Pt.
Foger and Anderson (ref. 7) cleverly chose to vary the charge compensating cation after
the Pt clusters were formed. This was done to ensure an identical metal particle size
among their samples. In various studies the charge compensating cations have included
Na^+, H^+, Ca^{2+}, Ce^{3+}, La^{3+}, and a mixture of rare earth ions. Protons are always generated
in the zeolite during reduction of the platinum.

Gallezot et al. have used electron microscopy (ref. 11) and X-ray scattering (ref. 12)
to determine the size of the Pt clusters in NaY. The size was found to approximately 1 nm.
Hydrogen uptake measurements show the platinum to be close to 100% dispersed, where dispersion is defined as the fraction of surface atoms in a metal particle. Location of the
platinum clusters within the supercages of the zeolite has been inferred from the in-
accessibility of hydrogenation sites to liquid phase reactants or bulky molecules (refs.
13, 14) and from the great resistance of the clusters to migration and sintering (ref. 15).

The acidity of the zeolite is related to the electric field gradients produced by the
charge compensating cations. Zeolites which contain multivalent cations or protons as
the principal charge compensating cations are generally recognized to be acidic (ref. 16).
When the charge compensating cation is Na^+, the zeolite behaves like a non-acidic oxide
support. No quantitative measure of acidity will be used here, only a qualitative measure
of the zeolites' ability to withdraw electrons is invoked.

Very strong evidence that the properties of platinum clusters can be modified greatly
by support effects alone is presented by Foger and Anderson (ref. 7). They report XPS
and catalytic activity measurements on clusters supported on NaY, CaY, and LaY. Their
data supports the idea that increased acidity of the support induces electron deficiency
in the metal clusters. For example, it is possible to estimate from their data that the
Pt $4f^{7/2}$ peak shifts 0.5 eV to higher energy in the XPS spectrum of PtLaY compared to its
position for PtNaY or Pt metal. It is reasonable to suppose that the average size of Pt
particles was the same in all their samples because of the preparation procedure they used,
as discussed above. Thus this shift in the Pt $4f^{7/2}$ line appears to depend only on the
acidity of the zeolite.

Additional evidence for a strong metal-support interaction clusters comes from X-ray
absorption measurements (ref. 9). Platinum clusters supported on NaY and HY were prepared
with metal dispersions of 92% and 86% as measured by H_2 uptake. Thus each sample contained
metal particles of about the same size. For PtNaY, the Pt L_{III} edge did not shift from
the position measured for bulk metal. However, the absorption edge for similarly sized
clusters in PtHY moved 0.6 eV to higher energy. This implies that the Pt 2p electrons are
more tightly bound in the clusters supported on the acidic HY zeolite, possibly because
they are less shielded from their nuclei following withdrawal of valence electron density
by the support. Diminished occupancy of the valence levels in the Pt clusters on HY was
directly observed as an increase in their L_{III} threshold peak area. The peak areas of Pt
foil and Pt clusters on NaY were 1.5 and 1.2 times smaller. Similar indications of
electron deficiency were displayed by other samples of platinum on acidic zeolites (see
Table 1).

Recent results from O_2 uptake measurements at room temperature and Extended X-ray
Absorption Fine Structure (EXAFS) spectroscopy on the same samples are summarized in
Table 1 (ref. 17). They are consistent with the view that electron deficiency in the
Pt clusters is a support effect. The Pt clusters supported on the non-acidic NaY zeolite
displayed normal, Wilson-Hall stoichiometry (ref. 18) for oxygen uptake on small particles
-- the ratio, H:O of atoms taken up was 1.96:1. However for the Pt clusters encaged in the
acidic HY zeolite the H:O ratio rose to 3.98:1. In the latter case the platinum may not
have been able to chemisorb as much oxygen because the necessary electrons were involved
in a strong metal-support interaction.

Radial distribution functions (rdf) derived from EXAFS measurements on samples of
PtNaY, PtCaY and PtHY under H_2 show a contraction of the Pt-Pt nearest neighbor distance
for the clusters on the two acidic supports (ref. 17). However, the number of nearest
neighboring atoms, indicated by the intensity of the Pt-Pt rdf peak, was the same in all
samples. The lattice contraction does not appear to arise from particle size. Rather it
was caused by support interaction with the CaY and HY zeolites which removed electron
density from the metal clusters. Molecular orbital theory suggests that lattice contraction would accompany electron transfer from a cluster. Indeed, X-alpha scattered
wave calculations (ref. 19) on a cuboctahedron of 13 Pt atoms show the highest occupied
levels to be anti-bonding between adjacent centers. If electron density were withdrawn
from such a cluster it would come from these levels and, in agreement with the experimental
findings, allow the bond distances to shorten. In the absence of support acidity and in
the case of hydrogen covered clusters, no contraction of the Pt-Pt bond distances was
observed either from EXAFS (ref. 20) or X-ray scattering measurements (ref. 12). Except
for the reduction in neighbor density expected for a small cluster, the rdf curve for
PtNaY in the latter experiment showed a face-centered cubic arrangement of the platinum
atoms at the distances of bulk metal.

It would be foolhardy to suggest that a parameter measured coarsely in eV like electron
deficiency would correlate with every aspect of the chemistry of this form of platinum.
For some reactions like the hydrogenolyses of neopentane (refs. 2,7), ethane and propane
(ref. 4) such a correlation does exist. The Arrhenius activation energy for all these
reactions falls by about 20 kJ/mol when the zeolite support is made acidic. On the other
hand, while the rate of hydrogenation of ethylene is sensitive to the identity of the
charge compensating cation around the platinum clusters, (ref.2), the rate of hydrogenation of benzene is not (ref. 6). It is also not our intention to belittle the importance
of particle size on the properties of these materials. Certainly none of the support
effects would have appeared without the Pt clusters being small enough to ensure intimate
contact with the zeolite. Size and shape distributions of the platinum clusters may play
a large role in determining their catalytic chemistry (ref. 7). We conclude from the
physical and chemical measurements that the electronic structure of platinum particles
in the size range of 1 nm is affected strongly by the acidity of the carrier.

418

Table 1 - Indications and Effects of Electron Deficiency
in Pt Clusters Encaged in Y Zeolites

Sample	Support Acidity	Metal Dispersion %	Ratio of H:O taken up	Activity for Hydrogenolysis	Pt L_{III} Edge Shift/eV	Pt L_{III} Peak Area	Pt Lattice Contraction/pm ±5
Pt	--	--	1:1	normal	0.0	1.0	0
PtNaY	non-acidic	92	2:1	normal	0.0	1.2	0
PtCaY	acidic	--	2:1	enhanced	0.3	1.4	5
PtCeY	acidic	--	--	enhanced	0.5	1.5	--
PtHY	acidic	86	4:1	enhanced	0.6	1.6	10

REFERENCES

1. P. Gallezot, Catal. Rev., (in press).
2. R.A. Dalla Betta and M. Boudart, Proc. 5th Int. Congr. Catalysis, Palm Beach, 1972, Vol. 2, North Holland, Amsterdam, 1973, p. 1329.
3. J. Datka, P. Gallezot, J. Massardier, and B. Imelik, Acta Revista Portug., (in press).
4. C. Naccache, N. Kaufherr, M. Dufaux, J. Bandiera, and B. Imelik, in "Molecular Sieves - II" (J.R. Katzer, ed), American Chemical Society, 1977, p. 538.
5. J.A. Rabo, V. Schomaker, and P.E. Pickert, Proc. 3rd Int. Congr. Catalysis, Amsterdam, 1964, Vol. 2, North Holland, Amsterdam, 1965, p. 1264.
6. P. Gallezot, J. Datka, J. Massardier, M. Primet, and B. Imelik, Proc. 6th Int. Congr. Catalysis, London, 1976, Vol. 2, The Chemical Society, London, p. 696.
7. K. Foger and J.R. Anderson, J. Catal. 54 (1978), 318-335.
8. J.C. Vedrine, M. Dufaux, C. Naccache, and B. Imelik, J. Chem. Soc. Faraday Trans. I, 74 (1978), 440-449.
9. P. Gallezot, R.S. Weber, R.A. Dalla Betta, and M. Boudart, Z. Naturforsch. 34a (1979), 40-42.
10. T. Kubo, H. Arai, H. Tominaga, and T. Kunugi, Bull. Chem. Soc. Japan, 45 (1972), 607-612.
11. P. Gallezot, I. Mutin, G. Dalmai-Imelik, and B. Imelik, J. Microsc. Spectrosc. Electron, 1 (1976), 1-6.
12. P. Gallezot, A.I. Bienenstock, and M. Boudart, Nouv. J. Chim., 2 (1978), 263-266
13. V. Penchev, N. Davidova, V. Kanazirev, H. Minchev, and Y. Neinska, Adv. Chem. Ser., 121 (1973), 461- 468.
14. R. Madon, PhD Dissertation, Stanford Univ., 1975.
15. P. Gallezot, A. Alarcon-Diaz, J.A. Dalmon, A.J. Renouprez, and B. Imelik, J. Catal., 39 (1975), 334-349.
16. D. Barthomeuf in "Molecular Sieves - II," (J.R. Katzer, ed.), American Chemical Society, Washington, 1977, p. 453.
17. R.S. Weber, P. Gallezot, R.A. Dalla Betta, and M. Boudart, (to be submitted to J. Catal.).
18. G.R. Wilson and W.K. Hall, J. Catal. 17 (1970), 190-206; J. Catal., 24 (1972), 306-314.
19. R.P. Messmer, S.K. Knudsen, K.H. Johnson, J.B. Diamond, and C.Y. Yang, Phys. Rev. B. 13 (1976), 1396-1415.
20. B Moraweck, G. Clugnet, and A.J. Renouprez, Surface Sci., 81 (1978), 1631-1634.

420

DISCUSSION

R.S. WEBER, M. BOUDART, P. GALLEZOT

Fraissard - Avez-vous d'autres exemples de telles propriétés métalliques dans les zéolithes ?

Gallezot - Nous avons étudié les propriétés électroniques du palladium. Les états de grande dispersion présentent également un caractère déficitaire en électrons.

Yates - As I understand, you have obtained your EXAFS data either under oxygen or hydrogen. Did you obtain any data under vacuum ?

Gallezot - No, but we have studied recently the structure of the 10 Å particles under vacuum by the radial electron distribution from X-ray data. It appears that there is a contraction of the interatomic distances and the structure is perturbed (broader smaller electron density peaks). However these particles are trapped in the zeolite supercages and are therefore surrounded by several tens of oxygen anions which may deeply perturb the structure under vacuum.

Fraissard - La déficience électronique doit elle être imputée à la petite taille de la particule ou à l'influence du support zéolithique.

Gallezot - Les tailles des particules doivent être petites et le support acide pour que l'on observe le caractère déficitaire en électron, mais il est difficile d'évaluer l'importance relative de ces deux effets. Le transfert électronique du métal vers le support est d'autant plus facile que la taille est plus petite c'est à dire qu'un plus grand nombre d'atomes sont en contact avec le support.

J. BOURDON (Editor)
Growth and Properties of Metal Clusters, pp. 421—434
© 1980 Elsevier Scientific Publishing Company — Printed in The Netherlands

Adsorption d'hydrogène sur petites particules de platine.

Etude par EXAFS et diffusion inélastique des neutrons

A. Renouprez, P. Fouilloux et B. Moraweck

Institut de recherche sur la Catalyse - Villeurbanne - France

ABSTRACT

The geometric and electronic structure of 12 $\overset{o}{A}$ Pt particles in Y zeolite and of 18 $\overset{o}{A}$ particles on SiO_2 was studied with the EXAFS method.

In vacuum, the distance between first neighbours was found respectively 7 and 5 % shorter than in the bulk metal. Moreover, the structure of the finest particles is found close to the icosaedral model while that of the 18 $\overset{o}{A}$ is cubic.

Upon hydrogen adsorption, the distance measured between first neighbours relaxes to the value of the bulk. This phenomenon of relaxation agrees with the results of neutron inelastic spectroscopy which indicate that hydrogen occupies C_{3v} and C_{4v} surface sites as well as atop positions on Pt atoms.

Oxygen adsorption at 80 K produces a large perturbation in the superficial structure, shortening and lengthening of the first neighbours distances explains the partial filling of the hollow surface sites and hence the surface stoichiometry of oxygen chemisorption which is half that of hydrogen.

INTRODUCTION

L'interaction de l'hydrogène et de l'oxygène avec le platine est un problème important du point de vue fondamental et de la catalyse par ce métal. Il est intéressant d'essayer de déterminer la structure des complexes de surfaces ainsi que les modifications éventuelles subies par le substrat au cours de l'adsorption. Dans une étude récente |1| nous avons examiné le bilan global de ces adsorptions tiré des mesures volumétriques. Pour l'hydrogène, nous avons conclu qu'il existe 2 états d'adsorption correspondant à des énergies ne différant que de quelques kilocalories. Le nombre des atomes fixés par le métal excède largement le nombre d'atomes de platine en surface, mais ne correspond cependant pas à une saturation de tous les sites disponibles. Nous avons admis qu'il se produit un remplissage partiel des sites C_{3v} et C_{4v} et fixation sur les atomes de métal en position terminale. Avec l'oxygène, le volume chimisorbé est inférieur de moitié à celui mesuré pour l'hydrogène. Nous avons admis que dans ce cas seul les sites "creux" se remplissent en partie.

Dans la présente étude nous rendrons compte des résultats obtenus par la méthode EXAFS concernant les modifications induites sur le métal par ces adsorptions et nous montrerons comment les expériences de diffusion inélastique des neutrons confirment les hypothèses avancées pour la structure du complexe adsorbé.

I ETUDE DES STRUCTURES GEOMETRIQUES PAR EXAFS

I-1 échantillons.   Le premier échantillon est constitué de platine déposé sur silice
(Pt - SiO$_2$) contenant 6,7 % de métal préparé par décomposition et réduction sous hydrogène
du complexe Pt (NH$_3$)$_4$ (NO$_3$)$_2$ déposé. Il comporte des grains, dont le diamètre mesuré par
diffusion centrale des rayons X est de 18 Å. Cela représente des ensembles de 150 à 200
atomes. Un second échantillon est préparé par échange des ions sodium d'une zéolite NaY(2).
Il renferme 15 % de métal sous formes de grains de 10 à 12 Å situés dans les grandes cavités de la zéolite. Ces particules comportent 50 à 60 atomes de métal.

I-2 structure géométrique - modifications sous l'effet de l'adsorption.   Nous avons étudié
la discontinuité d'absorption L III du platine sur l'anneau DCI (LURE) dans un domaine de
1 300 ev au dessus du seuil. Les expériences sont effectuées dans une cellule raccordée à
un dispositif de pompage et à une rampe à gaz.

Cette cellule permet à la fois d'effectuer les traitements sous atmosphère contrôlée
jusqu'à 800 K et de mesurer le spectre EXAFS à 80 K.

On sait d'après les travaux de Stern |3| que le coefficient d'absorption normalisé
obtenu après soustraction du fond continu, conduit par transformation de Fourier à une
courbe de distribution radiale présentant une succession de pics à des distances Ri, correspondant aux   couches successives entourant un atome pris comme origine.

Les valeurs Ri mesurées expérimentalement sont déplacées vers les faibles distances
en raison du déphasage entre l'onde émise par l'atome central et celles rétrodiffusées par
les autres atomes. Une méthode très répandue pour évaluer ce déphasage consiste à le mesurer sur la courbe de distribution obtenue avec un corps de structure connue (ici une feuille de Pt de 3µ d'épaisseur).

Les échantillons disposés dans la cellule EXAFS sont retraités à 700 K sous hydrogène
évacués à cette température durant 2 heures et refroidis à 80 K pour l'expérience.

Le tableau n° 1 indique les distances entre premiers, seconds et troisième voisins
après correction du déphasage. Ces valeurs peuvent être comparées à celles calculées par
deux modèles : un icosaèdre de 55 atomes dont le paramètre moyen est contracté de 7 % et
un cubooctaèdre contracté de 5 %.

On remarque que sous vide, les deux échantillons ont un réseau contracté par rapport
à celui du métal massif. Pour le Pt-zéolite, cette contraction est de 7 % et les distances
entre second et troisièmes voisins (3,55 et 4,30 Å) se rapprochent d'avantage de celles qui
seraient obtenues avec un icosaèdre (3,60 , 4,30) qu'avec un cubooctaèdre (3,60 et 4,45).
Pour Pt-SiO$_2$, cette contraction est également observée - 4,5 % - mais les distances entre
voisins sont plus proches de celles calculées pour le modèle cubique.

Il apparait donc que comme le prévoyaient les travaux théoriques de Gordon et Cyrot|4|
les particules de 10-12 Å seraient plus stables sous la forme d'icosaèdres et que celles

de 18-20 Å sous forme cubique. En second lieu, les réseaux sont contractés par rapport à celui du métal massif, le phénomène étant d'autant plus important que le diamètre des particules est plus faible.

Tableau 1.

		1er voisins d Å ± 0,03	2e voisins d Å ± 0,07	3e voisins d Å ± 0,1
Feuille 3μ		2,77	3,90	4,80
Cubooctaèdre théorique contracté de 5 %		2,64	3,71	4,57
$PtSiO_2$	vide 80 K	2,64	3,76	4,67
	H_2 80 K	2,74	3,90	4,74
	H_2 200 K	2,76	3,87	4,65
	H_2 600 K	2,77	3,87	4,82
Icosaèdre théorique contracté de 7 %		2,57	3,60	4,30
Pt zéolite	vide 80 K	2,57	3,55	4,30
	H_2 80 K	2,77	3,70	4,52
	H_2 300 K	2,77	3,72	4,72
	H_2 800 K	2,77	3,75	4,74

Lors de l'adsorption d'hydrogène, une relaxation se produit. Elle ne concerne que les premiers voisins à 80 K et devient complète à 300 K. A cette dernière température le réseau devient cubique avec pratiquement les paramètres du solide massif.

Il faut cependant remarquer qu'on ne connait pas dans le cas de Pt-zéolite l'influence du réseau sur ces modifications de structure du métal. Les particules sont en effet prisonnières de cavités dont les dimensions sont de 12 Å c'est à dire approximativement la taille des grains de métal.

Nous avons étudié l'effet de l'adsorption d'oxygène entre 80 et 300 K sur les solides. Le tableau 2 indique les positions des principaux pics mesurés, comparés à l'oxyde platine de référence.

On constate évidemment l'apparition d'un important pic Pt-O situé entre 1,65 et 1,75 Å, mais à 80 K, les distances platine-platine sont fortement modifiées. Deux distances sont apparentes ; l'une aux environs de 2,45-2,55 Å correspond à une compression de certaines paires et l'autre aux environs de 2,90-2,95 Å à une dilatation.

Il est raisonnable de penser qu'un site sur deux de la surface est occupé par l'oxygène et que cette occupation modifie fortement la forme du puits de potentiel : dilatation de 7 à 8 % pour les puits occupés, contraction pour les puits libres.

Enfin il faut noter que lorsque la température croit (dès 200 K pour Pt-zéolite et à 300 K pour $Pt-SiO_2$) un désordre complet s'installe dans la structure et qu'aucune distance

424

ne devient mesurable. Ceci n'est pas en désaccord avec l'étude bibliographique qui montre que l'obtention de composé PtO parfaitement cristallisé n'est possible que sous haute pression (plusieurs centaines de bars) et haute température (> 1 200°C).

Tableau 2.

Echantillon	Traitement		Distances	
PtO, xH_2O			1,70	
PtSiO$_2$	O_2	80 K	1,60 + 2,42 - 2,82	
	O_2	200 K	1,68 - 2,35 - 2,84	
	O_2	300 K	1,70	amorphe
Pt zéolite	O_2	80 K	1,70	2,40 - 2,86
		200 K	1,70	amorphe
		300 K	1,70	amorphe

II structure électronique.   Depuis les travaux de Y. Cauchois on sait que la structure au seuil d'absorption X est liée à l'état électronique de l'élément étudié. L'existence d'un pic important après le seuil (raie blanche) apparait lorsque le matériau présente une bande d incomplète. Ce pic est produit par la transition électronique d'un niveau de coeur vers un niveau non occupé. Pour la discontinuité L III de Pt, il s'agit d'une transition du niveau 2p vers le niveau 5d ou 6s. La principale difficulté expérimentale consiste en fait à séparer cette structure électronique qui se prolonge jusqu'à quelques dizaines d'ev du seuil du spectre EXAFS proprement dit. Nous avons choisi de reprendre la méthode utilisée par Wei et Lytle |5| dans le cas du tantale, consistant à représenter analytiquement cette structure par une loi de Breit-Wigner-Fano et à intégrer cette courbe analytique jusqu'à 10 ev au-dessus du seuil.

L'intensité ou seuil s'écrit :

$$I(\Sigma) = a \frac{(q + \Sigma)^2}{1 + \Sigma^2} + b \qquad \text{avec} \qquad \Sigma = 2 \frac{E - E_o}{\Gamma}$$

où les paramètres a, b, q, Γ et E$_o$ sont optimisés à partir des données expérimentales. a et b sont des constantes fixant la position de l'asymptote, E$_o$ est le seuil, q un paramètre de forme et Γ la largeur de la courbe. On peut comparer dans le tableau III ces intégrales à celle du témoin qu'est la feuille de Pt. Les figures 1 et 2 montrent les résultats de l'ajustement à cette loi.

Pour Pt-SiO$_2$ qui a un support neutre avec une interaction géométrique faible entre Pt et support, l'échantillon sous vide conduit à la même valeur que le témoin. Sous action de l'hydrogène, l'aire du pic diminue ce qui correspond à un transfert d'électrons de l'adsorbat vers le métal. Sous oxygène, le métal cède des électrons à l'oxygène et on se rapproche de la valeur mesurée pour PtO$_2$.

La situation est sensiblement différente avec le Pt-zéolite qui apparait largement déficitaire en électrons. Il est surprenant de constater que l'adsorption d'oxygène entraine une légère diminution d'aire. Ceci peut s'expliquer en admettant que des électrons

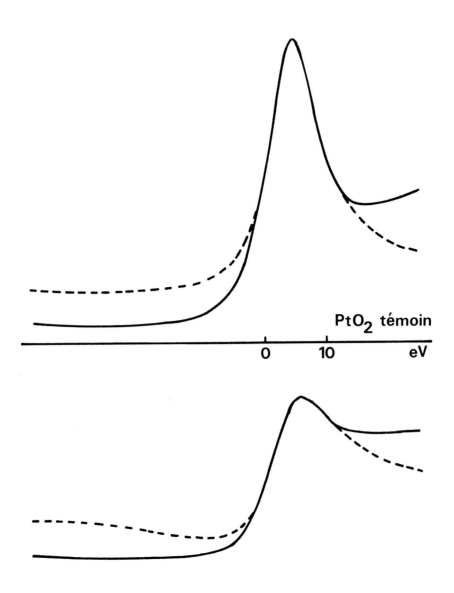

PtO$_2$ témoin

0   10   eV

Pt SiO$_2$ O$_2$ 80 K

0   10   eV

FIG. 1 : AJUSTEMENT DU SEUIL À LA LOI DE BREIT-WIGNER

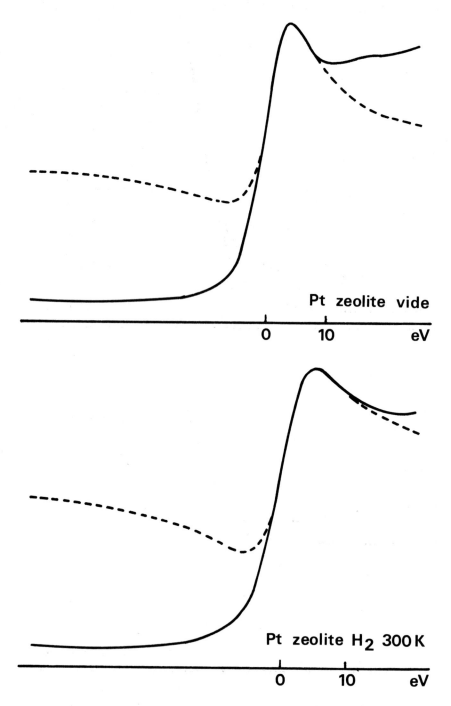

Pt zeolite vide

0   10   eV

Pt zeolite H$_2$ 300 K

0   10   eV

FIG. 2 : AJUSTEMENT DU SEUIL À LA LOI DE BREIT-WIGNER

sont transférés du support vers l'oxygène et le platine. Avec l'hydrogène la diminution d'aire est beaucoup plus importante et les électrons sont transférés de l'hydrogène au platine.

Tableau 3.

Echantillon	Traitement	Aire normalisée rapportée à Pt-3μ
Pt 3μ		1
PtSiO$_2$	vide 80 K	1
	H$_2$ 80 K	0,9
	H$_2$ 200 K	0,88
	H$_2$ 600 K	0,91
	O$_2$ 80 K	1,05
	O$_2$ 200 K	1,07
PtO$_2$, xH$_2$O		1,12
Pt-zéolite	vide 80 K	1,09
	H$_2$ 80 K	0,93
	H$_2$ 200 K	0,93
	H$_2$ 300 K	0,91
	H$_2$ 800 K	0,91
	O$_2$ 80 K	1,02
	O$_2$ 200 K	1,03
	O$_2$ 300 K	1,07

En résumé, pour Pt-SiO$_2$ on obtient le comportement prévisible en ce qui concerne le sens des transferts électroniques mais avec le Pt-zéolite le rôle du support dans l'état électronique du métal semble prépondérant.

III STRUCTURE DES ESPECES ADSORBEES PAR DIFFUSION INELASTIQUE DES NEUTRONS

A l'inverse des méthodes de la spectroscopie optique, la diffusion inélastique des neutrons n'est pas soumise à une règle de sélection. De plus, les vibrations ont une intensité qui est proportionnelle au déplacement carré moyen des atomes et à la section de diffusion du noyau considéré. Parmi les éléments, l'hydrogène a une section incohérente environ 10 fois supérieure à celle des autres noyaux |6|.

Par contre, même au réacteur à haut flux de l'ILL, le nombre des neutrons diffusés est faible et la résolution en énergie n'est que de 5 mev en dessous de 130 mev et 10 mev entre 130 et 250 mev.

La figure 3 montre le spectre de diffusion obtenu avec l'échantillon Pt-zéolite sous 2 pressions partielles 10^{-2} torr et 300 torr.

Sous forte pression, 5 vibrations sont détectées à 2 100 - 2 200 cm^{-1}, 1 350, 1 000

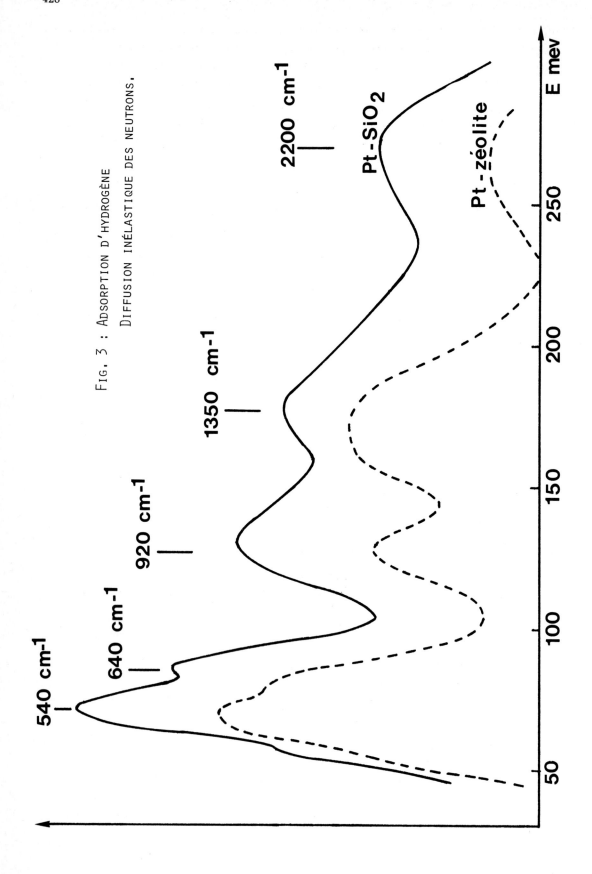

Fig. 3 : Adsorption d'hydrogène
Diffusion inélastique des neutrons.

660 et 520 cm^{-1}. Lorsqu'on pompe à 300 K sur l'échantillon, l'intensité des 2 vibrations à 520 et 2 200 cm^{-1} est réduite. On constate également une diminution du fond continu entre les bandes (vers 800 cm^{-1} par exemple). On remarque enfin que les bandes, situées au-dessous de 1 000 cm^{-1} ont une largeur très supérieure à la résolution de l'instrument.

On peut comparer ces résultats à ceux qu'avaient obtenus Howard et Waddington |7| lors de l'étude d'adsorption d'hydrogène sur le noir de platine par diffusion inélastique des neutrons et de Baro, Ibach et Buchmann sur Pt(111) par perte des électrons |8| (Tableau 4).

Tableau 4.

Howard et Waddington ν cm^{-1}	ν cm^{-1}	Baro, Ibach ν cm^{-1}	présent travail ν cm^{-1}	attribution I + II	ou I + III
1 torr	600 torr				
512	496	550	540	ν'_1	ν'_2
616	616		640	ν''_1	ν'_1
856	848	1 230			
936	936	(1 100-1 400)	950 - 980	ν_2	ν_2
1 296	1 296		1 350	ν'_2	ν'_3
1 696	1 656				
2000-2250	2000-2550		2 000 - 2 200	ν_1	ν_1

On doit noter tout d'abord que l'équipe britannique a travaillé sur un substrat qu'il est difficile de bien dégazer sans provoquer un frittage important et qu'elle admet qu'un certain nombre des vibrations mesurées peuvent être dues à de l'eau résiduelle. Ce serait le cas des deux bandes situées à 850 et 1 650 cm^{-1}.

En ce qui concerne les résultats obtenus sur monocristaux, il apparaît que la vibration mesurée à 1 230 cm^{-1} est en fait très large et s'étend de 1 100 à 1 400 cm^{-1}. Par contre aucune intensité n'est détectée au-delà de 1 500 cm^{-1}.

L'accord avec les travaux |7| de spectroscopie neutronique est donc satisfaisant si on tient compte du fait que la structure du substrat est probablement assez différente. D'autre part l'absence de vibration détectée à 2 000 cm^{-1} par diffusion des électrons peut s'expliquer par le fait que les pressions d'équilibre - 10^{-6} torr contre 10^{-2} ou 10^{2} torr - sont plus faibles que lors des expériences de neutrons. Enfin il faut noter que dans des mesures effectuées par IR sur Pt-MgO, Primet, Fouilloux et CANDY |9| avaient détecté une vibration aux environs de 2 200 cm^{-1} qui disparaissait par pompage à 300 K mais qu'ils n'avaient mesuré aucune vibration à basse énergie en raison de l'absorption due au support.

Finalement l'attribution certaine du système observé n'est pas possible. On peut avancer deux hypothèses représentées sur la figure 4 :
La première s'accorde avec les travaux de Ho et al (10) et correspondrait à la coexistence des états I et III avec adsorption en position terminale et en position pontée. La seconde hypothèse en meilleur accord avec les travaux de Ibach donnerait

430

Etat I

ν_1 2200 ν_2 = 930

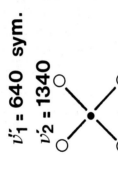

H

Pt

Etat II

ν''_1 = 640 sym.
ν'_2 = 1340

ν'_1 = 540 sym.
ν'_2 = 1350

Etat III

ν'_1 = 640

ν'_3 = 1350

ν'_2 = 540

H

FIGURE IV

une coexistence des états I et II avec adsorption sur les positions terminales et dans les sites (111) et (100) au centre des faces.

IV CONCLUSION

Des expériences d'EXAFS il ressort que le réseau initialement contracté des petites particules de platine se relaxe pour retrouver la structure cubique sous l'effet d'une adsorption d'hydrogène. Cette adsorption d'hydrogène qui provoque un apport d'électrons au métal, se produit probablement par remplissage progressif des sites C_{3v} et C_{4v} de la surface puis adsorption en position terminale sur le métal. La saturation obtenue à 300 K sous 300 torr ne correspond cependant pas à un remplissage de tous les sites disponibles, ce qui explique qu'aucune structure ordonnée n'ait jamais été détectée par diffraction des électrons sur les monocristaux.

Le nombre des modes de vibration détectés par diffusion des neutrons est en bon accord avec cette hypothèse de 2 types de sites. A l'heure actuelle il n'est cependant pas possible d'en faire une attribution absolument certaine. Il faudrait pour cela disposer de molécules modèles où les atomes d'hydrogène soient disposés dans chacune des symétries envisagées. La largeur des bandes de vibration qui comme dans le cas des études sur monocristaux est très supérieure à la résolution instrumentale, appuie également l'hypothèse d'une surface énergétiquement hétérogène mais où les énergies d'adsorption entre différents puits ne varient que de quelques kilocalories/mole.

Enfin la relaxation de réseau sous l'effet d'une adsorption d'hydrogène est un phénomène logique et sa grandeur est comparable aux variations qui sont mesurées sur les hydrures où les atomes d'hydrogène occupent une position interstitielle.

Dans le cas de l'adsorption d'oxygène où les mesures volumétriques montrent que près de 2 fois moins d'atomes s'adsorbent que pour l'hydrogène, il est logique de penser que seuls les sites C_{3v} et C_{4v} se remplissent en partie. Il y a bouleversement profond de la structure superficielle du métal donnant lieu à un rapprochement des atomes métalliques pour les sites vacants et un écartement pour ceux qui sont occupés.

En fait à la température ambiante la surface est quasi amorphe à l'échelle atomique.

REFERENCES

1 J.P. Candy, P. Fouilloux et A. Renouprez, Hydrogen adsorption on platinum catalysts, Trans. Far. Soc. (sous presse).

2 P. Gallezot, A. Alarcon, J. Dalmon, A. Renouprez et B. Imelik, J. Catal. 39 (1975) p. 334.

3 E.A. Stern, D.E. Sayers et F.W. Lytle, Phys. Rev. B 11 (1975) p. 4 836.

4 M.B. Gordon, thèse, Université de Grenoble (1978).

5 P.S.P. Wei et F.W. Lytle, Phys. Rev. B 19 (1979) p. 679.

6 A. Renouprez, P. Fouilloux, G. Coudurier, D. Tocchetti, R. Stockmeyer, Trans. Far. Soc. 73 (1977) p. 1.

7 J. Howard, T.C. Waddington, C.J. Wright, Intern. Symp. neutron scattering Vienne 1977.

8 A.M. Baro, H. Ibach and H.D. Bruchmann, Surf. Sci. (sous presse).

9 W. Ho, R.F. Willis and E.W. Plummer, Phys. Rev. Lett. 40 22 (1978) p. 1 463.

DISCUSSION

A. RENOUPREZ, P. FOUILLOUX, B. MORAWECK

Martin - You have shown that the surface stoichiometry of hydrogen adsorption on platinum is larger than that on nickel. Would it be possible to account for the smaller activity in ethane hydrogenolysis observed on platinum catalysts, hydrogen acting as a protecting film towards the hydrocarbon adsorption, thus decreasing the hydrogenolysis activity.

Renouprez - I think that the difference in activity for these two metals for C-C bond rupture should be looked at in terms of differences in the electronic structure.

Bonzel - Regarding the question by Dr Martin, the saturation coverage of hydrogen on W(100) is H/W = 2 (see Froitzheim et al., Surface Science). Since tungsten is a good catalyst for hydrogenolysis, it appears that there is no basis for a correlation between high hydrogen saturation coverage (Pt, W) and poor hydrogenolysis activity (Pt).

Yacaman - Will your results challenge the usual assumption that is made in measuring chemisorption of hydrogen on platinum in which a stoichiometry of one hydrogen to 1 platinum is assumed ?

Renouprez - This assumption is really an assumption. Our results definitively rule out this long living error.

Yates - I do not agree that the stoichiometry of H_2 adsorption on Pt is in any way arbitrary. Considerable work has been done on Pt black with H_2 chemisorption and argon physical adsorption. In all cases, one H atom is found to be adsorbed per surface Pt atom. Therefore, if you can definitely prove that more than 1 H atom is adsorbed per Pt atom, I think that you are the first person to do this. We have measured very many times the surface area of Pt on Al_2O_3 catalysts, and have never found a H/M ratio of a value greater than 1. Possibly, exceptions can be found for metals in zeolites ; have you considered that your excess H_2 is not on the Pt at all but is just mobile inside the surface of the zeolite ?

Renouprez - 1°/ Most of the errors in stoichiometry determination are due to insufficient cleaning of the surface, i.e. the last traces of H_2 and H_2O are only eliminated above 500° C.

2°/ Pt black is very frequently contaminated by alcaline metals or hydrocarbons (if they are prepared from organic salts).

3°/ We found for Raney-Pt (a porous unsupported metal) for which the surface was measured by 85 Kr adsorption, the same figures i.e. 1.4 - 1.6 H atom per surface Pt atom. In the case of Pt-zeolite, the stoichiometry is lower (1. to 1.2) either because of the size, or more probably because part of the metal is masked by the zeolite.

A detailed analysis of the literature compared to these results and to results on single crystals will shortly appear in Trans. Far. Soc.

Salem - Est-il certain qu'il n'y a pas d'hydrogène moléculaire dans les deux atomes H observés par atome de Pt ?

Renouprez - 1°/ Il n'a jamais été mesuré de vibration H-H dans la région des 4.000 cm^{-1} correspondant à de l'hydrogène moléculaire.

2°/ La vibration à 2.000 - 2.200 cm^{-1} observée par spectroscopie IR et neutronique correspond à une vibration Pt-H. Cette vibration est observée dans de nombreux complexes organométalliques dont la structure est connue et où l'hydrogène est en position terminale.

3°/ L'échange H-D se fait très rapidement sur Pt même au-dessous de la température ambiante.

434

Fraissard - Avec Pt/SiO$_2$, une partie de l'hydrogène adsorbé se trouve sur SiO$_2$ et réagit très rapidement dans certaines réactions (échange H-D par exemple). Ne pensez-vous pas que cette espèce peut fausser les valeurs que vous attribuez à l'adsorption de l'hydrogène uniquement sur le platine ?

Renouprez - 1°/ Pour Pt/SiO$_2$, les chiffres obtenus pour la stoechiométrie sont peu différents de ceux mesurés sur Pt-Raney où il n'y a pas de support.

2°/ La présence d'hydrogène migrant sur le support à grande distance de la particule de Pt est exclue : la quantité mesurée pour des échantillons de concentration variable en Pt, ayant la même taille de particule, reste proportionnelle à la concentration en Pt.

3°/ Il n'est pas exclu qu'il existe des atomes d'hydrogène situés en position pontante entre le Pt et l'oxygène du support, en particulier lorsque l'adsorption est faite au-dessus de 400-500° C.

J. BOURDON (Editor)
Growth and Properties of Metal Clusters, pp. 435—449
© 1980 Elsevier Scientific Publishing Company — Printed in The Netherlands

A SPECTRUM OF LANDING AREAS FOR ADSORPTION AND ITS RELATION TO CATALYST SELECTIVITY

E. Ruckenstein and Dady B. Dadyburjor
(State University of New York at Buffalo, Buffalo, NY 14214, USA and Rensselaer Polytechnic
Institute, Troy, NY 12181, USA)

ABSTRACT

   The concept of multiple landing areas available for adsorption of a gas phase molecule
on a solid surface is introduced. The distribution of adsorbed molecules in these different
landing areas varies with temperature, pressure and the properties of the surface. Consequently the variation in selectivity and activity of a catalyst can be explained from the
landing area point of view. Increasing the pressure favors adsorbed forms on fewer sites.
Increasing the temperature may have the same or the opposite effect, depending upon the
heats of adsorption for the various landing areas. For catalysts consisting of metal
clusters supported on a substrate, a change in the metal dispersion may change the fraction
of surface sites available to one or more landing areas. This could explain the facile or
demanding nature of activity and/or selectivity of the catalyst. The metal catalyzed
hydrogenolysis and isomerization reactions of hydrocarbons are used to illustrate these
points. The models agree well with experimental data.

1. Introduction

   For reactions catalyzed by clusters of noble metals supported on an inert substrate,
and in fact for solid-catalyzed reactions in general, the adsorption of one or more reactants on the surface of the solid catalyst is an indispensible step. The simplest
analysis of this process, associated with Langmuir, Hinshelwood, Watson, and Hougen,
assumes a homogenous surface, non-interacting absorbates and less than monolayer coverage.
An implicit assumption is that all molecules of a given species form only a single type of
adsorbate on a given surface under given conditions.

   The first three restrictions have been relaxed in later work. For a good discussion
of this see, for example, Thomas and Thomas (ref. 1). It is the postulate of the present
work that, even for a uniform homogenous surface, a molecule can adsorb in one of several
forms on the surface. The set of sites or atoms of the surface corresponding to a particular
adsorbed form is the landing area of that form.

   Adsorption on a large number of sites may occur in several steps.   A precursor,
or a molecule in its initial state of adsorption (probably on not more than one or two
sites), may have a choice of several final adsorption forms, depending on which landing
areas are available at that moment.

   Landing areas are postulated to consist of two types of sites. Some sites are attached
to the adsorbate by strong bonds. Such sites form the umbra or core of the landing area.
Other sites, in the penumbra, or periphery, are more loosely bound and perhaps are due to
the (limited) mobility of the adsorbate. For the final adsorbed form, a dynamic equilibrium

436

may exist between adjacent free sites and penumbra sites, with a given site changing from
one that is free to one in the penumbra.

A molecule adsorbed in one form can change to another form quite simply by freeing
up certain (umbra) sites and tying up others, so that its new landing area is that of the
other adsorbed form. Of course when thermodynamic equilibrium is reached, these inter-
changes would cancel one another out. At thermodynamic equilibrium, the distribution of
adsorbed forms/landing areas will depend upon the temperature and pressure. A non-
homogenous surface also influences the landing area distribution. For energetic or geometric reasons, a fraction of such a surface may be unavailable for one or more landing
areas/adsorption forms. Varying the landing area possibilities varies the activity and
selectivity of the catalytic reaction, since it may be supposed that each adsorbed form
contributes differently to the overall reaction.

In this work we illustrate the effectiveness of the landing area approach to understanding the effects of pressure, temperature, and a heterogenous catalyst surface using
a single set of reactions. The reactions considered are the isomerization, hydrogenolysis
and scrambling processes involving a straight chain hydrocarbon and hydrogen, and catalyzed
by Pt clusters on a support of alumina. The overall reaction network is represented in a
quantitative landing area framework in the next section. Three different landing areas are
described, some with further subdivisions, and it is possible to see the relationships with
one another and with their precursors. The effect of temperature is shown in Section 3.
In Section 4 the effect of pressure is illustrated using a simpler model for the process.
The heterogenity of the surface is taken into account in Section 5 by use of the selectivity
effectiveness factor, analogous to the conventional (activity) effectiveness factor.

2. Landing Area Formulation of Metal Cluster Catalyzed Hydrogen-Hydrocarbon Reaction Set

For the greater part of this work, we specify the hydrocarbon to be n-pentane, although
some C_6 reactions are considered briefly later. In both cases, the reactions with hydrogen
catalyzed by metal clusters are known to occur via the cyclic mechanism and the bond-shift
mechanism. Details of these mechanisms will not be repeated here; see for example ref. 2.
We postulate that each intermediate (or final adsorbed form) of the two mechanisms has a
characteristic landing area, i.e., requires a distinct set of surface sites. Then the
variations in temperature, pressure, and surface characteristics change the distribution
of this spectrum of landing areas. This alters the concentration of the different intermediates, thus varying the activity and selectivity of the overall reaction.

The careful tracer experiments of Garin and Gault (ref. 3), which furnish the experimental data for evaluation of our analysis, have been performed on n-pentane-2^{13}C. Consequently in Figure 1 are indicated the reaction network and the different intermediates
corresponding to this compound. Clearly there are numerous landing areas possible for the
adsorption of the C_5 compound. In principle the probability of any of these is finite, and
they all should be considered as part of the landing area spectrum. In practice, some insights on the selectivity of the process can be obtained by using relatively few of these
choices, and this has been done in Figure 1.

A minimum of three sets of landing areas can be accounted for in this reaction network, and the corresponding intermediates are identified as X, Y, and Z. The intermediate
corresponding to the X-type landing area is adsorbed on two non-adjacent C-atoms, while

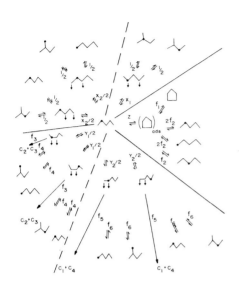

Figure 1. Reaction set for n-pentane-2-^{13}C. The dot denotes the location of ^{13}C and arrows denote points of attachment to the surface. Fractions f_1-f_6 denote reaction probabilities for the products. See the text for an explanation of landing areas corresponding to X, Y, and Z.

the Y-type intermediate is adsorbed on two adjacent C-atoms. The intermediate for the Z-type landing area is the adsorbed ring structure. The X_1 and Y_1 intermediates are adsorbed on at least one end C-atom, while the X_2 and Y_2 intermediates are adsorbed only on the inner C-atoms. The unsymmetric ^{13}C-atom in the molecule leads to two slightly different intermediates being formed, with roughly equal probability, on each of the two X-type and two Y-type landing areas. Each of these eight intermediates forms two different isomers via the bond shift mechanism. Also formed from the X and Y landing areas are low molecular weight hydrogenolysis products after reaction with hydrogen. Desorption of the intermediate from the Z-type landing area yields cyclopentane by the cyclization reaction, after removal of hydrogen. Breaking any one of the (symmetric) bonds of the cyclic intermediate returns n-pentane to the gas phase, but now the ^{13}C is randomly positioned in the hydrocarbon chain. This is the so-called scrambling reaction.

It is reasonable to believe that an intermediate on the Y-type landing area ties up the fewest number of sites, while that on the Z-type of landing area ties up the greatest number. However, the number of sites tied up in each case cannot be simply related to the points of attachment of the adsorbed form because of the role, as yet unclear, of the moderate interactions with the penumbra sites.

To represent Figure 1 in a landing area framework of equations, let x_1, x_2, y_1, y_2, z represent the number of sites tied up with the corresponding landing areas, and let w_i represent the number of sites tied up for a precursor adsorbed on the i-th C-atom. We have shown elsewhere (ref. 4) that hydrogen too adsorbs on different landing areas; however, we assume here that only a single landing area predominates. That landing area ties up h sites and is occupied in a single step, i.e., no separate precursor exists. Intermediates, precursors and the gas phase molecules are in equilibrium, and the process is controlled by the reaction of the intermediates to form the products. Then the formation of a precursor adsorbed on an end C-atom, for example, is governed by the reversible reaction

$$\text{\textbf{M}} + (w_1 + h)S \rightleftharpoons [\text{\textbf{⌂}} -S(w_1)] + [H - S(h)] \tag{1}$$

where the dot denotes the location of the ^{13}C-atom, and the arrow denotes the point of attachment of the precursor to the catalyst surface. Square brackets denote an adsorbed species, and S is a surface site. Similarly the formation of an intermediate, say x_2, from this precursor follows

$$[\text{\textbf{⌂}} -S(w_1)] + (x_2 - w_1 + h)S \rightleftharpoons [\text{\textbf{⌂}} - S(x_1)] + [H - S(h)] \tag{2}$$

The hydrogen adsorption-desorption reactions are

$$H_2 + 2hS \rightleftharpoons 2[H - S(h)] \qquad (3)$$

The formation of products from intermediates follows reactions such as

$$[\diagup\!\!\!\diagdown - S(x_1)] + 2[H - S(h)] \rightarrow \diagup\!\!\!\diagdown + (x_1 + h)S \qquad (4)$$

for isomerization. In principle this reaction too is reversible. At least for short reaction times, however, the reverse reaction can be neglected. Since reactions (1) through (3) are assumed to equilibrate rapidly

$$K_1 \, C_{pentane} \, \theta_S^{w_1+h} \;=\; \theta_{w_1} \theta_H \qquad (5)$$

$$K_2 \, \theta_{w_1} \, \theta_S^{x_2-w_1+h} \;=\; \theta_{x_1} \theta_H \qquad (6)$$

$$K_3 \, C_{hydrogen} \, \theta_S^{h} \;=\; \theta_H^2 \qquad (7)$$

Here the K_i represent equilibrium constants. The C_i are the gas phase concentrations, and θ_S, θ_{w_1}, θ_{x_1}, θ_H are the fractional number of sites that are empty, tied up by precursor, tied up by intermediate, and tied up by hydrogen. The rate of formation of the product of equation (4) is

$$r_4 = k_4 \, \theta_{x_1} \, \theta_H^2 \qquad (8)$$

where k_4 is a reaction rate constant. In principle the reaction rate of this and other products could be evaluated provided the equations analogous to (5), (6), and (8) were written out for all precursors, intermediates, and products. Such rates would be expressed in terms of forward and reverse rate constants, reactant concentrations, and site characteristics w_i, x_i, y_i, and z. Again in principle, comparison with experimental rate data would yield best fit values of the unknown kinetic parameters and site characteristics.

Such a task is too cumbersome to attempt at present, although a simpler model along these lines is evaluated in Section 4. In the next sections, we use initial rate data for n-pentane to estimate the distribution of landing areas on the catalyst surface.

3. <u>Analysis of Initial Rate Data - Effect of Temperature on the Distribution of Landing Areas.</u>

In Table I are shown some of the data obtained by Garin and Gault (ref. 3) by tracer analysis of the reaction products of n-pentane-2-^{13}C and hydrogen over a Pt/Al_2O_3 catalyst. Each column of data represents two separate runs under roughly similar conditions. One yields the relative distribution of pentane isomers, while the other measures the amounts of all products formed. The two columns correspond to two different temperatures. In both cases the partial pressure of hydrogen is 760 mm. The conversion of the pentane is assumed to be small enough that initial rate conditions apply.

From Figure 1 we obtain in Table II the relations between the number of moles of n-pentane that are adsorbed as intermediates on each of the different landing areas X_1, X_2,

TABLE I

Tracer Analysis Data of Garin and Gault (ref. 3)

T°C	283	269
Distributions, moles/100 miles of n-pentane-2-^{13}C		
/\/\	3.1	0.8
/\/\	87.4	94.0
/\/\	1.6	0.4
$CH_4 + C_4H_{10}$	1.3	0.95
$C_2H_6 + C_3H_8$	2.9	1.9
⬠	0.32	0.2
/\/	0.45	0.2
/\/	1.45	0.7
/\/ + /\/	1.7	0.85

Y_1, Y_2, and Z, and the product distributions of Table I. At low conversions of n-pentane, the number of moles of an intermediate is a measure of the concentration of the corresponding landing area on the surface of the catalyst. The contributions of the different landing areas are shown in Table III by solving the equations of Table II using the data of Table I.

TABLE II

Relations between products formed and intermediates adsorbed on the catalyst surface. <<i>> denotes moles of product i per 100 moles of feed, and <J> the moles of feed adsorbed on a J-type landing area per 100 moles of feed. Fractions f_1 through f_6 correspond to product distributions as shown in Figure 1.

$$<<\!/\!\backslash\!/\!\backslash\ >> = 2f_2<Z> + <X_2>/4 + f_4<Y_1>/2 + f_6<Y_2>/2$$

$$<<\!/\!\backslash\!\backslash\ >> = f_2< Z>$$

$$<<⬠\ >> = f_1<Z>$$

$$<<\ /\!\!\!\backslash\!/\ >> = <X_2>/4 + f_4<Y_1>/2 + f_6<Y_2>/2$$

$$<<\ /\!\!\!\backslash\!/\ >> = <X_1>/2$$

$$<<\ /\!\!\!\backslash\!/\ >> = <X_1>/2 + <X_2>/4 + f_4<Y_1>/2 + f_6<Y_2>/2$$

$$<<C_1+C_4>> = f_5<Y_2>$$

$$<<C_2+C_3>> = f_3<Y_1>$$

$$f_1 + 5f_2 = 1$$

$$f_3 + 2f_4 = 1$$

$$f_5 + 2f_6 = 1$$

First note that an intermediate on a Y_1 or Y_2 landing area forms, to a good approximation, only hydrogenolysis products. Intermediates on X_1, X_2 and Z landing areas may form isomerization (including scrambling) and cyclization products.

TABLE III

Distribution of landing areas on Pt/Al_2O_3 catalyst at different temperatures
Solution of equations in Table II using the data of Table I

T°C	283	269
Reaction fractions (Figure 1)		
f_1	0.05	0.09
f_2	0.19	0.18
f_3	1	1
f_4	0	0
f_5	1	1
f_6	0	0
Moles of reactant on landing area of type:		
X_1	2.9 (17)	0.95 (19)
X_2	1.8 (10)	1.9 (11)
Y_1	2.9 (17)	0.8 (26)
Y_2	1.3 (8)	1.4 (13)
Z	8.3 (48)	2.2 (31)

The landing area distributions can now be compared at the two temperature levels. The X_1 and X_2 landing areas are about as abundant at the higher temperature as they are at the lower one. There is a significant drop in the percentage of landing areas that are of the Y_1 and Y_2 type at the higher temperature, and a corresponding increase in the contribution of Z-type landing areas. Recall that we had earlier semi-quantitatively assigned the number of sites for the different landing areas in the order Y < X < Z. Since the number of moles of reactant on Y landing areas decreases drastically, while that on X landing areas decreases slightly, and that on Z landing areas increases, it appears that the higher temperature favors landing areas and adsorbed forms corresponding to the larger number of sites.

In an earlier work (ref. 4), we have shown that this need not be true in general. In fact an (i+1)-site landing area will be preferred over an i-site landing area if $(Q_{i+1}/i+1)$ is less than (Q_i/i) where Q_j is the heat of adsorption for a j-site landing area. Hence larger site landing areas will always be preferred at higher temperatures if Q_{i+1} is less than Q_i. However the preference may be in the same direction even if Q_{i+1} is greater than Q_i, depending upon the value of i and the relative values of Q_{i+1} and Q_i.

4. A Simplified Landing Area Model for Kinetics of Metal-Catalyzed Insomerization and Hydrogenolysis Reactions: The Role of Pressure

The essential features of this reaction set, in particular the reaction order with respect to hydrogen, can be obtained from a simpler model than the full scale one outlined in Section 2. The reactants are represented as R and H_2. The H_2 molecule is dissociatively adsorbed on two adjacent vacant sites. An R molecule can adsorb on one of three landing areas, comprising 2, 3, or 5 sites. Adsorbed species on these areas form, respectively, hydrogenolysis products, collectively termed P_h, isomerization products, P_i, and scrambling

TABLE IV

Reactions of the model system

H_2 + 2S	$\rightleftharpoons$	2[HS]
R + 4S	$\rightleftharpoons$	$[R - S_2]$ + 2[H - S]
R + 5S	$\rightleftharpoons$	$[R - S_3]$ + 2[H - S]
R + 6S	$\rightleftharpoons$	$[R - S_5]$ + [H - S]
$[R - S_2]$ + 4[H - S]	$\longrightarrow$	P_h + 6S
$[R - S_3]$ + 2[H - S]	$\longrightarrow$	P_i + 5S
$[R - S_5]$ + [H - S]	$\longrightarrow$	P_s + 6S

products, P_s. These reactions are collected in Table IV and are analogous to the example reactions of equations (1) through (4). Equilibrium relations and rate expressions analogous to equations (5) through (8) are shown in Table V. A site balance is also included.

TABLE V

Equilibrium relations for the model system:

$$K_5 C_R \theta_S^6 = \theta_5 \theta_H$$
$$K_3 C_R \theta_S^5 = \theta_3 \theta_H^2$$
$$K_2 C_R \theta_S^4 = \theta_2 \theta_H^2$$
$$K_H C_{H_2} \theta_S^2 = \theta_H^2$$

Site balance:

$$\theta_H + \theta_2 + \theta_3 + \theta_5 + \theta_S = 1$$

Rate expressions:

$$r_h = k_h \theta_2 \theta_H^4$$
$$r_i = k_i \theta_3 \theta_H^4$$
$$r_s = k_s \theta_5 \theta_H$$

Solutions to the equations of Table V are illustrated in Figures 2 through 4. In Figure 2 the fractions of the surface occupied by the three landing area conformations of R are shown as functions of the concentration of R. Note that for all values of C_R here, we have $\theta_2 > \theta_3 > \theta_5$. This relative order is not significant, however, and could be easily changed by using different values of the equilibrium constants K_2, K_3 and K_5. What is significant is the change in the fraction occupied by each conformation when the concentration of R changes. The conformation requiring the smallest number of sites increases monotonically with increasing C_R. The conformation requiring the largest number of sites decreases with increasing C_R. The intermediate conformation initially increases with C_R, reaches a maximum value, and then decreases. As the partial pressure of the species is increased, consequently, the smaller site conformations ($[R-S_2]$ and, initially, $[R-S_3]$) increase at the expense of the larger site conformations $[R-S_5]$ and, later, $[R-S_3]$). This

442

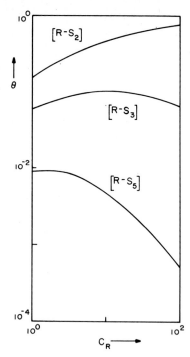

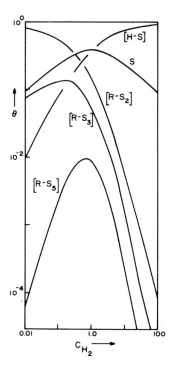

Figure 2. Variation of surface coverage with concentration of R. The model of Tables IV and V is used with $C_H =1$, $K_H= K_2=K_3=K_5=1$, all in arbitrary units.

Figure 3. Variation of surface coverage with concentration of H_2. Here $C_R=1$ and all the K values are the same as in Figure 2.

is consistent with our demonstration elsewhere (ref. 4) that in general higher pressures favor landing areas of smaller size.

Similar observations may be made from Figure 3, where the concentration of R is kept constant while that of H_2 is varied. Increasing the H_2 partial pressure decreases the relative amount of R in the gas phase. Hence [R-S_2] decreases, while [R-S_3] first increases and then decreases. [R-S_5] does not increase monotonically with increasing H_2, but instead passes through a maximum value. This is because most of the surface sites are occupied by [H-S] at the larger concentrations of H_2.

The rates of formation of products P_h, P_i, and P_s are plotted in Figure 4 as functions of H_2

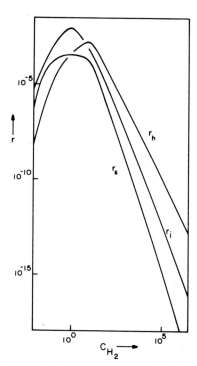

Figure 4. Reaction rates of Tables IV and V as a function of H_2 concentration. Parameter values of Figure 2 are used, with $k_h=k_i=k_s=1$ all in arbitrary units.

concentration. The slopes of these curves, drawn in logarithmic coordinates, represent reaction orders with respect to hydrogen. In all three cases, the slopes are positive at low H_2 concentrations, pass through zero, and then tend to an apparently asymptotic value which is negative. This trend can be compared with experimental reaction orders for hydrogenolysis, isomerization and scrambling products, obtained by Garin and Gault (ref. 3). The experimental orders are invariably negative and are constant. However the model is not inconsistent with the measured values, since the experiments were performed at values of hydrogen in large excess. Under these conditions the model yields only negative values for the slopes of the log-log curves. Further note that the experimental range of hydrogen pressures is approximately half an order of magnitude. In this relatively narrow range (cf eight orders of magnitude in Figure 4) straight lines can always be drawn, leading to pseudo-constant values of the slope.

The experimental reaction orders obtained by Garin and Gault (ref. 3) are compared with asymptotic values of the slopes of Figure 4 in Table VI. Note first that for almost all the products, the observed reaction orders are smaller in absolute magnitude than the asymptotic slopes of the model calculations. This implies that the partial pressure of hydrogen used in the experiments, while large enough to yield a negative slope, is not sufficiently large to enable the asymptotic portion to be valid.

TABLE VI

Hydrogen reaction order from the experiments of Garin and Gault (ref. 3) compared with the asymptotic slopes of Figure 4.

Reaction	(-b) obsd	(-b) calcd	Model product
$\wedge\wedge\wedge \rightarrow \wedge\wedge\wedge$	3.4 ± 0.1	3	P_s
$\wedge\wedge\wedge \rightarrow \wedge\!\!\!\vee$	1.8 ± 0.1	2.5	P_i
$\wedge\wedge\wedge \rightarrow C_3H_8 + C_2H_6$	1.3 ± 0.2	2.0	P_h
$\wedge\wedge\wedge \rightarrow C_4H_{10} + CH_4$	0.6 ± 0.2	2.0	P_h
$\wedge\!\!\!\vee \rightarrow \wedge\wedge\wedge$	2.3 ± 0.15	2.5	P_i
$\wedge\!\!\!\vee \rightarrow \wedge\!\!\!\vee$	1.9 ± 0.2	3.0	P_s
$\wedge\!\!\!\vee \rightarrow X$	1.65 ± 0.15	2.5	P_i
$\wedge\!\!\!\vee \rightarrow C_3H_8 + C_2H_6$	1.65 ± 0.2	2.0	P_h
$\wedge\!\!\!\vee \rightarrow C_4H_{10} + CH_4$	0.7 ± 0.1	2.0	P_h

Furthermore different products of the same type of reaction with the same reactant correspond to different reaction orders, all smaller in absolute magnitude than the limit of the asymptotic slope for that type of reaction. See for example the two sets of hydrogenolysis products, $C_2 + C_3$ and $C_1 + C_4$, in Table VI. The simplified model does not account for more than one set of product per reaction type, of course. However we have shown elsewhere (ref. 4) that variations in the thermodynamic equilibrium constants can lead to changes in the (nonasymptotic) values of the slopes at constant values of the reactant concentration. In particular, values of the slope increase with an increase in K_2 or K_3, and decrease with an increase in K_H and K_5. Then if we assume that K_2 has a larger value for the Y_2 landing area configuration (yielding $C_1 + C_4$) than for that on a Y_1 landing area (yielding $C_2 + C_3$), the smaller slope (in an algebraic sense) for the latter products can be satisfactorily explained. Similarly the different reaction orders with respect to hydrogen for isomerization products neo-pentane and normal-pentane formed from iso-pentane can be accounted for by using different values of K_3 for the two corresponding landing areas.

From Table VI the values of b are also altered when different reactants are used. For both sets of hydrogenolysis products, reactions with $i-C_5$ give rise to measured values of b that are smaller, algebraically, than those using $n-C_5$. Consequently K_2 with $i-C_5$ as the reactant must have a smaller value than that with $n-C_5$ as the reactant. Similarly K_5 with $i-C_5$ as reactant must be smaller than when the reactant is $n-C_5$, to account for the smaller algebraic value of the scrambling reaction order in the former case.

5. The Selectivity Effectiveness Factor - Role of the Heterogenous Catalytic Surface

In the previous sections we have assumed that all sites are equivalent, i.e., that subject to the availability of appropriate surrounding vacant sites, a particular site would as likely be a part of one type of landing area as another type. This is not strictly true in general (although it is worth noting that under certain conditions the assumption does not affect the results of the analysis). For clusters of supported metals, the active surface can be heterogenous because of the shape of the clusters and of the corners and edges they present. In the landing area framework, a surface is heterogenous when a fraction ψ is incapable of accomodating a particular landing area. The fraction is termed the un-availability factor for this landing area. Hence the heterogenity of the surface, through the factors ψ, plays a role in the distribution of the spectrum of landing areas and consequently affects the selectivity of the process. This is analogous to the roles of pressure and temperature described above. (Note that a heterogenous surface where the values of ψ are the same for all possible landing areas may be considered equivalent to a homogenous surface.)

The unavailability factor is dependent upon the size and shape of the landing area and upon the size and shape of the clusters. The size of the clusters is often quantified by the dispersion parameter d, the fraction of metal on the surface. It is possible that one or more (or none) of the landing area availability factors change with the dispersion d. Then the activity and/or the selectivity of the process could vary with the dispersion (i.e., particle size) or could be independent of it. Using the terminology of Boudart (ref. 5) and of Chambellan et al (ref. 6), the reaction would be demanding (structure-sensitive) or facile (structure-insensitive) in activity and/or selectivity. See ref (4) for more details of this analysis.

The dispersion and the unavailability factor can be combined to form the parameter $\eta_s \equiv d(1-\psi)$. This quantity defines the fraction of the metal catalyst that is "seen" by the particular landing area corresponding to ψ. Noting the similarity between this and the conventional effectiveness factor for activity, we term it the selectivity effectiveness factor. It can be related to the shape and size of the corresponding landing area and of the metal clusters present.

We can now relate the selectivity of a particular product to the changes in the selectivity effectiveness factor. We consider as before the reaction set described in Table IV.

As mentioned earlier, changing the factor d in the values of η_s without changing the values of ψ, or changing the values of ψ for landing areas equivalently, results in no effective change in the selectivity. It is of greater interest to alter the value of ψ for one landing area alone, and to note its influence on the selectivity of the corresponding product. Consequently, Table IV is modified in that only a certain fraction of the surface of the catalyst is available for the landing area corresponding to the intermediate [R-S$_5$]. Of course this fraction, and in fact the entire surface, is available for intermediates [H-S], [R-S$_2$], and R-S$_3$]. The new set of equations is given in Table VII.

TABLE VII
Relations for the reaction model incorporating an unavailability factor ψ_5 for [R-S$_5$]. Here θ_{ai} denotes the number of sites occupied by i in the portion of the surface available to [R-S$_5$], expressed as a fraction of the total number of sites

Equilibrium relations:

$$K_5 C_R \theta_{as}^5 \theta_s = \theta_{a5} \theta_H$$
$$K_3 C_R \theta_s^5 = \theta_3 \theta_H^2$$
$$K_2 C_R \theta_s^4 = \theta_2 \theta_H^2$$
$$K_H C_{H_2} \theta_s^2 = \theta_H^2$$

Site balances:

$$\theta_H + \theta_2 + \theta_3 + \theta_{a5} + \theta_s = 1$$
$$\theta_{aH} + \theta_{a2} + \theta_{a5} + \theta_{as} = 1 - \psi_5$$

Distribution of sites:

$$\frac{\theta_{aH}}{\theta_H - \theta_{aH}} = \frac{1 - \psi_5 - \theta_{a5}}{\psi_5} = \frac{\theta_{a2}}{\theta_2 - \theta_{a2}} = \frac{\theta_{a3}}{\theta_3 - \theta_{a3}}$$

Rate expressions:

$$r_h = k_h \theta_2 \theta_H^4$$
$$r_i = k_i \theta_3 \theta_H^2$$
$$r_s = k_s \theta_{a5} \theta_H$$

Figures 5 and 6 illustrate the results of these equations as functions of the H$_2$ partial pressure when values of the unavailability factor ψ_5 for [R-S$_5$] range from 0 to 0.9. The rate of formation of P$_s$ is shown in Figure 5. The other rates of this model, r_i and r_h, are independent of ψ_5, as might be expected, and are as shown in Figure 4. The curve of r_s for ψ_5=0 shown in Figure 5 is that when the entire surface is available to [R-S$_5$], and is identical to the corresponding curve in Figure 4.

For increasing values of ψ_5, first note that the slopes of the curves in Figure 5 are not appreciably changed. In other words, the reaction order (b in the previous section) is virtually independent of the unavailability factor.

However, the actual rates r_s decrease considerably, at the same H$_2$ concentration, when

446

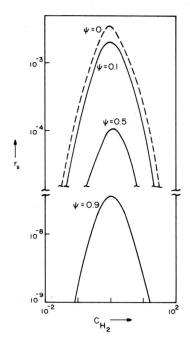

Figure 5. Variation of r_s with H_2 concentration at different values of ψ, the unavailability factor for [R-S$_5$]. Other landing areas have constant values of $\psi(=0)$. Values of parameters used are those of Figure 4.

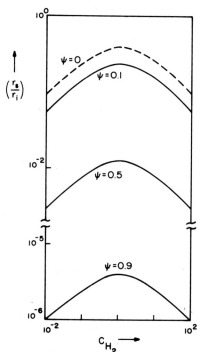

Figure 6. The selectivity of P_s with respect to P_i at different values of the unavailability factor ψ for [R-S$_5$]. Other parameters are as in Figure 5.

ψ_5 is increased. When 10 percent of the surface is unavailable for [R-S$_5$], the rate of formation of P_s drops by almost 50 percent at its maximum point. This maximum rate drops by five orders of magnitude when 90 percent of the surface is unavailable. Apparently the other intermediates with smaller landing areas compete effectively with [R-S$_5$] even in the relatively small fraction of the surface available to this landing area.

In order to make some comments concerning facile or demanding activity, note that r_i and r_h are much greater than r_s, even for $\psi_5=0$. Consequently the specific rate of disappearance of R, the sum of r_i, r_h, and r_s, will be negligibly changed when ψ_5 is changed. If the decrease in ψ_5 is due to a change in particle size, which also changes d, the specific rate of disappearance of R will be more or less constant while d changes. In other words the reaction is facile in activity.

However the relative importance of the rates could be changed if different values were used for k_i, k_h, and k_s. If the new values of the rate constants were such that r_s was greater than $r_i + r_h$, the specific activity of R would in fact change with d. Hence the reaction would be demanding in activity.

Figure 6 shows the variation in selectivity when ψ_5 is changed. The selectivity is drastically reduced when ψ_5 is increased. Again if the increase in ψ_5 is accompanied by a change in d, then the selectivity changes with the dispersion of the metal clusters. The reaction therefore is demanding in selectivity.

It may be of interest to comment on some experimental data on selectivity using the landing area framework. In this regard consider the work of Dartigues et al (ref. 7) on the isomerization of C_6 compounds. It should be noted that such reaction sets contain features not included in the present model, based upon Figure 1 for C_5 compounds. In particular the five-membered ring adsorbate formed from a C_6

compound could form methylcyclopentane, or the straight chain hexane, or substituted pen-
tanes. In other words, the corresponding landing area could give rise to cyclization, or
scrambling, or isomerization products. In contrast, the Z-type landing area of Figure 1
can only give rise to cyclization and scrambling products. Further, although the C_6
reaction set could be characterized by X, Y, and Z types of landing areas, the relative
demand of these areas for sites need not be in the same direction as for the C_5 reaction
set, viz Y < X < Z. Umbra sites for a particular landing area may be equivalent in both
reaction sets. However the different mobilities and chain lengths of the adsorbates for
the different reaction sets could give rise to different penumbra requirements of the
same type of landing area.

The results of Dartigues et al (ref. 7) reproduced in Table VIII, are presented as the
ratio of the cyclic contribution for the formation of the isomerization product 3-methylpen-
tane (3MP) to the bond shift contribution for the same reaction. Different dispersions of
the Pt/Al_2O_3 catalyst are used, and the experiment is performed using 2-methylpentane (2MP)
and n-hexane (nH) separately as reactants. In general Table VIII shows an increasing contribution of the cyclic mechanism at increasing dispersions (decreasing particle sizes).
Further for all dispersions when nH is the reactant, the cyclic contribution is greater
than when the reactant is 2MP.

TABLE VIII
Selectivity results of Dartigues et al (ref. 7) expressed as the relative contribution
of the cyclic and bond shift mechanisms to the formation of 3-methylpentane as a function
of catalyst dispersion. Catalysts A and B contain different Al_2O_3 supports for Pt metal.
2-methylpentane and n-hexane are separately used as reactants

Dispersion	Cyclic/bond shift for			
d	2MP $\longrightarrow$ 3MP		nH $\longrightarrow$ 3MP	
	Catalyst A	Catalyst B	Catalyst A	Catalyst B
0.05	0.33		0.92	
0.07	0.19		1.2	
0.12		0.25		
0.35		0.19		2.0
0.55		0.43		
0.70		1.6		4.9
1.0		5.3		>200

Increasing the dispersion probably results in decreasing the unavailability factor for
the different areas, perhaps to different extents. In an approximate way, the ratio of
Table VIII can be compared to the selectivity ratio r_s/r_i of Figure 6, or to the ratio of
Z-type landing areas to X-type landing areas. The X-type intermediate required to form
3MP from 2MP is $\bigwedge$, while the appropriate intermediate from nH is $\bigvee$. Of the two
X-type intermediates, the former probably requires the smaller landing area. Consequently
its unavailability factor may be less than that of $\bigvee$ for the same dispersion. The cyclic
intermediate (corresponding to the Z-type landing area) is the same for both reactants.
Consequently it is to be expected that the bond shift mechanism plays a lesser role in the
formation of 3MP from nH, compared to 2MP as the reactant. Further it may be reasonable
to assume for the C_6 reaction set that the Z-type landing area corresponding to the cyclic

448

intermediate ties up fewer sites than the X-type landing areas. This is perhaps related
to the larger numbers of penumbra sites required by the latter landing area for the more
mobile C_6 chains. Then an increase in the dispersion will increase the unavailability
factor for the Z-type landing area less than that for the X-type landing areas. This may
account for the increasing contribution of the cyclic process compared to the bond shift
process when the dispersion is increased.

6. Conclusions

A molecule adsorbing on the surface of a metal cluster can land in a variety of ways.
The arrangement of sites for each adsorbed form is termed the corresponding landing area.
A landing area comprises two types of sites. Umbra sites are those which are directly
bound to the adsorbed form, while penumbra sites are relatively loosely bound. An adsorbed
form is associated with one or more products (after desorption from the surface). Hence
the distribution of landing areas on the surface of a supported metal catalyst plays a key
role in questions concerning the selectivity of the process.

In general a particular surface site is not associated uniquely with one and only one
type of landing area. Successive gas phase molecules may adsorb on this site (amongst
others) in different forms/landing areas. Alternatively a molecule in one configuration
can change to another by altering its landing area. The equilibrium distribution of
landing area sites over an entire surface is, however, fixed. It will depend upon the
temperature, pressure, and the dispersion of the metal clusters. In general an increasing
partial pressure of the molecule in the gas phase increases the number of smaller landing
areas at the expense of the larger ones. The reverse process occurs after an increase in
the temperature. In general smaller clusters (i.e. larger dispersions) favor the smaller
landing areas. However the dependence on the dispersion, more than on any other process
parameter, is influenced by the shape of the landing area (and the shape of the metal
clusters) as well as by the size. The unavailability factor and the selectivity effectiveness factor are introduced in order to quantify these qualitative arguments.

A simple model in the landing area framework is introduced for the isomerization and
hydrogenolysis reactions of hydrocarbons in hydrogen catalyzed by the metal component of a
supported metal catalyst. The model predicts the reaction order with respect to hydrogen,
and can be used to explain the effects of temperature and dispersion on the selectivity of
the process.

References

1. J.M. Thomas and W.J. Thomas, Introduction to the Principles of Heterogenous Catalysis,
   Academic, New York, 1967, p. 14.
2. B.C. Gates, J.R. Katzer and G.C.A. Schmit, Chemistry of Catalytic Processes, McGraw
   Hill, New York, 1979, p. 260.
3. F. Garin and F.G. Gault, J. Am. Chem. Soc. 97 (1975) 4466-4476.
4. E. Ruckenstein and D. B. Dadyburjor, submitted for publication.
5. M. Boudart, Adv. Catal. 20 (1969) 153.
6. A. Chambellan, J.M. Dartigues, C. Corolleur and F.G. Gault, Nouv. J. Chim 1 (1977)
   41-48.
7. J.M. Dartigues, A. Chambellan and F.G. Gault, J. Am. Chem. Soc. 98 (1976) 856-857.

DISCUSSION

E. RUCKENSTEIN, D.B. DADYBURJOR

Dalmon - 1°/ Do you think that all the atoms of a given landing area are bonded to the adsorbed molecule corresponding to this area ?

2°/ When the particle size decreases you said that some important landing areas are no more available. Have you any idea on the critical diameter corresponding to this inhibition ?

Dadyburjor - In the written paper we have postulated two types of bonding : a relatively strong bonding corresponding to the "umbra" and a weaker type of bonding, the "penumbra". Bonds of the latter type may be broken and reformed without any change in "umbra" sites.

A critical size effect was observed experimentally by Gaûlt's group. We have not attempted to correlate this with our model as yet.

Crucq - The model proposed by the authors seems very similar to the one proposed by Frennel and al. (J. Catalysis 1977) and leads to very similar conclusions concerning the dependence upon H_2 and hydro carbon partial pressure. I have two questions :

1°/ What are the main differences between your model and the one of our Laboratory ?

2°/ We have measured the area of the landing site for CH_4 (around 7 surface metal atoms) and C_2H_6 (around 9 surface metal atoms). Your values for pentane seem much lower (4.5 or 6) for a larger molecule. How do you define a single site ?

Dadyburjor - 1°/ I am familiar with the elegant development of the model of your group. The major difference with this work is qualitative as well as quantitative. We postulate that a large number of different landing areas are simultaneously possible. Each type of landing area can tie up one or more surface sites uniquely. You have fitted the experimental data to obtain one value for the number of sites tied up by the adsorbing species. Further, the shape of the landing areas used in the present work are not necessarily spherically symmetric.
Finally, you have considered the surface sites to be energetically and geometrically homogeneous. When several landing areas are possible, as in the present case, it is possible that a certain fraction of the surface cannot accomodate one or more of these (via the unavailability factor). This allows consideration of selectivity structure sensitivity in a natural fashion.

2°/ We have implicitly defined a single site to be a single atom of surface metal.

J. BOURDON (Editor)
Growth and Properties of Metal Clusters, pp. 451—466
© 1980 Elsevier Scientific Publishing Company — Printed in The Netherlands

SKELETAL REARRANGEMENTS OF HYDROCARBONS ON METALS WITH VARIOUS PARTICLES SIZES [*]

F.G. GAULT, F. GARIN, G. MAIRE
Université L. Pasteur, Laboratoire de Catalyse 4, rue Blaise Pascal 67000 STRASBOURG

This paper was partially written by F.G. GAULT before his sudden death 4.8.1979

SUMMARY

    The relative contributions of the various reaction mechanisms may be drastically
changed by modifying the size of the metal particles. In the case of platinum catalysts for
instance, two minimal particle sizes may be defined for the occurrence of selective cyclic
and bond shift mechanisms respectively. The peculiar properties of the highly dispersed
platinum catalysts with metal particles smaller than 10 Å may be explained either by the
presence of pseudo-crystals with uncommon symmetry or, better, by electronic properties for
the very small clusters that differ from the ones in the infinite crystal.

I. INTRODUCTION

    A major problem in heterogeneous catalysis is the characterization of the active sites.
A possible solution, especially for metals, is to find a correlation between particle size
and some catalytic property.

    Although the first investigation of particle size effect was devoted to a change in
selectivity with metal dispersion (1, 2) (hydrogenolysis of the five cyclic bonds in methylcyclopentane), most of the work was focussed on determination of specific rates, defined as
the number of converted molecules per superficial metal atom and per time unit (3,4,5).

    For most reactions investigated, specific rates remained remarkably constant even when
the metal accessibility (the ratio between superficial and total metal atoms) varied by
several orders of magnitude.

    Specific rates greatly depended on the size of the metal particles for only a few
reactions : hydrogenolysis and isomerization of neopentane on platinum (3a) exchange of
benzene (6) and dehydrocyclisation of n-heptane (7).

    Recently, a revival of the selectivity approach to the study of particle size effects
resulted in a systematic study of the isomerization of hexanes on metal films and supported
catalysts (8,9). Skeletal isomerization of hexanes has three major advantages over other

[*] Part of this paper comes out from "Isomerization on metals. Correlation between metal
particle size and reaction mechanisms " by J.M. DARTIGUES, A.CHAMBELLAN, S. COROLLEUR,
F.G. GAULT, Laboratoire de Catalyse, Université Louis Pasteur, 67000 STRASBOURG
and A. RENOUPREZ, B. MORAWECK, P. BOSCH-GIRAL, G. DALMAI, Institut de Recherche pour la
catalyse - CNRS, Bld du 11 Novembre 1918 - 69626 VILLEURBANNE (N.J. Chimie in press).

reactions :

1) It only occurs according to two well characterized mechanisms, the bond shift mechanisms corresponding to a simple carbon-carbon bond displacement (10) and the cyclic mechanism involving a cyclopentane intermediate (8a).

2) The use of ^{13}C-labeled molecules allows a distinction between these two mechanisms and, consequently, evaluation of their relative contributions.

3) Isomerization of hexanes is highly sensitive to metal-particle size : while the cyclic mechanism predominates on highly dispersed catalysts (11a) bond shift is favoured on large platinum crystallites (11b).

At the same time, improvements of crystallographic techniques, especially electron microscopy and small-angle X-ray scattering make possible now the study of small metal aggregates ; they allow for example, the determination of particle size distributions in supported metal catalysts (12,13), or the structural characterization of small metal aggregates epitaxially deposited on well oriented substrates (14-17).

From both experimental and theoretical data, however, several alternative models emerge, providing reasonable explanations for particle-size effects in metal catalysis :
- According to the first and most simple model, different reactivities are associated with surface atoms of different coordination number. According to the "mitohedrical" theory developped by Poltorak (4), face atoms ("hedron") and edge atoms ("mitôs") in metal crystallites may act as specific active centers.
- According to a second model, groups or "ensembles" of atoms with a specific geometrical arrangement are required for some catalytic reactions. Examples of such ensembles are the B_5 sites used by VAN MONTFOORT, VAN HARDEVELD and HARTOG (18) to explain the adsorption of nitrogen and carbon monoxide.
- A third possible explanation of particle-size effects, proposed recently by BURTON (19) relates the occurrence of some catalytic properties to the existence of non-lattice symmetries (D_{5h} or icosahedral) observed in the case of very small metal aggregates (14-17).
- Lastly, on going further down in the range of particle size, the most stable clusters with less than 60 atoms are, according to some computations by HOARE and PAL (20-21), polytetrahedral aggregates rather than normal or distorted micro-crystalline fcc type clusters.

In order to chose between the possible above interpretations of the particle size effect, the hydrogenolysis of methylcyclopentane and the isomerization of ^{13}C-labeled hexanes were studied, using a series of platinum-alumina catalysts with a metal dispersion extending from 4 to 100 %. Four test reactions were used :

1) <u>Hydrogenolysis of methylcyclopentane</u> which may occur according to a selective or a non-selective mechanism (2)

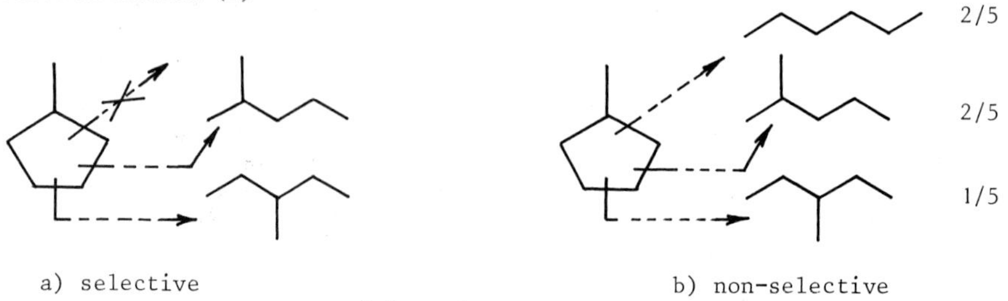

a) selective

b) non-selective

Scheme 1

And three isomerization reactions, for which three labeled hexanes allow to distinguish
between cyclic and bond-shift mechanisms. These reactions are :

2) <u>methyl migration</u> : (2MP → 3MP)

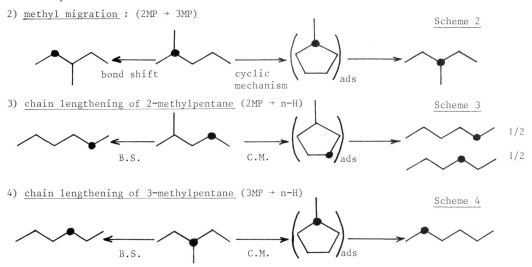

Scheme 2

3) <u>chain lengthening of 2-methylpentane</u> (2MP → n-H)   Scheme 3

4) <u>chain lengthening of 3-methylpentane</u> (3MP → n-H)   Scheme 4

Lastly, the isomerization of 2-methylpentane-2-^{13}C to n-hexane, allows an estimation of the
selective contributions of the two bond-shift mechanisms (A) and (B) involving terminal and
internal C-C bond respectively.

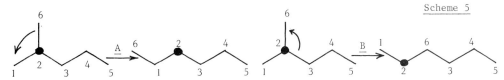

Scheme 5

II. CATALYSTS PREPARATION

Instead of using a series of catalysts progressively sintered (7,22) or changing the
nature of the carrier or the mode of preparation, a series of eleven Pt-Al$_2$O$_3$ catalysts
were prepared by impregnating an inert alumina obtained from WOELM with a chloroplatinic
solution. In all cases reduction was performed at 100°C with a hydrogen flow rate of
10 ml/min, and completed at 200°C for 48 hr. Although the physico-chemical properties of
the carrier were the same, two samples of alumina were distinguished, A and A', differing
in the number of their hydroxyl groups exchangeable with deuterium. The difference in size
of the metal particles between the 8 % platinum catalysts prepared with alumina A and A'
induced us to further dehydroxylate (or dehydrate) alumina A'. A series of alumina,
referred to as B'$_{nH}$, were then prepared by calcining A' at 600°C for n hr.

The dispersion of the metal phase for a series of 8% Pt-Al$_2$O$_3$ catalysts, characterized
by the ratio a = H/Pt between the number of chemisorbed hydrogen atoms and the number of
metal atoms, increased from 0.05 to 0.35 with increasing calcination time, as shown in
table 1.

In order to obtain "atomically" dispersed catalysts (a=1), decreasing amounts of
platinum down to 0.2% were deposited on alumina B' or A'. A complete set of catalysts with
a dispersion ranging from 0.04 to 1 was thus prepared (we verified that both non-calcined

Pt %	10	2.25	8.5	8.0	8.4	7.5	7.1	4.1	2.5	0.3	0.2
On Al_2O_3	A	A	A'	B'	B'	B'	B'	B'	B'	B'	A'
calcined during (hours)	0	0	0	2	10	24	210	210	210	210	0
a = H/Pt (d̄ X) Å	0.04 (200)	0.05 (120)	0.05 (90)	0.07	0.12	0.23	0.35	0.55	0.70	1.0	1.0
r = 3MP/n-H	4.6	3.2	2.4	2.0	1.3	0.9	0.7	0.4	0.4	0.4	0.4
N.S.H. %	11	15	20	24	36	50	63	100	100	100₁	100
Cl %	-	0.52	0.88	-	0.6	-	0.76	0.6	0.6	0.22	0.18

N.S.H. : non selective hydrogenolysis   d̄X : particle size determined by X-ray diffraction

Table 1 : Correlation between metal dispersion and selectivity in the hydrogenolysis of methylcyclopentane at 220°C

and calcined alumina were catalytically inactive for the skeletal isomerization of
2-methylpentenes at 300°C).

Besides this series of home-made catalysts, an industrial 5% Pt-Al$_2$O$_3$ catalyst, interesting
for its narrow particle-size distribution (around 30 Å) was purchased from Matheson-Coleman.

III. CATALYSTS CHARACTERIZATION

      Besides chemisorption, oxygen-hydrogen titration (23) and X-ray line broadening, which
give an estimate of the <u>mean</u> diameter of the metal clusters, particle-size distributions
were obtained by electron microscopy, small-angle X-ray scattering, and analysis of the
X-ray diffraction line profile.

The agreement between these three techniques is emphasized in Figure 1, which shows the
particle-size distributions for the 7.1% Pt-Al$_2$O$_3$ B'$_{210H}$ catalyst .

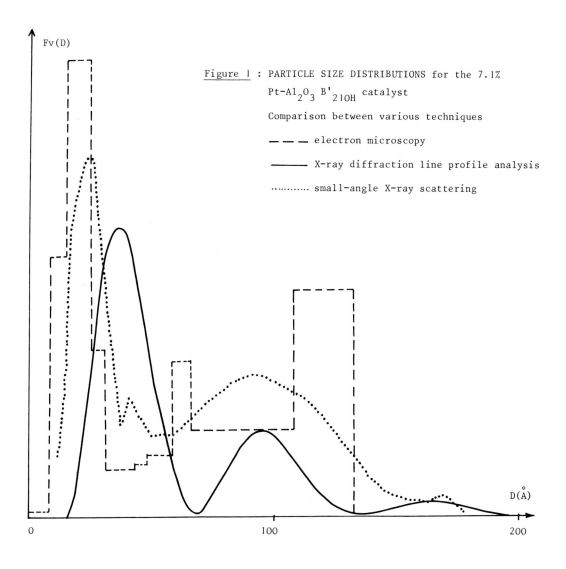

Fv(D)

Figure 1 : PARTICLE SIZE DISTRIBUTIONS for the 7.1%

          Pt-Al$_2$O$_3$ B'$_{210H}$ catalyst

          Comparison between various techniques

                – – – electron microscopy

                ――― X-ray diffraction line profile analysis

                ·········· small-angle X-ray scattering

D(Å)

0   100   200

IV. CATALYTIC EXPERIMENTS

The isomerization of labeled hexanes has been studied at 254°C under 1 atm of hydrogen on the series of prepared Pt-Al$_2$O$_3$ catalysts and the Matheson Coleman catalyst.

A) In the isomerization of 2-methylpentane to 3-methylpentane (table 2) the percentage of cyclic mechanism remained practically constant and equal to 18 ± 2 for a very wide range of metal dispersion (0 < a < 0.5). It increased sharply for highly dispersed catalysts but did not reach the maximum value of 100 even for the "atomically" dispersed catalysts. On the industrial catalyst, the cyclic mechanism was a minor process (7%).

catal. % Pt	a = H/Pt			cyclic mech. %
2,25 A	0.05	25	75	25
8.5 A'	0.05	16	84	16
8.4 B'$_{1OH}$	0.12	20	80	20
7.1 B'$_{21OH}$	0.35	16	84	16
4.1 B'$_{21OH}$	0.55	30	70	30
2.5 B'$_{21OH}$	0.70	62	38	62
0.2 A'	1.0	83	17	83
0.3 B'$_{21OH}$	1.0	84	16	84
5 M.C.	0.20	7	93	7

Table 2 : Isomerization of

B) In the isomerization of 2-methylpentane to n-hexane, the percentages of cyclic mechanism increased steadily from 70 % to 100 % (table 3) with increasing metal dispersion.

On the Matheson Coleman catalyst it was again much lower than on the series of prepared catalysts.

catal. % Pt	a = H/Pt			cyclic mech. %
2.25 A	0.05	65	35	70
8.5 A'	0.05	64	36	72
8.4 B'$_{1OH}$	0.12	58	42	84
7.1 B'$_{21OH}$	0.35	55	45	90
4.1 B'$_{21OH}$	0.55	57	43	86
2.5 B'$_{21OH}$	0.70	51.5	48.5	97
0.2 A'	1.0	50	50	100
0.3 B'$_{21OH}$	1.0	51	49	98
5 M.C.	0.20	74	26	52

Table 3 : Isomerization of

C) The percentage of bond shift A in chain lengthening (isomerization of 2-methylpentane to n-hexane) decreased with metal dispersion (table 4).

457

Catal. % Pt	a = H/Pt	![molecule]	![molecule]	Bond shift A(%)
2.25 A	0.05	90	10	10
8.5 A'	0.05	94	6	6
8.4 B'$_{1OH}$	0.12	94	6	6
7.1 B'$_{21OH}$	0.35	94	6	6
4.1 B'$_{21OH}$	0.55	99	1	1
2.5 B'$_{21OH}$	0.70	100	0	0
0.2 A'	1.0	100	0	0
0.3 B'$_{21OH}$	1.0	100	0	0
5 M.C.	0.20	90	10	10

Table 4 : Isomerization of

D) In hydrogenolysis of methylcyclopentane

The ratio r = 3MP/n-H (Table 1) decreased regularly from a very high value to a limit of 0.4 reached for an accessibility "a" of roughly 0.50.
If one assumes for methylcyclopentane hydrogenolysis (2b) the existence of two mechanisms, one completely selective (r_b equals infinity), and one non-selective (r_a = 0.4), one can estimate from the observed ratio r the contribution in percent of the non-selective mechanism. (Table 1, line 6). The absence of any chlorine effect in selectivity change, already demonstrated by comparing Pt-Al$_2$O$_3$ catalysts of various dispersion prepared from chloroplatinic acid and platinum tetrammine hydroxide (24), is obvious since the chlorine content remained practically constant throughout the series of catalysts from a = 0.05 to a = 0.70.

Since cyclic isomerization involves dehydrocyclisation and the reverse step, ring opening, one should distinguish between a selective and a non-selective cyclic isomerization mechanism according to whether hydrogenolysis of the methylcyclopentane intermediate is selective or not.

V. PARTICLE SIZE DISTRIBUTION (figure 2)

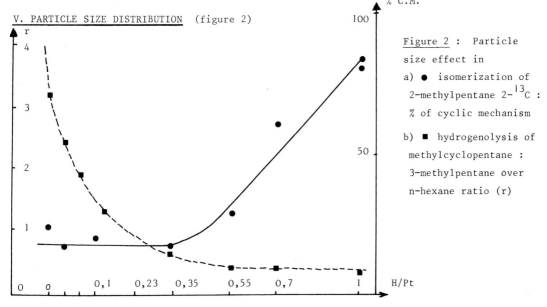

Figure 2 : Particle size effect in
a) ● isomerization of 2-methylpentane 2-^{13}C : % of cyclic mechanism
b) ■ hydrogenolysis of methylcyclopentane : 3-methylpentane over n-hexane ratio (r)

The most striking result obtained was the sharp increases of the percentage of cyclic mechanism in the isomerization of 2-methylpentane to 3-methylpentane for a dispersion "a" larger than about 0.4. Noticeable also was the break at the same dispersion in the curve representing the selectivity factor $r = \frac{3M.P}{n-H}$ in methylcyclopentane hydrogenolysis.

A comparison of the particle size distributions in the 7.1% $Pt-Al_2O_3$ B' (just before the break) and in the 4.1 and 2.5% $Pt-Al_2O_3$ B' (after the break) seems desirable.

Histograms representing the surface frequency law (f_s) for these three catalysts and also for the industrial catalyst are given in the figure 3.

We can see that very small particles, less than 10 Å, were present in the two highly dispersed catalysts (4.1 and 2.5% $Pt-Al_2O_3$). They did not exist in the industrial catalyst, and were present in negligible amounts in the 7.1% $Pt-Al_2O_3$ catalyst.

On the other hand, there were virtually no particles larger than 20 Å in the highly dispersed catalysts (4.1% B' and 2.5% B') where methylcyclopentane hydrogenolysis was purely non-selective, while they were in increasing amounts in the catalysts of lower dispersion.

Figure 3 : Particle size distribution of platinum particles : F(S) vs d (Å)

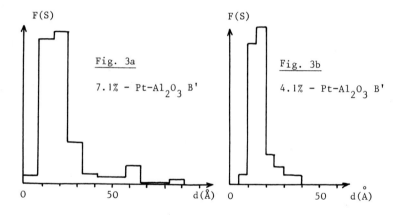

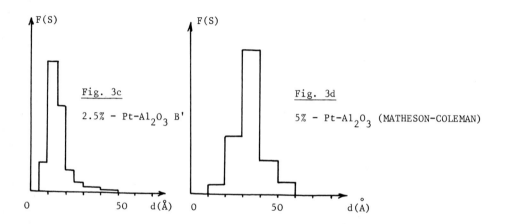

VI. DISCUSSION

Four major points have been raised
1. In the isomerization of 2-methylpentane to 3-methylpentane, the percentage of cyclic mechanism, remains constant over a very large range of metal dispersion (a < 0.5)
2. However its character changes continuously from selective to non-selective, as the size of the metal particles decreases
3. On very small particles (d < 10 Å), the bond shift mechanism is drastically decreased and the non-selective cyclic mechanism becomes predominant.
4. Methylcyclopentane hydrogenolysis is selective on metal particles larger than 20 Å and non-selective on smaller ones.

A) Mithohedrical theory

The constancy of the percentage of cyclic mechanism in the isomerization of 2-methylpentane to 3-methylpentane when accessibility "a" is smaller than 0.5 (mean particle size larger than 20 Å) allows to rule out the mitohedrical theory. If one assumes that edge or corner atoms of normal fcc crystallites are linked with the cyclic mechanism, and face atoms with bond shift, the relative contributions of the two mechanisms should differ greatly when passing from the 7% B' (a = 0.35) to the 8.5% A' catalyst (a = 0.05). For instance, when the number of atoms n on the edge of a regular octahedron varies from 30 to 5, with a corresponding change of accessibility from 0.06 to 0.37, the ratio (N_c/N_f) between corner and face atoms is multiplied by 70 and the ratio (N_e/N_f) between edge and face atoms by 7.4. If one follows then Anderson's argument linking cyclic mechanism with corner atoms and bond shift with face atoms (9), the percentage of cyclic mechanism should increase from 16 to 93% and if one assumes that edge atoms are responsible for the cyclic mechanism, from 16 to 60%. However it remains constant.
Therefore, the sites for the bond shift and cyclic mechanisms must be topographically similar, located both either on the face or on the edge of the metal particles. Since isomerization also takes place on very dispersed catalysts (a > 0.5), where edge atoms predominate, we believe that both types of isomerization sites include edge atoms.

B) B_5 sites

How can be explained then the decrease of the bond shift mechanism in the extremely dispersed catalysts ? A possible explanation would associate bond shift with some specific sites in fcc crystallites, including edge atoms and disappearing below a critical size. Such sites - the B_5 sites including five edge and face atoms in (110) or (311) configuration - arise when incomplete layers are added over (111) and (100) faces of fcc crystals. VAN HARDEVELD and HARTOG calculated the maximum number N_{B_5} of these sites as a function of particle size (18). The ratio between the maximum number of B_5 sites and the number of edge and corner atoms remains practically constant for particles larger than 20 Å and then decreases sharply to zero for the smallest particles. If one assumes then that bond shift and cyclic mechanisms involve B_5 sites and isolated edge atoms, respectively, the percentage of bond shift should vary like this ratio, first remaining constant and then decreasing below a critical particle size. The fact that some bond-shift mechanism remains even in the more dispersed catalyst would be due to the rather wide particle size distribution.

However, careful examination of the particle-size distributions shows that the model of incomplete cubooctahedron is not consistent with the observed results. The decrease in the bond shift mechanism is clearly related to the appearance of metal particles smaller than 10 Å, which is much below the critical size where the B_5 sites disappear in the incomplete fcc cubooctahedron.

C) Pseudocrystals with uncommon symmetry

Two types of explanations then, geometrical or electronic, could be provided to explain the special properties of these very small particles. In the first geometrical one, proposed by BURTON (25), it could be supposed that below a critical size the more stable metal aggregates would not retain the normal fcc lattice symmetry.

On the one hand, small particles with D_{5h} or icosahedral symmetry, have been characterized in epitaxial deposits of metals (14-17). One could imagine that very small platinum particles with such abnormal symmetry are present in highly dispersed catalysts and that they have some special catalytic properties, favoring, in the case of hexane isomerization, the non-selective cyclic mechanism.

On the other hand, HOARE and PAL, calculating the free energy of very small clusters (2-60 atoms) by using either LENNARD-JONES (6-12) or MORSE potential, showed that polytetrahedral aggregates obtained by packing 4-atom tetrahedra together face-to-face were more stable than any regular lattice microcrystallites of the fcc or hcp types and also than the pentagonal bipyramid (23 atoms) obtained by multiple twinning of fcc tetrahedra (20-21).

When constructing these stable aggregates, atom by atom, polytetrahedral packing may be carried out according to three different growth sequences whose first two complete shells have tetrahedral, pentagonal D_{5h} and icosahedral symmetry, respectively. When a third shell is added, however "the symmetry of the central seed structure does not propagate outwards through the cluster" and, between 35 and 55 atoms (7 to 12 Å), the more stable aggregates consist of a superficial quasi-amorphous layer of highly mobile atoms surrounding a solid symmetrical core.

The existence of these highly mobile quasi-isolated atoms could provide a new possibility for catalytic reactions on very small crystallites with the participation of mononuclear superficial complexes.

Although these hypotheses, which rest essentially on some very special geometrical properties of small metal aggregates, may appear attractive, they should be used with care : it is difficult indeed to decides unambiguously from either physicalmeasurements or theoretical calculations whether very small metal particles have fcc or non-lattice symmetry.

D) Electronic Factors

On the other hand, experimental evidences seem to indicate that electronic rather than geometrical factors should be considered when interpreting changes of reaction mechanism.

The importance of this electronic factor is clearly demonstrated when considering the predominant isomerization mechanism on various supported metal or alloy catalysts with large particle sizes (100-200 Å). Besides platinum, two metals, palladium and iridium, catalyze the isomerization of 2-methylpentane to 3-methylpentane. While on platinum the bond shift mechanism is largely predominant for this reaction, non-selective and selective cyclic mechanisms are favoured on palladium (26) and iridium (27) respectively. On the other hand, alloying platinum with gold or copper (28, 29) increases the contribution of the non-selective mechanism, while on platinum - nickel alloy catalysts, methylpentane isomerization takes place mostly according to a selective cyclic mechanism (30).

Similarly the observed particle size effect in the case of platinum catalysts could be accounted for by changes in electronic properties. CYROT-LACKMANN and coworkers showed recently that the local density of states and the asphericity of the charge density around a surface metal atoms varied with decreasing the particle size (31).
If one assumes then that the contributions of the two reaction mechanisms, bond shift and cyclic, depend primarily upon the electronic properties of the metal, the particle size effect observed in skeletal isomerization could easily be explained.

E) Geometrical factors

Two different species, metallocyclobutane and metallocarbene, with different electronic requirement, were proposed as precursors in bond shift and cyclic mechanism respectively (32, 33). The bond shift mechanism is very similar to the mechanism of metathesis involving metallocyclobutanes A and metallocarbenes B (scheme 6).

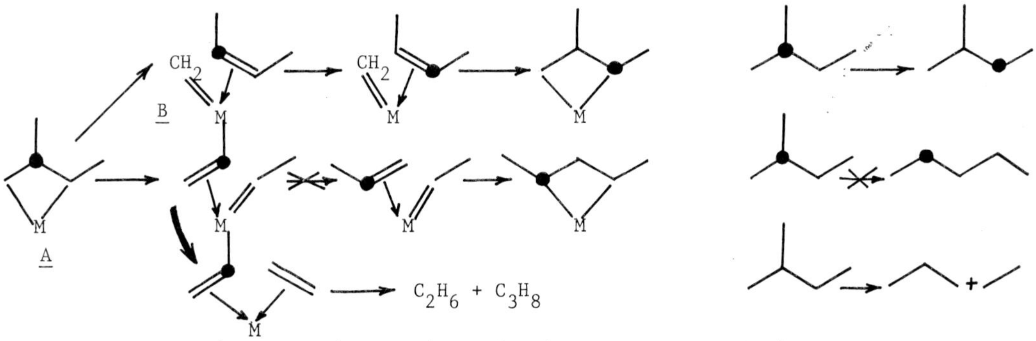

Scheme 6 : Bond shift mechanism for isomerization and hydrogenolysis

On the other hand, in the non-selective cyclic type of isomerization, the formation of carbon-carbon bonds including quaternary carbon atoms is not allowed : ring closure then takes place only between carbon atoms belonging either methylene ($>CH_2$) or methyl ($-CH_3$) groups. The dehydrocyclisation step therefore could be described as a dicarbene recombination (33) similar to the metallocarbene dimerization observed in coordination chemistry (34) (scheme 7a). Finally, in the selective cyclic mechanism, which does not interconvert methylpentanes and n-hexanes, two methyl groups in the 1-5 position are required for the dehydrocyclisation step.

Scheme 7a : non selective cyclic mechanism

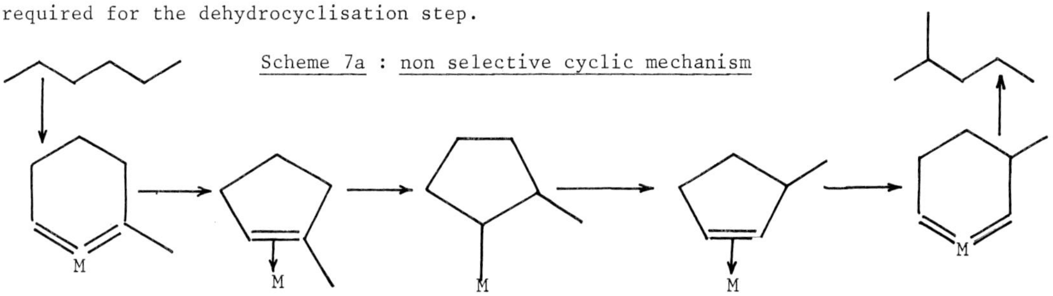

Scheme 7b : Selective cyclic mechanism

M D M   M E M   M   M   M   M

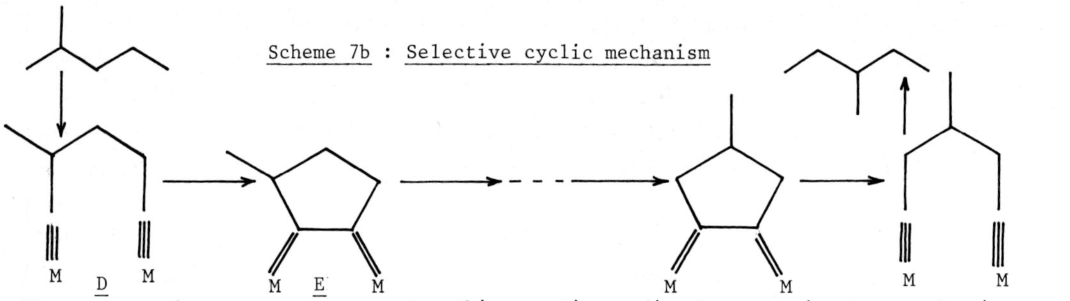

We suggest, then, as a precursor for this reaction a dicarbyne species D transforming into an ααββ tetraadsorbed cyclopentane intermediate (Scheme 7b). Although dicarbyne recombination has no analogue yet in homogeneous catalysis, metallocarbynes have been isolated (35). On account of the linear arrangement of the metal and the two carbon atoms in the M≡C-C group, species E should involve at least two metal atoms of the metal surface well separated and this requirement could explain why the selective cyclic mechanism only takes place on rather large metal crystallites.

Although we believe that the electronic properties of the metal primarily determine the nature, cyclic or bond shift, of the reaction mechanism, the geometrical factors should not be completely discarded, especially if one assumes that some intermediate species require not one, but two surface metal atoms. Geometrical factors could then become more important than the electronic ones, especially in the range 20-30 Å of metal particles, where both hydrogenolysis of methylcyclopentane and cyclic-type isomerization of methylpentanes change from selective to non-selective. The size of 20 Å indeed corresponds to a cubooctahedron of four atoms on the edge, the smallest structure in which a diadsorbed species involving two contiguous edge atoms may be formed.

VII. CONCLUSION

The particle size effects revealed in this study may be considered as resulting from the combination of two distinct factors (scheme 8)

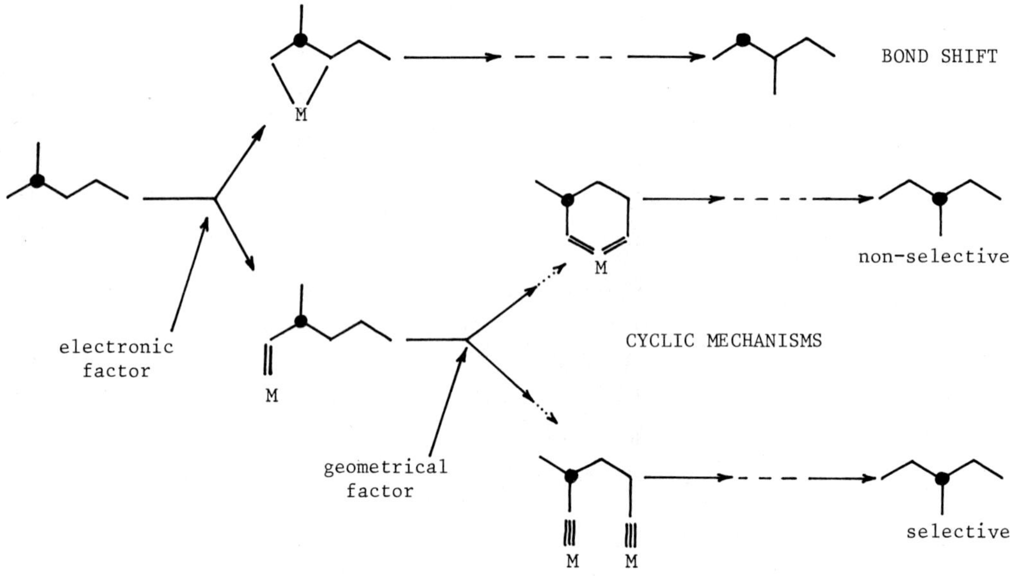

BOND SHIFT

electronic
factor

CYCLIC MECHANISMS

non-selective

geometrical
factor

selective

Scheme 8

First an electronic factor, appearing mostly when the metal particles are smaller than
10 Å, regulates the concentrations of the precursor species metallocyclobutane and
metallocarbene, and hence the relative contributions of the cyclic and bond shift
mechanisms. Secondly a geometric factor regulates the formation, from the metallocarbene,
of the reactive species - dicarbyne or dicarbene - responsible for selective and non
selective dehydrocyclisation respectively.

ACKNOWLEDGMENT : We thank Dr L. HILAIRE for a critical reading of this paper.

REFERENCES

1. R.L. BURWELL and R.H. TUXWORTH, J. Phys. Chem. 60, (1956), 1043
2 a). F.G. GAULT, C.R. Acad. Sci. 245 (1957), 1620
   b) G. MAIRE, G. PLOUIDY, J.C. PRUDHOMME and F.G. GAULT, J. Catal. 4, (1965) 556
3 a) M. BOUDART, A.W. ALDAG, L.D. PTAK and J.E. BENSON, J. Catal 11 (1968), 35
   b) M. BOUDART, Adv. Catalysis 20, (1969) 153
4. I.M. POLTORAK and V.S. BORONIN, Zh. Fiz. Khim. 40, (1966), 2671
5. K. FOGER and J.R. ANDERSON, J. Catal 54, (1978), 318
6. R. VAN HARDEVELD and A. VAN MONFOORT
   a) Proc. Intern. Congr. Catal 4th T. II 295 (1971)
   b) Adv. Catal. 22 (1972), 75
7. H.J. MAAT and L. MOSCOU, Proc. Inter. Congr. Catal. 3rd (1965), 1276
8. Y. BARRON, G. MAIRE, D. CORNET, J.M. MULLER and F.G. GAULT
   a) J. Catal 2 (1963) 152
   b) J. Catal. 5 (1966) 428
9. J.R. ANDERSON, R.J. Mc DONALD and Y. SHIMOYAMA, J. Catal. 20 (1971) 147
10 a) J.R. ANDERSON and B.G. BAKER, Proc. R. Soc. London Ser A 271 (1963) 402
   b) J.R. ANDERSON and N.R. AVERY, J. Catal 5 (1966), 446
11. a) C. COROLLEUR, S. COROLLEUR and F.G. GAULT, J. Catal. 24 (1972), 385
    b) C. COROLLEUR, D. TOMANOVA and F.G. GAULT, J. Catal 24 (1972) 406
12. P.C. FLYNN and E. WANKE, J. Catal. 37, (1975) 432
13. G. DALMAI-IMELIK and G. LECLERCQ, J. Microsc. (1972) 306
14. S. INO, J. Phys. Soc. Japan 21 (1966), 346
15. J.G. ALLPRESS and J.V. SANDERS, Surf. Sci. 7 (1967) 1
16. a) E. GILLET, J.F. ROUX, M. GILLET, Bull. Soc. Fr. Minéral. Cristallogr. 90 (1967), 54
    b) E. GILLET and M. GILLET, J. Crystal. Growth 13/14 (1972), 212
    c) E. GILLET and M. GILLET, Thin Solid Films 15 (1973) 249
17. a) K. KIMOTO and I. NISHIDA, J. Phys. Soc. Japan 22, (1967) 940
    b) T. KOMODO, Japan J. Appl. Phys. 7, (1968), 27
18. a) R. VAN HARDEVELD and A. VAN MONTFOORT, Surf. Sci. 4 (1966), 396
    b) R. VAN HARDEVELD and F. HARTOG, Ibidem 15, (1969), 189
19. J.J. BURTON, Catal. Rev. Sci. Eng. 9, (1974), 209
20. M.R. HOARE and P. PAL
    a) Nature Phys. Sci. 230 (1971), 5
    b) Adv. Physics 20, (1971) 161
21. M.R. HOARE and P/ PAL
    a) Nature Phys. Sci. 236 (1972), 35
    b) J. Crystal Growth 17 (1972) 77
22. T.A. DORLING and R.L. MOSS, J. Catal. 5 (1966), 111
23. J.E. BENSON and M. BOUDART, J. Catal. 4 (1965) 704
24. G. MAIRE, C. COROLLEUR, D. JUTTARD and F.G. GAULT, J. Catal 21, (1971), 250
25. J.J. BURTON, Catal. Rev. Sci. Eng. 9 (1974), 209
26. M. HAJEK, G. MAIRE, A. O'CINNEIDE, C. COROLLEUR, F.G. GAULT, J. Chim. Phys. 71 (1974) 1328
27. F. WEISANG and F.G. GAULT, J.C.S. Chem. Soc. (1979) 519
28. A O'CINNEIDE, F.G. GAULT, J. Catal. 37, (1975) 311
29. H.C. DE JONGSTE, V. PONEC, F.G. GAULT, J. Catal, in press
30. J.J. ALMON, Thèse Docteur-Ingénieur, Strasbourg 1976
31. M.B. GORDON, F. CYROT-LACKMANN and M.C. DESJONQUERES, Surf. Sci. 68 (1977), 359
32. F. GARIN and F.G. GAULT, J. Am. Chem. Soc. 97, (1975), 4466

464

33. V. AMIR-EBRAHIMI and F.G. GAULT, J.C.S. Faraday Transactions, in press
34. a) E.O. FISCHER, C.G. KREITER, Angew. Chem. Int. Ed. 8 (1969), 761
    b) R.L. ANDERSON, C.P. CASEY, J. Chem. Soc. Chem. Commun. (1975) 895
35. E.O. FISCHER, G. KREIS, F.R. KREISSL, J. MULLER, G. HUTTNER, H. LORENZ, Angew. Chem.
    Int. Ed. 12 (1973) 564

DISCUSSION

F.G. GAULT, F. GARIN, G. MAIRE

<u>Che</u> - It is assumed throughout your discussion that the particle size distribution remains constant during the catalytic reaction. Have you thus checked that the same particle size distribution was found after the reaction ?

<u>Garin</u> - On Chini catalysts, prepared by O. Zahraa in our Laboratory, with 2-3 % platinum on alumina $\left(a = \dfrac{H}{Pt} = 1 \right)$, the mean diameter of the metal cluster was obtained by J.L. Schmitt with high resolution electronic transmission microscopy. We found that the particles sizes remained constant and equal to 15 ± 5 Å before and after the isomerization reactions performed at 275-300° C. On the other hand the catalyst remains remarkably active and the selectivities unchanged during a number of experiments ; this shows that there is no modification of the catalyst with time.

<u>Dalmon</u> - What is the effect of alloying for the Bond-shift mechanism ? Is this effect in agreement with an electronic effect ?

<u>Garin</u> - On catalysts with large particle sizes (d > 100 Å) the major isomerization mechanisms are : Bond shift on platinum and non selective cyclic mechanism on palladium (1). On the other hand, alloying platinum with gold or copper (2,3) increases the contribution of non selective mechanism, while on platinum nickel alloy catalysts, methylpentane isomerization takes place mostly according to a selective cyclic mechanism (4). The importance of the electronic factor is thus clearly demonstrated.

<u>Gallezot</u> - Je pense qu'il n'est pas nécessaire de faire appel à des structures icosaédriques pour interpréter les mécanismes réactionnels. D'une part, nous avons montré que sous hydrogène, c'est-à-dire dans des conditions d'hydrogénolyse ou d'hydrogénation, les petites particules de platine sont cubiques à faces centrées. D'autre part, la différence d'énergie entre les structures cubo-octaédrique et icosaédrique est très faible comparée aux énergies d'adsorption de l'hydrogène ou des hydrocarbures.

<u>Martin</u> - D'après les résultats obtenus dans le groupe du Professeur Maurel à Poitiers sur platine, et à l'Institut de catalyse sur nickel, les activités et les sélectivités semblent dépendre plus de l'histoire du catalyseur, que de la dimension du grain métallique. Avez-vous essayé de faire des mesures sur des échantillons de granulométrie comparable, mais obtenus par exemple, par des traitements thermiques à des températures différentes (par exemple, au dessous de 500° C et vers 1000° C ?

<u>Garin</u> - Gault (1) avait montré l'effet d'un traitement thermique à 400° C sous hydrogène, sur une série de catalyseurs Pt/Al$_2$O$_3$ du type A, en étudiant la sélectivité de l'hydrogénolyse du méthylcyclopentane sous pression. Il avait noté que pour des catalyseurs concentrés en platine (> 6 %) ou peu concentrés en platine (< 0,6 %), la sélectivité dans l'hydrogénolyse du méthylcyclopentane ne variait pas. Par contre, entre 0,6 et 6 % de platine, il a observé un changement de sélectivité après traitement thermique.

Juttard (2) a conduit une étude similaire sur une série de catalyseurs du type A' et a montré que le rapport de sélectivité dans l'hydrogénolyse du méthylcyclopentane ne variait pas lors du traitement thermique.

Dartigues (3) a constaté, dans la série d'alumine A, après un traitement thermique à 400° C, un complet changement de sélectivité dans l'hydrogénolyse du méthylcyclopentane pour des teneurs en platine comprises entre 0,6 et 6 %.

Par contre, nous n'avons effectué aucune étude sur des catalyseurs traités à 1000° C.

(1) M. Hajek, G. Maire, A. O'Cinneide, C. Corolleur, F.G. Gault J Chim. Phys. <u>71</u>, 1239 (1974)
(2) A. O'Cinneide, F.G. Gault J. Catalysis <u>37</u>, 311 (1975)
(3) H.C. De Jongste, V. Ponec, F.G. Gault J. Catalysis in Press
(4) J.J. Almon Thèse Docteur Ingénieur Strasbourg 1976

466

Crucq - Les résultats décrits par l'auteur en ce qui concerne la sélectivité ont été obtenus à pression partielle constante des réactifs. Pour les différentes réactions étudiées, quels sont les ordres de réaction vis à vis de l'hydrogène ? Est-il possible de caractériser les divers mécanismes - bond-shift ou cyclique - par une valeur donnée de cet ordre ?

Garin - Des ordres très négatifs par rapport à l'hydrogène ont été trouvés pour l'isomérisation des C_5 (1) (tableau 1) et des C_6 (2). Par contre des ordres positifs (voisins de l'unité) ont été observés pour l'isomérisation des méthylhexanes et du 2,3 diméthylpentane (3). En étudiant la position du carbone -13 dans les molécules en C_7 isomères, on peut affirmer qu'il n'y a pas de processus répétitifs dans ces expériences même avec un ordre positif. Ceci montre que quelque soit l'ordre de la réaction par rapport à l'hydrogène, l'étape lente est l'étape de réarrangement du squelette.

Un modèle cinétique récemment proposé par Frennet et son équipe (4) permet d'interpréter la grande variation des ordres observés. Ils supposent que l'hydrocarbure et l'hydrogène sont en compétition sur de mêmes sites "potentiels" de la surface lors de la chimisorption. Alors que la chimisorption de l'hydrogène ne nécessite qu'un seul de ces sites, un groupement de Z sites contigus est nécessaire pour l'adsorption de l'hydrocarbure.

En appliquant ce modèle à l'isomérisation de squelette, il permet d'expliquer les ordres négatifs observés pour l'isomérisation du pentane et du n-hexane et l'ordre positif trouvé pour l'isomérisation du 2,3-diméthylpentane ce qui montre que la fraction de surface Θ_C couverte par les radicaux hydrocarbonés est plus importante dans le cas des heptanes que dans le cas des hydrocarbures en C_5 et C_6.

De ce fait, nous voyons qu'il n'est pas possible de caractériser les divers mécanismes d'isomérisation en fonction des ordres de réaction.

(2) A. Chambellan Thèse d'Etat Caen 1975
(3) P. Parayre, V. Amir Ebrahimi, A. Frennet, F.G. Gault Transactions Faraday in Press
(4) A. Frennet, G. Liennard, A. Crucq and L. Degols J. Catalysis 1978, 53, 150
(1) F. Garin and F.G. Gault J. Amer. Chem. Soc. 1975, 97, 4466.

J. BOURDON (Editor)
Growth and Properties of Metal Clusters, pp. 467—478
© 1980 Elsevier Scientific Publishing Company — Printed in The Netherlands

467

SURFACE AND CHEMISORPTION PROPERTIES OF SMALL NICKEL PARTICLES AS STUDIED BY HIGH FIELD
MAGNETIC METHODS, AND CATALYTIC ACTIVITY WITH RESPECT TO ETHANE HYDROGENOLYSIS AND BENZENE
HYDROGENATION.

By G.A. MARTIN, R. DUTARTRE and J.A. DALMON,
Institut de Recherches sur la Catalyse, 2, avenue A. Einstein 69626 Villeurbanne Cédex France

SUMMARY :

Magnetic properties of divided nickel catalysts prepared by reduction at various temperatures of unsupported, supported on silica, and antigorite precursors have been investigated in magnetic fields up to 70 kOe. Saturation magnetization is found to be nearly equal
to that of bulk nickel. It is concluded (i) that studied samples are probably completely
reduced, (ii) magnetic surface moments are equal to bulk ones, (iii) and that reduction of
the silica support and Ni-Si alloy formation is unlikely. Adsorption and catalytic studies
suggest that nickel catalysts reduced at high temperatures have (111) surface planes, on
which adsorbed hydrogen could be partly bonded to several metallic atoms and which exhibit
low activity with respect to hydrocarbons conversions (ethane hydrogenolysis and benzene
hydrogenation).

I. INTRODUCTION

One of the major problems in catalysis by metal is the understanding of the sensitivity
to the surface structure of catalytic reactions. By surface structure, it is meant [1]
coordination number of surface atoms as it can be varied by exposing different crystallographic planes and making steps and kinks [2], or by varying particle size in a large range
as done with supported metals.

Among all possible approaches, the study of catalytic activity at low and high pressure
of well-defined single crystal on which characterization on the atomic scale can be performed, has been proved to be fruitful [2] . An alternative way is to gain informations on the
surface structure of metallic powders which are generally well-characterized from the view
point of catalytic activity. As an example, it has been shown by electron diffraction and
microscopy, that nickel particles prepared by decomposition and reduction of the nickel
antigorite, a basic nickel silicate [3], show probably (111) surface planes [4,5]. The determination of the surface structure is made possible in that pecular case owing to the fact
that nickel particles are epitaxially grown on flat sheets of silica. Furthermore, the activity of this sample with respect to ethane hydrogenolysis, is smaller than that observed
on unorientated nickel catalysts [6], in accordance with the relatively low activity exhibited by the (111) face of single crystal for this kind of reaction [7]. It seemed to us
of interest to extend this type of study to other nickel catalysts. The determination of
the atomic surface structure by the technique used for the reduced antigorite, however, is
not possible for these samples which exhibit no chemoepitaxy. This led us to try to characterize the surface of nickel particles by studying chemisorption of gases (H_2, CO, C_6H_6)
with the help of high fields magnetic methods, and catalytic activities (ethane hydrogenolysis and benzene hydrogenation). Such a study was expected to give indirect informations
on surface structure, by comparing with data obtained on single crystals and on the

well-characterized reduced antigorite.

II. MATERIALS AND EXPERIMENTAL PROCEDURE

The methods of preparation and some morphological characteristics (degree of reduction, average particle size) were partly reported in previous works [6,8]. Let us recall that the precursor of sample I is a nickel hydroxyde obtained by evaporating ammonia from a solution of nickel nitrate hexammine. $Ni(OH)_2/SiO_2$ precursors are obtained by adding "Aerosil" silica from Degussa (surface area, 200 $m^2 g^{-1}$) into a solution containing various concentrations of nickel nitrate hexammine. Nickel antigorite, $Ni_3(OH)_4Si_2O_5$, is prepared by hydrothermal treatments at 623 K of stoichiometric mixtures of "Aerosil" silica and nickel hydroxyde [3].

TABLE 1

Methods of preparation and morphology of catalysts

Samples	Precursors	Ni loading wt %	Reduction temperature (K)	σ_s emu cgs a	Degree of reduct.	D_s (nm)	S_{Ni} $m^2 g^{-1}$
I	$Ni(OH)_2$	62	573	59.1	1.01 ∓ 0.1	–	10.8
II	$Ni(OH)_2/SiO_2$	4.5	800	70	0.95	2.5 a, b	–
III	$Ni(OH)_2/SiO_2$	23	920	61.6	0.984	6.3 b	–
IV	$Ni(OH)_2/SiO_2$	23	1200	60.3	~ 1	14 b	–
V	$Ni_3(OH)_4Si_2O_5$	45	970	57.4	~ 1	–	147
Bulk nickel	–	–	–	58.53	–	–	–

a measured at 4.2 K, 70 kOe (this paper)

b measured at 300 or 77 K, 20 kOe (see refs 6 and 8)

Reductions are performed in a stream of very pure hydrogen at temperatures listed in Table 1. Prior to reduction, precursors I, II and V are treated in vacuo at the same temperature as that used for the subsequent reduction. After outgassing at ca. 720 K for 1 hr (573 K only in the case of sample I), the powder is cooled to room temperature, and gas adsorption experiments are readily performed in a classical volumetric apparatus.

Magnetic measurements are carried out in a superconductive coil (70 kOe) at 4.2 K, using the Weiss method. Gaseous helium is added in sample-holder to ensure a good thermal contact. The accuracy and the repeatability of magnetization measurements are better than 10^{-4} in most cases. The system is calibrated using a Ni monocrystalline sphere with the 111 axis in the direction of magnetic field. The catalytic studies are performed in a flow system with a fixed-bed reactor at atmospheric pressure. Conversions are always smaller than a few percent.

III. EXPERIMENTAL RESULTS

III.1. Samples morphology

Magnetic measurements give informations on morphological characteristics of nickel powders. The surface average size of nickel particles of samples II, III and IV, D_s, calculated from the magnetization-field strength curves at 77 and 300 K in moderate fields (20 kOe), have been already reported [6, 8] ; they are listed in Table 1. The Curie points of samples II and III were also determined from static magnetic measurements and ferromagnetic resonance [9]. Let us recall that to a first approximation, they are nearly equal to that of bulk nickel. This allowed us to speculate on the degree of cleanness of nickel powders : Neugebauer [10] have obtained very similar results on thin nickel films prepared in ultrahigh vacuum conditions, in sharp contrast with films evaporated in less stringent conditions. It suggested to us that degrees of pollution of nickel powders are comparable with those of films obtained in good vacuum conditions [9].

Variations of magnetization of sample I, II, III, IV and V with field strength, H, at 4.2 K up to ca 70 kOe are shown in Figs. 1, 2, 3, 4 and 5, respectively. Saturation seems to be attained at ca. 40 kOe, as in the case of polycrystalline nickel [11], and corresponding magnetizations are calculated by extrapolating at H = 0 the high field linear part of the curves. Specific saturation magnetizations thus obtained are collected in Table 1. Superimposed susceptibilities deduced from slopes of the linear part of magnetization curves beyond 40 kOe are of the same order of magnitude as the bulk susceptibility, $(0.115 \, 10^{-3}$ emu cgs/atom gram of Ni) : observed values lie between 0.12 (sample V) and $0.4 \, 10^{-3}$ emu cgs/atom gram of Ni (sample II). It is very hard to decide wether these differences are significant owing to the uncertainty resulting from diamagnetism corrections of glass sample-holder and catalyst support.

The remanent to saturation magnetization ratio, M_r/M_s of sample I at 4.2 K is found to be 0.35, a figure which was already obtained in the case of unsupported Raney nickel catalysts [12] and which was attributed to the superposition of cubic magnetocrystalline anisotropy and uniaxial anisotropy due to stresses in polydomain particles. For sample II, the ratio M_r/M_s at 4.2 K is found to be 0.03, indicating that only 6 wt % of nickel particles have diameters larger than 5 nm after the Néel-Weiss method [13, 14]. The average diameter calculated from the low field part of the curve 8 is 2.5 nm, in good agreement with earlier determinations at 77 and 300 K [6, 8]. Ratios M_r/M_s of sample V at 300, 77, 4.2 and 1.7 K are found to be 0.0027, 0.012, 0.376 and 0.445, respectively, and the coercive field extrapolated at 0 K is 900 Oe. The volume distribution function of the diameters of equivalent spheres thus calculated [13, 14], exhibits a maximum at ca 4.5 nm; in agreement with electron microscopy data [4, 5] (equivalent spheres are defined as spheres having the same volume). If the shape anisotropy, measured from electron microscopy [4, 5], is taken into account, the surface area which is deduced from the distribution curve (147 m²/g) is in good agreement with electron microscopy data (150 m²/g) [4, 5]. Granulometries of samples III and IV have been already reported in ref. 8.

Electron diffraction techniques were unsuccessful to define the surface structure of samples I to IV. This technique requires the presence of ordered domains, 20 nm at least, to obtain sharp diffraction feature [2], a condition which is fulfilled only for sample V, as already stated [4, 5]. Now, how far chemisorption studies can help us to elucidate the surface structure of these samples ?

III.2. Hydrogen chemisorption

The saturation magnetization at 4.2 K decreases linearly, as the volume of adsorbed hydrogen at room temperature increases. This behavior is illustrated in Fig. 5 for samples I and V. The slopes of the curves, α, which can be considered as an electronic characteristic of the bond [22], vary from one sample to another as illustrated in Table 2. Samples IV and V have a common feature : Their α-values are relatively large, suggesting some similarities in surface structure.

470

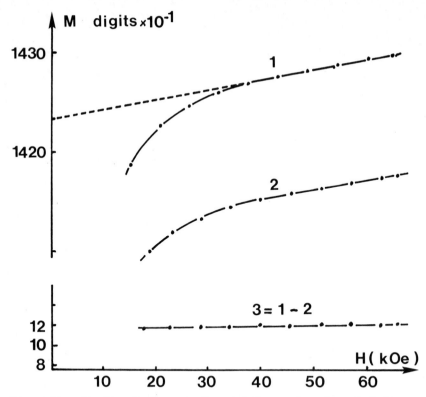

Fig. 1 Magnetization M of sample I at 4.2 K as a function of field strength H. Curve 1, outgassed sample. Curve 2, sample covered with H_2. Curve 3, difference between curves 1 and 2.

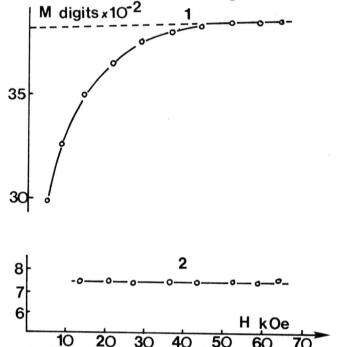

Fig. 2 Magnetization at 4.2 K of sample II (curve 1) and decrease of magnetization due to H_2 chemisorption, as a function of field strength H(2).

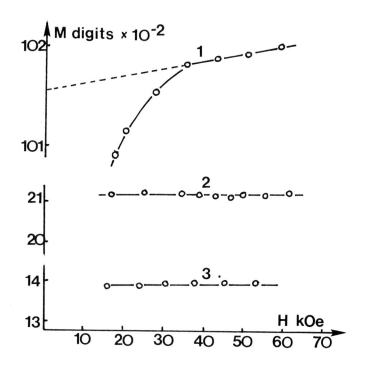

Fig. 3 Magnetization at 4.2 K of sample III (curve 1) and decrease of magnetization upon H_2 (curve 2) and CO chemisorption (curve 3), as a function of field strength H.

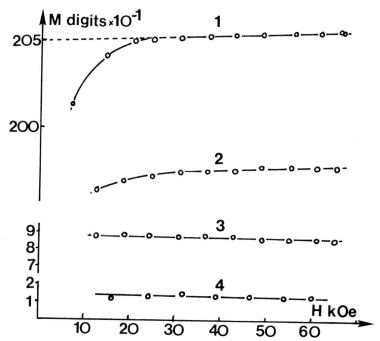

Fig. 4 Magnetization M of sample V at 4.2 K as a function of field strength H. Curve 1, outgassed sample. Curve 2, after H_2 adsorption. Curve 3, difference between curves 1 and 2. Curve 4, decrease of magnetization upon benzene chemisorption.

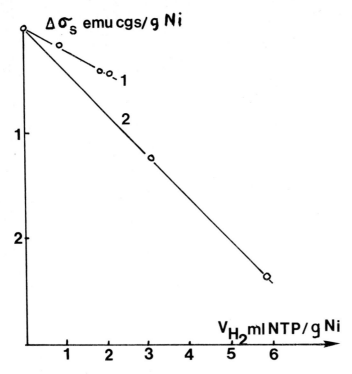

Fig. 5. Saturation magnetization of nickel as a function of the volume of adsorbed hydrogen on sample I (curve 1) and V (curve 2).

TABLE 2

Characteristics of H_2 chemisorption.

Samples	Surface area (m^2/g)	D_s (nm)	V_{H_2} (ml NTP/gNi) 100 Torr	Saturation	Psat. (Torr)	α_{H_2} B.M./molecule a	H/Ni_s
I	10.8	–	2.8	3.55 ∓ 0.4	$10^{3.1}$	0.90 ∓ 0.04	1.1
II	–	2.5	60	86.5 ∓ 5	$10^{5.6}$	1.41 ∓ 0.02	0.9
III	–	6.3	25	34.6 ∓ 2	$10^{5.4}$	1.46 ∓ 0.02	0.9
IV	–	14	8.1	10.5 ∓ 1	$10^{3.8}$	1.70 ∓ 0.02	0.6
V	150	–	8.0	10.8 ∓ 1	$10^{3.5}$	1.58 ∓ 0.02	0.20

[a]in Bohr magnetons per adsorbed molecule (B.M./molecule) ; average values from 3 determinations.

   In Table 2 are also listed the volumes of adsorbed hydrogen at room temperature under 100 Torr, and the volumes at saturation. Let us recall briefly how the latter are obtained [15] : Adsorption isotherms of each sample are measured at different temperatures from 10 to 300 Torr. The data are best represented by the Freundlich relation, $V = kP^a$, V = adsorbed volume, P = hydrogen pressure. The exponent a is pressure independent and varies with temperature. In a log-log graph, all isotherms converge to the point S, which can be considered as characterizing the saturation of the surface [16] (this point corresponds to the cancellation of the heat of adsorption). Corresponding saturation pressures ($P_{sat.}$) and adsorbed volumes are listed in Table 2. The comparison of the volume of adsorbed hydrogen at saturation with the number of surface nickel atoms, Ni_s, as deduced from surface area and average diameter determination, allows us to calculate the surface stoechiometry, H/Ni_s. It is assumed that :

(i) the cross sectional area of the surface nickel atom is an average of the values of (111), (100) and (110) planes (0.0677 nm^2) for sample I, and of (111) and (100) planes (0.0577 nm^2) for the other samples, which are prepared at relatively high temperatures and, hence, should exhibit smaller concentrations of low density surface planes.

(ii) the shape of nickel particles in samples II, III, and IV is spherical, as suggested by electron microscopy.

(iii) a part of the nickel crystallites in supported catalysts (samples II, III, IV and V), in contact with the support is not accessible to gas chemisorption, owing to the fact that a certain number of nickel atoms are utilized as a "glue" between the metal and the support. The percentage of these atoms is arbitrarily taken to be 10.

From Table 2, it can be seen that when going from sample I to IV, on one hand the ratio H/Ni_s is decreasing, on the other, the slope α is increasing. The accessibility to hydrogen chemisorption of sample V is probably very small, since the ratio H/Ni_s is equal to 0.2. This is probably to be due to embedding of nickel particles into the silica support, as evidenced by electron microscopy and nickel extraction experiments by bromine-methanol solutions [4, 5].

III.3. CO chemisorption

The carbon monoxide adsorption is performed at room temperature. The equilibrium pressure in the gas phase is smaller than 1 Torr to prevent nickel carbonyl formation. As already reported [8], and as illustrated in Fig. 2 for sample II, saturation magnetization of nickel decreases upon CO chemisorption. The decreases of saturation magnetization at 4.2 K, α, per adsorbed molecule are listed in Table 3. Observed values for samples II and III (1.1 and 1.15 B.M./molecule) are very near [8] to those measured at 77 K under 20 kOe (1.1 and 1.11 B.M./molecule). From the Table 3, it can be seen that, to a first approximation, α is not very sensitive to the origin of the catalyst. Similarly, the ratio of the volume of adsorbed hydrogen at saturation to that of adsorbed CO at 300 K under 1 Torr, V_{H_2} sat/V_{CO}, 1 Torr, is roughly constant except for sample I, indicating that most of the nickel atoms which are accessible to hydrogen adsorption are also involved in CO adsorption. (The ratios exceed 1 probably because surface is not saturated by CO under 1 Torr).

TABLE 3

Characteristics of CO and C_6H_6 chemisorption

Samples	α_{CO} B.M./molecule	$\dfrac{V_{H_2} \text{ sat.}}{V_{CO}, \text{ 1 Torr}}$ a	$\alpha_{C_6H_6}$ B.M./molecule	$\dfrac{V_{H_2}}{V_{C_6H_6}}$ a
I	-	1.8	4.3 ∓ 0.3	10.5
II	1.10 ∓ 0.05	2.9	4.6 ∓ 0.1	12.4
III	1.15 ∓ 0.05	2.3	4.3 ∓ 0.1	12.5
IV	1.13 ∓ 0.1	2.6	-	13.5
V	1.1 ∓ 0.1	2.5	4.1 ∓ 1	23

a comparisons of volumes of adsorbed gases are done on catalysts obtained from the same batches.

III.4. Benzene adsorption

After benzene adsorption at room temperature, reversible species are removed by pumping with a trap cooled at 77 K. The decreases of saturation magnetization at 4.2 K upon benzene irreversible adsorption thus observed (Fig. 4), are listed in Table 3. The value corresponding to sample III previously reported [17] - α = 4.8 B.M./molecule, measured at 300 K under 20 kOe - is in good accordance with the present determination. The ratios, V_{H_2} sat. / $V_{C_6H_6}$, where $V_{C_6H_6}$ is the total amount of irreversibly adsorbed benzene at room temperature, can also be compared in Table 3. To a first approximation, it can be seen that α is roughly constant for all samples. Moreover, the ratio V_{H_2} sat. / $V_{C_6H_6}$ is found to be ca.12 for samples I to IV, and significantly larger for sample V (the ratio is equal to ca.23). It means that a fraction of nickel atoms in sample V which are accessible to hydrogen and carbon monoxide molecules cannot be reached by larger molecules like benzene. The pecular behavior exhibited by this sample is considered in calculating catalytic activities : The rates of reaction are expressed in molecules converted in unit time per unit area of the metallic surface accessible to adsorption of large molecules.

III.5. Catalytic activities

The rates of ethane hydrogenolysis, r_1, and of benzene hydrogenation (r_2) measured in standard conditions can be compared in Table 4. Some results dealing with hydrogenolysis have been already reported [15, 19]. The observed parallel variations of rates r_1 and r_2 suggest that both reactions probably take place on the same type of metallic surface. Results in Table 4 show that benzene hydrogenation should be considered as a structure sensitive reaction. This observation will be discussed in details in another paper [20]. Another point to be considered in Table 4 is that samples IV and V show a very similar behavior from the catalytic viewpoint : Both have a very low activity, which confirms the resemblance between these samples already suggested by α_{H_2} measurements.

TABLE 4

Comparizon of the rates of ethane hydrogenolysis, r_1, and of benzene hydrogenation, r_2

Samples	r_1 x 10^{-11}	r_2 x 10^{-11}
	a	b
I	10	9
II	6	17
III	8	15
IV	0.7	1.8
V	2	4.5

[a] in molecules/sec/cm^2 Ni, measured at 507 K, P_{H_2} = 160 Torr, $P_{C_2H_6}$ = 6.3 Torr.
[b] in molecules/sec/cm^2 Ni, measured at 300 K, P_{H_2} = 600 Torr, $P_{C_6H_6}$ = 3 Torr.

IV. DISCUSSION

Saturation magnetization measurements allow us to speculate on degrees of reduction and values of surface magnetic moments.

For sample I, the ratio σ_s / σ_s bulk is equal to 1.01 $\pm$ 0.01. No firm conclusions on the magnetic moment of surface atoms can be drawn since only 2 % of nickel atoms are located on the surface, as shown by the B.E.T. surface area measurement reported in Table 1. It suggests, however, that the reduction is almost complete.

The saturation magnetization of sample II is a little larger than the bulk one (respectively 70 and 58.53 emu cgs/gNi). This difference could be due to an increase of the surface magnetic moment. This hypothesis can be ruled out, however, owing to the fact that the Curie point of this sample is equal to the bulk one [8]. Experimental data are best explained assuming that small amounts of nickel are not reduced : Separate experiments have shown that precursor II is ferromagnetic at 4.2 K, and that the saturation magnetization is ca. 250 emu cgs/gNi [18] . These magnetic properties are not changed by the treatment in vacuo at 800 K prior to reduction. Then, one can calculate that ca. 5 % of this unreduced phase would push σ_1 at 4.2 K as high as 70 emu cgs/gNi, the observed value. This suggests that the degree of reduction of this sample is only 0.95 (Table 1). The same reasoning can be used for sample III which has the same Curie point as bulk nickel [9] : The degree of reduction thus calculated is 0.984 (Table 1).

The Curie points of samples IV and V have not been measured. It is not therefore possible to determine surface magnetic moments without making hypotheses on degrees of reduction. These latter are probably equal to unity since both samples are prepared by reduction at high temperatures (the degree of reduction of sample IV is larger than that of sample III, itself equal to 0.984, since the former is obtained by reduction of the same precursor at higher temperature). Hence, surface magnetic moments of both samples are also equal to the bulk moment.

The possibility of support reduction and of Ni-Si alloy formation can be considered, specially for samples prepared at high temperatures : silicon addition in nickel is known to decrease saturation magnetization by 4 Bohr magneton per added atom. Then, formation of only 1 % of alloy would decrease saturation magnetization by 7 %. This is clearly the upper limit which can be proposed from saturation magnetization measurements reported in Table 1.

The main results of this magnetic study can be summarized in the following way :
(i) there is probably no alloy formation between nickel and silicon coming from a possible reduction of the support.
(ii) all studied samples are nearly completely reduced. This result is of importance since we know that the presence of large amounts of unreduced residues changes drastically on one hand physical properties of metallic nickel, as illustrated by Curie points shifts observed on partially reduced nickel [9], on the other hand, chemisorptive properties of the nickel surface, as shown in the case of CO adsorption [8].
(iii) surface magnetic moments are nearly equal to bulk moments, at least for samples II, III, IV and V, indicating that the curves of density of electronic states in the Fermi level region are probably similar to the bulk one. This conclusion confirms calculations performed in the tight-binding approximation by Desjonquères and Cyrot-Lackmann [21] which have predicted that the local density of state of various nickel surface planes is similar to that of bulk nickel.

The observed decrease of nickel saturation magnetization when gases are chemisorbed can be interpreted assuming that nickel atoms involved in the bonding, cease to participate in the collective ferromagnetism. This hypothesis is the basis of a method which is used to calculate the "bond number" [22] ; it consists in comparing the change of magnetic moments, α, produced by one molecule of an adsorbate, with magnetic moment of one nickel atom, μ. The bond number, n, is given by : $n = \dfrac{\alpha}{\mu}$

This method has received experimental confirmation in the case of CO chemisorption [8, 23], and has been proved to be fruitful for hydrocarbons adsorption studies 17 . In a recent paper [24] , Desjonquères and Cyrot-Lackmann have proposed a possible explanation of the mechanism of demagnetization of nickel surface atoms in the case of oxygen adsorption on (100)Ni : they have calculated in the tight-binding approximation that a broad level should appear at about 5 eV below the Fermi level and a state near the bottom of the Ni d-band resulting in a decrease of the density of state at the Fermi level. On the basis of the Stoner criterion (the existence of ferromagnetism is related to a high density of state at the Fermi level), the nickel layer involved in the gas-metal bond is expected to become non-ferromagnetic, in agreement with experimental data. This approach, which establishes the validity of the bond number method in the case of O_2 chemisorption can be extended to the case of hydrogen adsorption on nickel : U.P.S. studies [25] reveal that the density of state of the (111) Ni face decreases when H_2 is chemisorbed : Then, nickel surface atoms should lose their ability to contribute to ferromagnetism. Hydrogen bond numbers calculated from data in Table 2 for samples IV and V are found to be 2.7 and 2.8 respectively. This result indicate that multicentered species, like $\underset{H}{\overset{H}{Ni\diagdown Ni}}$, are probably present on the surface of these samples beside linear species $\underset{Ni}{\overset{|}{H}}$: Values of the ratios H/Ni_s for sample IV reported in Table 2 are consistent with this hypothesis.

The parallel behavior exhibited by sample IV and V (similar α_{H_2} - values, low catalytic activity) suggests that they have the same surface structure. This means that nickel parti-cles in sample IV, like those of sample V, the well-defined reduced antigorite, have proba-bly (111) surface planes. This is in agreement with the fact that particles are well-facetted as seen from electron microscopy [6]. The appearance of (111) faces, which are the most stable, would result from the high reduction temperature at which sample IV was prepared and from the relatively large particle size. It is interesting to note that CO and C_6H_6 adsorptions do not seem structure sensitive, at least as seen from magnetic expe-riments, in contrast with H_2 chemisorption. This behavior is rather unexpected and would require further investigations to be confirmed, particularly by infrared spectroscopy in the case of CO adsorption.

It can be concluded that comparison of chemisorption and catalytic properties of nickel catalysts with well-defined samples and single crystals has been shown to be fruitful. It has led us to suppose that Ni/SiO_2 catalysts reduced at high temperatures have (111) surface planes, which exhibit probably a low activity with respect to ethane hydrogenolysis and benzene hydrogenation and pecular properties towards hydrogen adsorption.

REFERENCES

1 M. Boudart, in G.C. Bond, P.B. Wells and F.C. Tompkins (Eds), Proc. 6th Int. Congress Catalysis, London, July 1976, The Chemical Society, London, 1977, p. 1.
2 G.A. Somorjai, in D.D. Eley, H. Pines, and P.B. Weisz (Eds), Advances in Catalysis, Academic Press, New York, 1977, p. 1.
3 G.A. Martin, B. Imelik and M. Prettre, C.R. Acad. Sci., série C, 264 (1967) 1536.
4 G. Dalmai-Imelik, C. Leclercq, J. Massardier and A. Maubert-Muguet, J. Chim. phys., 73 (1976) 176.
5 G. Dalmai-Imelik, C. Leclercq and A. Maubert-Muguet, J. Solid State Chem., 16 (1976) 129.
6 G.A. Martin and J.A. Dalmon, C.R. Acad. Sci. série C, 286 (1978) 127.
7 J. Massardier, J. Barbier and G. Dalmai-Imelik, J. Chim. phys., 75 (1978) 815.
8 M. Primet, J.A. Dalmon and G.A. Martin, J. Catalysis, 46 (1977) 25.

9 E.G. Derouane, A. Simoens, C. Colin, G.A. Martin, J.A. Dalmon and J.C. Védrine, J. Catalysis, 52 (1978) 50.
10 C.A. Neugebauer, Phys. Rev., 116 (1959) 1441.
11 J.P. Rebouillat, Thèse, Grenoble (1972).
12 G.A. Martin and P. Fouilloux, J. Catalysis, 38 (1975) 231.
13 L. Néel, Ann. Geophys., 5 (1949) 99.
14 L. Weil, J. Chim. phys., 51 (1954) 715.
15 G.A. Martin, J. Catalysis, in press.
16 D.O. Hayward and B.M.W. Trapnell, Chemisorption, Butterworth, London 1964, p. 159.
17 G.A. Martin and B. Imelik, Surface Sci., 42 (1974) 157.
18 G.A. Martin and J.A. Dalmon, C.R. Acad. Sci., série C, 272 (1971) 304.
19 G.A. Martin and J.A. Dalmon, C.R. Acad. Sci., série C, 286 (1978) 127.
20 G.A. Martin and J.A. Dalmon, in preparation.
21 M.C. Desjonquères and F. Cyrot-Lackmann, Solid State Commun. 18 (1976) 1127.
22 P.W. Selwood, Chemisorption and Magnetization, Academic Press, New York 1975.
23 J.A. Dalmon, M. Primet, G.A. Martin and B. Imelik, Surface Sci., 50 (1975) 108.
24 M.C. Desjonquères and F. Cyrot-Lackmann, Surface Sci., 8 (1979) 208.
25 H. Conrad, G. Ertl, J. Küppers and E.E. Latta, Surface Sci. 58 (1976) 578.

478

DISCUSSION

G.A. MARTIN, R. DUTARTRE, D.A. DALMON

Jacobs - The curves you showed : catalytic activity against dispersion showing a maximum around 5 nm remember very much the work of A. Vannice. This author has done extensive work on methanation. Do you think methanation of CO is more (or less) structure sensitive than e.g. hydrogenolysis of ethane ?

Martin - My colleague Dalmon has studied variations of the activity versus the particle size for the same catalysts as those I talked about. He has observed first an increase of intrinsic activity when the diameter increases then a smooth maximum at ca. 50 Å, and a slow decrease. This shows that the Sabatier reaction is less structure sensitive than the hydrogenolysis reaction.

Bonzel - Your results showed that the specific reaction rates for ethane hydrogenolysis and benzene hydrogenation are about equal for the Ni/SiO_2 sample IV and the unsupported Ni (antigorite). You interpreted this equality as evidence for the predominance of (111) facets on the Ni particles of both catalysts. On the other hand, does this near equality imply that there are no support effects for these reactions ? How do the absolute specific reaction rates compare for SiO_2 and Al_2O_3 supported Ni (of equal dispersion) ?

Martin - Actually, the nickel antigorite is supported on nickel, like sample IV. You raise the question of support effect in this type of reaction. We have not performed systematic studies with respect to this question. However, we have some data on catalyst activities when unsupported or supported on silica samples : they show the same activity (for a given diameter) under the condition that they are prepared at moderate temperatures, indicating that there are probably no support effects. The temperature of reduction seems to be the determining parameter for catalytic activity, rather than the nature of the support. At high temperatures, high density planes are probably formed, and these planes are less active than rough surfaces. We think now, that is possible to shed some light on the puzzling situation of structure sensitivity of benzene hydrogenation and ethane hydrogenolysis in the literature. An examination of bibliographic data shows that there are two types of catalysts : those which are prepared at low temperatures ($<500°$ C), on which these reactions are found to be facile ; those which are prepared at high temperatures, on which reactions are structure sensitive. We understand this situation by assuming that low temperature catalysts exhibit rough surface planes, whose nature is independent of the particle diameter. High temperature allows faceting and formation of dense planes which are less active, the variations of activity reflecting the variation of concentration of dense planes.

J. BOURDON (Editor)
Growth and Properties of Metal Clusters, pp. 479—491
© 1980 Elsevier Scientific Publishing Company — Printed in The Netherlands

USE OF FISCHER-TROPSCH SYNTHESIS OF HYDROCARBONS FOR THE CHARACTERIZATION
OF BIDISPERSE PARTICLE SIZE DISTRIBUTIONS AND BIMETALLIC CLUSTERS IN
ZEOLITES

H.H. NIJS, P.A. JACOBS, J.J. VERDONCK, J.B. UYTTERHOEVEN
Centrum voor Oppervlaktescheikunde en Colloïdale Scheikunde, K.U. Leuven,
De Croylaan 42, B-3030 Leuven (Heverlee), Belgium.

ABSTRACT

A detailed analysis of Fischer-Tropsch reaction products on ruthenium
loaded zeolites Y has shown that the reactivity and the selectivity of the
catalyst can yield valuable information on metal particle size distribution. It is demonstrated that inside the zeolite crystals, very uniform
particle dimensions exist.

Furthermore using the same method evidence is obtained that for RuCuY
and RuNiY zeolites alloys are formed outside the zeolite. In the Ni-Ru
agglomerates surface sites composed of each metal catalyze the Fischer-
Tropsch reaction independently.

Information obtained from temperature programmed oxidation of the metal
phase confirms the picture.

INTRODUCTION

Numerous data exist now on the structure and properties of small metal
particles (ref. 1). A wide variety of physical, chemical and physico-
chemical techniques have been used to obtain information on the surface
area and particle size distribution of supported metals and on the surface
composition of multimetallic agglomerates (ref. 2).

The limits of the most common methods are well-known. Chemisorption
experiments sometimes fail due to the not-well-known reaction stoichiometry between metal surface atoms and chemisorbed probe molecules. X-ray
line broadening has a lower detection limit around 3.5 nm (ref. 3). Transmission electron microscopy does not always allow to achieve a resolving
power of .5-1 nm, mainly in the case of supported metals. Small angle
X-ray scattering is able to resolve small particles on support, but the
interference scattering has to be masked.

The main disadvantage of most methods is that the metal catalyst is not
characterized in working conditions. Therefore it would be most suitable
if a test reaction could give information on the particle size distribution

of supported metals and the surface composition of multimetallic agglome-rates. The dependence of the rate of CO hydrogenation upon metal particle size has been reported several times. For supported Ni, an optimum par-ticle size exists (ref. 4). For Ru it is reported that larger ruthenium aggregates have higher specific activities for CO conversion (ref. 5). It was found recently that for Ru-Y zeolites a particle size effect also determines selectivity (i.e. hydrocarbon chain length) (ref. 6). The same information can be derived from recently published Fischer-Tropsch selec-tivity data on Co on alumina catalysts (ref. 7).

In this work, Fischer-Tropsch synthesis of hydrocarbons was carried out on Ru-Y zeolites and on Ru-Ni and Ru-Cu bimetallic systems. Ruthenium was taken for its very high polymerization activity so that an altered physical state of the metal would be most clearly visualized in changes of reaction selectivity. Zeolites were taken as support since this porous matrix is known to give rise to binodal (ref. 8) and even to trinodal (ref. 9) metal particle size distributions. In the case of bimetallic zeolites, it is clear that metal alloys are formed at the external surface (ref. 10, 11). Whether metal-metal interaction occurs in the inner voids of the zeolite crystals is not unequivocally established (ref. 12, 13, 14). The present method also allows to draw conclusions in this matter.

EXPERIMENTAL

Materials

NaY zeolite with a SiO_2/Al_2O_3 molar ratio of 4.85 was from Union Carbide (Linde). $La(NO_3)_3$, $Ni(NO_3)_2$ and $Cu(NO_3)_2$ were analytical grade from Merck A.G.. $Ru(NH_3)_6Cl_3$ was from Strem Chem. and checked for its purity by U.V. spectroscopy. All gaseous reactants (H_2, O_2, CO, He, Ar) were from L'Air Liquide with a purity of at least 99.99 % by volume.

The samples were prepared by ion exchange in a dilute suspension (10 g zeolite/dm^3) from a dilute solution (0.01 mol dm^{-3}) as follows :

Ru(40)Y, Ru(60)Y : exchange of NaY with $Ru(NH_3)_6^{3+}$.

Ru(40)Ni(1)Y, Ru(40)Ni(10)Y, Ru(40)Cu(1)Y, Ru(40)Cu(1)Y : partial exchange of NaY with Cu^{2+} or Ni^{2+} and subsequent exchange with the Ru^{3+} complex.

Ru(40)Ni(55)Y : complete exchange with Ni^{2+} (68 %) and subsequent partial exchange with Ru^{3+}.

Ru(14)LaY : exchange with La^{3+} (1 mol dm^{-3}) at reflux, drying, cal-cining at 873 K and exchange with Ru^{3+}.

The values in brackets denote percentage values of the cation exchange capacity, the remaining cations being Na^+. In some cases, reduction temperatures in K follow this sample notation.

Methods

The catalytic experiments were done in a continuous flow fixed bed reactor. The <u>standard conditions</u> were : total pressure, 14 kg cm^{-2}; H$_2$/CO molar ratio, 1.5; reaction temperature, 473 K; contact time, 0.4 s^{-1}. The catalyst (2.5 10^{-4} kg) was diluted with quartz (1 10^{-3} kg) to avoid heat transfer gradients. The catalysts were reduced in flowing hydrogen prior to the reaction. Accurate carbon balances could be obtained using argon as an internal standard. The analysis was done on-line over a 1.5 m carbosieve column connected to a thermal conductivity detector (to analyze CO, CO$_2$, Ar and CH$_4$) and over a 150 m OV 101 capillary column connected to a FID detector (to analyze the hydrocarbons). All hydrocarbons up to C$_{16}$ could be eluted from this column. Samples were drawn from the reactor after 2400 s.

After this reaction time, the adsorbed gases were removed from the catalyst surface by treating it with pure hydrogen at reaction temperature for 3600 s. Then, the catalyst was cooled, removed from the reactor and charged to a recirculation reactor for a temperature programmed oxidation (TPO) as described earlier (ref. 9). The heating rate employed in these experiments was 0.0833 Ks^{-1}. Experimental points were taken every 180 seconds.

RESULTS AND DISCUSSION

1. <u>Correlation between particle size in RuY zeolites and hydrocarbon chain length in Fischer-Tropsch synthesis</u>

TPO of metals in zeolites has been used to determine the bidisperse nature of the distribution of particle sizes (ref. 15). A thorough investigation of RuY zeolites by TPO revealed that the maximum in the rate of oxidation shifted to higher temperatures according to the series :

Ru(14)LaY < Ru(40)Y < Ru(60)Y

This shift is clearly demonstrated in Fig. 1.

Besides the maxima shown, each catalyst contains a minor amount of pyrophoric ruthenium (< 5 %) which is not given in Fig. 1. Zeolite Ru(14)LaY has a sharp maximum at 610 K with practically no tail. The maximum for Ru(40)Y is shifted to 640 K and is significantly broader. For Ru(60)Y a very broad curve is centered around 830 K. It is confirmed again that the position of the TPO maxima can be correlated to metal particle size dimensions. Indeed, a combination of X-ray diffraction methods, transmission electron microscopy and hydrogen chemisorption measurements indicate an average particle size diameter of 2, 4 and 14 nm for the 3 samples respectively. It is clear that the particles on Ru(60)Y must be located outside the zeolite crystals as a second phase.

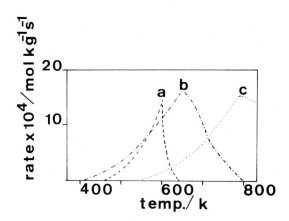

Fig. 1. TPO curves of RuY zeolites after FT reaction and subsequent reduction at 473 K : a, Ru(14)LaY; b, Ru(40)Y; c, Ru(60)Y.

The particles on Ru(40)Y are located in holes formed by the hydrolizing activity of water on the zeolite structure (ref. 9). For Ru(14)LaY, it is presumed that these holes cannot be formed due to the steam stability of the LaY-structure. Therefore the metal particle dimensions are limited by the supercage diameter (± 1.5 nm). Differences in reduction temperature (573 and 673 K) could not be resolved by TPO for these samples.

The catalytic results obtained in Fischer-Tropsch (FT) synthesis on Ru(40)Y, Ru(60)Y and Ru(14)LaY zeolites are given in Table 1.

TABLE 1

Catalytic characterization under standard reaction conditions of RuY zeolites in FT synthesis after different pretreatments

Catalyst	Reduction temp./K	Conversion of CO/%	C_{12}^+/%(a)
Ru(40)Y	573	20.6	0.0
Ru(40)Y	673	23.5	0.0
Ru(60)Y	573	28.3	64.6
Ru(60)Y	673	32.7	66.5
Ru(14)LaY(c)	573	18.2	0.0(b)
Ru(14)LaY(c)	673	20.2	0.0(b)

a, weight % of total carbon containing products; b, C_5^+; c, contact time, 0.8 s^{-1}.

The most striking difference between these catalysts is in the maximum chain length of the hydrocarbons produced. Only minor changes are observed with rising reduction temperature. In order to reach a better understanding of these phenomena a detailed product distribution is given in Fig. 2.

The Ru(40)Y catalyst does not catalyze the formation of hydrocarbons beyond dodecane. This has been reported earlier (ref. 6) and has recently been confirmed on FeY catalysts (ref. 16). It is clearly shown that within the C_1-C_{12} range a variation in the product distribution can be obtained by changing the reduction temperature, higher temperatures shifting the distribution closer to C_{12}. There is a very abrupt interruption of the polymerization activity beyond C_5 on Ru(14)LaY (C_5 = 52 %). The Ru(60)Y zeolite produces a very high C_{12}^+ content in the hydrocarbon product, which is comparable with a Ru/SiO$_2$ catalyst containing 15.5 % ruthenium (ref. 6). Since the zeolite crystal structure cannot be held responsible for the individual differences among these faujasite based catalysts, other physical characteristics of the catalyst must be found which do change significantly over these catalysts.

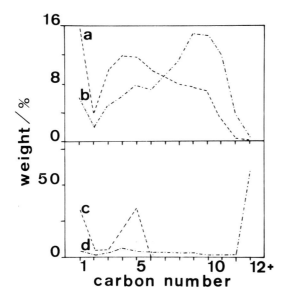

Fig. 2. FT product distribution in terms of carbon number : a, Ru(40)Y-573; b, Ru(40)Y-673; c, Ru(14)LaY-573; d, Ru(60)Y-573. All hydrocarbons containing more than 12 C-atoms are represented by one single point.

Although differences in particle size distributions for Ru(40)Y reduced at different temperatures could not be resolved by TPO, the shift at higher reduction temperatures to higher carbon number without exceeding C_{12} can be understood if more particles grow to a maximum size imposed by the zeolite structure.

Combining the product distribution curves with the TPO data, the following conclusions can be drawn :

i. The maximum size of the metal particles in the catalyst is correlated to a maximum hydrocarbon chain length detected in a FT product distribution.

ii. The shape of the hydrocarbon product distribution reflects the particle size distribution as it is also described by a TPO curve. The former probe is more sensitive towards minor changes in the particle size distribution.

iii. In zeolites, near monodisperse particles can be obtained due to their specific structural characteristics. This can lead to very selective catalysts.

In order to use this reaction as a probe to evaluate metal particle size distributions, it should be kept in mind that only reaction conditions yielding high growth rates of the hydrocarbon chains can lead to meaningful results. Indeed, a polymerization reaction with a small growth probability at every carbon number will stop before the point of growth inhibition by particle size limitations will be reached.

2. Decreased FT activity and increased selectivity suggests compound formation and surface site dilution in RuCuY zeolites

If particle size distribution can be determined by the FT reaction, it was thought that with the same method information might be obtained on the physical nature of the surface state of bimetallic compounds. Therefore, besides ruthenium, copper was exchanged into the zeolite. FT activities and product distributions are shown in Table 2 and Fig. 3.

TABLE 2

Characterization of RuCuY zeolites in FT under standard reaction conditions

Catalyst	Reduction temp./K	Conversion of CO/%	C_{12}^{+}/%
Ru(40)Cu(1)Y	573	13.0	20.9
Ru(40)Cu(1)Y	723	24.5	31.3
Ru(40)Cu(10)Y	573	0.0	0.0
Ru(40)Cu(10)Y	723	2.4	1.8

The following remarks can be made on these results :

i. In the presence of Cu^{++}, ruthenium appears to be reduced less easily, resulting in less activity for both catalysts at reduction temperatures of 573 K.

ii. At higher reduction temperatures, a comparable activity to Ru(40)Y is found on Ru(40)Cu(1)Y. The presence of a small amount of Cu however results in the appearance of a much higher amount of C_{12}^+ products. The Ru(40)Cu(10)Y zeolite exhibits an activity decreased by one order of magnitude compared to the original sample. The selectivity however is drastically shifted to lower carbon numbers. It was reported earlier that the reduction of RuCuY zeolites results in Ru particles with a much broader distribution then in RuY (ref. 13). This would explain why the Ru(40)Cu(1)Y yields more C_{12}^+ hydrocarbons than Ru(40)Y. On the other hand the Ru(40)Cu(10)Y exhibits a remarkable selectivity in the C_4-C_7 region.

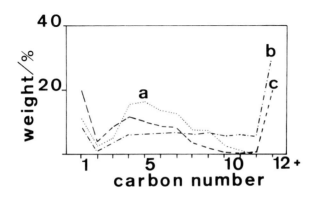

Fig. 3. FT product distribution over RuCuY zeolites in terms of carbon number; a, Ru(40)Cu(10)Y-723; b, Ru(40)Cu(1)Y-723; c, Ru(40)Cu(1)Y-573.

The understanding of both phenomena requires the following assumptions :
i. Ru and Cu form alloys at the external surface of the zeolite crystals as revealed by the low activity and product distribution on Ru(40)Cu(10)Y-723.
ii. Cu causes Ru to move preferentially out of the zeolite, derived from the high amount of C_{12}^+ on the less active catalysts.
iii. Relatively large amounts of Cu dilute the surface of large Ru particles located outside the zeolite. The average size of the ruthenium sites being small, the catalyst selectivity should be comparable to the one observed for very finely dispersed RuY systems. This is observed for Ru(40)Cu(10)Y. The low activity of the catalyst rather suggest that

bulky Ru particles are present. If the FT synthesis is a demanding reaction, it means that for a Ru catalyst sintering can be compensated by a higher turnover number within a certain range of particle sizes. However in a Ru-Cu system, particle size growth takes place without increase of the number of active sites. In other words, surface enrichment has occurred. The net result is a decrease in the amount of active sites without a rise in turnover number.

The observations demonstrate how the FT synthesis can reveal significant information on a bimetallic system, consisting of an inactive and an active metal.

3. Independent Fischer-Tropsch catalysis on ruthenium and nickel sites at an alloy surface in RuNiY

In order to obtain information on the physical state of bimetallic zeolites where both metals are Fischer-Tropsch active, Ru and Ni were exchanged into NaY. These two metals were chosen because of their very opposite FT properties, ruthenium having the highest polymerization activity known, nickel the lowest. These characteristics should make their behaviour in a bimetallic catalyst clearly visible. The catalytic activity and product distribution of these catalysts are given in Table 3 and Fig. 4.

TABLE 3

Characterization of RuNiY zeolites in FT under standard reaction conditions

Catalyst	Reduction temp./K	Conversion of CO/%	C_{12}^+/%	CO_2/%
Ru(40)Ni(1)Y	573	28.7	0.3	4.1
Ru(40)Ni(1)Y	723	38.6	53.5	3.8
Ru(40)Ni(10)Y	573	24.5	0.0	10.4
Ru(40)Ni(10)Y	723	11.1	0.0	8.7

These data show that :

i. In the presence of Ni^{2+}, Ru^{3+} is more readily reduced at 573 K, resulting in a more active catalyst. This behaviour is opposite to that of Cu.

ii. Reduction temperatures of 723 K cause the Ru(40)Ni(1)Y to sinter. Very little difference in activity or selectivity can be found compared to pure RuY zeolites where the metal is found outside the zeolite cages.

iii. For Ru(40)Ni(10)Y, the activity decreases considerably at higher sintering temperatures. In both cases very narrow product distributions are observed with a high methane content. The product distribution is no mere overlap of a NiY distribution (CH_4 > 95 %) and the previously shown Ru(40)Y distribution. From the activity decrease with increasing reduction temperature, it seems that the compensation effect of growing turn-

over numbers with growing particle size, is much smaller compared to the
pure RuY system.
iv. A Ru sample rich in Ni, shows a superposition of the characteristics
observed for Ru(40)Ni(10)Y and for a sintered RuY.

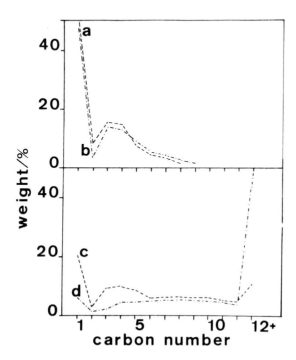

Fig. 4. FT product distribution over RuNiY zeolites in terms of carbon
number; a, Ru(40)Ni(10)Y-573; b, Ru(40)Ni(10)Y-723; c, Ru(40)Ni(55)Y-723;
d, Ru(40)Ni(1)-723.

As far as the physical nature of the catalyst is concerned, the following picture can be derived :

i. On Ru(40)Ni(10)Y, an alloy is readily formed upon reduction. These
alloyed particles are to be found outside the zeolite matrix and are
relatively large. No evidence of segregation can be found since no higher
hydrocarbons are formed.

ii. The reasons for the decrease of activity with reduction temperature of
Ru(40)Ni(10)Y can be attributed to the same phenomena as for Ru(40)Cu(10)Y
since nickel has a lower intrinsic activity than ruthenium (ref. 4).

iii. Nickel dilutes the ruthenium active sites causing them to restrict
the growth probability at a relatively short chain length. Particles of
nickel on the surface act as independent methanation sites. Indeed, an
electronic nickel-ruthenium interaction could exist resulting in properties which lie in between the characteristics of each metal in FT syn-

488

thesis. This would mean that the growth probability would be somewhere in between those of nickel and ruthenium (± 0.05 and ± 95 respectively). This assumption could account for the high yield of methane but not for the growth probabilities found at the C_2-C_4 level which are close to those found on pure RuY catalysts. Therefore, at the surface of the metal particle, ruthenium and nickel sites catalyze the FT reactions in an independent manner.

iv. For a Ni rich Ru sample metal phase segregation at the outer zeolite surface becomes increasingly important.

CONCLUSIONS

From the evidence presented in this work the following general conclusions may be drawn :

i. The Fischer-Tropsch synthesis can be used to obtain a qualitative picture of the metal particle size distribution. The method is limited by analytical problems when hydrocarbons with very high molecular weight are formed or by metal characteristics when a high growth probability cannot be attained.

ii. Under the same conditions it is possible to observe the formation metal-metal interaction inside or outside the zeolite. An estimation can be made to which degree surface enrichment occurs, even when both metals are Fischer-Tropsch active.

iii. Fischer-Tropsch catalysis can yield valuable information on metal-metal interactions in bimetallic compounds.

ACKNOWLEDGMENT

The authors wish to acknowledge the financial support from the Belgian government (Diensten van het Wetenschapsbeleid). They are particularly grateful for the permission to publish these results. P.A. Jacobs acknowledges a permanent research position as "Bevoegdverklaard Navorser" from N.F.W.O. (Belgium).

REFERENCES

1 J.R. Anderson, Structure of Metallic Catalysts, Academic Press, London, New York, San Francisco, 1975, Ch. 5, pp. 244-286.

2 id., ibid., Ch. 6 and 7, pp. 289-440.

3 G. Fagherazzi, G. Cocco, L. Schiffini, S. Enzo, A. Benedetti, R. Passerini, G.R. Tauszik, Chim. e L'Ind., 60 (1978) 892-900.

4 M.A. Vannice, Adv. Chem. Ser., 163 (1977) 15-32.

5 D.L. King, J. Catal., 51 (1978) 386-397.

6 H.H. Nijs, P.A. Jacobs, J.B. Uytterhoeven, J.C.S. Chem. Comm., (1979) to be published.

7 D. Vanhove, P. Makambo, M. Blanchard, J.C.S. Chem. Comm., (1979) 605-606.

8 P.A. Jacobs, H.H. Nijs, J.J. Verdonck, F.G. Derouane, J.P. Gilson, A.J. Simoens, J.C.S. Faraday Trans. I, 75 (1979) 1196-1205.

9 J.J. Verdonck, P.A. Jacobs, M. Genet, G. Poncelet, J.C.S. Faraday Trans. I, 75 (1979), to be published.

10 W.G. Reman, A.H. Ali, G.C.A. Schuit, J. Catal., 20 (1971) 374-381.

11 Kh.M.G.V. Minachev, G.V. Antoshin, E.S. Shpiro, Yu.A. Yusikov, in G.C. Bond, P.B. Wells, F.C. Tompkins (Eds.), Proc. 6th Int. Congr. Catal., London, July 12-16, 1976, The Chem. Soc., 1977, pp. 621-632.

13 D.J. Elliott, J.H. Lunsford, J. Catal., 57 (1979) 11-26.

14 J.B. Uytterhoeven, Acta Phys. Chem., 24 (1978) 53-69.

15 P.A. Jacobs, J.P. Linart, H. Nijs, J.B. Uytterhoeven, H.K. Beyer, J.C.S. Faraday Trans. I, 73 (1977) 1745-1754.

16 D. Ballivet-Tkatchenko, G. Coudurier, H. Mozzanega, I. Tkatchenko, Fund. Res. Homog. Catal. (1979), to be published.

DISCUSSION

H.H. NIJS, P.A. JACOBS, J.J. VERDONCK, J.B. UYTTERHOEVEN

Perrichon - At the beginning of your lecture, you have shown that FT synthesis depends upon the Ru particle size. In the last slide, you have presented the work of Blanchard who uses catalysts with alumina support presenting 60 Å pores, and you suggest that the pores of the zeolites may play a role in the selectivity. In your opinion, what is the factor the more important in selectivity : the particle size or the porosity of the zeolite more or less modified by the metallic particle.

Jacobs - I think definite evidence is in the paper which shows that there exists a particle size effect in Fischer-Tropsch synthesis of hydrocarbons. The zeolite Y due to its particular porosity confines a definite shape and size to the metal particles, which in their turn determine the product selectivity. The zeolite cages exert therefore no direct action on the product distribution as is clearly shown in reference 6 of the paper.

Perrichon - The catalytic results can be modified by a partial trapping of the hydrocarbon products in the cavities of the zeolites, which can explain particular drop in FT selectivity. This phenomenon can change with time. In your case, what is the change in activity and selectivity with the reaction time ?

Jacobs - Deactivation of zeolite-based Fischer-Tropsch catalysts may be the result of the following two phenomena :
. gradual decrease in crystallinity of the support, as a result of its operation under hydrothermal conditions ; consequently the metal particles agglomerate. This phenomenon can be overcome by using steam-stable zeolites.
. carbon deposition on the active metal.

In the case of a steam-stable support, the catalyst remains stable over a rather long period of time. Upon deactivation, the selectivity changes gradually towards shorter hydrocarbon chains. In any case, the selectivity can be perfectly regenerated by a hydrogen treatment at reaction temperature. Trapping of part of the hydrocarbons in the pores can be excluded as an explanation of the particular selectivity. Indeed, if long chain hydrocarbons are added to the feed (e.g. $n-C_{12}$ or 1-decene) they do not undergo any cracking. In the case of 1-decene, only double-bond shift and cis-trans isomerization is observed.

Dalmon - 1°/ My first question is also on the particle size effect on the chain length. If I well understand you consider geometric effects : have you any idea of the number of surface atoms needed to achieve a given chain length ?

2°/ In the case of Cu-Ru bimetallic catalysts, did you try to control the surface composition by hydrogen titration ?

Jacobs - 1°/ From the results in the paper it can be derived than on 1.5 and 4 nm Ru particles the maximum hydrocarbon chain length is C_5 and C_{11} respectively. Since these particles are strongly encaged in the zeolite matrix, it may well be that the whole surface is not accessible. It is therefore impossible for the moment to advance a minimum number of surface atoms which are required for the synthesis of a hydrocarbon with a given chain length.

2°/ For all catalysts mentioned in the paper, the conclusions derived from the Fischer-Tropsch activity and selectivity are confirmed by chemical and physical methods as : temperature programmed oxidation of the metal phase, temperature programmed desorption of chemisorbed hydrogen, electron microscopy and X-ray line broadening.

Bonzel - If the maximum in the product distribution C_n increases with increasing particle size (regardless of the support) one should not observe C_1 - C_6 products in Fischer-Tropsch synthesis in single crystals or extended polycrystalline samples under similar reaction conditions. However, such a conclusion seems to be at variance with recent results on Fe samples (Dwyer and Somorjai, J. Catal. ; and Bonzel + Krebs, Surface science) and probably also on clean Ru (Madey and Goodman, NBS Washington, unpublished).

Jacobs - If polymerization during Fischer-Tropsch synthesis occurs at a low growth rate, the formation of longer chains will stop long before the point of growth inhibition by particle size effect will be reached and a product distribution will be obtained which obeys the Schulz-Flory law :

$$W_n = \alpha^{n-1} (1-\alpha)^2$$

where W_n is the weight fraction of a carbon number n, and α the growth probability. If on large Ru particles, synthesis is done under conditions where $\alpha \geqslant 0.8$, waxes will be found. If a Schulz-Flory distribution terminating below n=10 is obtained, this means that the catalyst is working at very low α factors. The same is true for iron and cobalt.

Gallezot - How do you interpret the fact that the smallest particles give the smallest chain lengths ? Are there any secondary reactions such as hydrogenolysis or cracking.

Jacobs - Addition of long-chain olefins (C_{10}) to the feed, which are considered to be the primary products in a Fischer-Tropsch synthesis, allowed us to decide that no secondary hydrogenolysis or cracking of long chain molecules has occurred in the reaction conditions.

J. BOURDON (Editor)
Growth and Properties of Metal Clusters, pp. 493—503
© 1980 Elsevier Scientific Publishing Company — Printed in The Netherlands

THE STRUCTURE AND SELECTIVITY OF SUPPORTED METAL PARTICLES

by J.M. Domínguez[+] and M. José Yacamán[++]

Instituto Mexicano del Petróleo, Av. de Los Cien Metros and
[++]Instituto de Física, UNAM, Apartado Postal 20-364, México 20, D.F.

1. INTRODUCTION

In modern catalysis studies one of the most important aspects is the correlation between shape and crystallography of small metallic particles and
kinetic data. At the present time very little is known about the detailled
structure of supported metal catalyst. The main reason being the difficulty
to apply conventional electron and X-ray diffraction methods to nanometer
size particles. However some recent developments on weak beam electron microscopy (ref. 1 - 2) and small area diffraction (ref. 3) seem to make possible the full characterization of the particles.

In the present paper we characterize particles of Pt supported on graphite
using weak beam electron microscopy. We correlate the particle shape with
the kinetics data for the conversion of neopentane. This reaction is of the
"demanding" type (ref. 4) ie; the activity is influenced by the particle
size and more general by the mode of catalyst preparation. This system appears to be very convinient for the correlation sought because the reaction
has the metal as sole site of catalytic activity (ref. 5).

2. EXPERIMENTAL TECHNIQUES

a) Sample Preparation.

The preparation of Pt/C catalyst was made using materials of high purity.
The support was a graphite LONZA - LT10, type ex-anthracite, with 99.9% of
carbon, as reported by the supplier. The surface area determined by B.E.T.
adsorption of N_2 equals 18 m^2/g and the density equals 2.2 g/cm^3. The metal
Pt, was deposited on the support from chloroplatinic acid (H_2PtCl_6, $6H_2O$)
using the method of Bartholomew and Boudart (ref. 5).

The 10% in weight Pt/C catalyst was obtained from a solution of 10 ml. of
ethanol by 1 gr. of support. The mixture was shaken during 24 hrs. and then
the excess of solvent was eliminated by heating the powder at 100°C in an
evaporator during several hours. The sample was then air dried at 80°C during 12 hrs. The obtained powder was placed in a quartz cell and heated at
850°C in the presence of an hydrogen flow. Thus the sample was left 16 hrs.
in a static atmosphere of hydrogen and then was purged with Argon (99.99%)
until room temperature was reached.

b) Kinetic Measurements.

The activity data of the neopentane conversion over a Pt/C catalyst was collected in a differential reactor flow system coupled with a Varian Aerograph

1200 chromatograph. The gas coming from the reactor was analyzed by passing it through a column 6 m. long, filled with chromosorb W (80 mesh) impregnated with dimethyl-sulfolane (20%). The chromatographic analyses were performed at a reactor temperature of 300 and 360°C respectively and at a total pressure of 1 atmosphere. The reagent gas flowing through the reactor was a mixture of neopentane (Fluka, 99.9% purity) diluted in helium and hydrogen (Air Liquide, 99.95%) with an hydrogen to neopentane ratio equal to 10. These conditions were kept constant during the experiment and are similar to the ones described by Boudart and Ptak (ref. 7). The products detected were methane, ethane, propane, isobutane and isopentane.

Initial reaction rates were measured after 5 minutes of reaction. The percent of isomerization (selectivity) gives the amount of neopentane transformed in isopentane ($0 \leq S_i \leq 100\%$).

c) Electron Microscopy.

Samples were mounted on 200 Mesh grids covered with a layer of carbon which was evaporated from standard electrodes at a vacuum of 10^{-6} Torr.

The Pt/C powder was ultrasonically dispersed in ethanol and mounted on the grid, where a drop of the suspension was then air dried.

Observations were carried out in a Jeol 100-C electron microscope fitted with a high resolution top entry goniometer stage. Dark field images were obtained by tilting the electron beam so as to make the diffraction spot spatially coincident with the current center of the microscope. Astigmatism was corrected using the phase contrast features of the carbon film. Lattice images of Mn_2O_3 whiskers were used to calibrate the magnification.

3. SHAPE AND CRYSTALLOGRAPHY OF THE SMALL Pt PARTICLES

When observed in bright field microscopy the Pt clusters show two main profiles, hexagonal and elongated hexagonal. These types are shown in figure 1. A systematic study was made to obtain the correspondent 3-D shape for these particles. Dark field images using a reflection close to the Bragg condition showed the complete hexagonal profile (figure 2). That indicated that the particles were not multiple twinned icosahedra (ref. 8) which also have and hexagonal bright field profile but in dark field they only show part of the particle iluminated.

The regular hexagonal particles (H_1) are observed only in (220) - type of reflections. The elongated hexagons are observed in (111), (200) and (220) type of reflections.

Some micro diffraction experiments were performed using a STEM attachment for the microscope. The diffraction patterns for regular hexagonals were consistenly indexed as corresponding to an FCC crystal with a <111> zone axis. A typical pattern of this type is shown in figure 3.

The patterns of particles of the H_2 type indicated an FCC in a < 110 > zone axis. This data suggested the 3-D shape of the particles was a cubo-octa-hedron bounded by {111} and < 110 > faces. The particle H_1 will correspond to a cubo-octahedron sitting on a < 111 > face. The H_2 particle will corres-pond to a cubo-octahedron sitting in a < 110 > face and is produced probably by 9 particle growth in contact with some special type of sites on the sub-strate. This model was comfirmed by weak beam thickness fringes (ref. 2) which give a direct indication of the 3-dimensional shape. An example of thickness fringes for an H_2 particle which is slighty tilted is shown in fi-gures 4 a) and b). The profile correspond exactly to the cubo-octahedron when observed along a <110> axis.

Fig. 5a) thickness fringe profile for a H_1 particle in bright and dark field (fig. 5a) and 5b)). The dark field image shows a triangular fringe at the top to the hexagonal particle which shows that the {111} faces of the cubo-octahedron are triangular rather than hexagonal as shown in the model in fi-gure 6. A further information is that the cubo-octahedron is truncated to some extent. The exact amount of truncation can be obtained from the number of fringes present and their total size. We have observed that the trunca-tion tend to be larger for smaller particles.

An additional confirmation for the cubo-octahedron model is the relative orientation between the $\vec{g}$ vector corresponding to a (220) planes for a <111> oriented cubo-octahedron and their corresponding dark field image which is unique for this figure as described elsewhere (ref. 8).

4. ORIENTATION RELATIONS PARTICLE-SUBSTRATE

A important point in order to understand the mechanism of growth for the par-ticles is to determine the orientation relationship between the particles and the substrate. In order to do that the following experiment was perform-ed; a region of graphite of the order of 1500 Å containing a large number of particles was examined. This graphite had a surface corresponding to a basal plane i e ; <0001> zone axis with the corresponding hexagonal sym-metry. Dark field images of H_1 particles where taken in several positions of the objective aperture. In these images the rotation of the cubo-octa-hedron with respect to a < 0020 > graphite reflection was measured. This gives the orientation of the particles with respect to the substrate orien-tation. It was confirmed by examining the diffraction pattern that the orientation of the graphite did not change along the area observed. That allow us to make some statistical measurements of the particle orientation. A plot of the relative frecuencies vs. the particle rotation is shown in Fig. 7. As it is apparent the particles are not located at random but they present well defined preferred orientations.

The behavior shown in figure 7 indicates that particles grow epitaxially and they might be able to rotate on the substrate to acomodate in a minimum ener-gy configuration this point is relevant with respect to the sintering be-havior of the particles.

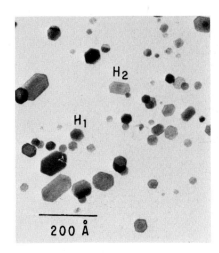

Figure 1. Bright field image of a Pt - Graphite catalyst showing regular hexagonal particles H_1 and elongated hexagonal particles H_2.

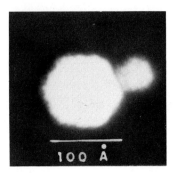

Figure 2. Dark field image using a (220) reflection of an H_1 particle. The complete hexagonal profile is observed.

5. KINETIC MEASUREMENTS

The corresponding data to the isomerization of neopentane are shown in Table 1. This Table shows the kinetic data which correspond to the two parallel reactions, hydrogenolysis and isomerization of neopentane at 300 and 360° C respectively. The data collected in table 2 are those taken at initial conditions, as mentioned above. These figures show that the isomerization rather than hydrogenolysis is favored by Pt/C catalyst at both 300 and 360°C with the selectivity being equal to 87.2 and 82.8% of the total conversion, respectively. Another important aspect is that the distribution of hydrogenolysis products: CH_4 and iso- C_4H_{10} are more favored than intermediates C_2H_6 and C_3H_8; which means the breaking of only one bond of the neopentane molecule is more likely. The quantity of iso-butane formed decreases with an increase in the temperature from 300 to 360°C. Is possible that in latter case the secondary reactions become important, such as the

Figure 3. Micro-diffraction pattern of an hexagonal particle showing < 111 >
zone axis. Some graphite reflections are observed.

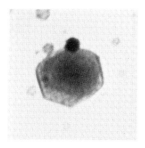

Figure 4a). Bright field image of an H_2 particle.

Figure 4b). Weak beam dark field image corresponding to the particle in
figure 4a). Thickness fringes and moire patterns are observed.

iso- C_5H_{12} transformation into light hidrocarbons giving CH_4 as the principal final product. It has been suggested by Boudart et al. (ref. 4) that
atom arrays of 3 sites (B_3 type sites) could favour the tri-adsorption of
neopentane molecule (precursor of isomer). This mechanism is squematically
represented in figure 8 in which the different steps of the reactions are

indicated. B$_3$ sites are present in { 111 } crystal planes. Foger and Anderson (ref. 11) have correlated the percent of atoms in { 111 } planes with selectivity (Si). Those authors assumed a cubo-octahedral and octahedral shapes.

A   B

Figure 5a) Bright field image of an hexagonal particle showing a triangular fringe.

Figure 5b) Weak beam dark field image corresponding to the particle in figure 5a) showing thickness fringes.

Figure 6. Cubo-octahedron shaped cluster showing the different type of sites which are present on the surfaces.

In view of these ideas and the results of the present work a calculation was made of the number of B$_3$ sites (ref. 12) for a regular cubo-octahedron as a function of the average particle diameter. The results are plotted in fig. 9 which includes some experimental selectivity points. The Si values were obtained from references (ref. 4 and 11) and from the present measurements. In fig. 9 we have not normalized the curves as proposed by Anderson

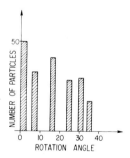

Figure 7. Plot of the orientations of the hexagonal particles with respect
to the graphite substrate.

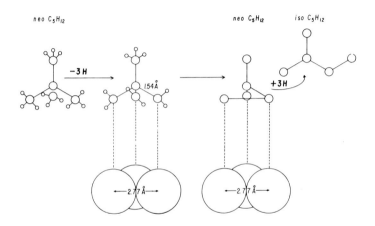

Figure 8. Squematic representation of model for isomerization of neo pentane

$(S_i = 90\%$ for a 100% < 111> oriented film) because a value of $S_i > 90\%$ has
been reported for a Pt/ γ -Al$_2$O$_3$ catalyst $(S_i = 100\%)$ treated at high
temperatures (ref. 13). As can be seen from the figure the best experimental agreement is found for larger sizes. It should noted that discre-
pancies exist with the data reported by the authors of(ref. 4 and 11),
who used different preparation conditions and different supports from the
ones in the present work. Indeed there is no evidence that the particles
in those catalysts were cubo-octahedrons.

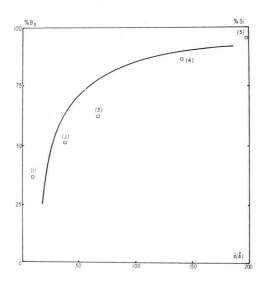

Figure 9. Change on the percent of 3 - atom arrays in { 111 } surfaces of a
perfect cubo-octahedral particle (continuos line) as a function
of diameter of the particle. Selectivity points are shown by
squares. Point 1.2 and 3 are from ref. 10, and point 5 is from
ref. 4.

6. DISCUSSION AND CONCLUSIONS

The data plot in figure 9 represents a very encouraging correlation between
the particle shape and crystallography with selectivity for isomerization
data. It seems that indeed the electron microscopy is a very powerfull technique to obtain such data.

The platinum that have been characterized are cubo-octahedron having { 111 }
and { 100 } facets. It is worth to mention that in the case of large single
crystals of Pt Leed experiments (ref. 14-15) show that the (100) surface
is reconstructed to an hexagonal array. At the present time there is no
experimental evidence of that reconstruction also occurs in small metal
clusters. However a theoretical considerations indicate that those effects
should be more dramatic in the case of small finite crystalls. If reconstruction of (100) surfaces is present the number of B_3 sites will be
increased. We are currently investigating these effects by matching experimental and computer calculated images for a number of particle sizes.

The experimental evidence shows that the shape of the H_1 and H_2 particles is
a cubo-octahedron in <111> and <110> orientation. The figures being either
complete or truncated. Although hexagonal Pt particles have been reported
in other works (ref. 16 and 17). This is the first time that an unambigous
determination of the reol shape is made. The 'Pill-box 'shape reported by
Boñker et al. (ref. 17) migth correspond to a truncated cubo-cotahedron particle of figure 5. All the particles observed were single crystalline in
contrast with the findins of Chen and Schmidt (ref. 16) who reported for

T A B L E No. 1

Activity of Pt/C catalyst in neopentane reaction at
300 and 360°C, H_2/neopentane = 10 , 1 atm.

Product	(300°C)	(360°C	specific rate at 300°C ($x\ 10^8$ moles-s^{-1}-g^{-1})	specific rate at 360°C ($x\ 10^8$moles-s^{-1}-g^{-1})
	Hydrogenolysis		Total specific activities of hydrogenolysis reported to 1 gram of Pt	
methane	43	50.7		
ethane	13.5	14.9	7.6	14.9
propane	12.3	16.5		
isobutane	31.1	17.8		
isomerization selectivity			specific rate of isomerization	
isopentane	87.2	82.8	51.8	72.1

Pt in S_1O_2 about of 20% of twinned particles. In adition the particles were found in an epitaxial orientation with respect to the rubstrate. These two facts suggest that there is an strong interaction between the support and the clusters. This interaction is likely to play an important role in the catalitic properties of the Pt-C system.

The present results also indicate that the lattice parameter of the Pt cluster remains very close to the bulk value. That is in agreement with the EXaFS measurements of Moraweck et. al. (ref. 18) that found an interatomic distance for Pt clusters very close to the bulk value.

R E F E R E N C E S

(1)   M. José Yacamán and T. Ocaña. Phys. Stat. Sol. a) 47, 571 (1977).

(2)   M. José Yacamán , K. Heinemann and H. Poppa Chemistry and Physics of Solid Surfaces III Edited by R. Vanselow. CRC. Press.

(3)   J.B. Warren . In introduction to analytical electron microscopy Edited by J.J. Hren, J. Goldstein and D. Joy. Plenum Press (1979).

(4)   M. Boudart, A.W. Aldag, L.D. Ptak and J.E. Benson. J. of Catal. 11, (1968) 35.

(5)   J. R. Anderson and N.R. Avery. J. Catal. 2, 542-544 (1963).

(6)   C.H. Bartholomew and M. Boudart . J. Catal 25, (1972) 173.

(7)   M. Boudart and L.D. Ptak. J. of Catal. 16 (1970) 90.

(8)   M. José Yacamán, K. Heinemann , C. Yang and H. Poppa. J. of Cryst. Growth.

(9)   M. José Yacamán and J.M. Domínguez. Surface Science in Press.

(10) A. Gómez and D. Dingley. To be published.

(11) K. Foger and J.R. Anderson. J. of Catal. 54, 318 (1978).

(12) R. Van Hardeveld and A. Van Montfort. Surf. Sci. 4 (1966) 369-430.

(13) J. M. Domínguez . Ph.D. Thesis (1977). Claude Bernard University Lyon.

(14) K. Muller, P.Heilmann, K. Heinz and K. Muller. Surface Science 83 (1979) 487.

(15) K. Muller , P. Helmann , K. Heinz and G.G. Waldecker. Vakuum. Rech. 8 (1976) 227.

(16) M. Chen and L.D. Schmidt. J. Catal. 55, (1978) 348.

(17) R.T. Baker, E.B. prestridge and R.L. Garten J. Catal. 56 (1979) 390.

(18) B. Moraweck, G. Clugnet and A.J. Renouprez. Surf. Sci. 81, (1979) L631.

DISCUSSION

J.M. DOMINGUEZ, J. YACAMAN

<u>Renouprez</u> - Down to what particle size can you obtain a diffraction pattern ? What is the influence of diffraction by the support on the quality of the metal diffraction pattern ?

<u>Yacaman</u> - By using dynamical diffraction theory, one can find orientations in which the beams coming from the particles will travel in the substrate without being diffracted or suffering strong anormalous adsorption. In those conditions the substrate influence is reduced to a minimum. With the tilting stage on the microscope, we can reproduce those conditions in practice.

<u>Wynblatt</u> - 1°/ Are the particular sets of orientations you observe, for particles on graphite, consistent with coincidence type models of a (0001)-graphite/metal interface ?

       2°/ How difficult is it to distinguish between the thickness fringes you obtain and, say, interfacial dislocations ?

<u>Yacaman</u> - 1°/ Yes, all the orientations that we observed are predicted by the coincidence model.

       2°/ Interfacial dislocations will not interact with thickness fringes. As can be seen in figure 5b) moire fringes and thickness fringes can coexist. Moire fringes on the other hand will be very difficult to distinguish from interfacial dislocation. That is why we prefer not to use the moires for quantitative measurements.

<u>Gillet</u> - Are the shapes you observe equilibrium shapes ? If so, what is the influence of the substrate ? Are those shapes taken during the growth or are they due to different treatments during catalytic processes ?

<u>Yacaman</u> - We have observed the particles after and before the reaction and the shape is not altered. Moreover, the treatment undergone by the particles leads them to their equilibrium shapes. The fact that the particles are in a well defined relation with the substrate suggests a strong particle-substrate interaction, which has to be considered when calculating the equilibrium shape.

J. BOURDON (Editor)
Growth and Properties of Metal Clusters, pp. 505—513
© 1980 Elsevier Scientific Publishing Company — Printed in The Netherlands

PROPRIETES CATALYTIQUES DES AGREGATS DE PLATINE SUPPORTE SUR SILICES ET SUR ZEOLITHES.

par Jean BANDIERA

Institut de Recherches sur la Catalyse, 2 avenue Albert Einstein, 69626 VILLEURBANNE - FRANCE

INTRODUCTION

Le platine est souvent utilisé dans des procédés mettant en jeu des réactions d'hydrogénation, de deshydrogénation ou d'hydrogénolyse. De l'ensemble des travaux antérieurs (réf.1)
il ressort que les performances catalytiques (activité, durée de vie et sélectivité) d'un
système platine supporté dépendent de ses nombreuses "caractéristiques". Ces "caractéristiques" qui ne sont pas forcément indépendantes concernent soit la phase métallique (taille,
forme et localisation des particules - structure électronique des atomes superficiels de
platine), soit le support (morphologie, degré de cristallinité, acidité et propriétés
d'adsorption). Ainsi, la morphologie du support peut influer sur la taille et sur la localisation des particules de métal, alors que la structure électronique des atomes superficiels
de platine semble dépendre du caractère électrophile de la surface du support (réf. 2) et
de la taille des agrégats métalliques (réf. 3).

La multiplicité et l'interdépendance de ces "caractéristiques" rendent délicate la mise
en évidence du rôle de chacune d'elles dans l'activation de liaisons Carbone-Carbone et
Carbone - Hydrogène d'autant plus que, pour une liaison donnée, ce rôle peut encore dépendre
de la géométrie de la molécule à convertir.

Dans la présente communication, nous nous proposons justement de rapporter des résultats
concernant les propriétés hydrogénantes, deshydrogénantes et hydrogénolysantes du platine
supporté sur des silices ou occlus dans des matrices zéolithiques pour essayer de préciser,en
regard du type de liaison à activer, quelle est (ou quelles sont) la (ou les) "caractéristique (s)" d'un système catalytique qui joue (nt) un rôle important dans une réaction donnée.
Afin de minimiser les éventuels effets stériques qui peuvent résulter, selon la morphologie
du support, de la géométrie de la molécule à convertir, nous n'avons mis en oeuvre que la
conversion de molécules de géométrie semblable.

DESCRIPTION DES SYSTEMES CATALYTIQUES

Le catalyseur de référence (nous avons choisi le catalyseur "EUROCAT") contient 6,4 % de
platine en poids supporté sur une silice ; sa phase métallique, homodisperse, est constituée
de cristallites de 20 Å de diamètre. Les autres supports utilisés sont : une silice micro-
poreuse (SiO_2 Davison), des zéolithes du type faujasite (Na Y et NH_4 Y) et une zéolithe
de type mordénite (Na Z).

Selon leurs conditions d'élaboration, les phases métalliques des systèmes catalytiques
étudiés peuvent.différer par la taille des particules de platine, par le fait qu'elles
peuvent être homo- ou hétérodisperses et (ou) par leur localisation comme le montre l'examen
du tableau I dans lequel sont résumées les "caractéristiques" essentielles des catalyseurs.

TABLEAU I

Conditions d'élaboration de la phase métallique et "caractéristiques" essentielles des différents catalyseurs platine supporté.

| %Pt en poids | Support | Traitements thermiques | | Morphologie | Phase métallique Ø | Localisation | n_s (a) | Cat. |
| | | T_{O_2} | T_{H_2} | | | | | |
		(°C)			(Å)			N°
6,4	SiO2	-	-	cristallites	20	-	3,5	1
2,6	SiO2 Davison	500	500	cristallites	40 - 60	orifices des micropores	1,1	2
		350	350	cristallites	15	micropores	1,9	2'
7,85	Na Y	500	500	cristallites Pt atomique	15 - 20 / -	occluses / -	1,4	3
3,6	NH4 Y	500	500	cristallites Pt atomique	15 / -	occluses / -	0,8	4
		350	350	agrégats	< 12	supercages	2,3	4'
5,85	Na Z	500	500	agrégats cristallites	< 10 / 20 200	internes / externes	3,0	5
		-	500	batonnets cristallites	- / -	externes	0,6	5'

(a) n_s désigne le nombre de micromoles de platine superficiel contenues dans 20 mg de catalyseur.

Remarques sur le tableau I

- Dans la dernière colonne, figure un nombre qui, dans la suite de cet exposé, servira à répertorier les différents catalyseurs.

- Avec une zéolithe Y comme support, l'obtention de cristallites de platine de 15 à 20 Å de diamètre (cat. N°s 3 et 4) s'accompagne d'une formation de platine atomiquement dispersé qui, n'adsorbant pas l'hydrogène à température ambiante, sera considéré comme catalytiquement inactif.

- Les batonnets qui constituent une fraction de la phase métallique supportée par la surface d'un grain de zéolithe Na Z (cat. N° 5') possèdent des plans cristallographiques orientés parallèlement aux canaux de cette mordénite.

DEFINITION ET FORMULATION DES DIFFERENTES REACTIONS "TEST"

Le choix des réactions mises en oeuvre est guidé par l'impératif suivant : activer, séparément ou compétitivement, différents types de liaisons appartenant à des molécules de géométrie semblable. Pour ce faire, nous avons fait appel à des hydrocarbures aromatiques et nous avons étudié :

- L'interconversion toluène - méthylcyclohexane

$$CH_3 - C_6H_5 + 3 H_2 \underset{V_{DH}}{\overset{V_H}{\rightleftharpoons}} CH_3 - C_6H_{11}$$

- L'hydrocraquage du benzène en méthane

$$C_6H_6 + 9 H_2 \xrightarrow{V_{HC}} 6 CH_4$$

- L'hydrométhylation du toluène

$$CH_3 - C_6H_5 + H_2 \xrightarrow{V_{HDM}} CH_4 + C_6H_6$$

Dans ce cas si x désigne la fraction de noyaux aromatiques hydrocraqués, la réaction globale se formule par

$$CH_3 - C_6H_5 + (1 + 9x) H_2 \rightarrow (1 + 6x) CH_4 + (1 - x) C_6H_6$$

En désignant par V_1 et V_6 les vitesses de formation du méthane et du benzène, on montre facilement que :

$$x = \frac{V_1 - V_6}{V_1 + 6 V_6} \qquad V_{HDM} = \frac{V_1 + 6 V_6}{7}$$

Pour compléter les résultats quantitatifs obtenus pour ces 4 réactions, nous décrirons quelques résultats plus qualitatifs sur la conversion de l'éthylbenzène en un mélange de toluène, benzène et méthane.

Toutes les réactions sont effectuées sur le même échantillon de 20 mg de catalyseur, à la pression atmosphérique et sous un débit de 10 $1h^{-1}$.

RESULTATS

1. Stabilité de l'activité et durée de vie d'un catalyseur

Quels que soient le catalyseur et la réaction, l'activité catalytique est pratiquement stable après une heure de travail de sorte qu'il est alors possible de déterminer l'énergie apparente d'activation de la réaction. La bonne stabilité catalytique des systèmes étudiés est confirmée par le fait qu'un catalyseur ayant effectué le cycle des réactions précédemment décrites a une activité hydrogénante peu différente de celle qu'il avait après seulement une heure de travail à température ambiante.

2. Activités hydrogénante et déshydrogénante

Les résultats obtenus sont résumés dans le tableau II dans lequel figurent les vitesses et les énergies apparentes d'activation d'hydrogénation du toluène (V_H et E_H) et de deshy-drogénation du méthylcyclohexane (V_{DH} et E_{DH}), ainsi que les valeurs de $a = V/n_s$ qui, pour une réaction donnée, mesurent en h^{-1} l'activité par site superficiel de platine (n_s est défini dans la légende du tableau I).

TABLEAU II

Activités hydrogénante et deshydrogénante du platine supporté sur silice ou occlus dans une matrice zéolithique.

Catalyseurs N°	Hydrogénation du toluène à 25°C			Deshydrogénation du méthylcyclohexane à 250°C		
	V_H (a)	E_H (b)	a_H (h^{-1})	V_{DH} (a)	E_{DH} (b)	a_{DH} (h^{-1})
1	95	11,5	27	569	26	164
2	7,0	10	6,5	191	19,5	179
2'	7,6	9,5	4,0	221	19,5	115
3	309	11,5	215	923	26,5	641
4	205	8	253	540	25,5	667
4'	120	10	53	400	21	175
5	inactif	-	0	124	14,5	41
5'	16	9	26	268	17	447

(a) V_H et V_{DH} en micromoles de réactif converties par heure, pour un échantillon de 20 mg de catalyseur.

(b) E_H et E_{DH} en kilocalories mole^{-1}.

De l'examen de ce tableau, nous retiendrons que les valeurs expérimentales de la vitesse, de deshydrogénation V_{DH} variant de 124 à 923 micromoles h^{-1}, l'équilibre thermodynamique méthylcyclohexane - toluène n'est certainement pas atteint dans nos conditions expérimentales comme le prouve encore le fait que le taux de conversion augmente quand le débit diminue, même pour le catalyseur le plus actif (N° 3).

3. Activités et sélectivité du platine supporté pour l'hydrocraquage du benzène et l'hydrodéméthylation du toluène.

Les principaux résultats, établis à partir des valeurs expérimentales de V_1 et de V_6, sont résumés dans le tableau III dans lequel a_{HC} et a_{HDM} désignent les activités par site superficiel de platine pour respectivement l'hydrocraquage de C_6H_6 et l'hydrodéméthylation de $CH_3 - C_6H_5$.

L'examen du tableau suivant indique que :

- A 500°C, la vitesse d'hydrodéméthylation V_{HDM} est supérieure à la vitesse d'hydrocraquage V_{HC} pour tous les catalyseurs étudiés.

- La sélectivité, pour l'hydrodéméthylation du toluène, s = 1 - x du platine supporté sur silice ou sur zéolithe Y (Cat. N°s 1 à 4) est bonne (s > 90 %) et elle diminue lorsque la température augmente alors que, pour un support Na Z (cat. N°s 5 et 5'), le pouvoir hydro-craquant du platine est plus grand (13 < x < 34 %) mais s croit avec la température de réaction.

TABLEAU III
Performances (activité a et sélectivité s) catalytiques de différents systèmes platine supporté pour l'hydrocraquage du benzène et l'hydrodéméthylation du toluène.

Catalyseurs No	Hydrocraquage de C_6H_6 à 500 °C		Hydrodéméthylation du toluène					
	V_{HC} (a)	a_{HC} (h^{-1})	T $(°C)$	V_{HDM} (a)	a_{HDM} (h^{-1})	x $(\%)$	s = 1-x $(\%)$	E_{HDM} (b)
1	23,1	6,6	400 500	11 354	3 102	1,5 1	98,5 99	36 35,5
2	2,9	2,7	400 500	3,2 27	3 26	1,5 8,5	98,5 91,5	22 22
3	128	89	400 500	97 1927	67 1338	0 5	100 95	31,5 30
4	50,5	62	400 500	15 504	18 622	3 4,5	97 95,5	34 39,5
5	125	42	400 500	10 336	3 112	34 23	66 77	35 40
5'	66	111	400 500	8,5 311	14 519	20 14	80 86	34 38

(a) V_{HC} et V_{HDM} en micromoles de réactif converties par heure, pour un échantillon de 20 mg de catalyseur.

(b) E_{HDM} en kilocalories mole^{-1}.

4. AUTRES RESULTATS

Ils concernent la conversion, à 400°C, de l'éthylbenzène en un mélange de toluène, benzène et méthane. La réaction principale

$$C_6H_5 - CH_2 - CH_3 + H_2 \xrightarrow{V_{HG}} CH_4 + C_6H_5 - CH_3$$

est appelée hydrogénolyse de l'éthylbenzène parce qu'elle met en jeu l'activation de la liaison carbone-carbone du groupe éthyle.

Les résultats obtenus montrent que :

- A 400°C, la vitesse d'hydrogénolyse V_{HG} est supérieure à la vitesse d'hydrométhylation V_{HDM} pour tous les catalyseurs étudiés.

- La sélectivité du platine pour l'hydrogénolyse de l'éthylbenzène est comprise entre 40 et 80 % ; elle varie, selon le support, comme la sélectivité pour l'hydrodéméthylation du toluène.

Enfin, dans le tableau IV, sont rassemblées, pour toutes les réactions étudiées, les activités relatives A des différents catalyseurs, le catalyseur Nº 1 ("EUROCAT") étant pris comme référence ; pour ce dernier, A = 1 quelle que soit la réaction envisagée.

510

TABLEAU IV

Activités relatives A pour: $_H$ l'hydrogénation du toluène, $_{DH}$ la deshydrogénation du méthylcyclohexane, $_{HG}$ l'hydrogénolyse de l'éthylbenzène, $_{HDM}$ l'hydrodéméthylation du toluène
et $_{HC}$ l'hydrocraquage du benzène.

Catalyseurs	Activités relatives				
Nº	A_H 25 °C	A_{DH} 250°C	A_{HG} 400 °C	A_{HDM} 500 °C	A_{HC} 500 °C
1	1	1	1	1	1
2	0,25	1,1	0,3	0,25	0,5
2'	0,15	0,7	-	-	-
3	8	4	5	13	13
4	9	4	-	6	9
4'	2	1	-	-	-
5	0,0	0,25	0,2	1	6,4
5'	1	3	1,5	5	17

DISCUSSION

Les résultats ci-avant rapportés dont une synthèse est représentée dans le tableau IV
indiquent que pour des particules de 15 à 20 Å de diamètre, le platine occlus dans une
zéolithe Y (Cat. N°s 3 et 4) est toujours plus actif que lorsqu'il est supporté sur une
silice (Cat. N°s 1 à 2'), mais il convient de remarquer que son activité relative diminue
quand on passe de l'hydrogénation du toluène (A_H = 8 - 9) à la deshydrogénation du méthylcyclohexane (A_{DH} = 4) puis augmente à nouveau pour l'hydrogénolyse de l'éthylbenzène (A_{HG} = 5),
l'hydrodéméthylation du toluène (A_{HDM} = 6 - 13) et l'hydrocraquage du benzène (A_{HC} = 9 - 13).
Au contraire, le platine bien divisé qui est occlus dans les canaux étroits (Ø < 7,5 Å) d'une
mordénite (Cat. N° 5) n'hydrogène pas le toluène à température ambiante alors qu'à 500°C,
son activité pour l'hydrodéméthylation du toluène et l'hydrocraquage du benzène devient
égale (A_{HDM} = 1) et supérieure (A_{HC} = 6) à celle du platine supporté sur une silice. Il
n'en est pas de même pour le platine mal divisé situé à la surface d'un grain de mordénite
(Cat. N° 5') : son activité hydrogénante est normale (A_H = 1) alors qu'il est plus performant
que Pt/SiO$_2$ pour toutes les autres réactions.

L'exaltation de l'activité hydrogénante des catalyseurs Pt - zéolithe Y a été discutée
et interprétée par ailleurs (réf. 4). Elles résulterait du fait que, contrairement aux
silices, les zéolithes Y adsorbent du toluène de manière irréversible à 25°C ; les molécules
de toluène ainsi adsorbées seraient activées et facilement converties en méthylcyclohexane
au contact d'hydrogène activé sur le platine, suivant une réaction de catalyse bifonctionnel-
le. Au contraire, une zéolithe Na Z n'adsorbe du toluène que si elle ne contient pas de platine ; il semble donc que les canaux d'une mordénite soient obstrués par les petits agrégats
de platine qu'ils contiennent, la plupart de ces derniers étant, tout du moins à température
ambiante, inaccessible au toluène et par voie de conséquence non actifs en hydrogénation.
Il apparaît donc que pour un support à structure peu ouverte vers l'extérieur, seule la
fraction de l'aire métallique située sur la surface d'un grain de mordénite soit active pour
l'hydrogénation du toluène. Une situation analogue (capacité d'adsorption réduite quand elle

contient du platine) se retrouve avec un support SiO_2 Davison ; corrolairement, l'activité hydrogénante relative du platine est inférieure à 1 (tableau IV : Cat.N°s 2 et 2') et ce d'autant plus que la taille des cristallites de métal est plus petite.

L'accessibilité d'une phase métallique, nécessairement liée à la morphologie du support et à la taille des particules de platine, apparaît jouer un rôle fondamental dans l'hydrogénation des hydrocarbures aromatiques ; c'est pourquoi, il ne nous est pas possible de préciser sans ambiguité si l'activité hydrogénante d'un atome superficiel de platine dépend ou ne dépend pas de la taille de la particule à laquelle il appartient.

Cet "effet de structure", spécifique des supports microporeux (Cat. N°s 2, 2', 5 et 5'), est moins manifeste pour des réactions se développant à des températures plus élevées ($A_{DH} > A_H$), comme si, consécutivement à une élévation de température, une fraction de plus en plus grande de platine interne devenait accessible au réactif. Or, le platine finement divisé occlus dans une matrice Na Z n'a toujours aucune activité hydrogénante à température ambiante même après avoir effectué l'hydrodéméthylation du toluène à 500°C. Il est donc permis de postuler que c'est la véhiculation d'une molécule de géométrie donnée à travers un réseau microporeux qui est facilitée par une élévation de température ; cette hypothèse est d'ailleurs corroborée par les faits expérimentaux suivants :

- Le platine supporté sur un grain de mordénite est 10 fois plus deshydrogénant à 250°C et seulement 5 fois plus actif pour l'hydrodéméthylation du toluène à 500°C que le platine occlus dans cette matrice zéolithique (tableau IV : Cat. N°s 5 et 5').

- L'énergie apparente d'ativation de deshydrogénation E_{DH} est d'autant plus faible que le support est plus microporeux (tableau II) : à 250°C, une fraction du platine situé dans les micropores d'un support est accessible au méthylcyclohexane mais des phénomènes de transfert de matière résultant de la valeur élevée de la vitesse de deshydrogénation ($V_{DH} > 120$ micromoles h^{-1}) limitent cette vitesse dans le cas d'un support microporeux.

- Pour l'hydrodéméthylation du toluène (tableau III), la vitesse de réaction n'est limitée par les phénomènes de transfert de matière que pour le Cat. N° 2 Pt/SiO$_2$ Davison : $E_{HDM} = 22$ kcal. mole^{-1}. Avec les catalyseurs Pt - Na Z (N°s 5 et 5'), l'énergie apparente d'activation est plus grande qu'avec Pt - Na Y (Cat. n° 3) et elle augmente légèrement avec la température : à 500°C, tout le platine occlus dans une mordénite (Cat. N° 5), est accessible au toluène ($A_{HDM} = 1,1$ d'après le tableau IV) et les phénomènes de transfert de matière ne limitent pas la vitesse d'hydrodéméthylation ($E_{HDM} = 40$ kcal. mole^{-1} d'après le tableau III).

Quant au caractère irréversible de l'adsorption du toluène sur une zéolithe Y, il disparaît totalement au dessus de 350°C. Il convient donc de chercher ailleurs l'origine de la plus grande (par rapport à l'EUROCAT) activité du platine occlus dans une zéolithe Y ou supportée sur un grain de mordénite vis-à-vis de réactions se développant à ces températures et mettant en jeu la rupture de liaisons carbons-carbone. Nous avons constaté qu'à une même température $V_{HG} < V_{HDM} < V_{HC}$ et ce quel que soit le catalyseur considéré ; ce résultat tend à indiquer que le caractère "exigeant" de ces réactions est de plus en plus marqué quand on passe de l'hydrogénolyse (liaison activée : $H_2C - CH_3$) à l'hydrodéméthylation (liaison activée : $\emptyset - \overset{\cdot}{C}H_3$) et à l'hydrocraquage (liaison activée : HC - CH). Des travaux de BOUDART et DALLA BETTA (réf. 5), de SINFELT (réf. 6) et de GRENOBLE (réf. 7) ont montré que la rupture catalytique d'une liaison carbone-carbone dépend énormément du métal catalyseur, probablement de par la structure électronique de ses atomes superficiels. Il semble donc que les meilleures performances hydrogénolysantes des systèmes Pt-zéolithe Y soient dües au caractère déficitaire en électrons des particules de platine constituant leur phase métallique (réf. 2 et 3). Pour le platine supporté sur un grain de mordénite, sa bonne activité vis-à-vis de la rupture des liaisons carbone-carbone pourrait résulter du fait que sa phase métallique est essentiellement constituée de "batonnets" prismatiques possédant des plans cristallographiques particuliers qui auraient, comme certains plans du nickel pour l'hydrogénolyse du cyclopentane (réf. 8), une meilleure activité hydrogénolysante que la surface d'une cristallite supposée sphérique supportée sur une silice.

CONCLUSION

L'étude d'un ensemble de réactions ne mettant en jeu que des molécules de géométrie semblable (C_6H_6, $C_6H_5 - CH_3$, $C_6H_{11} - CH_3$ et $C_6H_5 - CH_2 - CH_3$) permet de constater que l'importance relative d'une "caractéristique" donnée d'un catalyseur platine supporté dépend du type de liaison à activer.

Pour l'hydrogénation des hydrocarbures aromatiques, le support joue un rôle fondamental. Il peut :

- soit se comporter comme un cocatalyseur du platine, en activant par adsorption irréversible les noyaux aromatiques : il en est ainsi des zéolithes du type faujasite ;

- soit avoir un "effet structural" résultant de sa morphologie (il en est ainsi pour la mordénite Norton et pour la silice Davison), rendant tout ou partie de la surface métallique située dans les micropores de tels supports inaccessible aux molécules aromatiques et par voie de conséquence non active pour leur hydrogénation.

La taille, la forme et la localisation des particules de métal dépendant évidemment de la morphologie du support, l'existence d'une "effet structural" pour les supports microporeux n'autorise pas de conclure quant à l'influence des facteurs géométriques (dimensions et forme des particules de platine) dans l'hydrogénation des hydrocarbures aromatiques. Enfin, nous n'avons observé aucune influence de l'acidité d'une zéolithe Y pour l'hydrogénation du toluène.

"Effet catalytique" des zéolithes Y et "effet structural" des supports microporeux s'amenuisent puis disparaissent quand la température de réaction augmente de sorte que pour la rupture d'une liaison carbone-carbone les facteurs électroniques (caractère déficitaire en électrons des cristallites de platine occluses dans une zéolithe Y) et géométriques (plans cristallographiques particuliers du platine supporté sur un grain de mordénite) apparaissent jouer un rôle prépondérant. La morphologie d'un support intervient encore en hydrogénolyse, en augmentant le pouvoir hydrocraquant du platine contenu dans les canaux étroits d'une mordénite. Quant à l'acidité d'une zéolithe NH_4 Y, elle induit parallèlement aux réactions d'hydrogénolyse se développant sur le platine des réactions de transalkylation qui produisent des hydrocarbures aromatiques plus lourds que le réactif.

REFERENCES

1 G.C. Bond, in "Catalysis by Metals" (G.C. Bond, Ed.), Academic Press, New York and London, 1962, p. 320.
  J.R. Anderson, Adv. in Catalysis, 23 (1973) 1.
  J.H. Sinfelt, Adv. in Catalysis, 23 (1973) 91.
2 J.C. Védrine, M. Dufaux, C. Naccache et B. Imelik, J.C.S. Faraday Trans. I, 74 (1978) 440.
3 P. Gallezot, J. Datka, J. Massardier, M. Primet et B. Imelik, Proc. Int. Congress Catalysis 6th, 1976, A11.
4 J. Bandiera, J. Chim. phys., sous presse.
5 R.A. Dalla Betta et M. Boudart, Proc. Int. Congress Catalysis 5th, 1972, North Holland Pub. Company, Vol. 2, 1973, p. 1329.
6 J.H. Sinfelt, Catal. Rev., 3 (1969) 175 et J. Catal., 27 (1972) 468.
7 D.C. Grenoble, J. Catal., 56 (1979) 32-39 et 40-46.
8 J. Massardier, J. Barbier et G. Dalmai-Imelik, J. Chim. phys., 75 (1978) 815-818.

J. BOURDON (Editor)
Growth and Properties of Metal Clusters, pp. 515—524
© 1980 Elsevier Scientific Publishing Company — Printed in The Netherlands

STUDY OF THE PREPARATION OF HIGHLY DISPERSED PLATINUM-RUTHENIUM ALLOY PARTICLES SUPPORTED BY γ ALUMINA

by Gilbert BLANCHARD and Henri CHARCOSSET

Institut de Recherches sur la Catalyse - C.N.R.S. - 2, avenue Albert Einstein
69626 VILLEURBANNE Cédex - FRANCE -

SUMMARY

The Temperature Programmed Titration of oxygen chemisorbed on platinum-ruthenium supported catalysts, by means of a 1 % H_2 in Argon flow, is shown to be very sensitive and able to distinguish between metal surface Ru atoms and small particles of alloyed Ru. Successive impregnation of Al_2O_3 by H_2RuCl_6 and H_2PtCl_6 in water, coimpregnation of Al_2O_3 by H_2RuCl_6 + H_2PtBr_6 in water, and coimpregnation of Al_2O_3 by H_2RuCl_6 + H_2PtCl_6 in ethanol + water were used to prepare the bimetallics. Only the last method gives rise altogether to reasonably well alloyed and dispersed alloy phase.

INTRODUCTION

Bimetallic catalysts, with a low metal content deposited on a suitable support i.e. γ alumina, are of practical importance in various catalytic processes such as the reforming of crude oils, the automotive exhaust gases post-combustion, etc... Different mechanisms are likely to account for the variations in the properties of bimetallics according to the element added to the base element. For instance, the beneficial effect of tin in the Pt/Al_2O_3 reforming catalysts is likely to be due to ionic Sn species on the support[1] while the effect of Re in Pt based reforming catalysts most probably arises from the formation of (Pt, Re) alloy particles [2].

In the present paper we deal with the : (Pt, Ru)/γAl_2O_3 which has been patented for the reforming of naphthas [3] but which does not seem up to now to have been used in industrial units.. In the presence of Pt, Ru was shown to be easily reduced to Ru^o [4], therefore the alloying effect may be determining. More specifically, we now consider two questions : - how to distinguish between (Pt) + (Ru)/γAl_2O_3 and (Pt, Ru)/γAl_2O_3, the second case corresponding to the alloy state while the first one refers to a mixture of Pt and of Ru particles on the support. For that purpose we used the so-called TPT method (Temperature Programmed Titration of chemisorbed O, by H_2) ; - the effect of impregnation processes on the degree of alloying of the metal phase : successive impregnation of the γ Al_2O_3 pellets in aqueous medium by H_2RuCl_6 and then by H_2PtCl_6 - coimpregnation of γ Al_2O_3 by aqueous solutions of H_2RuCl_6 + H_2PtBr_6 - coimpregnation of γ Al_2O_3 by H_2RuCl_6 and H_2PtCl_6 in ethanol plus water.

As a reference let us investigate silica supported, bimetallic platinum-ruthenium catalysts already known to be easily obtainable [5] with a small % of dispersion, hence easy to characterize by X-Ray Diffraction Analysis.

MATERIALS AND EXPERIMENTAL PROCEDURE

1. Catalysts

a) $(Pt, Ru)/SiO_2$ alloys : prepared by coimpregnation of Aerosil Degussa powder by aqueous solutions H_2PtCl_6, H_2RuCl_6, followed by drying and subsequent H_2 reduction at 700°C, like in [4].

b) $(Pt, Ru)/\gamma Al_2O_3$ catalysts : the support was the GFS 400 Rhône-Poulenc Alumina (pellets of $\sim$ 1,5 mm in diameter, 15 mm in length ; S $\sim$ 200 m^2/g).

b1. Successive impregnation of H_2RuCl_6 and of H_2PtCl_6 in aqueous medium : as controlled by electron microprobe analysis, the obtention of a distribution of Pt and Ru, macroscopically homogeneous from the outside to the center of the pellets was thought to be impossible using coimpregnation [4]. Therefore we impregnated the support successively by H_2RuCl_6 in strongly acidic medium and following water washing, by H_2PtCl_6 without further addition of HCl ; experimental details are reported in [4].

b2. Coimpregnation of H_2RuCl_6 and of H_2PtBr_6, in aqueous solution : A paper by Summers and Ausen [6] pointed out a strongly higher reactivity of H_2PtBr_6 compared to H_2PtCl_6 towards Al_2O_3. We thought and found in fact to be possible to use the coimpregnation of Al_2O_3 in aqueous medium, using H_2PtBr_6 and H_2RuCl_6 as reagents. More specifically the amount of HCl to be added to the impregnation solution was nearly the same as for the Ru monometallic catalyst (See [4]).

b3. Coimpregnation of H_2RuCl_6 and of H_2PtCl_6 in ethanol plus water solution : The usefulness of non-aqueous solvents to prepare monometallic supported catalysts has already been reported (See for instance Murrel and Yates [7] for preparing Ru on basic supports catalysts). Following many exploratory experiments, we found suitable to coimpregnate H_2RuCl_6 and H_2PtCl_6 via a 75 vol % ethanol and 25 vol % water solution. The amount of HCl to add to the impregnation solution was the same for the Pt100, Pt50Ru50 and Ru100 catalysts, that is 6 x 10^{-4} ion gr Cl^-/gAl_2O_3.

Fig. 1 show the electron microprobe analysis results for the Pt50Ru50 catalyst, in its impregnated plus dried in air at 110°C state. The Pt profile is very homogeneous while the Ru profile shows a somewhat lower concentration in Ru in the center of the pellet. The Cl profile is very homogeneous.

2. The TPT method

The principle of the Hydrogen Temperature Programmed Titration of Oxygen chemisorbed on the catalysts was indicated in [4]. After hydrogen reduction at 500°C, the catalyst was outgassed by a helium flow at 500°C. After cooling down to room temperature, oxygen was chemisorbed from a 1 % O_2 in He mixture (frontal analysis method). The sample was subsequently purged by argon flow during 20 min. Afterwards, the Hydrogen Titration by a 1 % H_2 in Ar mixture was carried out firstly during 20 min at room temperature and subsequently up to 200°C (heating rate : 5 °C/min). Finally, the sample was cooled down to room temperature in the 1 % H_2/Ar mixture, by removing the furnace. A catharometer allowed to follow the variations in the H_2 concentration of the H_2/Ar mixture during the different steps. Fig. 2 shows, as a typical example of a TPT curve for the 0,73 % $Ru/\gamma Al_2O_3$ monome-

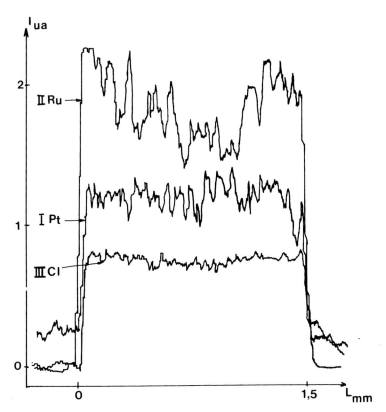

Fig. 1 : 0,94 % Pt + 0,47 % Ru/γ Al$_2$O$_3$, prepared by coimpregnation of H$_2$PtCl$_6$, H$_2$RuCl$_6$ in ethanol (75 %) plus water. Electron microprobe analysis results for Pt (curve I), Ru (curve II) and Cl (Curve III).

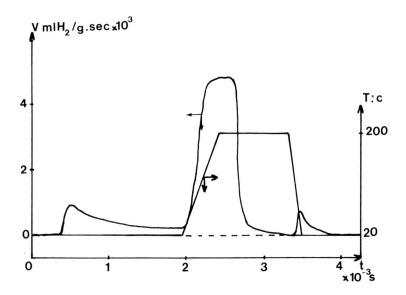

Fig. 2 : Temperature Programmed Titration of 0,73 % Ru/γ Al$_2$O$_3$ prepared by impregnation in ethanol plus water solution.

tallic catalyst prepared by impregnation in ethanol + water solution dried in air flow at 200°C in order to completely remove the ethanol, then reduced by hydrogen up to 500°C. The oxygen on Ru was negligibly titrated at room temperature (first small H_2 consumption peak), but was titrated during heating (main H_2 consumption peak). The small H_2 consumption during the final cooling arises from H_2 chemisorption on Ru^0.

EXPERIMENTAL RESULTS

1. (Pt, Ru) alloys/SiO_2

Fig. 3 shows the TPT curves for 10 wt % Pt/SiO_2 (A), 5 wt % Ru/SiO_2 (B), a mechanical mixture (50 % - 50 %) of Pt/SiO_2 plus Ru/SiO_2 (C), and the 50 at % Ru/(Pt + Ru) alloy/SiO_2 (D). It stands out that the oxygen chemisorbed on Pt is completely titrated at room temperature (fig. 3A), the oxygen chemisorbed on Ru is mainly titrated during the programmed heating (fig. 3B), the mechanical mixture behaves roughly as expected from the additivity of Pt and Ru (fig. 3C). Nevertheless, the water evolved during H_2 titration of oxygen on Pt is likely to inhibit the reduction of oxygen on Ru, hence the whole amount of oxygen on Ru should be titrated during the heating. The alloy catalyst (Fig. 3D) shows a platinum alike behaviour ; only a small H_2 consumption peak appears in the course of heating and is related to the presence of some unalloyed Ru, detected in fact by X-Ray Diffraction Analysis, in that catalyst. In Fig. 3 A to D, the intensity of the H_2 consumption peak during the final cooling from 200 to 25°C, is related to the Dispersion of the metal phase. The phenomenon will not be further discussed in the present paper.

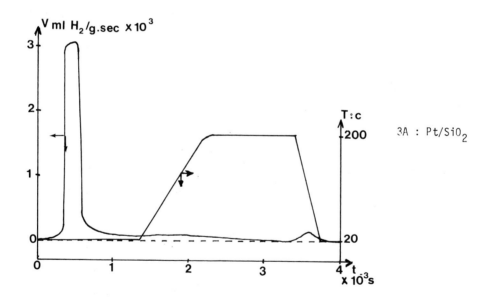

Fig. 3 A to D : Temperature Programmed Titration of 10 % Pt/SiO_2 (A), 5 % Ru/SiO_2 (B), a 50 % - 50 % mixture of Pt/SiO_2 and Ru/SiO_2 (C) and a 50 at % Ru/(Pt + Ru)/SiO_2, alloy (D).

519

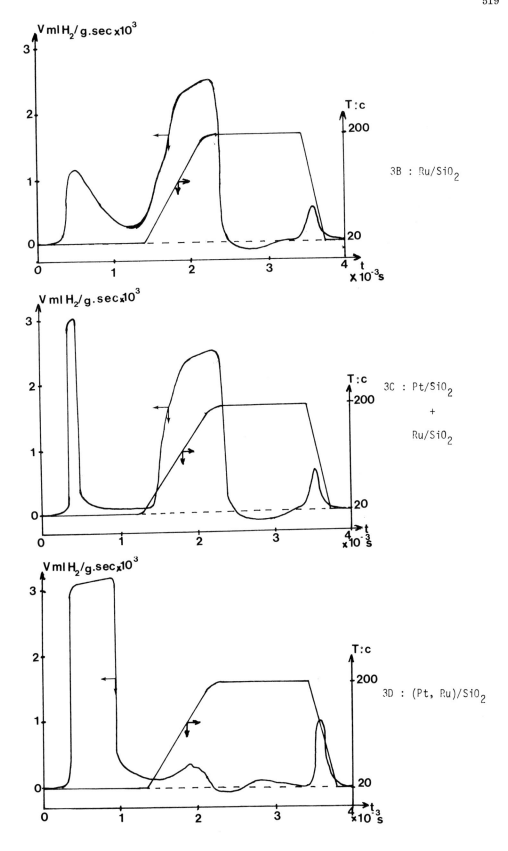

520

2. (Pt, Ru)/γ Al₂O₃ catalysts

a. <u>Prepared by successive impregnation of Ru and of Pt</u> : The Pt monometallic catalyst was completely titrated at room temperature, the Ru monometallic catalyst was completely titrated during the programmed heating [4], while a 0,93 % Pt + 0,37 % Ru/Al₂O₃ catalyst, directly reduced by H₂ at 500°C after air drying at 110°C following the impregnation, gave rise to the TPT curve in Fig. 4A. There are 2 strongly differentiated H₂ consumption peaks due to the titration, the first one related to Pt, the second one to Ru.

b. <u>Prepared by coimpregnation with H₂RuCl₆ and H₂BrCl₆ in water</u> : The Pt monometallics ex H₂PtBr₆ gave rise to quantitative H₂ titration at room temperature, with a H₂ consumption peak about 15 % in area compared to the monometallics ex H₂PtCl₆. That arised from a lower number in surface Pt atoms (Pt$_s$). Fig. 4B shows the TPT curve for the 1,04 % Pt + 0,47 % Ru/Al₂O₃ catalyst, ex H₂PtBr₆ + H₂RuCl₆ dried at 110°C and reduced at 500°C. Comparison to Fig. 4A shows a strong similarity apart in the areas of the two TPT peaks which are much lower for the ex H₂PtBr₆ catalyst (Fig. 4B) than for the ex H₂PtCl₆ catalyst (Fig. 4A).

c. <u>Prepared by coimpregnation with H₂RuCl₆ and H₂PtCl₆ in ethanol + water</u> : The Pt monometallics was titrated at room temperature, with a H₂ consumption peak about a half of that for Pt/Al₂O₃ ex H₂PtCl₆ in water. The Ru monometallics was almost completely titrated during heating (See Fig. 2). The TPT curve area for that catalyst is about 1.3 the area of the TPT curve for 0.88 % Ru/Al₂O₃ ex H₂RuCl₆ in water.

Fig. 4C shows the TPT curve for 0,94 % Pt + 0,47 % Ru/γ Al₂O₃, ex H₂RuCl₆ + H₂PtCl₆ in ethanol plus water, dried at 200°C in a dry air flow and subsequently reduced by H₂ at 500°C. That TPT curve differs stongly from that in Fig. 4A and 4B, in the sense that the ratio of the second peak area to the first peak area is considerably smaller.

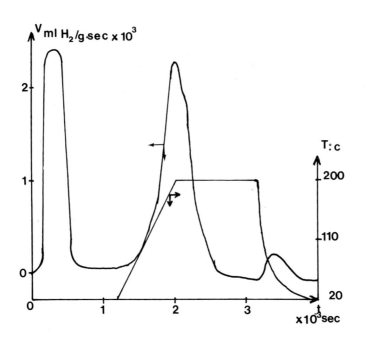

4A. Successive impregnation of H₂RuCl₆ and of H₂PtCl₆, in water.

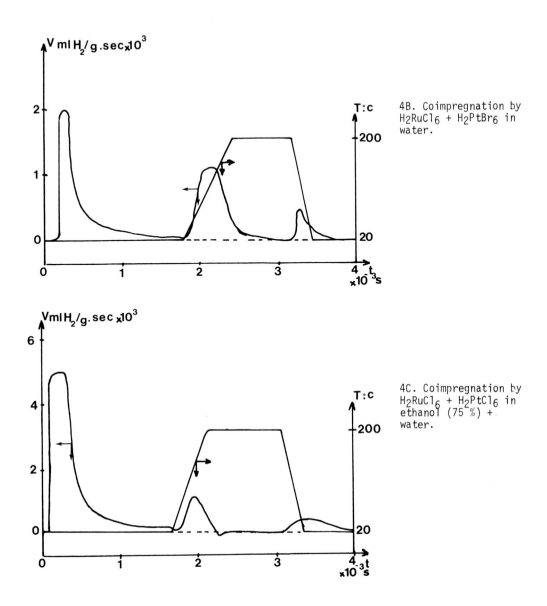

Fig. 4A to C : Temperature Programmed Titration of 40 to 50 at % Ru/(Pt + Ru) bimetallics, supported by γ Al$_2$O$_3$ and prepared by : successive impregnation of H$_2$RuCl$_6$ and H$_2$PtCl$_6$ in water (A), coimpregnation of H$_2$RuCl$_6$ and H$_2$PtBr$_6$ in water (B), and coimpregnation of H$_2$RuCl$_6$ and H$_2$PtCl$_6$ in ethanol (75 %) plus water (C).

DISCUSSION

The TPT method is able to give evidence for the state of the metal phase in highly dispersed Pt, Ru bimetallic supported catalysts. Fig. 3A to D show a considerable diffe-rence in behaviour between (Pt, Ru) (alloy phase) and (Pt) + (Ru) (mixture of pure metals). The platinum alike behaviour of (Pt, Ru) may not be ascribed to strong surface enrichment

522

of the alloy particles in Pt for two reasons : i) results of H_2 and of O_2 chemisorption measurements, to be reported elsewhere [8], were uncompatible with a surface composition nearly independent of the % Ru/(Pt + Ru). On the other hand those results were well accounted for by nearly equal surface and mean compositions of the metallic phase.

ii) Ramamoorthy and Gonzalez [5] when investigating (Pt, Ru) alloys /SiO$_2$ by Infrared Spectroscopy using CO and NO as adsorbates also arrived to the conclusion that the composition of the surface changes in the same way as that of the bulk.

The platinum alike behaviour of (Pt, Ru) could also be considered as the result of H^* spillover from Pt particles to Ru particles. Hydrogen spillover does not seem to play a significant role under our experimental conditions, because : i) H^* spillover should result in an increase in the reducibility of oxygen on Ru in the mechanical mixture of Pt/SiO$_2$ and Ru/SiO$_2$; that was not observed in fact.

ii) Also in the Al_2O_3 supported bimetallics prepared by successive impregnation (Fig. 4A) or by coimpregnation via H_2PtBr_6 (Fig. 4B), the Ru TPT peak was not shifted to lower temperatures, compared to the Ru TPT peak in the Ru monometallics.

iii) When using the same sort of approach (increase in the reducibility of oxygen on MeII$_s$ in (Pt, MeII) bimetallics due to alloying) to characterize (Pt, Re)/Al$_2$O$_3$ catalysts we found for certain activation procedures a platinum behaviour of the bimetallics, while for other activation procedures the behaviour of the final bimetallics was that of a Pt and Re particles mixture. In all cases the degree of hydration of the catalyst was approximately the same, hence a water or OH group catalyzed H^* spillover which should occur under certain circumstances is not likely.

Therefore we conclude that : i) the presence of a high temperature H_2 consumption peak during TPT is characteristic of the presence of surface Ru atoms (Ru$_s$) from pure Ru particles.

ii) and that the absence of such a peak may result from one or several of the three following effects :

1. Ru might not be reduced to the metallic state during reduction step. Temperature Programmed Reduction experiments showed that it is not the case for Ru in the three bimetallics of the present study, as shown in [4] for the H$_2$RuCl$_6$ followed by the H$_2$PtCl$_6$ impregnation procedure, and as shown in [8] for the two coimpregnation procedures.

2. Ru might be reduced to Ru^o particles with a Ru$_s$ number too low to give rise to a significant high temperature TPT peak. That could be easily recognized by using electron microscopy, eventually electron Diffraction, and X-Ray Diffraction Analysis to complete the characterization of the catalysts. In the three bimetallics/Al$_2$O$_3$, above mentionned, no metallic particle > 300 Å in size was detected by electron microscopy and no pure Ru^o was detectable by X-Ray Diffraction.

3. Ru might be reduced to Ru^o, with a significant number of Ru$_s$, but alloyed with Pt.

The main limitation of the TPT method arises from its unability to distinguish between (Pt, Ru) and Pt particles for samples containing lower than 75 at % Ru/(Pt + Ru). 15 at % Pt$_s$ in the surface of the metal phase are sufficient to improve the reducibility of oxygen on Ru$_s$ to a level which is comparable to that of oxygen on Pt$_s$.

As regard to the state of the metal phase in the three present bimetallics, Fig. 4A and 4B show clearly that at least most of the Ru is not alloyed to Pt, for the successive impregnation procedure (A) and for the coimpregnation by H_2RuCl_6, H_2PtBr_6 (B) procedure. On the other hand at least a very high percentage of the Ru is alloyed to Pt, following coimpregnation by H_2RuCl_6, H_2PtCl_6 in $C_2H_5OH + H_2O$ (Fig. 4C). In fact, the Ru was shown to be reduced to Ru^0, moreover the electron microscopy did not allow to detect any metallic particle larger than about 15 Å and also showed a very narrow particle size distribution The only possible situation is that of one alloy phase, the particle composition distribution of which may not be inferred from the present data since, as already outlined, the TPT method distinguishes essentially between the pure Ru phase and all of the platinum containing phases.

The reasons for the successively impregnated catalyst to be microscopically heterogeneous probably holds in the process of impregnation itself. Seggregation of Pt from Ru during the reduction step is unprobable since the reduction of the Pt and of the Ru species respectively was shown to occur approximately at the same temperature in the bimetallics [4].

The microscopically heterogeneous state of the bimetallics, prepared by coimpregnation with H_2RuCl_6 and H_2PtBr_6 is of much interest. In that case we followed the kinetics of impregnation of Al_2O_3 by the Ru and Pt species, at 0°C, by means of atomic absorption analysis. The following table shows the variation with time of impregnation of the relative % of the Ru fixed by the support and of the atomic Ru/Pt on the solid.

Table : Kinetics of coimpregnation of Al_2O_3 by H_2PtBr_6, H_2RuCl_6

TIME (min)	2	5	10	20	30	40	60
Relative % Ru on the solid	51	79	88	93	95	97	96
Atomic Ru/Pt ratio of the solid	1,41	1,27	1,14	1,13	1,19	1,26	1,25

The first measurement could only be done after 2 min, after which already 50 % of the Ru were attached to the support. Nevertheless, the table only shows a small variation in Ru/Pt on the solid, when the % Ru fixed on Al_2O_3 increases from ∿ 50 % up to 96 %. This suggests that the kinetics of impregnation of Al_2O_3 by the Pt and by the Ru species respectively, during coimpregnation, at most only moderately differ from each other.

Therefore, a reasonable degree of microscopic homogeneous distribution should be expected at the end of the coimpregnation step. The microscopic heterogeneity of the final catalyst is then probably due to seggregation during the drying or (and) reduction steps. In that respect it should be mentioned that H_2PtBr_6/Al_2O_3 was found to be much less reducible than H_2PtCl_6/Al_2O_3. Hence the reduction step would give rise successively to Ru particles and then to Pt particles at higher temperatures.

The reasons for the catalyst ex ($H_2RuCl_6 + H_2PtCl_6$) coimpregnated in $C_2H_5OH + H_2O$ to be altogether reasonably well dispersed and alloyed, are not yet established.

524

CONCLUSION

The Hydrogen Programmed Temperature Titration (TPT) of the oxygen chemisorbed on highly dispersed bimetallic supported catalysts is highly sensitive to detect unalloyed MeII particles in (Pt, MeII) bimetallic catalysts. That method allows then to get useful informations about the degree of microscopic homogeneity of the metal phase. It has clearly been shown in this way that preparing highly dispersed and reasonably well alloyed phases altogether is not a simple task.

The use of one ethanol plus water medium instead of water alone as solvent of the Pt and Ru precursor species has been found a promising method.

The present work is continued in particular from the point of view of the quantification of the TPT data in terms of the numbers of Ru_s from pure Ru particles, of Ru_s from (Pt, Ru) alloy particles and of Pt_s. Much progress has recently been done in that direction and the results will be published in a next future.

Acknowledgements

We acknowledge Mrs Martine Cattenot, Miss Nancy Martin and Mr Henri Urbain for all of the chemical analysis data. The french Institute of Petroleum is acknowledged for a grant to one of the authors (G.B.) and for the electron microprobe analysis data.

REFERENCES

(1) A.C. MULLER, P.A. ENGELHARD and J.E. WEISANG, J. Catal., 56, 65 (1979).

(2) H. CHARCOSSET, R. FRETY, G. LECLERCQ, E. MENDES, M. PRIMET and L. TOURNAYAN, J. Catal. 56, 468 (1979).

(3) G. MARTINO, J. MIQUEL and P. DUHAUT, Fr. Patent 2.234.924, 24 Janv. 1975 (CA 80, 20080 p).

(4) G. BLANCHARD, H. CHARCOSSET, M.T. CHENEBAUX and M. PRIMET, Second International Symposium : Scientific Bases for the Preparation of Heterogeneous Catalysts, Sept. 4-6, 1978, Louvain-la-Neuve, Belgium, Paper B8.

(5) P. RAMAMOORTHY and R.D. GONZALEZ, J. Catal., 58, 188 (1979).

(6) J.C. SUMMERS and S.A. AUSEN, CMR - 2549 Report, PCP-61, October 1977.

(7) L.L. MURRELL and D.J.C. YATES, Second International Symposium : Scientific Bases for the Preparation of Heterogeneous Catalysts, Sept. 4-6, 1978, Louvain la Neuve, Belgique, Paper C7.

(8) G. BLANCHARD, Thesis, to be published.

J. BOURDON (Editor)
Growth and Properties of Metal Clusters, pp. 525—533
© 1980 Elsevier Scientific Publishing Company — Printed in The Netherlands

INFLUENCE DE LA DISPERSION SUR LES PROPRIETES CATALYTIQUES DU PALLADIUM ET DU RHODIUM SUPPORTES

F.FIGUERAS[‡],S.FUENTES[+] et C.LECLERCQ

Institut de Recherches sur la Catalyse,Villeurbanne

adresses actuelles : [‡] Ecole Nationale Supérieure de Chimie –Montpellier
[+] Institut Mexicain du Pétrole –Mexico

Un atome métallique situé à la surface d'un cristallite de 10Å a-t-il les mêmes propriétés qu'un atome situé sur une particule de 50 à 100Å ? Cette question de l'influence de l'état de dispersion du métal sur les propriétés catalytiques reste une question très controversée dans la catalyse par les métaux.

Les résultats expérimentaux publiés jusqu'ici montrent que pour l'hydrogénolyse de l'éthane sur le nickel déposé sur silice, Yates et al (1) ont observé une variation avec la dispersion de l'activité par atome de métal superficiel, tandis que Ryndin et al (2) obtiennent une activité constante quelle que soit la dispersion et le mode de préparation. Dans le cas du platine, l'activité pour l'hydrogénolyse du cyclopentane est constante en fonction de la dispersion lorsque le catalyseur est fritté sous H_2 (3), mais dépend de la taille si on calcine d'abord le solide sous oxygène (4). Ces résultats suggèrent que la taille en soi n'est pas le paramètre déterminant les propriétés catalytiques. Bien que certains résultats puissent être attribués à la présence d'impuretés sur les supports (5), il est sûr qu'une influence modérée de la taille sur l'activité a pu être démontrée. On peut noter que dans le cas du platine (6) et du nickel (7) les différentes faces cristallines ont des activités différentes ; un changement de la morphologie des particules, induite par des conditions différentes de préparation du catalyseur pourrait également expliquer les contradictions observées puisque la forme des particules peut changer avec la nature du support, les impuretés qu'il contient, l'atmosphère à laquelle le métal est exposé. Dans l'état actuel des connaissances, cette hypothèse séduisante demande des vérifications expérimentales. Il serait en particulier intéressant de comparer des petites particules ayant une orientation cristalline définie aux catalyseurs, conventionnels, comme cela a été fait pour le nickel (8). En ce qui concerne les propriétés catalytiques, l'accent a été jusqu'à présent porté sur l'activité, les travaux concernant la sélectivité sont beaucoup plus rares et mériteraient d'être développés car c'est la propriété la plus importante sur le plan pratique.

Le présent travail concerne l'étude de l'effet de la taille des particules sur des catalyseurs Pd et Rh supportés. En modifiant le support et les conditions de préparation, nous avons pu préparer des catalyseurs présentant des distributions homogènes des tailles de particules et dans le cas du palladium un échantillon cristallographiquement orienté. Les réactions utilisées pour caractériser le catalyseur sont l'hydrogénation du benzène, connue comme insensible à la structure superficielle sur de nombreux métaux et l'hydrogénolyse du cyclopentane, qui en tant que rupture de liaison C-C pourrait être sensible à la structure superficielle.

Méthodes expérimentales

A - Préparation des catalyseurs

Les catalyseurs au palladium sont préparés par échange d'ions en utilisant une solution acide de $PdCl_2$ dans le cas de l'alumine et une solution aqueuse de K_2PdCl_4 dans celui de la magnesie.

Les catalyseurs au rhodium sont préparés :

a) par échange d'ion avec une solution acide de $RhCl_3, 3H_2O$, lorsque l'on veut préparer des catalyseurs bien dispersés,

b) par imprégnation avec une solution d'ammine $RhCl(NH_3)_5Cl_2$ lorsque l'on cherche à obtenir de grosses particules. Dans ce cas, on met l'alumine en contact avec la solution et l'on évapore lentement la phase aqueuse jusqu'à séccité.

Dans tous les cas, les solides sont séchés à l'étuve une nuit à 110°C et stockés.

Les catalyseurs sont réduits sous un courant d'hydrogène à des températures variables pour obtenir des dispersions variables de la phase métallique. D'une façon générale, une bonne dispersion est observée quand la pression de vapeur d'eau présente au cours de la réduction est faible. Dans le cas du rhodium, on peut utiliser le fait que la vapeur d'eau favorise le frittage pour préparer des catalyseurs à grosses particules ; cet effet de la vapeur d'eau, combiné avec les diverses méthodes de dépôt du métal permet d'obtenir une large gamme de dispersions(9).

B - Mesures de la dispersion

Les dispersions du palladium et du rhodium ont été mesurées par chimisorption d'hydrogène, d'oxygène et par titrage par l'hydrogène de l'oxygène préadsorbé. Dans le cas du palladium (5) les stoechiométries obtenues sont analogues à celles publiées pour le platine (10). Pour le rhodium par contre (9), une stoechiométrie simple est obtenue, correspondant à la réaction : $RhO + 3/2\ H_2 \longrightarrow RhH + H_2O$.

La distribution des tailles de particules peut également être obtenue en microscopie électronique. Les répliques extractives des échantillons (11) sont examinées au moyen d'un appareil JEM 100B, dont la résolution est de $2\overset{\circ}{A}$. Certains échantillons ont été examinés dans le microscope JEM 100C, dont la résolution est de $1,2\overset{\circ}{A}$. De nombreuses photographies sont obtenues à partir de chaque échantillons dont on déduit la distribution des tailles et le cas échéant, la forme des particules. La comparaison entre les dispersions mesurées par chimisorption et par microscopie nécessite un modèle de la particule métallique ; nous supposons une particule sphérique et une égale répartition des plans les plus denses à la surface de la particule.

C - Mesures d'activité

Les activités catalytiques sont mesurées au moyen d'un réacteur dynamique continu, à faible conversion (< 2%) pour éviter les limitations par les transferts de masse et de chaleur.

Dans l'hydrogénation du benzène, la désactivation du catalyseur est généralement négligeable, par contre, dans l'hydrogénolyse du cyclopentane, une variation notable d'activité est observée. Dans ce cas, l'activité au temps de travail zéro, considérée comme caractérisant le catalyseur frais, est obtenue en utilisant la loi de désactivation homographique (12). Notons que la sélectivité n'est généralement pas affectée par la désactivation.

Pour l'hydrogénation du benzène, les conditions sont : pression partielle de benzène 56 torr, pression partielle d'hydrogène, 704 torr, température : 50°C pour le rhodium et 140°C pour le palladium.

Pour l'hydrogénolyse du cyclopentane : la pression partielle de l'hydrocarbure est de 100 torr, le complément étant l'hydrogène, la température est de 225°C pour le rhodium et de 290°C pour le palladium.

Résultats et Discussion

Un exemple des distributions des tailles de particules obtenues avec le palladium est représenté sur la figure 1 :

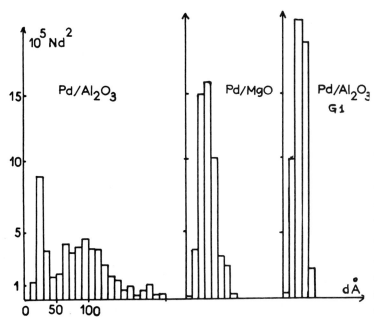

Distributions (normalisées à la même surface) des tailles de particules de 3 catalyseurs au palladium (Figure 1)

On peut préparer des échantillons contenant en majorité soit des petites particules (figure 2), soit plus grosses avec une distribution homogène, en fonction de la préparation utilisée. La forme des particules est fonction surtout du support utilisé : dans le cas de l'alumine par exemple, on peut obtenir certaines particules de 30 à 40Å dont le contour hexagonal indique un facettage, si le support est feuilleté. Cependant, aucune orientation cristalline n'existant sur ces échantillons, il est difficile de préciser la nature des plans exposés, qui sont selon toute probabilité, des plans denses (111) et (100). La majorité des particules se présente cependant dans ce cas sous une forme que l'on peut assimiler à une sphére.(Fig.3).

Dans le cas de MgO par contre, le support cristallise sous forme de plaquettes et le palladium se présente également sous forme de particules facetées (figure 4). L'orientation préférentielle du palladium sur la magnésie peut être mise en évidence par diffraction électronique sur un feuillet isolé recouvert d'une densité importante de cristallites métalliques : on voit sur le cliché six renforcements sur l'anneau 220 du palladium correspondant à l'orientation de ce dernier, qui se produit probablement par épitaxie du métal

528

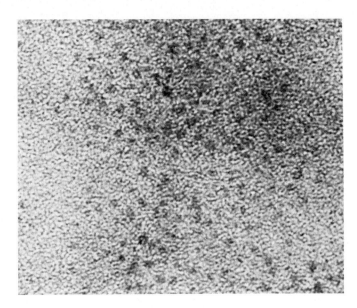

Catalyseur Pd/Al$_2$O$_3$ bien dispersé. Grossissement 1.200.000
Dispersion mesurée : 80% (Figure 2)

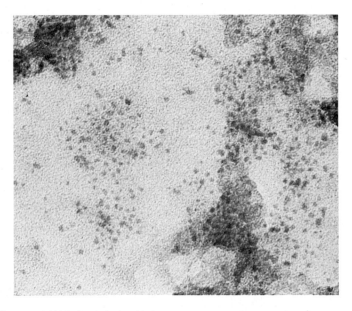

Catalyseur Pd/Al$_2$O$_3$ G-1 de dispersion moyenne (distribution
des tailles indiquées sur la figure 1). Grossissement 600.000
Dispersion mesurée : 40% (Figure 3)

sur MgO avec (111)Pd   (111)MgO et (0$\overline{1}$1)Pd   (0$\overline{1}$1)MgO (10). Dans ce cas particulier on peut donc préciser que la particule de palladium présente à la surface des plans denses (III) ou un mélange de plans (III) et (100).

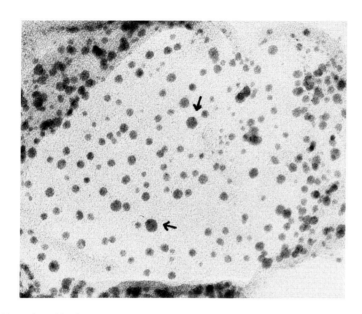

Echantillon de Pd/MgO. Grossissement 500.000. Distribution des tailles sur la figure 1. (Figure 4)

Cette hypothèse est par ailleurs confirmée par le bon accord obtenu alors entre les tailles de particules déterminées par chimisorption et par microscopie.

Dans le cas du catalyseur au rhodium sur alumine, pour lesquels la distribution des tailles est également homogène, les grosses particules ont également un contour hexagonal, donc un facetage (figure 5). Ce fait correspond probablement à une recristallisation du support γ alumine, compte tenu de la température utilisée pour la réduction, 600°C et la présence d'eau. Cet effet de facetage serait donc dû plus au support qu'à la taille des particules en soi.

Les petites particules de rhodium (figure 6) ont une forme imprécise que l'on peut supposer sphérique.

Les **activités catalytiques par** atome de métal superficiel et les sélectivités sont représentées sur les figures 7 et 8 en fonction du degré de dispersion. On note que dans le cas du palladium, ces activités sont constantes avec la dispersion et que les deux catalyseurs Pd/MgO ne se différencient pas des autres, tant pour l'hydrogénation du benzène que pour l'hydrogénolyse du cyclopentane. La sélectivité de l'hydrogénolyse reste inchangée, le seul produit étant le n-pentane.

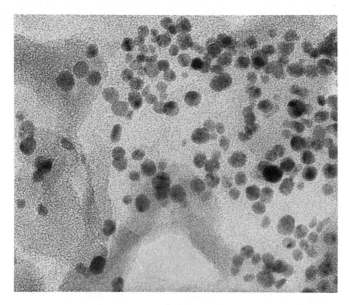

*Grosses particules de Rh obtenues après réduction à haute température.
Grossissement 800.000. Dispersion du métal 20% (Figure 5)*

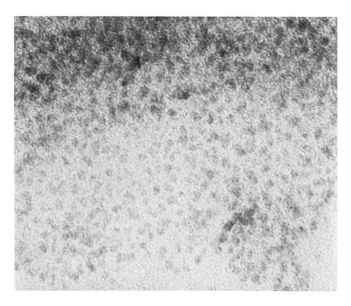

*Catalyseur Rh/Al₂O₃ bien dispersé. Grossissement 1.200.000.
Dispersion mesurée : 100% (Figure 6)*

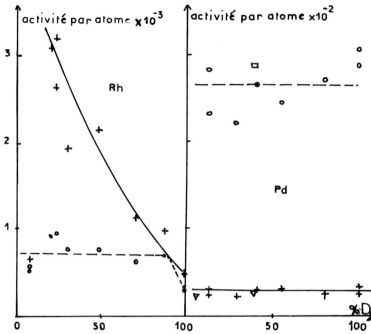

Activités par atome de métal superficiel pour l'hydrogénation du benzène (0) et l'hydrogénolyse du cyclopentane (X) en fonction de la dispersion. Les points ▽ et □ sont relatifs à Pd/MgO.(Figure 7)

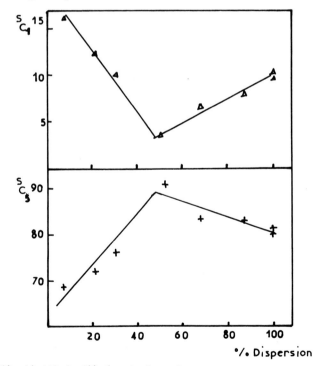

Sélectivité de l'hydrogénolyse du cyclopentane en CH$_4$(SC$_1$) et n-pentane (SC$_5$) en fonction de la dispersion pour Rh/Al$_2$O$_3$. (Figure 8)

Dans le cas du rhodium par contre, deux effets apparaissent :

1°) les catalyseurs très dispersés sont moins actifs pour l'hydrogénation du benzène : les particules de très faible taille, de l'ordre de 5 à 10Å ont un comportement analogue à celui des complexes homogènes du rhodium qui ne catalysent pas l'hydrogénation des aromatiques,

2°) une influence très nette de la dispersion sur l'activité et la sélectivité de l'hydrogénolyse, les catalyseurs les plus actifs étant les moins dispersés.

Des résultats analogues ont été observés pour l'iridium et le platine : variation d'activité avec la taille pour le platine (4), et constance d'activité pour l'iridium (13). Dans ce cas, ces résultats peuvent s'interpréter en fonction des données obtenues sur les faces monocristallines ; en effet, dans le cas du platine, une spécificité est observée (6) alors que les différentes faces de l'iridium ont le même comportement (14).

Les résultats décrits dans le présent travail peuvent s'interpréter dans le même sens puisque l'accroissement d'activité observé pour le rhodium correspond à une modification détectable expérimentalement, de la morphologie des particules. De ce fait, l'explication la plus simple est que l'activité par atome ne varie pas avec la structure superficielle dans le cas du palladium, alors que dans le cas du rhodium les faces denses (111),(100) auraient une activité supérieure à celle des faces peu denses auxquelles on peut assimiler une petite particule. Soulignons qu'on ne peut exclure une reconstruction de la surface sous l'influence des réactifs dans le cas du palladium, mais que les données publiées sur les monocristaux d'iridium montrent que l'hypothèse retenue est plausible.

Cette explication peut être généralisée à un certain nombre d'autres faits expérimentaux comme par exemple l'influence des additifs alcalins sur les catalyseurs au nickel dans la synthèse Fischer.Tropsch. Ces additifs peuvent induire une reconstruction de la surface et stabilisent la face (111), ce qui a été démontré dans le cas du platine monocristallin (15). La résistance au soufre améliorée par l'introduction d'alcalins peut alors être reliée à l'observation, rapportée par Oudar et al (16) que l'adsorption de soufre est plus faible sur les faces denses des métaux de transition que sur les faces à marches. Cette même hypothèse explique également que des modifications d'activité et de sélectivité soient attendues dans la synthèse car les propriétés thermodynamiques du carbone superficiel, qui est l'intermédiaire de la réaction, changent avec la face cristalline exposée (17).

En conclusion, des métaux aussi voisins que Pd et Rh, pour lesquels on peut préparer des catalyseurs ayant des aspects analogues par microscopie électronique, ont un comportement catalytique très différent lorsqu'on modifie la taille et la morphologie des particules. En particulier, un effet de la taille sur la sélectivité apparaît dans le cas du Rh qui n'est pas observé avec le palladium. Ces résultats peuvent s'interpréter en admettant que dans le cas du rhodium, et non dans celui du palladium, les propriétés catalytiques changent avec la face cristalline exposée. C'est une situation analogue à celle que l'on rencontre avec les faces monocristallines de platine et d'iridium. La raison profonde de ces différences reste à établir, cependant, il semble que l'on puisse raisonnablement étendre aux petites particules métalliques les résultats obtenus sur les faces monocristallines.

B I B L I O G R A P H I E

1.- D.J.C.Yates,W.F.Taylor et J.Sinfelt,J.Amer.Chem.Soc.,86,(1964),2996.

2.- Yu.A.Ryndin,B.N.Kutnetsov, et Yu.I.Yermakov,React.Kinet.Catal.Lett.,7,(1977),105.

3.- R.Maurel,G.Leclercq et J.Barbier,J.Catal.,37,(1975),324.

4.- A.Morales,Thesis,Poitiers,1978.

5.- S.Fuentes et F.Figueras,J.Chem.Soc.,Far.Trans.I,74,(1978),174.

6.- D.W.Blakely et G.A.Somorjai,J.Catal.,42,(1976),181.

7.- G.Dalmai-Imelik et J.Massardier,Proc.6th Intern.Congr.Catalysis,London 1976, (G.C.Bond,P.B.Wells et F.C.Tompkins Ed),The Chemical Society,1977,p 90. J.Massardier,J.Barbier et G.Dalmai-Imelik,J.Chim.Phys.,75,(1978),815.

8.- G.Dalmai-Imelik,C.Leclercq,J.Massardier,A.Maubert-Franco et A.Zalhout,Jap.J.Appl. Phys.,Supl.2,Part 2,(1974),489.

9.- S.Fuentes et F.Figueras,J.Catal.,sous presse.

10.- G.R.Wilson et W.K.Hall,J.Catal.,17,(1970),190.

11.- G.Dalmai-Imelik,C.Leclercq et I.Mutin,J.Microscopie,20,(1974),123.

12.- J.E.Germain et R.Maurel,Compt.Rend.Acad.Sci.,247,(1958),1854.
S.Fuentes et F.Figueras,J.Catal.,54,(1978),397.

13.- P.Marecot,Thèse de 3ème cycle,Poitiers,Sept.1979.

14.- B.E.Nieuwenhuys et G.A.Somorjai,J.Catal.,46,(1977),259.

15.- J.J.Mc Carrol,Surf.Sci.,53,(1975),297.

16.- J.Oudar,Conf on Catalyst Deactivation and Poisoning,24-26 mai 1978,Lawrence Berkely Laboratory,Berkeley.

17.- J.C.Shelton,H.R.Patil et J.M.Blakely,Surf.Sci.,43,(1974),493.
L.C.Isett et J.M.Blakely,Surf.Sci.,47,(1975),645 et 58(1976),397.
L.C.Isett et J.M.Blakely,J.Vac.Sci.Techn.,12,(1975),237.

J. BOURDON (Editor)
Growth and Properties of Metal Clusters, p. 535
© 1980 Elsevier Scientific Publishing Company — Printed in The Netherlands

POLYMER-BOUND TETRARUTHENIUM AND TETRAIRIDIUM CARBONYL CATALYSTS FOR OLEFIN HYDROGENATION

Z. Otero-Schipper, J. Lieto, J. J. Rafalko and B. C. Gates
Center for Catalytic Science and Technology
Department of Chemical Engineering
University of Delaware
Newark, Delaware 19711, U.S.A.

Tetraruthenium clusters with unique structures have been attached to solid polymeric supports and used to catalyze ethylene hydrogenation at 1 atm and 50-90°C. Polymer-bound analogs of $[H_4Ru_4(CO)_{12-x}(PPh_3)_x]$ (with x = 1,3, or 4) were synthesized by ligand exchange between $[H_4Ru_4(CO)_{12}]$ and poly(styrene-divinylbenzene) membranes functionalized with phosphine ligands. Rates of ethylene hydrogenation were measured with a flow reactor allowing simultaneous recording of the infrared spectra of the functioning catalyst. Each catalyst was stable, exhibiting undiminished activity after thousands of turnovers and presenting a carbonyl spectrum unchanged during catalysis and indistinguishable from that of the membrane incorporating the originally bound tetraruthenium cluster. The catalysts incorporating tri- and tetra-substituted clusters exhibited the same form of kinetics, indicating saturation in ethylene and a reaction order in H_2 of 0.8. The catalytic activity increased, the activation energy decreased, and the strength of bonding of ethylene to the catalyst increased with increasing substitution by electron-donor phosphine ligands on the cluster. The results suggest that the Ru_4 framework provided the catalytic sites, perhaps by reversible Ru-Ru bond breaking to form coordinatively unsaturated metal centers.

Unique tetrairidium carbonyl clusters were also anchored to phosphine-functionalized poly(styrene-divinylbenzene), the metal species being identified by carbonyl infrared spectra as the clusters analogous to $[Ir_4(CO)_{12-x}(PPh_3)_x]$ (x = 1, 2, or 3). The synthesis method was developed from that reported by J. J. Rafalko, J. Lieto, B. C. Gates, and G. L. Schrader, Jr., J. Chem. Soc. Chem. Commun. 540 (1978). Infrared spectra of polymer membranes functioning as catalysts for ethylene and cyclohexene hydrogenation in a flow reactor at 1 atm and 40-80°C indicated that the predominant metal species in each catalyst was the originally prepared tetrairidium cluster. The catalysts were stable, exhibiting unchanged spectra and undiminished activity for as many as 5000 turnovers at temperatures <90°C, but at temperatures >120°C, the iridium clusters aggregated to form crystallites. Catalytic kinetics measured at <90°C showed that for each olefin, the rate of hydrogenation decreased with an increasing number of phosphine substituents on the tetrairidium cluster (in contrast to the results observed with tetraruthenium clusters). The results suggest that the metal clusters provided the catalytic sites, possibly formed by reversible cleavage of Ir-Ir or Ir-P bonds to generate coordinative unsaturation.

J. BOURDON (Editor)
Growth and Properties of Metal Clusters, pp. 537—543
© 1980 Elsevier Scientific Publishing Company — Printed in The Netherlands

ADSORPTION D'HYDROGENE ET D'OXYGENE SUR PETITES PARTICULES DE PLATINE. DETERMINATION VOLUMETRIQUE DES DIFFERENTES ESPECES

A. Renouprez, P. Fouilloux, J.P. Candy

Institut de Recherches sur la Catalyse,
2, avenue Einstein, 69626 Villeurbanne Cédex FRANCE

ABSTRACT

A volumetric determination of hydrogen isotherms and thermodesorption curves was performed. On $Pt-SiO_2$ and Pt-zeolite two surface species β, and β_2 were detected. On the first sample, the surface stoichiometry corresponds to nearly twice the number of surface atoms. The two species are formed by the partial filling of hollow sites and atop positions. On Pt-zeolite the amount of adsorbed hydrogen is strongly reduced probably in reason of strong interaction between metal and support. In both cases, oxygen adsorption is only half that of hydrogen. The proposed model consists in partial filling of the hollow sites.

I. INTRODUCTION

Le platine sous forme divisée est utilisé depuis très longtemps comme catalyseur d'hydrogénation ou d'isomérisation. Cependant malgré de très nombreuses études, le mode d'adsorption de l'hydrogène sur ce métal est encore mal connu. En particulier, le nombre d'atomes d'hydrogène par atome de métal superficiel, l'existence de plusieurs états adsorbés font encore l'objet de vives controverses (1,2,3). Au cours de ce travail nous avons réexaminé ce problème en mettant à profit les progrès techniques de ces dernières années pour déterminer de façon précise les aires métalliques ainsi que les volumes adsorbés. Nous discuterons des résultats obtenus pour les différents modèles cristallographiques de petites particules.

II. TECHNIQUES EXPERIMENTALES ET ECHANTILLONS

II.1 Echantillons

Nous avons sélectionné 3 échantillons dont les caractéristiques sont très différentes :

(a) $Pt-SiO_2$. 6,7 % de métal sont déposés sur la silice à partir du complexe $Pt(NH_3)_4(NO_3)_2$ qui est ensuite réduit sous hydrogène à 700°K.

(b) Pt-zéolite Y. Cet échantillon est préparé par échange à partir d'une zéolite Na-Y (ref. 4). Le complexe ammonié du platine est décomposé à 570 K sous oxygène et la réduction en métal s'effectue à 770 K sous hydrogène. On obtient un échantillon comportant 15 % de platine.

(c) Pt-Raney. Ce matériau poreux est obtenu par attaque d'un alliage platine-aluminium comportant 50 % en poids d'aluminium. L'aluminium résiduel est éliminé par traitement à l'acide fluorhydrique. Une mesure par XPS permet de vérifier que la surface est exempte d'impureté.

II.2 Mesures d'aire métallique

En ce qui concerne les échantillons a et b, nous avons utilisé la diffusion des rayons X aux petits angles pour évaluer les aires métalliques et la distribution de la taille des particules du métal (réf. 5). La mesure est précise et aisée avec l'échantillon Pt-zéolite car le support produit une diffusion négligeable. Pour l'échantillon Pt-SiO$_2$, il est nécessaire de procéder à une correction pour la diffusion due au support, qui représente environ 20 % du phénomène mesuré.

Enfin, pour l'échantillon de Pt-Raney, qui ne comporte pas de support, la mesure par diffusion centrale ne conduit pas à l'évaluation de la surface accessible aux gaz, car cet échantillon initialement poreux comporte après traitement thermique une certaine proportion de pores fermés. Ces pores sont évidemment détectés dans la mesure par rayons X. Nous avons donc préféré une méthode mieux adaptée à la mesure des petites surfaces : la méthode BET d'adsorption du Kr^{85} avec détection par un scintillateur (réf. 6).

Les mesures d'aires ont été dans tous les cas faites avant les expériences d'adsorption et reprises après ces mesures de façon à tenir compte des effets de frittage. Le tableau n° 1 rassemble les caractéristiques des échantillons.

TABLEAU 1

Echantillon	% Pt	Traitement préalable 600° 10^{-7} torr	Surface m^2 g^{-1}	Diamètre moyen Å
Pt-SiO$_2$	6,7	30 h	120	20
Pt-zéolite	15	12 h	160	13
Raney	99,9	15 h + HF	1	

II.3 Mesures volumétriques

Elles ont été effectuées dans un système où le porte-échantillon peut être mis sous un vide de 10^{-7} torr. Le système de pompage comporte une pompe turbomoléculaire et un ensemble primaire avec pompe à diffusion et pompe à palette. Les isothermes d'adsorption sont établies en mesurant les pressions dans un volume étalonné, à l'aide d'une jauge Texas Instrument.

Les courbes de thermodésorption sont déterminées en mesurant à l'aide d'une jauge de Mac-Leod le volume de gaz éjecté dans la réserve de vide primaire, par le système de pompage. Lorsque les échantillons sont dans un état stable – à la suite de 3 à 4 cycles d'adsorption et de désorption – les volumes adsorbés et désorbés coïncident à 5 % près.

III. RESULTATS EXPERIMENTAUX

La figure 1 représente l'isotherme mesuré à 300 K sur PtSiO$_2$ et Pt-zéolite. La saturation est obtenue au-dessus de 100 torr avec l'hydrogène et 10 torr avec l'oxygène.

Après adsorption à 300 K, et refroidissement sous hydrogène à 77 K, on obtient les courbes de thermodésorption représentées sur la figure 2. On constate que la désorption se fait dès 100 K et qu'il existe deux inflexions sur la courbe intégrale. On peut donc dire que deux "espèces" β_1 et β_2 désorbent successivement. β_1 est éliminée au-dessous de 300-350 K et β_2 à 600-700 K.

Si on effectue l'adsorption à 900 K, les courbes de désorption mesurées entre 100 K et

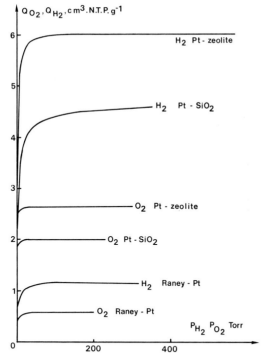

FIG. 1 : ISOTHERMES D'ADSORPTION DE H_2 ET O_2 À 300K

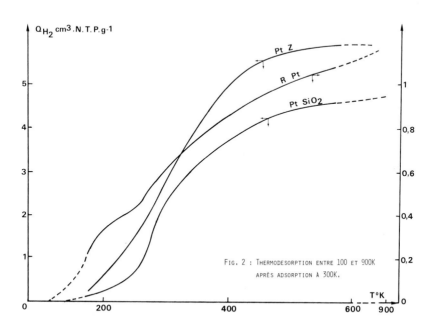

FIG. 2 : THERMODESORPTION ENTRE 100 ET 900K
APRÈS ADSORPTION À 300K.

540

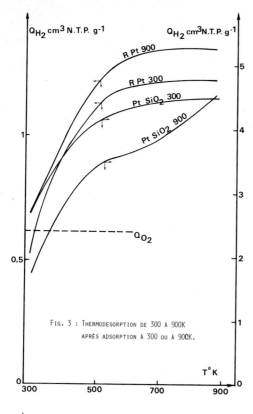

FIG. 3 : THERMODÉSORPTION DE 300 À 900K
APRÈS ADSORPTION À 300 OU À 900K.

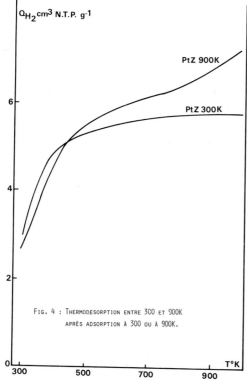

FIG. 4 : THERMODÉSORPTION ENTRE 300 ET 900K
APRÈS ADSORPTION À 300 OU À 900K.

900 K ont une forme fortement modifiée pour certains échantillons. Pour le Pt-Raney, la courbe de désorption est semblable à celle obtenue lors de l'adsorption à 300 K mais le volume désorbé augmente de 10 % environ. Pour le Pt-SiO$_2$, le volume désorbé à 700 K est inférieur de près de 30 % lorsque l'adsorption a été faite à haute température mais lorsque la température de désorption atteint 900 K, le volume recueilli est le même pour les deux températures d'adsorption. Il se forme donc une espèce supplémentaire β_3, ne désorbant qu'entre 700 et 900 K et qui prend naissance au dépend de β_1 et β_2 (Fig. 3).

Enfin, dans le cas de Pt-zéolite, la courbe de désorption est totalement différente de celle obtenue par adsorption à 300 K. Le volume désorbé est accru de 20 % et il est entièrement dû à la désorption d'une espèce β_3 formée à haute température et décomposée également entre 700 et 900 K (Fig. 4).

Le tableau II rend compte des volumes adsorbés (et désorbés) rapportés à l'unité d'aire métallique.

TABLEAU 2

Echantillon	Adsorption H$_2$ à 300 K at H cm^{-2} x 10^{15}	Adsorption H$_2$ à 900 K at H cm^{-2} x 10^{15}	Adsorption O$_2$ à 300 K at H cm^{-2} x 10^{15}
Pt-SiO$_2$	2,55	2,6	1,17
Pt-zéolite	1,4	1,9	0,65
Pt-Raney	2,1	2,4	1

IV. DISCUSSION

IV.1 Espèces adsorbées

Les courbes de thermodésorption déterminées après une adsorption à 300 K montrent que dans tous les cas 2 espèces (β_1 et β_2) sont présentes sur le platine. β_1, la plus faiblement liée, désorbe entre 100 et 350 K, β_2 entre 300 et 700 K. La différence d'énergie de liaison pour ces deux espèces n'est que de 4 à 5 kcal/mole. Dans une étude sur des faces (111) monocristallines, Ertl (réf. 7) a détecté également ces deux espèces. Il a attribué la présence de deux pics de thermodésorption à une hétérogénéité induite à la surface du métal.

Une autre hypothèse serait liée à la présence de plusieurs types de sites tels la position terminale sur un atome ou les puits de symétrie C_{3v} ou C_{4v} sur les facettes (111) et (100) ; les calculs de Bullett (réf. 8) montrent qu'une différence inférieure à 0,2 ev sépare les énergies de liaison sur ces différents sites. En l'absence de donnée spectroscopique précise sur la structure de ces espèces, on ne peut trancher entre ces hypothèses.

Après adsorption à 900 K, les courbes de désorption relatives aux catalyseurs supportés montrent l'existence d'une troisième espèce d'hydrogène adsorbé, ne désorbant qu'entre 700 et 900 K. Pour l'échantillon Pt-SiO$_2$ cette forme n'accroît pas le volume total d'hydrogène adsorbé et les 20 % du total qui sont recueillis entre 700 et 900 K proviennent de l'espèce β_2. Pour le Pt-zéolite, au contraire, il se forme à 900 K une forme β_3 qui n'est décomposée qu'au dessus de 700 K et qui accroît de près de 30 % le total de l'hydrogène adsorbé. Cette forme β_3 très stable est probablement due à des atomes en position pontante entre le métal et le support.

IV.2 Stoechiométrie de surface

Dans le tableau n° 3, nous avons considéré 3 formes cristallines ou pseudo cristallines. Le cubooctaèdre ou l'octaèdre tronqué gardent la symétrie cubique et nous avons montré

542

par ailleurs que les particules de 18 Å de Pt-SiO$_2$ conservent cette symétrie (réf. 9). Au contraire, les particules de 12 Å de Pt-zéolite auraient en majorité la symétrie C$_5$ de l'icosaèdre. On remarque que le rapport du nombre des sites (111 + 100) au nombre des atomes de surface varie dans des proportions considérables avec le diamètre de la particule et avec la symétrie considérée (de 1,2 à 2).

TABLEAU 3

Cubooctaèdre
6 faces (100), 8 faces triangulaires (111)

D Å	N_{at}	$N_{at\ surf.}$	Dispersion	(111) sites	(100)	$N_{sites}/N_{at\ surf.}$	N_{sites} cm^{-2}
6	13	12	0,92	8	6	1,17	
11	55	42	0,76	32	24	1,33	2 x 10^{15}
17	147	92	0,63	72	54	1,37	

Octaèdre tronqué
6 faces (100), 8 faces hexagonales (111)

8,5	38	32	0,84	48	6	1,69	2,5 x 10^{15}
17	201	122	0,61	192	24	1,77	

icosaèdre
20 faces (111)

6	13	12	0,92	20		1,67	
11	55	42	0,76	80		1,90	3 x 10^{15}
17	147	92	0,63	180		1,96	

Pour Pt-SiO$_2$, la population de surface (2,6 x 10^{15}) excède largement le nombre des sites du cubooctaèdre (2 x 10^{15}/cm^2) et même de l'octaèdre (2,5 x 10^{15}/cm^2). On doit donc admettre que ces sites se remplissent et que des atomes d'hydrogène se trouvent également en position terminale sur chaque atome de métal sans qu'on atteigne cependant une saturation qui correspondrait à $\sim$ 3,5 x 10^{15} at H/cm^2. Ce remplissage de 2 types de sites rendrait compte des 2 espèces β_1 et β_2 dont les énergies de formation sont légèrement différentes.

La situation est très différente par l'échantillon Pt-zéolite qui n'adsorbe que 1,4 et 1,9 x 10^{15} at H/cm^2 à 300 et 900 K. Le premier chiffre correspond "par hasard" exactement au nombre des atomes métalliques de surface. En fait dans ce cas les particules sont prisonnières du réseau silico-aluminate qui occulte exactement la moitié de la surface du métal. Il est donc beaucoup plus probable qu'également les sites C$_{3v}$ et les positions terminales soient occupés à 80 % et les zones occultées par le support ne contiennent pas d'hydrogène. A 900 K le coefficient de diffusion de l'hydrogène augmente de 2 puissances de 10 et les vibrations du réseau oxyde permettent aux atomes d'hydrogène de s'introduire dans les zones vides. Il se peut également que des liaisons du type Pt-H-O-Si se forment. Avec l'oxygène les populations de surface sont environ moitié de celles mesurées pour l'hydrogène. En raison des bouleversements de la structure superficielle du métal qui sont observés par EXAFS (réf. 9), il est logique de penser que l'oxygène se loge de préférence dans les sites C$_{4v}$ (ou C$_{3v}$) mais n'en occupe qu'une proportion réduite ($\sim$ 50 %) puisque la population de surface est respectivement de 0,7 et 1,2 x 10^{15} at O/cm^2 pour Pt-zéolite et Pt-SiO$_2$.

V. CONCLUSIONS

L'adsorption d'hydrogène à la surface du platine polycristallin finement divisé est donc un phénomène complexe. Il paraît cependant établi que dans les conditions usuelles (300 K, 300 torr) 2 types de sites se remplissent partiellement. On dépasse largement les stoechiométries de surfaces qui étaient ordinairement admises de 1 atome d'hydrogène par atome de métal superficiel. On doit cependant noter qu'on n'atteint pas la saturation des sites disponibles, probablement en raison des interactions dipoles-dipoles importantes à fort taux de recouvrement.

REFERENCES

1 J.R. Wilson and W.K. Hall, J. Catal., 17(1970)190.
2 D.E. Mears and R.C. Hansford, J. Catal., 9(1967)125.
3 J. Uchijima, J.M. Herrmann, Y. Inoue, R.L. Burwell, J. Butts, J.B. Cohen, J. Catal., 50(1977)464.
4 P. Gallezot, A. Alarcon Diaz, J.A. Dalmon, A.J. Renouprez, B. Imelik, J. Catal. 39(1975)334.
5 A.J. Renouprez, C. Hoang Van, P.A. Compagnon, J. Catal., 34(1974)411.
6 G. Beurton, P. Bussière, B. Imelik, Bull. Soc. Chim. (1967)1293.
7 K. Christmann, G. Ertl and T. Pignet, Surf. Sci., 54(1976)365.
8 D.W. Bullett, Surf. Sci., 68(1977)149.
9 A. Renouprez, P. Fouilloux, B. Moraweck, 33ème réunion Soc. Chim. Phys. n° 49.

J. BOURDON (Editor)
Growth and Properties of Metal Clusters, pp. 545—548
© 1980 Elsevier Scientific Publishing Company — Printed in The Netherlands

PANEL DISCUSSION

This discussion was held at the end of the poster session, and was steered by Drs. Ehrlich, Gillet, Hamilton, Imelik, Martino, Naccache, Wynblatt, and Yates.

The main topics under consideration during this discussion were :

- What constitutes a metal cluster ?
- How many metal atoms are needed for the cluster to bulk metal transition ?
- What is the difference in behaviour between clusters and bulk metal ?
- Role of the substrate on cluster formation and properties.
- Adsorption of gases (CO, N_2) on dispersed metals.

This discussion allowed, so to speak, to prolong in public the quite lively discussion which had taken place in front of most of the posters. Although some of the participants were too busy – or too lazy – to write down what they had said, we hope the remarks and comments which follow will give a reasonably fair idea of the climate in which the meeting was held.

546

What constitutes a cluster ?

Yates - This is not at all a simple matter. One characteristic could be that any particle less than, say 100 Å could constitute a cluster. Another definition could be that a cluster is an entity which is small enough so that it shows a very significant variation from the bulk properties of the parent material.

Wynblatt - I agree with what has been said by Dr Yates. A cluster may be defined, in an operational sense, as an aggregate of atoms which displays properties that deviate measureably from the properties of the bulk material. However, this definition is not entirely satisfactory, because the size at which an atomic aggregate begins to approach macroscopic behavior may be significantly different depending on the particular property under consideration (e.g. nearest neighbor distance, surface energy, catalytic behavior, etc.).

Difference of behaviour between cluster and bulk metal ?

Cyrot-Lackmann - There is now a general agreement among the scientific community that electronic properties of metallic clusters converge to the bulk ones only at large size, i.e. for clusters of at least a few hundred atoms. There is thus no hope for the near future that ab initio methods could reach these sizes, due to limitations in computing abilities. So far the validity of an approach of the chemisorption process based on a simulation of a surface by a small cluster is quite questionable.

Sahyun - 1°/ Cluster to metal transition may reflect the decreasing role of environmental domination with respect to the properties of the substance. A cluster has to be formed in some environment. Its surface to volume ratio is large compared to that of bulk metal. The electronic properties of this environment as well as its geometry tend to impose the cluster properties despite its natural tendency to behave as a metal at least geometrically.

2°/ It is easy to regenerate preconceptions in carrying out calculations. If one does calculations e.g. looking at only Van der Waals interactions in Lennard-Jones potentials, and ignoring the potential directionality of chemical bonds, then one may be condemned to generate a model of an amorphous material whether or not it exists in nature.

Hamilton - I would comment on behalf of my colleague Dr. Roger Baetzold who if he were here would agree with Dr. Cyrot-Lackmann that the quantum chemical calculations do not converge to bulk properties before sizes of several hundred atoms.

We have also explored the question experimentally, using as a criterion for bulk properties the width of the d-band as determined by photoelectron spectroscopy. For Pt, Pd, Rh and Ir, we find, in good agreement with calculations, that bulk band width is reached only when the cluster size is several hundred atoms.

Kreibig - I want to support the statement of Mme Cyrot-Lackmann that dielectric substrates may not influence essentially the transition cluster to bulk metal, though an influence could be expected.

There are, as far as I know, two papers, at this conference, which assign a specific size to this transition. The one by Hamilton et al. stating that the transition occurs at 200-300 atom-particles, the other being our own work showing that transition occurs in the 500 atom-particle range for gold. Although the substrates differ markedly, there appears to be no significant difference as far as the transition size is concerned in the case of gold.

Importance of cluster shape - Size-threshold for measuring cluster shape - Formation of metals on non-metallic substrates - Kinetic parameters in growth phenomena.

Gillet - Thickness fringes are a good test for determining the aggregates shape. What is the minimum size of aggregates on which it is possible to observe thickness fringes ?

Martino – Most particle size determinations are made on fresh catalysts, has anyone any indication on reactant-induced rearrangements ?

Yacaman – Regarding the question of third dimensionality of the clusters we should mention that the clusters produced by evaporation tend to achieve a third dimension for a diameter of the order of 20 Å. That is the case for noble metals growing on alkali halides. However when the substrate strongly interacts with the overgrowth the latter tends to assume a rather flat shape. In this latter case we have observed for instance heavily truncated cubo-octahedra.

In the case of Pt on γ – Al_2O_3 catalyst prepared by chemical reduction electron micrographs show that the particles are very flat and a few monolayers thick.

Wynblatt – There is no question that the equilibrium form of platinum on alumina is three dimensional, for any realistic value of metal loading. However, the point I tried to make in my lecture was that kinetic considerations strongly suggest that two-dimensional islands can be formed as a meta-stable intermediate in the transition from monomers to three-dimensional clusters, as long as the temperature is low enough. The formation of a meta-stable phase as a result of kinetic effects is not unusual, and indeed is a well studied and very common feature of solid-solid phase transitions.

Mutaftschiev – The role of the substrate in the nucleation is not always so important as one can think. In the case of condensation of gold upon vacuum evaporation onto NaCl substrate the gold – NaCl bond is so weak (~ 0.15 eV) in comparison to the cohesion energy of the gold (3.4 eV per bond) that its catalytic effect in the nucleation phenomena is negligible and so should be its influence on the structure and other (e.g. catalytic) properties of the gold particle.

The role of the substrate in this case is essentially :

- to provide to the gold atoms the opportunity to meet in a reduced two-dimensional space.
- to absorb and dissipate the heat of condensation when clusters are formed.

Clusters and catalysis.

Bonzel – As mentioned a moment ago, the existence of two-dimensional metallic islands on Al_2O_3 ("rafts") would imply a strong metal-support interaction, i.e. the metal-support bond energy would be comparable in magnitude with the metal-metal bond energy. If this is the case for the Rh rafts discussed by Yates in his paper, the following question arises with regard to CO chemisorption : how is it possible that Rh atoms in a raft – already bonded to the support as well as neighboring Rh atoms – are not only able to chemisorb two CO molecules per atom but in addition chemisorb these molecules in such a way that the measured CO I.R. spectra are almost identical to gaseous Rh carbonyls ? Should the strongly perturbed electronic configuration of the Rh raft atoms not entail a rather different CO chemisorption behavior relative to that of carbonyls ?

Ehrlich – The fact that in infrared measurements no nitrogen adsorption is observed on rhodium catalysts need not imply that the rhodium particles have electronic properties different from the bulk. Your observations could be rationalized by assuming that on atomically flat rhodium surfaces adsorption (and possibly also the transition moment) is much weaker than on the rough surfaces usually studied. In fact, in fieldemission experiments with nitrogen on rhodium, Hegne et al. did find a correlation with surface roughness.

Zecchina – The formation enthalpy of metal – CO bond is of the same order of magnitude as that of the metal-metal bond. Consequently CO adsorption on a coordinatively unsaturated atom of a very small cluster can be a complicated process where metal-metal bonds are broken and smaller carbonyl clusters formed (observations of this kind have been make in our laboratory for the Ru/Al_2O_3 – CO system). As a consequence the stoechiometry of the CO adsorption on extremely dispersed metals cannot be used to estimate the initial dimension of the adsorbing cluster.

Clusters and the photographic process.

Hamilton - Of the four poster papers on the photographic process, there was much diversity in the physical systems studied and the approaches. This is the application area which has traditionnally been concerned with clusters of the smallest size (two, three, four atoms). Ideas about how these act in photolysis and development are still subject to discussion.

Judging on the basis of a simple head-count during the poster session the most stimulating new concept is that in Dr Hoffman's paper. It is unique, in this symposium on small particles, that he wishes us to believe that the property we have always ascribed to a catalytic effort of small silver cluster is actually a bulk thermodynamic property of the silver halide crystal. In this sense it is an anti-cluster model.

Moisar - The silver specks involved in the photographic process are perhaps the smallest clusters (2...4 atoms) observed exhibiting catalytic properties. Their formation, particularly in early stages, is still obscure.
The technique of field ion microscopy as described by Ehrlich could be a very powerful tool to investigate the early stages of silver cluster formation, provided the method could be adapted to the relevant system e.g. Ag/AgBr.
Early stages of growth of these clusters in the developer could be investigated using Budewski's method.

Sahyun - Do Silver clusters formed in silver bromide and on inert supports exhibit the same catalytic behavior, especially with regard to the so-called "physical development" ?

Hamilton - We find that the experimentally determined size dependence of silver clusters on carbon is very close to that indicated by photographic experiments for silver latent image centers on silver bromide. Malinowski's results (to be presented tomorrow) are more direct and indicate no substrate effect.

The following comments of Budewski, Malinowski and Mutaftschiev have been made after a short presentation by Ruckenstein during the discussion panel of a paper published by Ruckenstein and Lee in Surface Science in 1975 (see also the comment made by Ruckenstein in connection with the lecture presented by Dr. Yates).

Budevski - Are you treating the deposited phase as a continuum ? And the question is : Is this allowed for small sized clusters ?

Ruckenstein - We treat the particle as a continuum using a hard sphere repulsion coupled with a Van der Waals attraction. Because the distances involved are large in our cases compared to the lattice spacing such an approximation is reasonable. In nucleation theory this condition is less well satisfied and is nevertheless often used.

Mutaftschiev - Are your computation of the equilibrium shape of small droplets performed for liquid or solid structures. If they regard liquids, how can you obtain information about the equilibrium shape ? Snap shot pictures of liquid clusters with these dimensions, during Monte-Carlo simulation, show that the particles are very far from being spherical or lense-shaped.

Malinowski - I know some calculations carried out by Baetzold (Kodak-Rochester) who showed that the equilibrium form depends on the size of the cluster and the substrate. But this is true for clusters of atomic dimensions. Nevertheless, you speak of large clusters and we, as well as Hamilton, have monitored the shape of aggregates 20-60 Å in diameter of different metals on various substrates. The shape of these clusters has been shown to be semi spherical up to sizes where facets were observed.

Ruckenstein - The equilibrium shapes have been computed using a hard sphere repulsion with Van der Waals attraction. Expressions have been derived for the asymptotic wetting angle valid for sufficiently large particles as well as for the variation of the angle near the edge. Detailed results can be found in the paper published by Ruckenstein and Lee in Surface Science, 1975.
Sizes below about 15 Å have unusual behaviour and this seems to agree with the experimental results mentioned by Malinowski.

AUTHOR INDEX